This second volume of James Clerk Maxwell's correspondence and manuscript papers begins in July 1862 with his first referee reports for the Royal Society, and concludes in December 1873 shortly before the formal inauguration of the Cavendish Laboratory at Cambridge. The volume documents his involvement with the wider scientific community in Victorian Britain, and the period of his scientific maturity. In the years 1862–73 Maxwell wrote the classic works on statistical molecular theory and field physics, including the *Treatise on Electricity and Magnetism*, which established his special status in the history of science. His letters and drafts of this period provide unique insight into this work, which remains fundamental to modern physics. Few of the manuscripts reproduced here have received prior publication in other than truncated form; and the volume includes Maxwell's correspondence with G. G. Stokes, Kelvin and P. G. Tait. The edition is annotated with a full historical commentary.

Note on this Paperback Re-issue:

This is Part Two of Volume Two of the Scientific Letters and Papers of James Clerk Maxwell. Volume Two was first published as a single hardback volume in 1995. This paperback impression of Volume Two is printed in two parts, the first of which contains pages i-469 of the original hardback, the second pages 470-999 of the original hardback.

THE SCIENTIFIC LETTERS AND PAPERS OF
JAMES CLERK MAXWELL

$$\left.\begin{array}{l} k\nabla^2\mu\alpha = 4\pi\mu\frac{d^2}{dt^2}\mu\alpha \\ k\nabla^2\mu\beta = 4\pi\mu\frac{d^2}{dt^2}\mu\beta \\ k\nabla^2\mu\gamma = 4\pi\mu\frac{d^2}{dt^2}\mu\gamma \end{array}\right\} \quad (69)$$

If we assume that α, β, γ are functions of $lx + my + nz - Vt = w$ the first equation becomes

$$k\mu\frac{d^2\alpha}{dw^2} = 4\pi\mu^2 V^2 \frac{d^2\alpha}{dw^2} \qquad (70)$$

or

$$V = \pm\sqrt{\frac{k}{4\pi\mu}} \qquad (71)$$

The other equations give the same value for V so that the wave is propagated in either direction with a velocity V.

This wave consists entirely of magnetic disturbances, the direction of magnetization being in the plane of the wave. No magnetic disturbance whose direction of magnetization is not in the plane of the wave can be propagated as a plane wave at all.

Hence magnetic disturbances propagated through the electromagnetic field agree with light in this, that the disturbance at any point is transverse to the direction of propagation, and such waves may have all the properties of polarized light.

The only medium in which experiments have been made to determine the value of k is air, in which $\mu = 1$ and therefore by equation (46)

$$V = v \qquad (72)$$

By the electromagnetic experiments of M. M. Weber & Kohlrausch

$$v = 310\,740\,000 \text{ metres per second}$$

is the number of electrostatic units in one electromagnetic unit of electricity, and this according to our result should be equal to the velocity of light in air or vacuum.

Velocity of light in air by M. Fizeau's experiments

$$V = 314\,858\,000$$

Leipzig Trans. V (1857) p 260 in Poggendorff's Annalen Aug 1856 p 10
in phil. Rev. vol XXIX (1864) p 90

The electromagnetic theory of light. From 'A dynamical theory of the electromagnetic field', October 1864 (Number 239).

THE SCIENTIFIC
LETTERS AND PAPERS OF
JAMES CLERK MAXWELL

VOLUME II
1862–1873
Part II
1869–1873

EDITED BY

P. M. HARMAN
Professor Emeritus of the History of Science, Lancaster University

CAMBRIDGE UNIVERSITY PRESS
Cambridge, New York, Melbourne, Madrid, Cape Town, Singapore, São Paulo, Delhi

Cambridge University Press
The Edinburgh Building, Cambridge CB2 8RU, UK

Published in the United States of America by Cambridge University Press, New York

www.cambridge.org
Information on this title: www.cambridge.org/9780521256261

© Cambridge University Press 1995

This publication is in copyright. Subject to statutory exception
and to the provisions of relevant collective licensing agreements,
no reproduction of any part may take place without the written
permission of Cambridge University Press.

First published 1995
This digitally printed version 2008

A catalogue record for this publication is available from the British Library

Library of Congress Cataloguing in Publication data
Maxwell, James Clerk, 1831–1879.
The scientific letters and papers of James Clerk Maxwell/edited by P. M. Harman
Includes bibliographical references and index.
1. Electromagnetic theory. 2. Light, Wave theory of. 3. Molecular theory – Statistical methods.
I. Harman, P. M. (Peter Michael), 1943–   . II. Title.
QC670.M385 1990   530.1′41   89–452

ISBN 978-0-521-10135-6 paperback (Volume 1)
ISBN 978-0-521-25625-4 hardback (Volume 1)
ISBN 978-0-521-10136-3 paperback (Volume 2 Set)
ISBN 978-0-521-74607-6 paperback (Volume 2 Part 1)
ISBN 978-0-521-74610-6 paperback (Volume 2 Part 2)
ISBN 978-0-521-25626-1 hardback (Volume 2)
ISBN 978-0-521-10137-0 paperback (Volume 3 Set)
ISBN 978-0-521-74614-4 paperback (Volume 3 Part 1)
ISBN 978-0-521-74617-5 paperback (Volume 3 Part 2)
ISBN 978-0-521-25627-8 hardback (Volume 3)
ISBN 978-0-521-75794-2 paperback (3 Volume Set)
ISBN 978-0-521-80952-8 hardback (3 Volume Set)

For Tim and Rosie

CONTENTS
Part I

Preface	*page* xi
List of texts	xiv
Editorial note	xxiv
List of plates	xxvii
Abbreviated references	xxix
Introduction	1
TEXTS 1862-1868	39

Appendix

Index

Part II

Preface	*page* xi
List of texts	xiv
Editorial note	xxiv
List of plates	xxvii
Abbreviated references	xxix
TEXTS 1869-1873	470
Appendix	971
Index	977

PREFACE

This second volume of James Clerk Maxwell's scientific letters and papers documents the period of his maturity. These manuscripts provide substantive evidence of the process in which the brilliant innovations of his scientific youth were transformed into the Maxwellian physics transmitted to posterity. The volume covers the years 1862–73, when Maxwell wrote the classic works on statistical molecular theory and field physics, including the *Treatise on Electricity and Magnetism*, which established his unique status in the history of science. The volume begins with his first referee reports for the Royal Society, signalling his involvement with the wider scientific community, and ends shortly before the inauguration of the Cavendish Laboratory at Cambridge.

Only a small number of the manuscripts reproduced in this volume have received prior publication in other than truncated form. Letters received by Maxwell, of which few are now extant, are reproduced on a selective basis, and third-party correspondence is also included. All the letters from his major correspondents – George Gabriel Stokes, William Thomson (later Lord Kelvin) and Peter Guthrie Tait – are reproduced complete, the correspondence with Tait being of especial interest.

This volume prints all of Maxwell's extant autograph letters from the period 1862–73. While these and other manuscripts provide profuse documentation of the evolution of Maxwell's science, his intellectual development, and the course of his public career, little information can be gleaned about his private affairs. Campbell and Garnett's *Life of Maxwell* contains no more than a very sparse selection of the documents, still extant at the time of his death, which related to his personal life in this period.

Much of the work on this volume has been carried out in the Cambridge University Library and the Harvard College Library. I am grateful to the President and Fellows of Clare Hall, Cambridge, and the Department of the History of Science, Harvard University, for hospitality in providing facilities for this work.

The edition owes much to the support of Cambridge University Press. Sir Alan Cook has taken a kind interest in the progress of my work on behalf of the Syndics. Richard Ziemacki, Simon Capelin, James Deeny and Fiona Thomson have been generous with advice and assistance. I am very grateful to Alan Winter and Richard Schermerhorn: the completion of this volume owes much to the help they kindly proffered. It is a pleasure to thank Susan

Bowring for her meticulous contribution as copy-editor; and to gratefully acknowledge the work of Pauline Ireland and of the draughtsmen and typesetters at the Press in the presentation of the edition in such an elegant form.

I have benefited from the helpfulness of archivists and librarians in many libraries. I thank especially Godfrey Waller of the Manuscripts Room of the Cambridge University Library and Alan Clark of the Library of the Royal Society, for their kindness and efficiency over many years.

I am grateful to many friends and colleagues who have been helpful in providing information about the location of manuscripts, in offering advice, and in fostering my work by various acts of kindness. I thank especially Jed Buchwald, I. Bernard Cohen, Francis Everitt, Tom Fuller, Ivor Grattan-Guinness, Erwin Hiebert, Bruce Hunt, Lord Jenkin, Robert Kargon, Martin Klein, Anne Kox, Sir Brian Pippard, A. I. Sabra, Robert Schulmann, Sam Schweber, Alan Shapiro, Daniel Siegel, Thomas Simpson, John Stachel, Carlene Stephens, The Hon. Guy Strutt, Garry J. Tee, Paul Theerman, Charles Webster, Tom Whiteside, L. Pearce Williams and David Wilson.

I am grateful to Ethel Dunkerley for typing the entire manuscript (from my handwritten transcriptions) with such dedication; to Isabel Matthews for valuable assistance in drawing the figures; and to Keith Papworth of the Cavendish Laboratory for his enthusiasm in preparing photographs of Maxwell's experimental apparatus.

It would have proved impossible to prepare this volume for publication without the opportunity to spend extended periods working in a research library. I am grateful to the Royal Society for awarding me a succession of research grants, and I thank Norman Robinson and Sheila Edwards for their interest. I am especially grateful to the National Science Foundation for substantial grants which supported two years work at Harvard; to thank Ronald J. Overmann for his generous interest and kindness, I can only say that without such support this volume would not have been completed.

For permission to reproduce manuscripts I am grateful to Lord Rayleigh; Professor Sydney Ross; Miss Margaret Tait; the Syndics of the Cambridge University Library; the Master and Fellows of Trinity College, Cambridge; the Master and Fellows of Peterhouse, Cambridge; the Cavendish Laboratory, Cambridge; the Librarian of Glasgow University Library; St Andrews University Library; Edinburgh University Library; the Trustees of the National Library of Scotland; the Royal Society; the Royal Institution; Imperial College London Archives; King's College London Archives; the University of London Library and the Athenæum; the Institution of Electrical Engineers, London; the Greater London Record Office; the Bodleian Library, Oxford; the Royal Greenwich Observatory; The General

Electric Company, p.l.c.; The Queen's University of Belfast Library; Columbia University Library; The Johns Hopkins University Library; the Smithsonian Institution Libraries; Harvard University Archives; and the Akademie-Archiv, Berlin.

I am grateful to the Cavendish Laboratory and the Whipple Museum of the History of Science, Cambridge for permission to reproduce photographs of Maxwell's apparatus, and to Dr I. B. Hopley for use of his photograph of the governor; and to the Syndics of the Cambridge University Library, the Librarian of Glasgow University Library, and the Royal Society for permission to reproduce photographs of documents.

To end on a very personal note, my deepest thanks are to Juliet, Tim and Rosie for so good-humouredly tolerating my absorption in this work.

LIST OF TEXTS

Part I and Part II

197	Letter to William Sharpey, 8 July 1862	*page* 41
198	Letter to George Gabriel Stokes, 14 July 1862	43
199	Letters to George Gabriel Stokes, 16 July 1862	46
200	Letter to George Gabriel Stokes, 21 July 1862	50
201	On a paper by Thomas Romney Robinson on the spectra of electric sparks, 10 September 1862	54
202	Letter to George Gabriel Stokes, 10 September 1862	58
203	On diagrams of forces, *c.* November 1862	60
204	Letter to John William Cunningham, 5 December 1862	61
205	On a paper by George Biddell Airy on stress in beams, late December 1862	62
206	Letter to George Gabriel Stokes, 29 December 1862	70
207	On the conduction of heat in gases, *c.* Spring 1863	72
208	Letter to John William Cunningham, 24 March 1863	86
209	Letter to George Biddell Airy, 14 May 1863	87
210	Letter to William Thomson, 29 May 1863	88
211	Letter to William Thomson, June 1863	93
212	Letter to George Gabriel Stokes, 9 June 1863	95
213	Letter to John William Cunningham, 27 June 1863	97
214	Letter to William Thomson, 31 July 1863	98
215	Letter to John William Cunningham, 10 August 1863	102
216	Letter to Robert Dundas Cay, 21 August 1863	103
217	Letter to George Phillips Bond, 25 August 1863	104
218	Letter to Fleeming Jenkin, 27 August 1863	110
219	Letter to William Thomson, 11 September 1863	112
220	On a paper by Charles Chambers on the magnetic action of the sun, late October 1863	117
221	On the equilibrium and stiffness of a frame, *c.* January 1864	119
222	Letter to Katherine Mary Clerk Maxwell, 28 January 1864	122
223	On a paper by William John Macquorn Rankine on fluid motion, late February 1864	123
224	On the theory of Saturn's rings, 1864	128
225	Letter to Hermann Helmholtz, 12 April 1864	146
226	Letter to John Tyndall, 20 April 1864	147
227	On the motion of the earth through the ether, *c.* 24 April 1864	148

228	Letter to George Gabriel Stokes, 6 May 1864	*page* 154
229	Letter to Robert Dundas Cay, 12 July 1864	157
230	On the determination of coefficients of self-induction, *c.* Summer 1864	158
231	Draft of 'A dynamical theory of the electromagnetic field', *c.* Summer 1864	160
232	Letter to Charles Hockin, 7 September 1864	164
233	On the determination of the number of electrostatic units in one electromagnetic unit of electricity, *c.* September 1864	165
234	Letter to William Thomson, 27 September 1864	172
235	Letter to William Thomson, 15 October 1864	176
236	On the explanation of the reflection and refraction of light by the electromagnetic theory of light, October 1864	182
237	Letter to George Gabriel Stokes, 15 October 1864	186
238	A dynamical theory of the electromagnetic field (abstract), [27 October 1864]	189
239	Cancelled passages in the manuscript and proofs of 'A dynamical theory of the electromagnetic field', October 1864	197
240	Letter to Charles Hope Cay, 5 January 1865	202
241	On the determination of the number of electrostatic units in one electromagnetic unit of electricity, *c.* February 1865	204
242	Letter to William Thomson, 25 February 1865	207
243	Torsion balance to compare an electrostatic attraction with an electromagnetic repulsion, 1 March 1865	213
244	Letter to Peter Guthrie Tait, 7 March 1865	214
245	Letter to Peter Guthrie Tait, 3 April 1865	216
246	Letter to William Thomson, 17 and 18 April 1865	218
247	Letter to Robert Dundas Cay, 28 April 1865	221
248	Letter to Thomas Graham, 1 May 1865	222
249	Letter to Peter Guthrie Tait, 17 June 1865	224
250	Letter to Henry Richmond Droop, 19 July 1865	226
251	Letter to Lewis Campbell, 21 November 1865	228
252	On the viscosity or internal friction of air and other gases (abstract), [23 November 1865]	230
253	On James Thomson's vortex turbine, *c.* late 1865	236
	Appendix I: On the stability of vortex motion, *c.* late 1865	239
	Appendix II: Letter to Robert Dundas Cay, 8 December 1865	240
254	On the stability of fluid motion, *c.* 1865	241
255	On a paper by John Tyndall on calorescence, 1 January 1866	245
256	Letter to Charles Benjamin Tayler, 2 February 1866	249
257	Letter to Hugh Andrew Johnstone Munro, 7 February 1866	250

258	On a paper by John Tyndall on radiation, 22 February 1866	page 253
259	Drafts of 'On the dynamical theory of gases', late 1865 – early 1866	254
260	Letter to William Thomson, 27 February 1866	267
261	On a paper by Joseph David Everett on the rigidity of glass, 1 March 1866	272
262	Letter to Peter Guthrie Tait, 4 April 1866	276
263	On the dynamical theory of gases (abstract), [16 May 1866]	279
264	On a paper by Thomas Graham on the absorption and separation of gases, 17 July 1866	285
265	On a paper by Edward Wyndham Tarn on the stability of domes, 18 December 1866	288
266	Letter to George Gabriel Stokes, 18 December 1866	291
267	Letter to James Joseph Sylvester, 21 December 1866	294
268	Letter to George Gabriel Stokes, 27 February 1867	298
269	On a paper by Joseph David Everett on the determination of rigidity, 4 March 1867	300
270	Reported comments on Brodie's chemical calculus, 6 June 1867	304
271	Letter to William Huggins, 10 June 1867	306
272	British Association paper on a stereoscope, [September 1867]	312
273	On reciprocal figures and diagrams of forces, *c*. September 1867	313
	Appendix: British Association paper on diagrams of forces, [September 1867]	317
274	Letter to William Thomson, 14 September 1867	318
275	Letter to Peter Guthrie Tait, 13 November 1867	321
276	Letter to Peter Guthrie Tait, 4 December 1867	323
277	Letter to Peter Guthrie Tait, 11 December 1867	328
278	Letter to Peter Guthrie Tait, 23 December 1867	335
279	On the principles of stereoscopic vision, *c*. 1867	340
	Appendix: exhibition of stereograms to the London Mathematical Society, 23 January 1868	342
280	Question to the London Mathematical Society on governors, 23 January 1868	343
	Appendix: draft on governors, *c*. January 1868	344
281	Letter to William Thomson, 20 February 1868	346
282	On a paper by Joseph David Everett on the rigidity of metal rods, *c*. 25 February 1868	348
283	Letter to George Biddell Airy, 12 March 1868	351
284	Letter to Peter Guthrie Tait, 12 March 1868	353
285	Letter to William Robert Grove, 27 March 1868	356
286	Letter to Mark Pattison, 7 April 1868	358

		List of texts	xvii
287	Letter to Mark Pattison, 13 April 1868		*page* 362
288	On papers by Francis Bashforth, James Atkinson Longridge and Charles Watkins Merrifield on the motion of projectiles, 19 May 1868		369
289	On a method of making a direct comparison of electrostatic with electromagnetic force; with a note on the electromagnetic theory of light (abstract), [10 June 1868]		375
290	On a paper by Alfred Des Cloiseaux on the optical properties of crystals, *c.* late May 1868		380
291	On a paper by Robert Moon on the impact of compressible bodies, 8 July 1868		383
292	On the measurement of surface tension, *c.* Summer 1868		386
293	Letter to Peter Guthrie Tait, 14 July 1868		389
294	Letter to Peter Guthrie Tait, 18 July 1868		391
	Appendix: comments on Thomson and Tait's *Natural Philosophy*, Chapter II, July 1868		395
295	Letter to William Thomson, 18 July 1868		398
296	Letter to Peter Guthrie Tait, *c.* 20 July 1868		407
297	Letter to John Tyndall, 23 July 1868		409
	Appendix: stability criteria for governors of the fifth order, *c.* late July 1868		410
298	On a paper by George Gabriel Stokes on the communication of vibration to a gas, 28 July 1868		412
299	Letter to Peter Guthrie Tait, 3 August 1868		416
300	On the absorption and dispersion of light, *c.* August 1868		419
	Appendix: Mathematical Tripos question, *c.* late 1868		420
301	Letter to William Thomson, 19 August 1868		422
302	Letter to William Thomson, 5 September 1868		424
303	Letter to William Thomson, 12 September 1868		428
304	On topology, *c.* September 1868		433
305	On continuity and topology, *c.* September 1868		439
306	Letter to William Thomson, 28 September 1868		443
307	Letter to William Thomson, 6 October 1868		446
308	Letter to William Thomson, 7 October 1868		449
	Appendix: on hollow solids, *c.* October 1868		450
309	Letter to William Huggins, 13 October 1868		451
310	Letter to William Thomson, 16 October 1868		453
311	Letter to William Thomson, 30 October 1868		457
312	Letter to Lewis Campbell, 3 November 1868		460
313	Letter to William Robert Grove, 7 November 1868		461
314	Letter to George Biddell Airy, 9 November 1868		462

315	Letter to William Thomson, 9 November 1868	page 463
316	Letter to William Thomson, 7 December 1868	464
317	On the topology of surfaces, 29 December 1868	466
318	On J. B. Listing's paper 'Der Census räumlicher Complexe', 11 February 1869	470
319	On a paper by Henry Moseley on the motion of glaciers, 2 March 1869	472
320	Letter to Arthur Cayley, 12 April 1869	476
321	Letter to William Thomson, 12 May 1869	479
322	Letter to William Thomson, 5 June 1869	483
323	Letter to George Gabriel Stokes, 26 June 1869	487
324	Letter to George Gabriel Stokes, 8 July 1869	489
325	On a paper by Norman Macleod Ferrers on the motion of a rigid body, 14 August 1869	492
326	Letter to William Thomson, 17 August 1869	496
327	Letter to William Thomson, 1 October 1869	498
328	Letter to William Thomson, 5 October 1869	501
329	Contents of the *Treatise on Electricity and Magnetism*, c. October 1869	502
330	Letter to the London Mathematical Society on the potential of a disc, November 1869	508
331	On a paper by George Oldham Hanlon on the *vena contracta*, November 1869	510
332	Letter to William Thomson, 16 November 1869	513
333	Letter to Peter Guthrie Tait, 10 December 1869	516
334	On reciprocal figures, frames, and diagrams of forces (abstract), [17 December 1869]	519
335	Drafts relating to Part IV of the *Treatise*, c. late 1869	522
336	Letter to Katherine Mary Clerk Maxwell, 3 January 1870	528
337	On a paper by William John Macquorn Rankine on fluid motion, 2 March 1870	529
338	On a paper by William John Macquorn Rankine on the thermodynamic theory of waves, 26 March 1870	535
339	Letter to William Thomson, 14 April 1870	541
340	Letter to John William Strutt, 18 May 1870	545
341	Letter to Cecil James Monro, 6 July 1870	550
342	On a paper by Charles Bland Radcliffe on animal electricity, c. July 1870	554
343	On the chromatic effects of polarised light on double refracting crystals: addition to a paper by Francis Deas, c. Summer 1870	559

344	Draft of the 1870 Presidential Address to Section A of the British Association, *c.* Summer 1870	*page* 564
345	British Association paper on hills and dales, [September 1870]	566
346	Letter to Peter Guthrie Tait, 7 November 1870	568
347	On the application of quaternions to electromagnetism, November 1870	570
348	Letter to Peter Guthrie Tait, 14 November 1870	577
349	Letter to John Hutton Balfour, 28 November 1870	580
350	Letter to John William Strutt, 6 December 1870	582
	Appendix: from the manuscript of the *Theory of Heat*, *c.* late 1870	584
351	Letter to George Gabriel Stokes, 11 January 1871	589
352	Draft letter to Peter Guthrie Tait, 23 January 1871	590
353	Letter to Peter Guthrie Tait, 23 January 1871	593
354	On a paper by John William Strutt on the theory of resonance, 31 January 1871	598
355	Letter to John William Strutt, 4 February 1871	605
356	Postcard to Peter Guthrie Tait, 14 February 1871	609
357	Draft letter to Edward William Blore, 15 February 1871	611
358	Letter to John William Strutt, 15 March 1871	614
359	Letter to Cecil James Monro, 15 March 1871	617
360	On colour blindness, *c.* March 1871	621
361	Letter to Katherine Mary Clerk Maxwell, 20 March 1871	623
362	Letter to William Thomson, 21 March 1871	624
363	Letter to Katherine Mary Clerk Maxwell, 22 March 1871	629
364	Plans for the physical laboratory, *c.* March 1871	630
365	Postcard to William Thomson, 30 March 1871	632
366	Postcard to Peter Guthrie Tait, 4 April 1871	634
367	Postcard to Peter Guthrie Tait, 3 May 1871	636
368	Postcard to Peter Guthrie Tait, 8 May 1871	637
369	Postcard to Peter Guthrie Tait, 11 May 1871	639
370	Question to the London Mathematical Society on spatial relations, 11 May 1871	641
	Appendix: note on spatial relations, 11 May 1871	642
371	Postcard to Peter Guthrie Tait, 12 May 1871	644
372	Postcard to Peter Guthrie Tait, 25 May 1871	645
373	Postcard to Peter Guthrie Tait, 27 May 1871	646
374	Postcard to Peter Guthrie Tait, 27 May 1871	648
375	Postcard to Peter Guthrie Tait, 3 June 1871	650
376	Postcard to Peter Guthrie Tait, 14 June 1871	652
377	On the history of the kinetic theory of gases: notes for William Thomson, *c.* Summer 1871	654

378	Letter to Charles William Siemens, 23 June 1871	*page* 661
379	Letter to John William Strutt, 8 and 10 July 1871	664
	Appendix: letter of reference for William Kingdon Clifford, *c.* July 1871	666
380	Postcard to Peter Guthrie Tait, 13 July 1871	667
381	Letter to James Thomson, 13 July 1871	668
382	Letter to James Thomson, 24 July 1871	670
383	Note for William Thomson and Peter Guthrie Tait, late August 1871	675
384	Postcard to Peter Guthrie Tait, 5 September 1871	677
385	Note for Fleeming Jenkin on electric circuits, *c.* September 1871	678
	Appendix: annotation on proof of Jenkin's *Electricity and Magnetism, c.* September 1871	680
386	Letter to Peter Guthrie Tait, 19 October 1871	681
387	Postcard to Peter Guthrie Tait, 23 October 1871	682
388	Letter to Peter Guthrie Tait, 2 November 1871	683
389	Postcard to Peter Guthrie Tait, 7 November 1871	686
390	Postcard to William Thomson, 7 November 1871	689
391	Letter to Robert Dundas Cay, 23 November 1871	690
392	Reported comments on the strains of an iron structure, 5 December 1871	691
393	Postcard to Peter Guthrie Tait, 7 December 1871	692
394	Postcard to Peter Guthrie Tait, 12 December 1871	694
395	On the geometrical mean distance of two figures on a plane, *c.* December 1871	695
396	Letter to Peter Guthrie Tait, 21 December 1871	699
397	Letter to William Milner Fawcett, 1 January 1872	701
398	Postcard to Peter Guthrie Tait, 1 January 1872	702
399	Postcard to Peter Guthrie Tait, *c.* 4 January 1872	704
400	Letter to George Gabriel Stokes, 8 January 1872	706
401	Postcard to Peter Guthrie Tait, 19 January 1872	707
402	Postcard to William Thomson, 8 February 1872	708
403	Postcard to Peter Guthrie Tait, 12 February 1872	710
404	Letter to George Gabriel Stokes, 12 February 1872	711
405	Abstract of paper on Arago's rotating disc, *c.* 15 February 1872	712
406	Letter to William Huggins, 2 May 1872	714
407	Letter to Peter Guthrie Tait, *c.* early May 1872	715
408	Postcard to Peter Guthrie Tait, 9 May 1872	716
409	Postcard to Peter Guthrie Tait, 14 May 1872	717

List of texts

410	On a paper by George Biddell Airy on the magnetic properties of iron and steel, 17 May 1872	page 718
411	Letter to Peter Guthrie Tait, 24 May 1872	727
412	Letter to Robert Dundas Cay, 27 May 1872	729
	Appendix: theorem on the potential function for the 1873 Mathematical Tripos, *c*. Summer 1872	730
413	Note to Peter Guthrie Tait, *c*. late June 1872	731
414	Postcard to Peter Guthrie Tait, 29 June 1872	732
415	On a paper by Latimer Clark on a standard of electromotive force, *c*. 2 July 1872	734
416	Letter to George Gabriel Stokes, 8 July 1872	738
417	Postcard to Peter Guthrie Tait, 15 July 1872	739
	Appendix: postcard to Peter Guthrie Tait, 7 August 1872	741
418	Letter to Latimer Clark, 16 July 1872	742
419	On the interpretation of Lagrange's and Hamilton's equations of motion, *c*. July 1872	744
420	Letter to William Thomson, 10 August 1872	748
421	Letter to James Thomson, 2 September 1872	751
422	Postcard to Peter Guthrie Tait, 4 October 1872	755
423	Letter to Peter Guthrie Tait, 9 October 1872	756
424	Letter to George Biddell Airy, 16 October 1872	758
425	Letter to Lewis Campbell, 19 October 1872	760
426	Letter to George Biddell Airy, 28 October 1872	761
427	Note to Peter Guthrie Tait, 12 November 1872	763
428	Letter to Peter Guthrie Tait, late 1872 – early 1873	764
429	Notes to Peter Guthrie Tait, *c*. December 1872	766
430	On electromagnetism, late 1872 – early 1873	767
431	On Forbes' work on colours, *c*. 1872	774
432	On the classification of the physical sciences, late 1872 – early 1873	776
433	Letter of reference for James Thomson, 7 January 1873	783
434	Postcard to William Thomson, 22 January 1873	784
435	Draft letter to the Duke of Devonshire, late January – early February 1873	785
436	On a problem in the calculus of variations in which the solution is discontinuous, February 1873	787
437	Lecture on Faraday's lines of force, early 1873	790
	Appendix: on dynamical principles, *c*. 1873	811
438	Letter to Henry Bence Jones, 4 February 1873	813
439	Essay for the Eranus Club on science and free will, 11 February 1873	814

440	Postcard to Peter Guthrie Tait, 12 February 1873	page 824
441	Letter to Peter Guthrie Tait, *c.* early 1873	825
442	On a paper by Frederick Guthrie on the electrical properties of hot bodies, *c.* 25 February 1873	827
443	Postcard to Peter Guthrie Tait, 3 March 1873	831
444	Postcard to Peter Guthrie Tait, 5 March 1873	832
445	Letter to Peter Guthrie Tait, 10 March 1873	833
446	Postcard to Peter Guthrie Tait, 12 March 1873	835
447	On a paper by James Jago on experiments on vision, *c.* 24 March 1873	836
448	Letters to William Thomson, 25 March 1873	839
449	Letter to Lewis Campbell, 3 April 1873	840
450	Review of Fleeming Jenkin, *Electricity and Magnetism*, *c.* April 1873	842
451	Letter to Peter Guthrie Tait, 2 May 1873	845
452	Letter to Peter Guthrie Tait, 7 May 1873	846
453	Letter to George Gabriel Stokes, 13 May 1873	847
454	Letter to Peter Guthrie Tait, 15 May 1873	848
455	On a paper by Dugald M'Kichan on the determination of the number of electrostatic units in one electromagnetic unit of electricity, *c.* 20 May 1873	849
456	Letter to Robert Dundas Cay, 22 May 1873	852
457	On the effect of gravity on the temperature of a column of gas, *c.* 25 May 1873	853
458	Letter to John William Strutt, 26 May 1873	856
459	Letter to Charles Tomlinson, 29 May 1873	858
460	On a paper by John William Strutt on theorems relating to vibrations, 26 June 1873	860
461	On the theory of anomalous dispersion, *c.* 1873	864
462	On a paper by Latimer Clark on a standard voltaic battery, 26 June 1873	866
463	Fixtures and instruments in the Cavendish Laboratory, June 1873	868
464	Draft letter to Henry Wilkinson Cookson, 5 July 1873	876
465	Postcard to Peter Guthrie Tait, *c.* 8 July 1873	877
466	Letter to Henry Augustus Rowland, 9 July 1873	879
467	Letter to Henry Augustus Rowland, 12 July 1873	881
468	Letter to Peter Guthrie Tait, 22 July 1873	884
469	Postcard to Peter Guthrie Tait, 24 July 1873	888
470	Draft of 'On Loschmidt's experiments on diffusion', late July 1873	890

List of texts xxiii

471	Postcard to Peter Guthrie Tait, 30 July 1873	*page* 897
472	Drafts of 'On the final state of a system of molecules in motion subject to forces of any kind', *c.* August 1873	898
473	Draft of 'On the final state of a system of molecules in motion subject to forces of any kind', August 1873	911
474	Letter to Peter Guthrie Tait, *c.* August 1873	915
475	On atoms and ether, 13 August 1873	917
476	Letter to John William Strutt, Lord Rayleigh, 28 August 1873	919
477	Note to Peter Guthrie Tait, late August – early September 1873	921
478	Drafts of lecture on 'Molecules', *c.* August – September 1873	922
479	Postcard to Peter Guthrie Tait, 2 September 1873	934
480	British Association paper on geometrical optics, [September 1873]	935
481	On the effect of gravity on the temperature of a column of gas, October 1873	937
482	Letter to John William Strutt, Lord Rayleigh, 22 November 1873	940
483	Letter to Peter Guthrie Tait, 1 December 1873	944
484	Letter to William Grylls Adams, 3 December 1873	949
485	On quaternions, December 1873	951
486	Letter to Herbert Spencer, 5 December 1873	956
487	Letter to Herbert Spencer, 17 December 1873	962
488	Examiner's report on the Natural Sciences Tripos (Physics) 1873, December 1873	964
489	The equation of continuity and physical analogy, 1873	965
490	On a paper by Osmond Fisher on the elevation of mountains, *c.* December 1873	968

EDITORIAL NOTE

The terms of reference of this edition of Maxwell's scientific letters and papers are described in the General introduction and Editorial note to the first volume. Maxwell's extant autograph letters and papers are supplemented by documents drawn from the *Life of Maxwell*, and by his shorter publications – letters, reviews, abstracts of contributed and published papers, and contributions to discussions – which were omitted from the memorial edition of his *Scientific Papers* published by Cambridge University Press in 1890. The texts are reproduced in chronological sequence, so far as can be determined. In the case of postcards, where there is generally no date written by Maxwell, the convention is adopted (in the absence of any other evidence) of dating the cards by their postmarks. In the case of abstracts of contributed and published papers the convention is adopted either of citing the date when the paper was read, or (in the case of papers read to the Royal Societies of London and Edinburgh) the date the paper was received by the Secretary.

The primary intention of this edition is the reproduction of an accurate text of all Maxwell's scientific letters and substantive manuscript papers. Manuscript fragments and jottings have been included on a selective basis. Special mention should be made of a series of six notebooks[1] that Maxwell kept during the years spanned by this volume. These notebooks, each of which was in use for two or three years, contain drafts of examination questions, journal references, calculations, and a miscellany of fragmentary jottings and notes. Some materials drawn from these notebooks have been reproduced as texts, and additional manuscript jottings have been included in the editorial annotations.

As already mentioned, the edition includes publications omitted from the *Scientific Papers*. Two classes of such published works have of necessity not been included: reports of the British Association Committee on electrical standards, of which Maxwell was a member[2] (the report for the year 1863

---

(1) There are three notebooks in the Maxwell Papers in the King's College London Archives; one in ULC Add. MSS 7655, V, k/9; one in the Cavendish Laboratory, Cambridge (of which there is a photocopy in ULC Add. MSS 7655, V, n/1); and one in ULC Add. MSS 7655, V, n/2).

(2) In the British Association *Reports* for 1863, 1864 and 1869; reprinted in Fleeming Jenkin, *Reports of the Committee on Electrical Standards appointed by the British Association for the Advancement of Science* (London, 1873).

including his paper, written with Fleeming Jenkin, on electrical units and dimensional relations);[3] and his series of questions set during five years as an examiner and moderator for the Cambridge Mathematical Tripos,[4] though some of these questions (being of special relevance) have been reproduced as texts or included in the editorial annotations.

Letters addressed to Maxwell are listed in the appendix. Because of the limited scope of these documents (as described in the General introduction to the first volume of the edition) these letters are reproduced on a selective basis. In the present volume all the letters written by his major correspondents, George Gabriel Stokes, Peter Guthrie Tait, and William Thomson, are printed *in extenso*. Other letters are reproduced complete, in extract, or are merely cited, as judged appropriate. Because of the generally patchy nature of the extant incoming correspondence, these letters are reproduced as annotations to the Maxwell texts. Third-party letters and other documents that contain information bearing on Maxwell's writings and work are included, generally in selective extract.

In accordance with the principles of modern scholarship the reproduction of the texts faithfully follows the manuscripts in spelling, punctuation, capitalization, and in preserving contractions; endpoints to sentences have been silently inserted. Where the texts are reproduced from printed sources the style of the original is followed. Trivial cancellations have been omitted without comment, but corrections deemed significant have been recorded. Minor deletions are placed within angle brackets ⟨...⟩ preceding the revised text; longer cancelled passages are reproduced by setting a double vertical bar against them in the left-hand margin. Appended passages are reproduced with a single vertical bar in the left-hand margin; appended phrases by corners ⌞...⌟ which enclose the added words. Annotations which were subsequently appended by Maxwell or by his correspondents are recorded. The name enclosed by brackets {...} denotes the annotator. The very few editorial insertions to the text, which have been introduced for the sake of clarity, are enclosed within square brackets.

In general I have attempted to preserve the layout of the manuscripts in their transformation to the printed page, but some necessary adjustments have been made for reasons of clarity. This applies especially to the reproduction of figures, which, like the transcription of handwriting, requires editorial interpretation. Some of Maxwell's figures are clearly drawn, but

---

(3) J. Clerk Maxwell and Fleeming Jenkin, 'On the elementary relations between electrical measurements', *Phil. Mag.*, ser. 4, **29** (1865): 436–60, 507–25; in Jenkin, *Reports of the Committee*: 59–96.

(4) In the *Cambridge University Calendar* for 1866, 1867, 1869, 1870 and 1873.

most are rough sketches. The aim has been to elucidate Maxwell's intentions as determined by study of both the figure and the corresponding text. The aim has been clarity rather than the precise reproduction of the originals. Figure numbers have been added; the captions are Maxwell's. In printing documents in the annotations to the texts, the convention is adopted of marking paragraph divisions and lines of poetry by a solidus.

The editorial commentary – the historical and textual notes and the Introduction – is intended to aid the reader in following Maxwell's arguments and his allusions to concepts, events and personalities. The Introduction provides a broad account of his intellectual development and career in the period covered by this volume, and an outline review of the texts here reproduced. In addition to clarifying obscurities in the texts, the historical notes seek to establish the context within which the documents were written, employing contemporary published as well as manuscript sources, including letters written to Maxwell, third-party correspondence, and fragmentary manuscript jottings not reproduced as texts. Reference to the first volume of the edition is made in the form 'Volume I: 438', meaning Volume I: [page] 438.

LIST OF PLATES

Part I

From 'A dynamical theory of the electromagnetic field', October 1864 (The Royal Society, PT.72.7, folio 62) (Number 239) *frontispiece*

I	The 'compound' governor, after 1863 (Cavendish Laboratory, Cambridge) (Number 219)	*facing page* 114
II	From a letter to William Thomson, 15 October 1864 (Glasgow University Library) (Number 235)	178
III	Drawing of torsion balance, 1 March 1865 (ULC Add. MSS 7655, V, c/14 (i)) (Number 243)	212
IV	Apparatus to determine the viscosity of gases, 1865 (Cavendish Laboratory, Cambridge) (Number 252)	230
V	Real image stereoscope, 1867 (Cavendish Laboratory, Cambridge) (Number 272)	312
VI	Stereograms of icosihedron in octahedron, lines of curvature of elliptic paraboloid and lines of curvature of hyperbolic paraboloid, 1867 (ULC Add. MSS 7655, V, i/11) (Number 274)	318
VII	Stereograms of lines of curvature of ellipsoid and Fresnel's wave surface, 1867 (ULC Add. MSS 7655, V, i/11) (Number 274)	319
VIII	Stereograms of conical point of wave surface and centres of curvature of ellipsoid, 1867 (ULC Add. MSS 7655, V, i/11) (Number 275)	322
IX	Stereograms of Gordian knots, 1867 (ULC Add. MSS 7655, V, i/11) (Number 277)	330
X	Stereograms of confocal spherical ellipses and concyclic spherical ellipses, 1867 (ULC Add. MSS 7655, V, i/11) (Number 277)	331
XI	Electrical torsion balance, 1868 (Cavendish Laboratory, Cambridge) (Number 289)	376
XII	Surface-tension microscope, 1868 (Whipple Museum, Cambridge) (Number 292)	386
XIII	Zoetrope or 'wheel of life' showing Helmholtz's rings, 1868 (Cavendish Laboratory, Cambridge) (Number 307)	446

| XIV | Zoetrope or 'wheel of life' showing motion through a fluid, 1868 (Cavendish Laboratory, Cambridge) (Number 310) | 456 |

Part II

| XV | Postcard to Peter Guthrie Tait, 7 November 1871 (ULC Add. MSS 7655, I, b/36) (Number 389) | 686 |

ABBREVIATED REFERENCES

Ann. Chim. Phys.	*Annales de Chimie et de Physique* (Paris).
Ann. Phys.	*Annalen der Physik und Chemie* (Leipzig).
Boase	*Modern English Biography containing Many Thousand Concise Memoirs of Persons who have Died since the Year 1850.* By Frederic Boase, 3 vols. and supplement (3 vols.) (Truro, 1892–1921).
Camb. & Dubl. Math. J.	*Cambridge and Dublin Mathematical Journal* (Cambridge).
Camb. Math. J.	*Cambridge Mathematical Journal* (Cambridge).
Comptes Rendus	*Comptes Rendus Hebdomadaires des Séances de l'Académie des Sciences* (Paris).
DNB	*Dictionary of National Biography.* Ed. L. Stephen and S. Lee, 63 vols. and 2 supplements (6 vols.) (London, 1885–1912).
Electricity	Michael Faraday, *Experimental Researches in Electricity*, 3 vols. (London, 1839–55).
Electrostatics and Magnetism	William Thomson, *Reprint of Papers on Electrostatics and Magnetism* (London, 1872).
Knott, *Life of Tait*	Cargill Gilston Knott, *Life and Scientific Work of Peter Guthrie Tait. Supplementing the two Volumes of Scientific Papers Published in 1898 and 1900* (Cambridge, 1911).
Larmor, *Correspondence*	*Memoir and Scientific Correspondence of the Late Sir George Gabriel Stokes, Bart.* Ed. J. Larmor, 2 vols. (Cambridge, 1907).
Larmor, 'Origins'	'The origins of Clerk Maxwell's electric ideas, as described in familiar letters to W. Thomson'. Communicated by Sir Joseph Larmor, in *Proc. Camb. Phil. Soc.*, **32** (1936): 695–750. Reprinted separately (Cambridge, 1937).
Life of Maxwell	Lewis Campbell and William Garnett, *The Life of James Clerk Maxwell. With a Selection from his Correspondence and Occasional Writings and a Sketch of his Contributions to Science* (London, 1882).
Life of Maxwell (2nd edn)	Lewis Campbell and William Garnett, *The Life of James Clerk Maxwell with Selections from his Correspondence and Occasional Writings*, new edition, abridged and revised (London, 1884).
Math. & Phys. Papers	William Thomson, *Mathematical and Physical Papers*, 6 vols. (Cambridge, 1882–1911).
Molecules and Gases	*Maxwell on Molecules and Gases.* Ed. Elizabeth Garber,

	Stephen G. Brush and C. W. F. Everitt (Cambridge, Massachusetts/London, 1986).
OED	*The Oxford English Dictionary*, 12 vols. (Oxford, 1970).
Papers	George Gabriel Stokes, *Mathematical and Physical Papers*, 5 vols. (Cambridge, 1880–1905).
Phil. Mag.	*Philosophical Magazine* (London).
Phil. Trans.	*Philosophical Transactions of the Royal Society of London* (London).
Proc. Camb. Phil. Soc.	*Proceedings of the Cambridge Philosophical Society* (Cambridge).
Proc. Roy. Soc.	*Proceedings of the Royal Society of London* (London).
Proc. Roy. Soc. Edinb.	*Proceedings of the Royal Society of Edinburgh* (Edinburgh).
Scientific Memoirs	*Scientific Memoirs, Selected from the Transactions of Foreign Academies of Science and Learned Societies, and from Foreign Journals.* Ed. Richard Taylor, 5 vols. (London, 1837–52).
Scientific Papers	*The Scientific Papers of James Clerk Maxwell.* Ed. W. D. Niven, 2 vols. (Cambridge, 1890).
Thomson and Tait, *Natural Philosophy*	Sir William Thomson and Peter Guthrie Tait, *Treatise on Natural Philosophy. Vol. 1* (Oxford, 1867).
Trans. Camb. Phil. Soc.	*Transactions of the Cambridge Philosophical Society* (Cambridge).
Trans. Roy. Soc. Edinb.	*Transactions of the Royal Society of Edinburgh* (Edinburgh).
Treatise	James Clerk Maxwell, *A Treatise on Electricity and Magnetism*, 2 vols. (Oxford, 1873).
ULC	Manuscripts in the University Library, Cambridge.
Venn	*Alumni Cantabrigienses. A Biographical List of all Known Students, Graduates and Holders of Office at the University of Cambridge, from the Earliest Times to 1900.* Compiled by J. A. Venn. Part II. From 1752 to 1900, 6 vols. (Cambridge, 1940–54).
Wiener Berichte	*Sitzungsberichte der Mathematisch-Naturwissenschaftlichen Classe der Kaiserlichen Akademie der Wissenschaften* (Vienna).
Wilson, *Stokes–Kelvin Correspondence*	*The Correspondence between Sir George Gabriel Stokes and Sir William Thomson, Baron Kelvin of Largs.* Edited with an introduction by David B. Wilson, 2 vols. (Cambridge, 1990).

TEXTS
1869-1873

COMMENTS ON J. B. LISTING'S PAPER 'DER CENSUS RÄUMLICHER COMPLEXE'[1]

11 FEBRUARY 1869

From the *Proceedings of the London Mathematical Society*[2]

[LISTING'S 'SURVEY OF SPATIAL COMPLEXES']

Mr. Clerk-Maxwell next drew attention to J. B. Listing's paper in the 10th vol. of the Göttingen Transactions, on the kinds of Cyclosis in lines, surfaces, and regions of space.[3] If p points are joined into a system by l lines, then since $p-1$ lines are sufficient for this purpose, the remaining $K = l-p+1$ lines give K independent closed paths.[4] Any other closed path must be compounded of these. If we call s the distance travelled by a point along any path, and[5]

$$L = \int \left(X \frac{dx}{ds} + Y \frac{dy}{ds} + Z \frac{dz}{ds} \right) ds,$$

the line-integral of the quantity, whose components are X, Y, Z, along the path, then if the line-integrals round each of the k cycles are $k_1 \ldots k_k$, the value of L from any one point to any other is

$$L = L_0 + n_1 k_1 + n_2 k_2 + \ldots + n_k k_k,$$

where $n_1, n_2 \ldots n_k$ are integral numbers.

As an instance, if

$$X = \frac{dw}{dx}, \quad Y = \frac{dw}{dy}, \quad Z = \frac{dw}{dz},$$

where w is the solid angle subtended at the point xyz by a closed curve, then if one of the cycles of the curve along which the line-integral is taken is enlinked with this closed curve, the corresponding value of k is 4π.

This will be the case if $L = \iint \frac{u}{r^3} ds\, ds'$,

---

(1) Remarks made at a meeting of the London Mathematical Society, 11 February 1869.

(2) *Proceedings of the London Mathematical Society*, **2** (1869): 165–6.

(3) Johann Benedict Listing, 'Der Census räumlicher Complexe oder Verallgemeinerung des Euler'schen Satzes von den Polyëdern', *Abhandlungen der Math. Classe der Königlichen Gesellschaft der Wissenschaften zu Göttingen*, **10** (1861): 97–182.

(4) Following Listing, Maxwell terms 'a loop or closed path ... a Cycle' (*Treatise*, **1**: 16 (§18)). The existence of cycles is termed 'Cyklose' by Listing, 'Der Census räumlicher Complexe': 111, 181, which Maxwell translates as 'Cyclosis'.

(5) See Number 305 esp. note (12).

where
$$\frac{u^2}{r^2} = \left[1-\left(\frac{dr}{ds}\right)^2\right]\left[1-\left(\frac{dr}{ds'}\right)^2\right]-\left(r\frac{d^2r}{ds\,ds'}\right)^2,$$

r being the distance from a point on the closed curve s to a point on the closed curve s', and the integral is taken round both curves. This integral is always $4\pi n$, and is a criterion of the curves being linked together or not, depending only on the relations of r, s and s'.[6]

---

(6) See Number 276 esp. note (8).

319

REPORT ON A PAPER BY HENRY MOSELEY[1] ON THE MOTION OF GLACIERS

2 MARCH 1869

From the original in the Library of the Royal Society, London[2]

REPORT ON CANON MOSELEY'S PAPER ON THE MECHANICAL POSSIBILITY OF THE DESCENT OF GLACIERS BY THEIR WEIGHT ONLY[3]

A considerable part of this paper including the general reasoning and the experimental investigation has been printed in the Proceedings.[4] The remainder consists chiefly of a mathematical determination of the work of shearing performed in the interior of a glacier and the work of friction at its surface as compared with the work performed by gravity during the same time.[5] This investigation if correct leads to the conclusion that the amount of work consumed in shearing the ice within the glacier and in rubbing its surface over the channel is greater, even in the most favourable case, than the work done by gravity. But this work is done, therefore there must be something in action besides gravity. The author does not in this paper state what this is, but he has given his views in former papers.[6]

We have therefore principally to consider the calculation of the work of shearing, and this both physically and mathematically. The author has determined experimentally the strength of ice to resist shearing force, and has

---

(1) St John's 1821, Professor of Natural Philosophy at King's College, London 1831–44, FRS 1839, Canon of Bristol 1853 (Venn, *DNB*).

(2) Royal Society, *Referees' Reports*, **6**: 191.

(3) Henry Moseley, 'On the mechanical possibility of the descent of glaciers, by their weight only' (Royal Society, AP. 51.8). The paper was received by the Royal Society on 21 October 1868, and read on 7 January 1869; see the abstract in *Proc. Roy. Soc.*, **17** (1869): 202–8.

(4) See note (3).

(5) Moseley subsequently published a corrected version of the mathematical portion (ff. 17–27) of his paper in the May 1869 number of the *Philosophical Magazine*; see Henry Moseley, 'On the mechanical impossibility of the descent of glaciers by their weight only', *Phil. Mag.*, ser. 4, **37** (1869): 363–70.

(6) Moseley had maintained that the descent of glaciers was the result of the successive elongation and contraction of sheets of ice, caused by changes of temperature. See Henry Moseley, 'On the descent of glaciers', *Proc. Roy. Soc.*, **7** (1855): 333–42; Moseley, 'On the motion of a plate of metal on an inclined plane, when dilated and contracted; and on the descent of glaciers', *ibid.*, **11** (1861): 168–77, esp. 177, where he contested Forbes' theory of glacier viscosity (see notes (11) and (12)) as explaining the descent of glaciers.

found that it requires about 75 lb weight per square inch to shear across a cylinder of ice made by stuffing a mould with ice and hammering it in. The radius of the cylinder was measured to the hundred thousandth part of an inch.

The author calls this coefficient of strength to resist shearing the *unit* of shear, an expression which I do not approve. Nothing is said about the time occupied in shearing the cylinder but I suppose it was cut in two as the requisite weights were applied.

Now if in any glacier the weight of the ice and the slope were great enough to shear the ice at any point right through then the glacier would descend,[7] and if the slope were a little greater the glacier would slide away with an accelerated velocity till the additional resistance due to concussion on the rocks reduced its speed. That is to say, it would be an avalanche. Glaciers which are not avalanches move very slowly so that the kind of resistance to deformation by which their motion is regulated must be one which depends on the *rate* of deformation. The simplest hypothesis which we can make is that the shearing force is proportional to the rate of deformation.[8] This is the hypothesis about the friction of fluids on which Stokes made his investigation of their action on pendulums.[9] It is probably true for all gases for water, oil, treacle, pitch, asphalt.

On the other hand, hard sharp sand has a resistance to shearing force which is independent of time, and seems to be proportional to the normal pressure as in friction of solid surfaces.

Soft clay, wet sand, mortar, and sanded asphalt have a combination of these two properties.

Another class of bodies such as broken ice and water mixed together, loaf

---

(7) From his experiments Moseley concluded that the 'unit of shear of ice...is therefore 75 lbs.' On the basis of the rate of descent of a glacier observed by John Tyndall in his paper 'On the physical phenomena of glaciers. Part I. Observations on the Mer-de-Glace', *Phil. Trans.*, **149** (1859): 261–78, Moseley's mathematical calculation gave the result that 'the unit of shearing force of the ice could not have been more than 1.3193 lb.' See Moseley, 'On the mechanical possibility of the descent of glaciers, by their weight only', *Proc. Roy. Soc.*, **17** (1869): 207.

(8) In his report on Moseley's paper (Royal Society, *Referees' Reports*, **6**: 192), dated 24 February 1869, W. J. M. Rankine noted: 'It may be remarked that the coefficient of resistance to shearing, or "Unit of Shear", as it is termed by the Author, is treated as being independent of the velocity with which the shearing motion goes on – in other words, it is assumed to be as great for an insensibly small velocity of shearing as for the considerable velocity with which the shearing must have taken place in the experiments from which the coefficient was deduced.'

(9) George Gabriel Stokes, 'On the effect of the internal friction of fluids on the motion of pendulums', *Trans. Camb. Phil. Soc.*, **9**, part 2 (1851): [8]–[106] (= *Papers*, **3**: 1–136). See Volume I: 597–8.

sugar and syrup, have a kind of plasticity depending on time but arising from different causes.

Bodies of the first class are called Viscous.[10] Some of them have the property of being sticky, but this is not implied in the use of this word by Forbes[11] and others.[12]

The word viscous is also applied to other bodies in which long continued force produces effects of a different kind from the same force acting for a short time.

Some bodies appear capable of resisting a small force of deformation for an indefinite time, though a greater force produces deformation at a rate depending on the force. Lead is probably of this kind and ice does not appear to alter its form under the action of small forces.

In the investigation in the paper, no notice is taken of the possible effect of time in allowing deformations to take place which would be prevented from happening at once by the strength of the ice.

The hypothesis on which the work of shearing seems to be calculated is that the surfaces, after being shorn asunder immediately freeze together so that the work done in sliding one on the other is equal to the shearing force multiplied by the distance of sliding. I should think that this hypothesis would apply well to the case of sharp sand or detritus, which we know lies permanently on a slope much steeper than that of a glacier, but when it comes to a steeper place it rushes down as a landslip, with a velocity like that of a falling body.

There seems to be a somewhat unnecessary complication in the calculation of the work of shearing on this principle, and I am doubtful whether it would be desirable to print it at full as a mathematical investigation, especially as the result, as stated in the part already printed follows readily from the statement of the hypothesis.

There is a note at p. 27 in which the viscosity of a fluid is treated but there

---

(10) See Number 252.

(11) J. D. Forbes, *Travels in the Alps of Savoy and of other parts of the Pennine Chain; with Observations on the Phenomena of Glaciers* (Edinburgh, 1843): 365; and Forbes, 'Illustrations of the viscous theory of glacier motion', *Phil. Trans.*, **136** (1846): 143–55, 157–75, 177–210, esp. 143 where he defines a glacier as a 'semifluid or viscous mass in motion'.

(12) Compare Thomson and Tait, *Natural Philosophy*: 591n; 'Forbes' theory is merely the proof by observation that glaciers have the property that mud (heterogeneous), mortar (heterogeneous), pitch (homogeneous), water (homogeneous), all have of changing shape indefinitely and continuously under the action of continued stress.' John Tyndall, 'On the physical phenomena of glaciers': 272–8, and in his *The Glaciers of the Alps* (London, 1860): 311–14, 325–7, had contested Forbes' theory of glacier viscosity, denying that ice possesses 'the "gluey tenacity" which the term viscous suggests' (on 327). See also Number 477.

is no statement of what is meant by μ[13] either in the interior or at the surface so that the value of the investigation is not easily understood.

On the whole I think that the reprinting of the whole paper with the omitted parts would but slightly increase the value of what we have in the Proceedings.[14]

JAMES CLERK MAXWELL
2nd March 1869
7 Kildare Terrace W.

(13) Moseley's 'unit of shear'. In the note on f. 7 of his manuscript (see note (3)) Moseley seems to be considering variations in μ in the interior of a glacier.

(14) Recording his 'dissent from [Moseley's]...conclusion', Rankine recommended publication in the *Philosophical Transactions*: 'Supposing that it should eventually be proved, that the shearing resistance of ice is a function of the velocity of shearing increasing towards a limit – viz: the coefficient found by the Author's experiments, – and that gravity alone is sufficient to account for the descent of glaciers, it will still be desirable that the details of Canon Moseley's investigation should be on record.' (see note (8)).

LETTER TO ARTHUR CAYLEY[1]

12 APRIL 1869

From the original in the Library of Trinity College, Cambridge[2]

86 Hereford Road
Westbourne Grove W
12 April 1869

Dear Sir

I have only just returned from Paris and found your paper of suggestions for surfaces lying here.[3] I send it on to Sylvester.[4]

Surface E, a tubular surface with a parabolic axis,[5] would I think be easily constructed by means of its circular sections which are lines of curvature, and the other lines of curvature pass through corresponding points of the circles.

Draw the parabola and a series of normals at proper intervals on a plane cut off the normals at a given length on each side. Draw the equidistant curves and the evolute of the parabola.

Make a number of semicircles of the proper size and place them on the normals at right angles to the plane.

When the normals intersect, the planes of these circles intersect, so that in the 'interesting' part of the figure there would be a great deal of honeycombing.

---

(1) Trinity 1838, Sadlerian Professor of Pure Mathematics at Cambridge 1863 (Venn).

(2) Trinity Portraits, Vol. C, page 50 *verso*.

(3) In his paper 'On the cyclide', *Quarterly Journal of Pure and Applied Mathematics*, **11** (1867): 111–26 (= *Scientific Papers*, **2**: 144–59), Maxwell drew stereoscopic diagrams of four varieties of the cyclide using his real image stereoscope (see Number 274). In a letter of 20 April 1868 (ULC Add. MSS 7655, II/29) Cayley had written to acknowledge receipt of some stereoscopic drawings. 'Dear Sir / I was very much obliged for the stereoscopic drawing of Steiner's surface – besides the ellipses, – & (I suppose less easily drawable) the intersections by the concentric spheres – I do not know if there are any other easily traceable curves on the surface. The axes are of course nodal lines – with two real sheets within the surface – and without any real sheets outside it – and I think it would bring out the stereoscopic figure if the axes were drawn upon it, and that rather more strongly than the other lines of the figure. I remain dear Sir / Yours sincerely / A. Cayley.' Maxwell very probably sent Cayley the figures in connection with his paper 'On the construction of stereograms of surfaces', *Proceedings of the London Mathematical Society*, **2** (1868): 57–8 (= *Scientific Papers*, **2**: 101), read to the London Mathematical Society on 23 January 1868, when stereograms of surfaces were exhibited; see Number 279 and Plate V.

(4) The paper mentioned by Maxwell was probably Cayley's 'On the quartic surfaces $(* \mathop{)} U, V, W)^2 = 0$', *Quarterly Journal of Pure and Applied Mathematics*, **11** (1870): 15–25. J. J. Sylvester was editor of the *Journal*.

(5) In his paper 'On the quartic surfaces': 21 Cayley discussed the case of a parallel surface of a paraboloid.

This part should be done separately by parallel sections the circular sections being drawn afterwards.

At the Conservatoire des Arts et Métiers there is a set of ruled surfaces capable of transformation, each line being a silk cord stretched by a separate weight. They work very well when they are quite dry and when not more than two strings pass through the same hole. The intersections of two such surfaces are indicated by beads through which two lines pass. There is also a cubic scroll by Michel Chasles[6] with cones & conics belonging to it. M. Tresca[7] has given me a plaster cast of Fresnels wave surface,[8] both the space between the sheets and the internal nucleus.

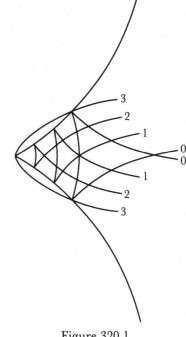

Figure 320,1

It would not be difficult to construct the symmetrical form of Steiner's surface[9] which you set a problem on.[10] Make a set of ellipses with constant major axis $= a$

---

(6) See Number 267 note (4).

(7) Henri Edouard Tresca, professor of mechanics at the Conservatoire des Arts et Métiers.

(8) The surface whose radii determine the speeds of wave fronts; see Augustin Fresnel, 'Mémoire sur la double réfraction', *Mémoires de l'Académie Royale des Sciences*, **7** (1827): 45–176, esp. 126–49. Cayley had published on the subject; see his papers 'On the wave surface', *Quarterly Journal of Pure and Applied Mathematics*, **3** (1860): 16–22; and 'Note on the wave surface', *ibid.*, **3** (1860): 142–4. See Number 274 and Plate VII.

(9) 'Steiner's surface' (suggested by Jacob Steiner), a fourth order surface such that on the surface there lie three double straight lines that intersect in a triple point, that has the property that each of its tangent planes cuts it in a pair of conics, had been made public by Karl Weierstrass in the *Monatsberichte der Akademie der Wissenschaften zu Berlin* (1863): 337–8. Cayley had published a paper on the surface: 'Note sur la surface du quatrième ordre de Steiner', *Journal für die reine und angewandte Mathematik*, **64** (1865): 172–4. Maxwell made a jotting 'Schröter on Steiner Surface' in a notebook (King's College, London Archives, Maxwell notebook (3)); see H. Schröter, 'Über die Steiner'sche Fläche vierten Grades', *Monatsberichte ... Berlin* (1863): 520–38. See Plate V.

(10) In his Smith's Prize paper of 3 February 1869 Cayley had set the following problem: 'Two tangents on a conic are harmonically related to a second conic: find the locus of the intersection of the two tangents. In plane geometry the angle in a semicircle is, in spherical geometry it is not, a right angle: show how these conditions follow from the solution of the above problem.'; see the *Cambridge University Calendar for the Year 1869* (Cambridge, 1869): 511, and Cayley's 'A "Smith Prize" paper; solutions', *Oxford, Cambridge and Dublin Messenger of Mathematics*, **5** (1869): 40–64.

and minor axis $a\sin 2\theta$. Place them with their minor axes coinciding with a fixed line and one extremity of the axis with a fixed point and with the plane of the ellipse inclined θ to a fixed plane. Then the ellipses are lines on Steiners surface.

After this week, address Glenlair
       Dalbeattie
       NB.

Yours truly
J. CLERK MAXWELL

321

LETTER TO WILLIAM THOMSON

12 MAY 1869

From the original in the University Library, Cambridge[1]

A. Cornu has set up a divided ring electrometer wh. he keeps charged with a dry pile.[2]

Glenlair
Dalbeattie
May 12 1869

Dear Thomson

I am finishing what I have to say on Statical Electricity & I should be glad to hear from you on some points.

1 I think I am right in saying that Poisson,[3] Plana[4] &c though they determined the distribution on a sphere due to an electrified point did not discover that the potential due to this distribution on the outside is that due to the image of the point and that this simplification of the theory, together with the whole theory of electrical inversion belongs to you.[5]

2nd The other problems solved by a general method (analogous to the harmonics) are

α Ellipsoids of revolution (planetary & ovary)[6] by J. Neumann, Crelle 37[7]

---

(1) ULC Add. MSS 7342, M 103. Previously published in Larmor, 'Origins': 736–8.

(2) Alfred Cornu was a professor at the École Polytechnique, Paris, whom Maxwell had presumably met on his visit to Paris: see his letter to Cayley of 12 April 1869 (Number 320). On Cornu's interest in electrometers see his paper 'Sur les mesures électrostatiques', *Journal de Physique Théorique et Appliquée*, **1** (1872): 7–17, 87–98, 241–6.

(3) Siméon Denis Poisson, 'Mémoire sur la distribution de l'électricité à la surface des corps conducteurs', *Mémoires de la Classe des Sciences Mathématiques et Physiques de l'Institut de France* (année 1811): 1–92, 163–274.

(4) Jean Plana, 'Mémoire sur la distribution de l'électricité à la surface de deux sphères conductrices complètement isolées', *Memorie della Reale Accademia delle Scienze di Torino*, ser. 2, **7** (1845): 71–401.

(5) Compare the *Treatise*, **1**: 191–5 (§155). On Thomson's method of electric images see Numbers 301, esp. note (10), and 310.

(6) Maxwell defines these terms in the *Treatise*, **1**: 187–8 (§§151–2), as ellipsoids which are figures of revolution about their conjugate and transverse axes, respectively. The terms 'ellipsoides planétaires' and 'ellipsoides ovales' are used by Gabriel Lamé, *Leçons sur les Fonctions Inverses Transcendantes et les Surfaces Isothermes* (Paris, 1857): 19, to which Maxwell refers below and in the *Treatise*, **1**: 181n (§147).

(7) Read: F. E. Neumann, 'Entwickelung der in elliptischen Coordinaten ausgedrückten

β Indefinite right cylinder Kirchhoff, Crelle 48.⁽⁸⁾

Has Liouville or any one else done it for the ellipsoid of 3 axes, except in the case of the charged ellipsoid in infinite field and the uncharged ellipsoid in field of uniform force.

In all the cases that have been done the position of a point in space is determined by three functions $\rho\,\mu\,\nu$. The equation of the conducting surface is

$$\rho = a.$$

For all internal points ρ is between 0 and a. For all external points ρ is between a and b which may be ∞.

The values of the potential are of the form

$$R\,M\,N$$

where R, M, N are functions of $\rho\,\mu\,\nu$ respectively.

For each value of M & N there are two values of R which fulfil Laplaces eq^n[9] one which vanishes at ∞ and another which does not become infinite within the surface.

M & N must be of the nature of periodic functions. See Lamé on Inverse Functions.[10]

The case of 2 dimensions has been pretty well solved by C. Neumann, Crelle 1861.[11]

Have you published anything about the theory of electrical images in the figure formed by four spheres which cut at right angles?[12]

For electrification to potential unity, if the radii are $r_1\ r_2\ r_3\ r_4$ the images are
At centre of 1st sphere, charge $= r_1$ (four points).

---

reciproken Entfernung zweier Punkte in Reihen, welche nach den Laplace'schen $Y^{(n)}$ fortschreiten; und Anwendung dieser Reihen zur Bestimmung des magnetischen Zustandes eines Rotations-Ellipsoids, welcher durch vertheilende Kräfte erregt ist', *Journal für die reine und angewandte Mathematik*, **37** (1848): 21–50.

(8) Gustav Kirchhoff, 'Ueber den inducirten Magnetismus eines unbegrenzten Cylinders von weichem Eisen', *Journal für die reine und angewandte Mathematik*, **48** (1854): 348–76.

(9) For the potential function V, $\nabla^2 V = 0$.

(10) Lamé, *Leçons sur les Fonctions Inverses Transcendantes*: 36–44. Compare the *Treatise*, **1**: 181–4 (§§147–9).

(11) Carl Neumann, 'Ueber die Integration der partiellen Differential-gleichung: $\dfrac{\partial^2\phi}{\partial x^2}+\dfrac{\partial^2\phi}{\partial y^2}$ $= 0$', *Journal für die reine und angewandte Mathematik*, **59** (1861): 335–66. Compare the *Treatise*, **1**: 234–5 (§190).

(12) Compare the *Treatise*, **1**: 211 (§170), where Maxwell outlines his treatment of this case.

At foot of perp from 3rd centre on the line between 1 & 2

$$\text{charge} = -\frac{1}{\sqrt{\frac{1}{r_1^2}+\frac{1}{r_2^2}}} \text{ (six points of this kind).}$$

At foot of perp from 4th centre on plane of 1 2 & 3

$$\text{charge} = +\frac{1}{\sqrt{\frac{1}{r_1^2}+\frac{1}{r_2^2}+\frac{1}{r_3^2}}} \text{ (four such points).}$$

At intersection of these four perpendiculars

$$\text{charge} = -\frac{1}{\sqrt{\frac{1}{r_1^2}+\frac{1}{r_2^2}+\frac{1}{r_3^2}+\frac{1}{r_4^2}}} \text{ (one point).}$$

The surface for which the potential due to these 15 points is unity consists of the 4 spheres. Of course the case of this figure influenced by a point comes out by inversion.[13]

Three spheres give the same expressions[14] and so do two.

If there are two spheres, centres A, B, radii α and β and a point O distant a from A & b from B the density at a point P on the sphere A induced by unit of electricity at O is

$$\sigma = \frac{1}{4\pi}\frac{a^2-\alpha^2}{\alpha r^3}\left(1 - \frac{\beta^3 r^3}{(\beta^2 r^2 + (b^2-\beta^2)(p^2-\beta^2))^{\frac{3}{2}}}\right)$$

radii of spheres α & β distance $AB = \sqrt{\alpha^2+\beta^2}$

$$OA = a \quad OB = b \quad OP = r \quad BP = p.\text{[15]}$$

I have been doing the charge on a proof plane in the form of a disk of radius a and thickness b.[16] I find that the charge is greater than that of the circle it

---

(13) On the method of 'electrical inversion', obtained from the geometrical method of inversion, see the *Treatise*, **1**: 199–203 (§§ 162–4). On the geometrical method of inversion see also Volume I: 484–5; and George Salmon, *A Treatise on the Higher Plane Curves* (Dublin, 1852): 306–7.

(14) See the *Treatise*, **1**: 210–11 (§ 169) for an analogous treatment of this case.

(15) See the *Treatise*, **1**: 207–9 (§ 168) (and Fig. IV appended to the volume) for the same result.

(16) On the theory of Coulomb's proof plane (a disc attached to the surface of a conductor) see the *Treatise*, **1**: 277–81 (§§ 223–5).

covers in the proportion of

$$1 + 8\frac{b}{a}\log\frac{8\pi a}{b} \text{ to } 1.^{(17)}$$

The thickness is supposed small compared with the radius and the radius small compared with the radius of curvature of the electrified surface to which the disk is applied.

I am now describing your absolute electrometer[18] & the quadrant d°.[19] To what class do you refer Coulombs Torsion Balance?[20]

Where are you to be found this summer. I may be at Ardhallow, Dunoon, between May 17 and May 31, and after that at Glenlair. How is the reprint of your electrical papers getting on?[21]

Yours truly
J. CLERK MAXWELL

---

(17) The value derived in the *Treatise*, **1**: 281 (§225).

(18) Thomson's guard-ring electrometer: see Number 289 esp. note (11).

(19) Thomson quadrant electrometer was described in his 'Report on electrometers and electrostatic instruments', *Report of the Thirty-seventh Meeting of the British Association* (London, 1868): 489–512, esp. 490–7 and Plate V (= *Electrostatics and Magnetism*: 262–81, with considerable augmentations). The instrument is described in the *Treatise*, **1**: 271–4 (§219).

(20) In his 'Report on electrometers and electrostatic instruments': 490, Thomson considered electrometers as falling under three classes: 'repulsion', 'symmetrical' (an example being the quadrant electrometer) and 'attracted disc' (an example being the guard-ring electrometer). Thomson made no mention of Coulomb's torsion balance, which Maxwell describes in the *Treatise*, **1**: 263–6 (§215). Coulomb described his electrometer in his paper 'Sur l'électricité et le magnétisme', *Mémoires de l'Académie Royale des Sciences* (année 1785): 569–77, 578–611, 616–38.

(21) The reprint of Thomson's papers on *Electrostatics and Magnetism* was published in 1872.

322
LETTER TO WILLIAM THOMSON
5 JUNE 1869
From the original in the University Library, Cambridge[1]

Glenlair
Dalbeattie
June 5 1869

Dear Thomson

I am anxious to know whether your views about contact electricity[2] are those which I attribute to you.

In the first place what is the potential of a metallic conductor. Is this it?[3] Make a hollow place in the conductor and place the end of the electrode of an electrometer in the hollow space, and carry off a great number of small particles from the end of the electrode to an infinite distance, then the potential indicated by the electrometer differs from that of the conductor by a constant quantity.

2nd The electromotive force from one metal to another is $J\Pi$ where Π is the Peltier effect[4] as defined in your RSE paper.[5] Now Π is a function of the temperature and of the 2 metals in contact and is such that at any one temperature for metals $a\ b\ c$

$$\Pi_{bc} + \Pi_{ab} + \Pi_{ca} = 0.$$

Hence $\quad \Pi_{ab} = P_a - P_b \quad \Pi_{bc} = P_b - P_c \quad \Pi_{ca} = P_c - P_a$

where $P_a\ P_b\ P_c$ are functions of the temperature for each metal.[6]

Also in any one metal owing to difference of temperature the difference of potentials of any two points is equal to the difference of the values of a

---

(1) ULC Add. MSS 7342, M 104. First published in Larmor, 'Origins': 738–9.

(2) William Thomson, 'On a self-acting apparatus for multiplying and maintaining charges, with applications to illustrate the voltaic theory', *Proc. Roy. Soc.*, **16** (1867): 67–72 (= *Electrostatics and Magnetism*: 319–25). See the *Treatise*, **1**: 299–300 (§§ 246–8).

(3) See the *Treatise*, **1**: 276 (§ 222).

(4) J. C. A. Peltier, 'Nouvelles expériences sur la caloricité des courants électriques', *Ann. Chim. Phys.*, ser. 2, **56** (1834): 371–86.

(5) William Thomson, 'On the dynamical theory of heat. Part V. Thermo-electric currents', *Trans. Roy. Soc. Edinb.*, **21** (1854): 123–71, esp. 133 (= *Math. & Phys. Papers*, **1**: 232–91); 'Π_1, Π_2, Π_3 &c denote the amounts (positive or negative) of heat absorbed at [the different junctions]... by a positive current of unit strength during the unit of time'.

(6) See the *Treatise*, **1**: 302–4 (§§ 250–1).

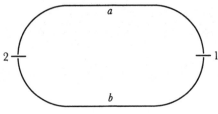

Figure 322,1

function Q of the temperature so that for a circuit of two metals a and b of which the junctions are at temperatures 1 and 2 the total electromotive force is

$$F = P_{a_1} - P_{b_1} + Q_{b_1} - Q_{b_2} + P_{b_2} - P_{a_2} + Q_{a_2} - Q_{a_1}$$
$$= P_{a_1} - Q_{a_1} - (P_{b_1} - Q_{b_1}) - (P_{a_2} - Q_{a_2}) + (P_{b_2} - Q_{b_2}).$$

Hence if we make $P_{a_1} - Q_{a_1} = R_{a_1}$ and so on

$$F = R_{a_1} - R_{a_2} - R_{b_1} + R_{b_2}.$$

If every P was equal to the corresponding Q thermo electric currents would be impossible but the Peltier effect at a junction might still exist so that by thermal experiments we might discover both the Ps and Qs in the way that you discovered the Qs.[7]

Could the Qs be measured by finding the difference of potential of air near hot & cold parts of the same piece of metal?

Here is my theory of the state of a dielectric called electric polarization.[8]

Draw any closed curve and through the points of this curve draw lines of inductive action so forming a tube of inductive action.[9] Draw two equipotential surfaces cutting the tube and enclosing between them a cell.

---

(7) Thomson, 'Thermo-electric currents': 141–5.

(8) On Maxwell's theory of dielectric polarisation, and the 'displacement of the electricity', see J. C. Maxwell, 'On physical lines of force. Part III. The theory of molecular vortices applied to statical electricity', *Phil. Mag.*, ser. 4, **23** (1862): 12–24, esp. 14–19 (= *Scientific Papers*, **1**: 491–6). See Maxwell's letters to Faraday and Thomson of 19 October and 10 December 1861 (Volume I: 683–9, 692–8). Maxwell had reformulated his concept of electric polarisation in Theorems C and D of his 'On a method of making a direct comparison of electrostatic with electromagnetic force; with a note on the electromagnetic theory of light', *Phil. Trans.*, **158** (1868): 643–57, esp. 654 (= *Scientific Papers*, **2**: 139). In the *Treatise* he develops this account of electric polarization: see the *Treatise*, **1**: 57–65, 131–4 (§§ 59–62, 109–11).

(9) Compare Maxwell's geometrical imagery in his paper 'On Faraday's lines of force', *Trans. Camb. Phil. Soc.*, **10** (1856): 27–83 (= *Scientific Papers*, **1**: 155–229). See Volume I: 337–50, 357–61.

The resultant electromotive force in the small cell is $\frac{A-B}{AB}$ in the direction perpendicular to A or B and from A towards B.

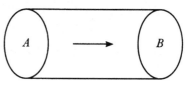

Figure 322,2

The electric displacement is a linear function of the electromotive force[10] and is parallel to the surface of the tube. In fluid dielectrics the displacement is in the direction of the electromotive force and is proportional to it.

The displacement through any section of the tube is the same and is

$$\frac{A-B}{AB} D \,(\text{area}) = Q$$

where D is the specific inductive capacity.[11]

Besides the internal displacement, which consists in a quantity of electricity Q being forced through every section from A towards B we must suppose a superficial distribution of Q on section A and $-Q$ on section B.[12] When the polarization is solenoidal[13] these superficial electrifications destroy one another except at the surface of the dielectric.[14]

The energy of the cell is $\frac{1}{2}FQ$[15] and its mechanical stress is a tension $= \frac{1}{2}\frac{FQ}{\text{volume}}$ on the surfaces A and B and a pressure of equal numerical value on the sides of the tube.[16]

---

(10) See the *Treatise*, **1**: 58–60 (§§59–60); Number 231 (equation (12)); and Maxwell's 'On a method of making a direct comparison...': 654–6 (= *Scientific Papers*, **2**: 139–42).

(11) On this Faradayan concept see the *Treatise*, **1**: 50 (§52).

(12) Compare Maxwell's discussion of the Leyden jar in the *Treatise*, **1**: 133 (§111). On Maxwell's theory of charge in the *Treatise* see J. Z. Buchwald, *From Maxwell to Microphysics* (Chicago/London, 1985): 20–40.

(13) See William Thomson's discussion of the 'solenoidal' distribution of magnetism in his paper 'A mathematical theory of magnetism', *Phil. Trans.*, **141** (1851): 243–85, esp. 270, 273 (= *Electrostatics and Magnetism*: 341–404). Thomson considers a magnet divided into an infinite number of 'solenoids' (a term derived from Ampère; see Number 410 note (19)), tubes 'which are either closed or have their ends in the bounding surface...the equation $\frac{d\alpha}{dx}+\frac{d\beta}{dy}+\frac{d\gamma}{dz}=0$ expresses that the distribution of magnetism is solenoidal', where α, β, γ are the components of magnetisation at any internal point x, y, z.

(14) Compare the *Treatise*, **1**: 133 (§111); 'all electrification is the residual effect of the polarization of the dielectric'.

(15) See Number 231; Maxwell, 'On a method of making a direct comparison...': 656 (= *Scientific Papers*, **2**: 142); and the *Treatise*, **1**: 63–4 (§62).

(16) Compare the *Treatise*, **1**: 126–31 (§§107–8).

It follows from this theory that the movements of electricity are like those of an incompressible fluid⁽¹⁷⁾ and that charging a body and putting it into a cubic foot of air does not increase the quantity of electricity in the cubic foot.

Yours truly

J. C. MAXWELL

(17) Compare the *Treatise*, **1**: 64 (§62); 'the motion of electricity is subject to the same condition as that of an incompressible fluid...it follows from this that every electric current must form a closed circuit'. See his comment on closed circuits in Theorem D of 'On a method of making a direct comparison...': 654 (= *Scientific Papers*, **2**: 139).

LETTER TO GEORGE GABRIEL STOKES

26 JUNE 1869

From the original in the University Library, Cambridge[1]

Glenlair
Dalbeattie
June 26, 1869

Dear Sir

As you have studied series of periodic functions[2] I should like to know from you whether there is any method of finding the coefficients of such a series

$$S = A_0 + A_1 \cos\theta + A_2 \cos 2\theta + \ldots + A_n \cos n\theta$$
$$+ B_1 \sin\theta + B_2 \sin 2\theta + \ldots + B_n \sin n\theta$$

so that between the limits $\theta = 0$ & $\theta = \alpha$ the series S shall have values given in terms of θ,

and between the limits $\theta = \alpha$ and $\theta = 2\pi$ some other series depending on S such as $\dfrac{dS}{d\theta}$ shall have values given in terms of θ.

For instance, can we find the values of the coefficients A in the series such that $A_0 + A_1 \cos\theta + A_2 \cos 2\theta + \ldots + A_n \cos n\theta$ shall be constant $= C$ for values of θ of the form $\theta = 2\pi n \pm \phi$ when ϕ is less than α and at the same time $A_1 \cos\theta + 2A_2 \cos 2\theta \ldots + nA_n \cos n\theta$ shall be zero for values of θ not within the above limits?

The question arises from the application of Fouriers theorem to the determination of the potential of an electrified grating consisting of a number of parallel strips all in one plane the breadth of each being $2a\alpha$ and the intervals between them being $2(\pi-\alpha)a$.

The potential is of the form

$$V = A_0 + A_1 e^{-\frac{y}{a}} \cos\frac{x}{a} + \&c + A_n e^{-n\frac{y}{a}} \cos\frac{nx}{a}$$

with the conditions $V = C$ on the strips and $\dfrac{dV}{dy} = 0$ in the intermediate spaces.

I have succeeded by a different method (that of transformation by

---

(1) ULC Add. MSS 7656, M 426. First published in Larmor, *Correspondence*, **2**: 29–30.

(2) George Gabriel Stokes, 'On the critical values of the sums of periodic series', *Trans. Camb. Phil. Soc.*, **8** (1848): 533–83 (= *Papers*, **1**: 236–313).

conjugate functions)⁽³⁾ in finding the effect of interposing a grating of fine parallel wires at potential zero between a plane at potential zero and an electrified parallel plane.⁽⁴⁾

If E be the electrification produced through the grating and E' that produced when the grating is away then

$$\frac{E'}{E} = 1 + \frac{\frac{1}{\alpha}}{\frac{1}{b_1}+\frac{1}{b_2}}$$

where b_1 & b_2 are the distances between the grating and the two planes and α is a line equal to $\frac{a}{2\pi}\log_e\left(\frac{1}{2}\operatorname{cosec}\frac{\pi c}{a}\right) = \alpha$ a being the distance between the axes of the wires and c their radius.

This is only true when a is much greater than c and when b_1 and b_2 are each much greater than a.

I have since got a method of finding the complete solution for cylindrical wires⁽⁵⁾ in a series of the form $A_0 F + A_1 \frac{dF}{dy} + A_2 \frac{d^2F}{dy^2} + \&c$, where

$$F = \log(e^y + e^{-y} - 2\cos x).$$

Can you tell me the value of the infinite series

$$\frac{1}{1.(1+\alpha)} + \frac{1}{2.(2+\alpha)} + \frac{1}{3.(3+\alpha)} + \&c,$$

where α is any fraction?

Excuse my troubling you with these questions, I wish you to answer them only if you can do so without trouble.

Yours truly
J. CLERK MAXWELL

---

(3) See Number 303 esp. note (3).
(4) See the *Treatise*, **1**: 248–51 (§§203–5); and Numbers 324 and 326.
(5) Compare the *Treatise*, **1**: 251–3 (§206).

324

LETTER TO GEORGE GABRIEL STOKES

8 JULY 1869

From the original in the University Library, Cambridge[1]

Glenlair
Dalbeattie
8 July 1869

Dear Sir

I am very much obliged to you for your information about Fouriers series &c.[2]

I am afraid I shall not be able to attend the meeting of the B.A. at Exeter[3] which I hope will be a great success. Jenkin is I believe with the Great Eastern[4] and will probably be busy for some time. Balfour Stewart knows most about the resistance experiments and Dr Joule has got the whole subject up independently in a most thorough manner so as to correct several numerical mistakes in the report.[5]

I know how to reduce the problem I sent you to a case of integration by a method which Thomson has applied to the complete solution of the electrification of a segment of a spherical shell.[6]

I first find by this method the distribution on an arc of a cylindric surface and then putting this in cylindric coordinates r & θ, the functions are periodic in θ. Then putting $r = ce^{\frac{2\pi x}{a}}$ and $\theta = \frac{2\pi y}{a}$, the functions become suited for rectangular coordinates and periodic in y.[7]

---

(1) ULC Add. MSS 7656, M 427. Previously published (in part) in Larmor, *Correspondence*, **2**: 30–1. (2) See Number 323.

(3) The 39th meeting of the British Association for the Advancement of Science, held at Exeter in August 1869.

(4) Fleeming Jenkin was engaged in laying the French Atlantic Cable aboard the *Great Eastern*, at Brest; see S. P. Thompson, *The Life of William Thomson, Baron Kelvin of Largs*, 2 vols. (London, 1910), **1**: 552.

(5) Jenkin, Joule and Stewart were members, with Maxwell, of the British Association's Committee on Standards of Electrical Resistance; see their brief 'Report' in the *Report of the Thirty-ninth Meeting of the British Association* (London, 1870): 434–8, which included Maxwell's 'Experiments on the value of v, the ratio of the electromagnetic to the electrostatic unit of electricity' (on which see Number 289 note (13)), giving his results on units and the figure of his apparatus as published in his paper 'On a method of making a direct comparison of electrostatic with electromagnetic force', *Phil. Trans.*, **158** (1868): 643–57, esp. 646, 651 (= *Scientific Papers*, **2**: 129, 135). The values given in the abstract (Number 289) differ: see Number 289 note (14).

(6) See Number 310 note (2).

(7) See the *Treatise*, **1**: 248–9 (§204): theory of a grating of parallel wires; and see Number 326.

The curves on the opposite page⁽⁸⁾ represent the equipotential surfaces & lines of force due to an infinite series of *wires* of which one is given at A placed parallel to a plane on the left hand which has an equal and opposite charge on its opposed surface.

Yours truly
J. Clerk Maxwell

---

(8) Compare Fig. XIII appended to the first volume of the *Treatise*.

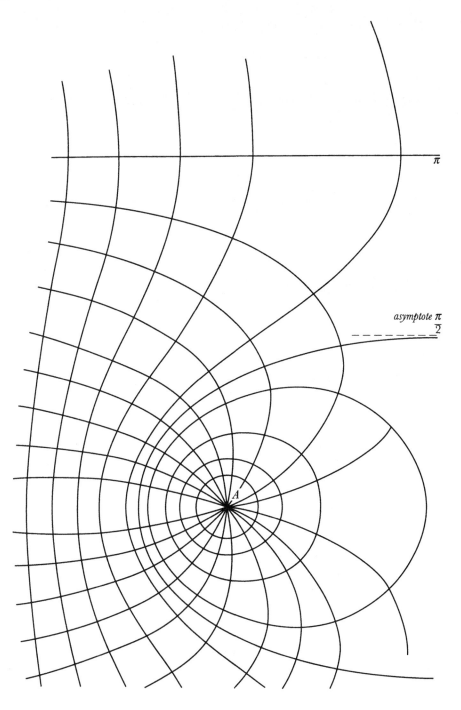

Figure 324,1

REPORT ON A PAPER BY NORMAN MACLEOD FERRERS[1] ON THE MOTION OF A RIGID BODY

14 AUGUST 1869

From the original in the Library of the Royal Society, London[2]

REPORT ON THE REVD. N. M. FERRERS' PAPER

NOTE ON PROF SYLVESTERS REPRESENTATION OF THE MOTION OF A FREE RIGID BODY BY THAT OF A MATERIAL ELLIPSOID[3]

Professor Sylvester in the paper to which this is a note has shown that the motions of different rigid bodies under different circumstances are related to one another in a simple manner.[4] Among other remarkable results he has found that the motion of a rough ellipsoid whose centre is fixed and whose surface rolls without sliding on a fixed plane is identical with that of a free body moving about the fixed point provided A B and C the moments of inertia of the ellipsoid are in the proportion of $\frac{G}{a^4}+\frac{H}{a^2}$, $\frac{G}{b^4}+\frac{H}{b^2}$ and $\frac{G}{c^4}+\frac{H}{c^2}$ where $a\ b\ c$ are the semiaxes of the ellipsoid.[5]

---

(1) Caius 1847, Fellow 1852 (Venn).

(2) Royal Society, *Referees' Reports*, **6**: 124.

(3) N. M. Ferrers, 'Note on Professor Sylvester's representation of the motion of a free rigid body by that of a material ellipsoid whose centre is fixed, and which rolls on a rough plane', *Phil. Trans.*, **160** (1870): 1–7. Under the title 'Note on Professor Sylvester's representation of the motion of a free rigid body by that of a material ellipsoid rolling on a rough plane', Ferrers' paper was received by the Royal Society on 29 May 1869, and read on 17 June 1869; see the abstract in *Proc. Roy. Soc.*, **17** (1869): 471–2. In recommending publication in a report dated 14 July 1869 (Royal Society, *Referees' Reports*, **6**: 123), Arthur Cayley suggested that: 'A slight change in the Title appears necessary – if the specification "rolling on a fixed plane" be inserted it is quite as necessary to state that the centre is a fixed point.' Ferrers adopted this emendation; and the paper as published in *Phil. Trans.* contains several lengthy additions dated February 1870.

(4) J. J. Sylvester, 'On the motion of a free rigid body acted on by no external forces', *Phil. Trans.*, **156** (1866): 757–79.

(5) Sylvester, 'On the motion of a free rigid body': 761–2. Maxwell here adopts the symbols employed by Ferrers; G and H are the angles between the principal axes of the ellipsoid and the 'instantaneous axis' (the line of contact). Sylvester's paper employed concepts derived from Louis Poinsot's *Théorie Nouvelle de la Rotation des Corps* (Paris, 1851), where the rotation of a body about an axis that varies in its position about a fixed point is represented by a cone whose summit is at this point, which rolls without sliding on the surface of another cone, whose vertex coincides with this point. The rotation of a body is represented by the 'central ellipsoid' which has its axes coincident with the principal axes of inertia of the body. Maxwell had employed Poinsot's theory

The moments of inertia of the free body must be in the proportion of $\frac{1}{a^2}$ $\frac{1}{b^2}$ and $\frac{1}{c^2}$ and the two bodies must have the same initial motion.

Professor Sylvester has investigated the pressure and friction between the ellipsoid and the rough plane at the point of contact. Mr Ferrers has also calculated the pressure and friction by a different process, in the course of which he has obtained an interesting relation between the absolute motion of the point of contact and the angular momentum resolved parallel to the fixed plane, this resolved part being proportional to the velocity of the point of contact and perpendicular to it.

In fact if h be the angular momentum about any axis parallel to the fixed plane and v the velocity of the point of contact resolved perpendicular to this axis

$$h = Gpv.^{(6)}$$

This is a remarkable result in the pure kinematics of a rolling ellipsoid and forms the basis of Mr Ferrers dynamical method.

In calculating the force exerted between the fixed plane and the end of the instantaneous axis it should be stated that this force is necessarily indeterminate since any force in the direction of the axis itself may be combined with it without altering its effect. Both Prof Sylvester & Mr Ferrers assume (what is the most convenient assumption) that the direction of the friction is perpendicular to the line joining the point of contact with the foot of the perpendicular from the fixed point. I find that if $X\,Y\,Z$ are the components of the force and if we put

$$K = \frac{G\left(A\omega_1^2 + B\omega_2^2 + C\omega_3^2\right)}{\dfrac{G}{p^2} + H}^{(7)}$$

$$X = K\frac{1}{a^2}\left(\frac{1}{a^2} - \frac{1}{b^2} - \frac{1}{c^2}\right)x + Lx$$

---

in his paper 'On a dynamical top', *Trans. Roy. Soc. Edinb.*, **21** (1857): 559–70 (= *Scientific Papers*, **1**: 248–62); see Volume I: 499–500.

(6) Here G is the mass of a particle situated at the point of contact of the ellipsoid and rough plane, p is the distance from the centre of the ellipsoid to the plane (these are Ferrers' symbols). Maxwell has generalised equations (8) of Ferrers' 'Note on Professor Sylvester's representation of the motion of a free rigid body': 4, where he states relations for the component angular momenta of the ellipsoid.

(7) ω_1, ω_2, ω_3 represent the component angular velocities of the ellipsoid about its principal axes.

$$Y = K\frac{1}{b^2}\left(\frac{1}{b^2} - \frac{1}{c^2} - \frac{1}{a^2}\right)y + Ly$$

$$Z = K\frac{1}{c^2}\left(\frac{1}{c^2} - \frac{1}{a^2} - \frac{1}{b^2}\right)z + Lz.$$

The coefficient L is indeterminate as far as the given conditions are concerned.

If however we assume that the friction is in the direction stated above

$$Xx\left(1 - \frac{p^2}{a^2}\right) + Yy\left(1 - \frac{p^2}{b^2}\right) + Zz\left(1 - \frac{p^2}{c^2}\right) = 0$$

or
$$K\left(\frac{2}{p^2} - \left(\frac{1}{a^2} + \frac{1}{b^2} + \frac{1}{c^2}\right)\right) + L(r^2 - p^2) = 0.$$

The friction then becomes

$$F = \frac{Kp}{q}\frac{(b^2 - c^2)(c^2 - a^2)(a^2 - b^2)}{a^4 b^4 c^4}xyz$$

where $\qquad r^2 = x^2 + y^2 + z^2 \quad$ and $\quad p^2 + q^2 = r^2$

r being the instantaneous semiaxis p the perpendicular on the fixed plane and q the distance of the point of contact from the foot of the perpendicular. This expression is not subject to the ambiguity of sign which is found in the expressions given by Prof Sylvester & Mr Ferrers with which however it agrees.[8] I find the pressure

$$P = p\left(\frac{Xx}{a^2} + \frac{Yy}{b^2} + \frac{Zz}{c^2}\right)$$

$$P = \frac{K}{pq^2}\left\{\left(\frac{1}{a^2} + \frac{1}{b^2} + \frac{1}{c^2}\right)q^2 + 2\left(\frac{1}{a^2} + \frac{1}{b^2} + \frac{1}{c^2} - \frac{1}{p^2}\right)p^2 - 2\frac{a^2 + b^2 + c^2 - r^2}{a^2 b^2 c^2}p^2 r^2\right\}.$$

This agrees with Prof. Sylvester but not with Mr Ferrers.[9] Mr Ferrers takes advantage of the result $h = Gpv$, which indicates that as far as motion about axes parallel to the fixed plane is concerned (on which alone the pressure depends) the angular momentum of the body is the same as that of a body of mass G, moving so as always to coincide with the point of contact. Hence if R is the resolved part of the force on the latter body in the direction of q (towards the foot of the perpendicular)

---

(8) Sylvester, 'On the motion of a free rigid body': 764; Ferrers, 'Note on Professor Sylvester's representation of the motion of a free rigid body': 5.
(9) Sylvester, 'On the motion of a free rigid body': 766; Ferrers, 'Note on Professor Sylvester's representation of the motion of a free rigid body': 5.

$$P = R\frac{p}{q} = \frac{p}{q}G\left(\frac{d^2q}{dt^2} - n^2q\right) \quad (10)$$

which agrees with Mr Ferrers result.[11]

In my copy of Poinsot I find $\dot{\phi} = \frac{h}{k} + \frac{(h^2-a^2)(h^2-b^2)(h^2-c^2)}{kh^3v^2}$[12] instead of Mr Ferrers $n = \lambda - \alpha\beta\gamma\frac{\lambda^2}{\mu^2}$[13] and I found independently of Poinsot that the sign is $+$ and not $-$.

This should be looked into but I have not time at present. I think the method might be made clearer by a division of the mass of the body into two parts corresponding to G and H so as to show that the external forces are due to G only and also by a comparison of one part of the external force to the force acting on a body $= G$ moving as the point of contact moves.[14]

The calculation of n and P should be reexamined and then I think the paper deserving of being printed in the Transactions.

J. CLERK MAXWELL

Glenlair 14 August 1869

---

(10) n is the angular velocity of the radius vector of the point of contact measured from the foot of the perpendicular on the rough plane.

(11) Compare equations (10) of Ferrers' 'Note on Professor Sylvester's representation of the motion of a free rigid body': 5.

(12) Poinsot, *Théorie Nouvelle de la Rotation des Corps*: 130; an 'expression trés-simple de la vitesse angulaire avec la pôle instantané de rotation tourne autour du centre de l'herpolhodie σ; cette vitesse, comme on le voit, est composée d'une partie constante, et d'une partie variable qui est réciproque au carré du rayon vecteur v, et, par conséquent, périodique comme ce rayon.' Poinsot's 'herpolhodie' is the curve traced by the point of contact on the plane when the ellipsoid rolls on the plane; see Volume I: 500n. The 1851 edition of Poinsot's text, here cited (see note (5)), is the edition in Maxwell's library (Cavendish Laboratory, Cambridge).

(13) Adopting Ferrers' symbols in place of Poinsot's. In a paper 'On the angular velocity of the instantaneous axis in space', *Quarterly Journal of Pure and Applied Mathematics*, **7** (1865): 74–5, Ferrers obtained an equation for n with a minus sign between the two terms. The sign is corrected to a plus sign in the published Royal Society paper; compare Ferrers, 'Note on Professor Sylvester's representation of the motion of a free rigid body': 5 (equation (12), there an equation for p).

(14) See Ferrers' addendum, dated February 1870, in the published text of his 'Note on Professor Sylvester's representation of the motion of a free rigid body': 6–7.

326

LETTER TO WILLIAM THOMSON

17 AUGUST 1869

From the original in the University Library, Cambridge[1]

Ardhallow
Dunoon
17 Aug 1869

(a)

Dear Thomson

I have not heard of you since you were at Brest[2] and should like to know if you are in these parts. We are to be here for 3 or 4 weeks, and I am sticking my electrostatics and electrokinetics together, and should like a little of your influence to assist me in brooding over the mass.

I have been doing the case of the influence of an electrified body on a conductor at potential zero separated from it by a grating of parallel wires also at potential zero.[3] I have not met with any examination of this case, have you? or have you done it yourself?

I find that if two planes A_1 and A_2 are at distances b_1 and b_2 on opposite sides of a grating and if A_2 is in metallic connexion with the grating and at potential zero and if A_1 is brought to some other potential then the electric density induced on A_2 through the grating is to that which would be induced on it if the grating were removed as 1 to $1 + \dfrac{2b_1 b_2}{\alpha(b_1 + b_2)}$ where α is a linear quantity whose approximate value is

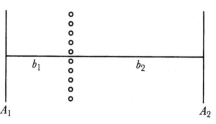

Figure 326,1

$$\alpha = \frac{a}{2\pi} \log_\epsilon \frac{a}{2\pi c}$$

where a is the distance between the axes of consecutive wires of the grating and $2\pi c$ is the circumference of one of the wires.[4]

This expression is approximate only when the distance between the wires is considerably greater than the circumference of a wire for it is manifest that

---

(a) {Thomson} I have made extract of this. T

(1) ULC Add. MSS 7655, II/33.
(2) Thomson had been aboard the *Great Eastern* at Brest in June 1869: see Number 324 note (4).
(3) See Numbers 323 and 324.
(4) See the *Treatise*, **1**: 248–51 (§§203–5).

α ought always to be positive when a is greater than $2c$ and to become zero when $a = 2c$.

I am also trying to reduce to the simplest form the mathematical conception of a dielectric bad conductor which shows electric absorption. I got a differential equation between the electromotive force and the current through the dielectric which may contain any number of differential coefficients of all orders such as

$$A_1 F + A_2 \frac{dF}{dt} + \&c = B_1 \gamma + B_2 \frac{d\gamma}{dt} + \&c.$$

If F is the electromotive force and γ the current

$$F = \left\{ r_1 \left(1 + \alpha_1 \frac{d}{dt}\right)^{-1} + r_2 \left(1 + \alpha_2 \frac{d}{dt}\right)^{-1} + \&c \right\} \gamma$$

where $r_1 + r_2 + r_3 + \&c = r$ the actual specific resistance and α_1 α_2 &c are *times* which in unabsorbing media are all equal to $\frac{r}{4\pi k}$.[5]

How is your reprint of electrical papers coming on.[6] The last I heard of was the electrified cup which I see you can do completely for any kind of influence.[7] I tried the case of an incomplete cylindric tube but found hard integrations in the way.

Can you let me see your *complete* version of the cup. I mean to describe it if I can without bagging it whole.[8]

Yours truly
J. CLERK MAXWELL

---

(5) k is the reciprocal of the specific inductive capacity; see Maxwell's discussion of conduction in dielectrics in the *Treatise*, **1**: 376–80 (§§ 328–29).

(6) See Number 321 note (21). (7) See Number 310 note (2).

(8) See the *Treatise*, **1**: 221–5 (§§ 176–81).

LETTER TO WILLIAM THOMSON

1 OCTOBER 1869

From the original in the University Library, Cambridge[1]

Ardhallow
Dunoon
1st October 1869

Dear Thomson

Many thanks for yours of the 22nd Sept. You see I am again on the Clyde & I propose to be in Glasgow on Tuesday 5th Oct and will call at Whites[2] about 12 or as I hear from you.

In which of your papers is there a discussion of Poissons k.[3] Thalén gives for Neumann's κ 32.32, 31.80, 32.61.[4]

---

(1) ULC Add. MSS 7342, M 105. First published in Larmor, 'Origins': 739–40.

(2) See Number 301 (note (2)).

(3) Thomson had discussed Poisson's theory of magnetism in his paper 'On the theory of magnetic induction in crystalline and non-crystalline substances', *Phil. Mag.*, ser. 4, **1** (1851): 177–86 (= *Electrostatics and Magnetism*: 465–80). In his discussion of 'Magnetic permeability, and analogues in electro-static induction, conduction of heat, and fluid motion' (dated March 1872), first published in the reprint of his papers on *Electrostatics and Magnetism*: 482–6, he terms Maxwell's quantity κ, which Maxwell calls 'Neumann's coefficient of Magnetization by Induction' (see the *Treatise*, **2**: 54 (§430), the 'magnetic susceptibility'. Thomson's 'magnetic permeability' is termed the 'Coefficient of Magnetic Induction' (μ) by Maxwell, who writes $\mu = 4\pi\kappa + 1$ (following Thomson). While k, 'Poisson's Magnetic Coefficient represents the ratio of the volume of the magnetic elements to the whole volume of the substance'; see the *Treatise*, **2**: 54 (§430). Maxwell writes the relation $k = 4\pi\kappa/(4\pi\kappa + 3)$. See Siméon Denis Poisson, 'Mémoire sur la théorie du magnétisme', and 'Second mémoire sur la théorie du magnétisme', *Mémoires de l'Académie Royale des Sciences*, **5** (1826): 247–338, 488–533.

(4) Tobias Robert Thalén, 'Recherches sur les propriétés magnétiques du fer', *Nova Acta Regiae Societatis Scientiarum Upsaliensis*, ser. 3, **4** (1863): esp. 31–43. Thalén obtains these values from three experiments on bars of soft iron. In the *Treatise*, **2**: 54 (§430) Maxwell takes $\kappa = 32$ and finds $k = 134/135$. F. E. Neumann's discussion is in his paper 'Entwickelung der in elliptischen Coordinaten ausgedrückten reciproken Entfernung zweier Punkte in Reihen, welche nach den Laplace'schen $Y^{(n)}$ fortschreiten; und Anwendung dieser Reihen zur Bestimmung des magnetischen Zustandes eines Rotations-Ellipsoids, welcher durch vertheilende Kräfte erregt ist', *Journal für die reine und angewandte Mathematik*, **37** (1848): 21–50, esp. 46–50, on the distribution of the magnetisation of an ellipsoid of revolution under the action of magnetic forces. Maxwell's brief notes on this paper are in ULC Add. MSS 7655, V, c/40. The paper is discussed by Wilhelm Weber, in his 'Bestimmung der rechtwinkeligen Componenten der erdmagnetischen Kraft in Göttingen in dem Zeitraume von 1834–1853', *Abhandlungen der Math. Classe der Königlichen Gesellschaft der Wissenschaften zu Göttingen*, **6** (1856): esp. 20 (= *Wilhelm Weber's Werke*, 6 vols. (Berlin, 1892–4), **2**: 333–73), referring to the 'Neumannsche magnetische Constante', which Maxwell denotes by the symbol κ.

I have written 40 pages on Magnetic Measurements[5] and am beginning Terrestrial Magnetism.[6]

I have put in Joule's method of swinging two magnets together, so as to eliminate induction.[7] I think that the magnets ought to be as heavy as a single silk fibre will safely carry and as short as is consistent with strong permanent magnetization.

I got into a mess with an investigation of the 2 best distances at which to place the deflecting magnet in order to deduce its moment by the eq^n

$$\frac{2M}{H} = \frac{D_1 r_1^5 - D_2 r_2^5}{r_1^2 - r_2^2}{}^{(8)}$$

supposing the relation between the probable error in the measurement of D the tangent of deflexion and r the distance to be known.

In fact I got a pair of impossible values for r_1 & r_2. If one distance only is used the best distance is when

$$\frac{\delta D}{D} = \sqrt{3}\frac{\delta r}{r}$$

where $\dfrac{\delta D}{D}$ is the probable percentage error of D and $\dfrac{\delta r}{r}$ that of r.[9]

Your bowl investigations are first rate.[10] I must find the induction through a round hole in a plate by means of them. Whether would you have me bag the whole thing for my book, or give results and references with an *account* of the method?[11]

Yours truly
J. CLERK MAXWELL

C. Neumanns theory of the transmission of Potentials is altogether unique, the Potential $\dfrac{mm_1}{r}$ $\left(\text{not the potential function } \dfrac{m}{r}\right)$ starts from m (with the consciousness of the value of r and m_1 at the instant) and travels along r with uniform velocity not absolute but relative to m till it reaches m_1 which

---

(5) See the *Treatise*, **2**: 88–119 (§§449–64).

(6) See the *Treatise*, **2**: 120–7 (§§465–74).

(7) J. P. Joule, 'On an apparatus for determining the horizontal magnetic intensity in absolute measure', *Proceedings of the Literary and Philosophical Society of Manchester*, **6** (1867): 129–35. See the *Treatise*, **2**: 105–6 (§457).

(8) M is the magnetic moment of the magnet, H the horizontal component of terrestrial magnetism.

(9) See the *Treatise*, **2**: 97–101 (§§453–4).   (10) See Number 310 note (2).

(11) In the *Treatise*, **1**: 221–5 (§§176–81) Maxwell follows the latter procedure.

receives it after a time t.[12] Truly those who supposed that Neumanns potential travelled like light were greatly mistaken.[13]

---

(12) Carl Neumann, 'Resultate einer Untersuchung über die Principien der Elektrodynamik', *Nachrichten von der Königl. Gesellschaft der Wissenschaften und der Georg-August-Universität zu Göttingen* (1868): 223–35, esp. 225–6; 'Das emissive Potential ist dasjenige, welches jeder Punct in dem gegebenen Augenblick aussendet, und welches erst einige Zeit später den andern Punct erreicht... [Das] emissive Potential $= \frac{mm_1}{r}$... Das receptive Potential anderseits ist dasjenige, welches jeder Punct in dem gegebenem Augenblick empfängt, welches also schon einige Zeit früher von dem andern Punct ausgesendet wurde. Das dem gegebenem Augenblick entsprechende receptive Potential ist demnach immer identisch mit dem einem früheren Augenblick entsprechenden emissiven Potential.'

(13) For further comments see the *Treatise*, **2**: 435–6 (§863).

LETTER TO WILLIAM THOMSON

5 OCTOBER 1869

From the original in the University Library, Cambridge[1]

Ardhallow
Dunoon
5 Oct 1869

Dear Thomson

I did not go to Glasgow today as you were not to be there. I can go on Thursday Friday or Saturday. We are going home the beginning of next week. There are but few other things I have to do in Glasgow.

In Shurrocks hairbrushing room I examined the endless band in motion. The velocity of propagation of a disturbance in space is in the case of a flexible tube with water going at velocity V when m = mass of tube μ of water in unit of length

$$\text{vel of disturbance} = \frac{\mu}{m+\mu}V \pm \sqrt{\frac{T}{m+\mu} - \frac{m\mu V^2}{m+\mu}}.$$

When the 2nd term is impossible, that is if T the effective tension (tension-pressure) is small compared with V the motion is unstable. When however $m = 0$ as at Shurrocks this cannot be.

When the shape of the tube is in equilibrium $T = T_0 + \mu V^2$ where T_0 is the statical value. Hence the velocity may be written

$$\frac{\mu}{m+\mu}V \pm \sqrt{\frac{T_0}{m+\mu} + \frac{\mu^2 V^2}{(m+\mu)^2}}$$

which shows that the velocities are always in opposite directions but when T_0 is small one of them is very small. Hence the sluggishness of the wave near the bottom of a loop of chain or flexible pipe, part of it darts up the ascending side and part slowly ascends the descending one but faster as it gets away from the bottom.

Can you tell me where you were getting *light* indiarubber cloaks when I was at Largs? last year.

Yours truly
J. CLERK MAXWELL

---

(1) ULC Add. MSS 7342, M 106. First published in Larmor, 'Origins': 740–1.

329

OUTLINE OF CONTENTS OF THE *TREATISE ON ELECTRICITY AND MAGNETISM*

circa OCTOBER 1869[1]

From the original in the King's College London Archives[2]

[*TREATISE ON ELECTRICITY AND MAGNETISM*: CONTENTS]

Introduction p 5	24[3]
Treatise on Electricity & Magnetism	

Part I Electrostatics

Ch.I[4] Experiments. Theory of 2 & of 1 fluid. Polarization Theory. Law of Force. Electric Balance. Definitions.	21
Ch.II[5] Elementary Mathematical Theory. Distribution in 3 2 & 1 dimension. Integration along a curve. Potential. Proof of Law of Inverse Square. Superposition. Energy of System. Riemanns Theorem.[6] Greens Function.[7]	34
Ch.III[8] General Mathematical Theory. Laplaces Equation. Characteristics of Potential. Greens Theorem.	12
	3
Ch.IV[9] Theory of the action of a Medium.	13
	107
Ch.V[10] Particular distributions of Electricity.	

---

(1) This date is conjectural. But see Numbers 327 and 333, which indicate progress in writing the *Treatise* roughly corresponding to this partial and preliminary outline of its contents. Other jottings in the notebook (see note (2)) support this conjectural dating.

(2) From Maxwell Notebook (3), King's College London Archives.

(3) The numbers in the right hand margin, indicating section numbers in the draft *Treatise*, were added in pencil. Compare the *Treatise*, **1**: 1–29 (§§1–26).

(4) Compare Part I Chapter I of the *Treatise*, **1**: 30–65 (§§27–62).

(5) Compare Part I Chapters II and III of the *Treatise*, **1**: 66–97 (§§63–94).

(6) It is unclear which theorem Maxwell intends to denote; but see Number 274 esp. note (10).   (7) See Number 274 esp. note (9).

(8) Compare Part I Chapter IV of the *Treatise*, **1**: 98–118 (§§95–102).

(9) Compare Part I Chapter V of the *Treatise*, **1**: 119–34 (§§103–11).

(10) Compare Part I Chapters VI, VII, VIII and IX of the *Treatise*, **1**: 134–80 (§§112–46).

Nuclei of any order & their spherical harmonics and axes. Points of Equilibrium and their spherical harmonics. Electrified sphere. $\sum Y_i Y_j dS.$[11]
Distribution of points of equilibrium. Instability of electrical equilibrium.   13

Ch.VI[12] Theory of Electrical Images.
Spherical Harmonic of order 0. Uninsulated sphere & electrified point. Charged sphere and electrified point or system. Internal spherical surfaces. Spherical Condensers. Theory of two spheres.   30

Ch.VII[13] Test of a particular set of surfaces being equipotential. Application to confocal quadrics.   16

Ch.VIII[14] Electrical Instruments.
Electrical Machines.[15] Electrophorus. Doubler. Revolving Doubler. Varleys multiplier.[16] Thomsons water dropping collectors & multipliers.[17] Condensers. Electrometers.

Part II Electrokinematics

Ch.I[18] On the Electric Current. How it is produced. Why it is called a Current. Its properties. 1 Transference of Electrical state. 2 Chemical action. 3 Magnetic action. 4 Resistance. 5 Production of Heat. Measurement of Currents.

Ch.II[19] Ohms Law of Resistance explained. Resistance of linear conductors in series.
——————————————in multiple arc.
Determination of the distribution of currents in any linear system. Minimum of Heat. Reciprocity of EMF & Current. Simple case. Wheatstone Bridge.[20] Different arrangements of the bridge.   12

---

(11) See Number 294 esp. note (20).
(12) Compare Part I Chapter XI of the *Treatise*, **1**: 191–225 (§§ 155–81).
(13) Compare Part I Chapter X of the *Treatise*, **1**: 181–9 (§§ 147–54).
(14) Compare Part I Chapter XIII of the *Treatise*, **1**: 254–87 (§§ 207–29).
(15) See Number 302.   (16) See Number 260 note (17).
(17) See Number 302 note (2).
(18) Compare Part II Chapters I, II and III of the *Treatise*, **1**: 288–306 (§§ 230–54).
(19) Compare Part II Chapters VI and XI of the *Treatise*, **1**: 329–37, 388–425 (§§ 273–84, 335–70).   (20) See Number 230.

Results & applications of the measurement of resistance.

Ch.III[21] Theory of conduction in crystallized bodies the equipotential surfaces being plane. General equations of conduction. The rotatory property probably nonexistent.[22]

Ch.IV[23] Theory of conduction in two dimensions. Equipotential Lines and Lines of Flow with their Conjugate Functions.[24] Theory of the transformation of results from one set of curvilinear coordinates to another. Graphic method of finding the resultant of the superposition of two systems. Examples of the solution of problems. Extension to cases in 3 dimensions symmetrical about an axis.   12

Ch.V Theory of Submarine Cables.[25] Electrolysis,[26] Bourgoin Ann de Ch IV, XV p 47.[27] Millers Chemical Physics 4th ed^n.[28] Daniell Phil Trans 1839 p 97.[29] D'Almeida Ann de Ch III, 4, 263.[30] Miller Phil Trans 1844, 16.[31] Magnus Pogg cii.[32]

---

(21) Compare Part II Chapters VII, VIII and IX of the *Treatise*, **1**: 338–73 (§§ 285–324).

(22) See Number 301 esp. note (5).

(23) Compare Part I Chapter XII of the *Treatise*, **1**: 226–53 (§§ 182–206).

(24) See Number 303 esp. note (3).

(25) Compare Part II Chapter X of the *Treatise*, **1**: 374–87 (§§ 325–34).

(26) Compare Part II Chapters IV and V of the *Treatise*, **1**: 307–28 (§§ 255–72).

(27) E. Bourgoin, 'Du role de l'eau dans l'électrolyse', *Ann. Chim. Phys.*, ser. 4, **15** (1868): 47–57.

(28) William Allen Miller, *Elements of Chemistry: Theoretical and Practical. Part I. Chemical Physics* (London, $_4$1867).

(29) J. F. Daniell, 'On the electrolysis of secondary compounds', *Phil. Trans.*, **129** (1839): 97–112; and also Daniell, 'Second letter on the electrolysis of secondary compounds', *Phil. Trans.*, **130** (1840): 209–24.

(30) J. Ch. D'Almeida, 'Décomposition par la pile des sels dissous dans l'eau', *Ann. Chim. Phys.*, ser. 3, **51** (1857): 257–90.

(31) J. F. Daniell and W. A. Miller, 'Additional researches on the electrolysis of secondary compounds', *Phil. Trans.*, **134** (1844): 1–19.

(32) Gustav Magnus, 'Elektrolytische Untersuchungen', *Ann. Phys.*, **102** (1857): 1–54.

Part III Magnetics

Ch.I[33] Experiments with magnets. Magnetization. Every particle a magnet with poles of equal strength. Induction of magnetism in soft iron and in steel. Gauss & Webers method for the Determination of the direction of the axis of a magnet and of that of the earths horizontal component.[34]
The dipping needle.
Determination of the strength of a magnet and of the Earths horizontal component. Joules method of eliminating the effects of induction.[35]

Ch.II[36] Mathematical Theory of the distribution of magnetization and of Magnetic Potential. Gauss' 24 coeffts of Terrestrial Magnetism.[37]

Ch.III[38] Theory of Magnetic Induction. Para & Diamagnetic bodies & Magnecrystallic phenomena. Weber's Theory.[39]

Ch.IV[40] Theory of the magnetism of Ships and of the correction of the compass by magnets by iron and by tables.

Ch.[41] Earths mag axis Gauss 77°50 N 296°29 E from Greenwich to 77°50 S 116°29′. Moment $= 947.08R^3$.[42]

---

(33) Compare Part III Chapters I and VII of the *Treatise*, **2**: 1–20, 88–119 (§§371–94, 449–64).

(34) Carl Friedrich Gauss, 'Ueber ein neues, zunächst zur unmittelbaren Beobachtung der Veränderungen in der Intensität des horizontalen Theiles des Erdmagnetismus bestimmtes Instrument', in *Resultate aus den Beobachtungen des magnetischen Vereins in Jahre 1837*, ed. C. F. Gauss and W. E. Weber (Leipzig, 1838): 1–19 (= Gauss, *Werke*, **5** (Göttingen, 1867): 357–73); translation in *Scientific Memoirs*, ed. R. Taylor, **2** (London, 1841): 252–67. Wilhelm Weber, 'Bemerkungen über die Einrichtung und den Gebrauch des Bifilar-Magnetometers', in *Resultate...in Jahr 1837*: 20–37 (= *Wilhelm Weber's Werke*, 6 vols. (Berlin, 1892–4), **2**: 43–57); trans. in *Scientific Memoirs*, **2**: 268–80. See *Treatise*, **2**: 107–111 (§§459–60).

(35) See Number 327 esp. note (7).

(36) Compare Part II Chapters II and III of the *Treatise*, **2**: 21–43 (§§395–423).

(37) Compare the *Treatise*, **2**: 124 (§469), and see below.

(38) Compare Part II Chapters IV, V and VI of the *Treatise*, **2**: 44–87 (§§424–48).

(39) See Numbers 278 esp. note (8) and 295.

(40) Compare the *Treatise*, **2**: 70–3 (§441).

(41) These notes are taken from Carl Friedrich Gauss, 'Allgemeine Theorie des Erdmagnetismus', in *Resultate...in Jahre 1838*, ed. C. F. Gauss and W. Weber (Leipzig, 1839): 1–57, 146–8 (= Gauss, *Werke*, **5**: 119–93); translation in *Scientific Memoirs*, **2**: 184–251.

(42) Gauss, *Werke*, **5**: 164; here R is the earth's major semi-axis.

$$\cos u = e \quad \sin u = f^{(43)}$$

$$P^{n,m} = \left(e^{n-m} - \frac{(n-m)(n-m-1)}{2(2n-1)} e^{n-m-2} + \&c.\right) f^m$$

$$P^n = g^{n,0} P^{n,0} + (g^{n,1} \cos \lambda + h^{n,1} \sin \lambda) P^{n,1}$$
$$+ (g^{n,2} \cos 2\lambda + h^{n,2} \sin 2\lambda) P^{n,2} +{}^{(44)}$$

$g^{1,0} = +925.782, \quad g^{1,1} = +89.024 \quad h^{1,1} = -178.744$

$g^{2,0} = -22.059, \quad g^{2,1} = -144.913 \quad h^{2,1} = -6.030$

$\phantom{g^{2,0} = -22.059,} \quad g^{2,2} = +0.493 \quad h^{2,2} = -39.010$

$g^{3,0} = -18.868 \quad g^{3,1} = +122.936 \quad h^{3,1} = +47.794$

$g^{3,2} = -73.193 \quad g^{3,3} = 1.396 \quad h^{3,2} = -22.766$

$h^{3,3} = -18.750 \quad g^{4,0} = -108.855 \quad g^{4,1} = -152.589$

$h^{4,1} = +64.112 \quad g^{4,2} = -45.791 \quad h^{4,2} = +42.573$

$g^{4,3} = +19.774 \quad h^{4,3} = -0.178 \quad g^{4,4} = 4.27$

$\phantom{g^{4,3} = +19.774 \quad h^{4,3} = -0.178 \quad} h^{4,4} = 3.175^{(45)}$

Webers magnet of 142 grammes $\frac{M}{H} = .08765$

metre gramme deflexion 11°24 at .450 when $H = 1.774$.[46]
Limiting magnetic moment of iron = 2100 per milligramme.
Best steel magnets 400 Weber.
Prof A Waltenhofen Sitzungsberichte der K Acad in Wien 1869 No 12.[47]

---

(43) u is the earth's latitude; e and f are Maxwell's own symbols.

(44) λ is the earth's latitude, g and h the coefficients of the harmonics of P, the potential of the distribution of the earth's magnetism. See Gauss, *Werke*, **5**: 142.

(45) Gauss' table of the 24 coefficients of the potential of the earth's magnetism: 3 for the first degree, 5 for the second, 7 for the third, and 9 for the fourth. See Gauss, *Werke*, **5**: 150.

(46) For these symbols see Number 327 note (8). The values are from Wilhelm Weber, 'Beschreibung eines kleinen Apparats zur Messung des Erdmagnetismus nach absolutem Maass für Reisende', in *Resultate... in Jahre 1836*, ed. C. F. Gauss and W. Weber (Leipzig, 1837): 63–89 (= Weber, *Werke*, **2**: 20–42), translation in *Scientific Memoirs*, **2**: 65–87, esp. 82–3.

(47) These two values are given by A. von Waltenhofen, 'Über die Grenzen der Magnetisbarkeit des Eisens und des Stahles', *Wiener Berichte*, Abtheilung II, **59** (1869): 770–88, esp. 777, 780.

Outline of contents of the Treatise, c. October 1869

Part IV Electromagnetics

Ch.I[48] Oersted's discovery of the action of a current on a magnet.[49] Ampère's experiments and mathematical theory.[50] Faraday's experiments on rotation of magnets & currents.[51]

Ch.II[52] Faraday's discovery of the induction of electric currents.[53] Faradays Theory of Lines of Force and of the Electrotonic State.[54]

Ch.III[55] Helmholtz and Thomsons deduction of the induction of currents from their electromagnetic action.[56] Theory of the coefficients of induction of two linear currents. The Induction Coil.[57]
V = potential of a plane area in xy bounded by a curve s density unity.

$$\frac{dV}{dz} = W \quad \frac{dV}{dy} = F \quad \frac{dV}{dx} = -G \quad H = 0.\text{[58]}$$

---

(48) Compare Part IV Chapters I and II of the *Treatise*, **2**: 128–61 (§§475–527).
(49) See Number 238 note (17).
(50) See Volume I: 305–6n; and Number 332 note (10).
(51) See Faraday, *Electricity*, **2**: 127–47.
(52) Compare Part IV Chapter III of the *Treatise*, **2**: 162–79 (§§528–45).
(53) See Number 238 note (15).
(54) See Number 238 notes (12) and (13).
(55) Compare Part IV Chapters III (the latter part), IV and VII of the *Treatise*, **2**: 176–83, 206–10 (§§543–52, 578–84).
(56) See Number 238 notes (9), (10) and (11).
(57) Compare Part IV Chapter XVII of the *Treatise*, **2**: 352–7 (§§752–7).
(58) See Maxwell's discussion of plane current-sheets in the *Treatise*, **2**: 264–5 (§657).

LETTER TO THE LONDON MATHEMATICAL SOCIETY ON THE POTENTIAL OF A DISC

NOVEMBER 1869[1]

From the *Proceedings of the London Mathematical Society*[2]

[ON THE POTENTIAL OF A UNIFORM CIRCULAR DISC]

Can the potential of a uniform circular disc at any point be expressed by means of elliptic integrals? Suppose V is the potential of the disc bounded by the circle

$$z = 0, \quad x^2 + y^2 = a^2;$$

then

$$\frac{dV}{dx} = 2x\left(\frac{a}{r}\right)^{\frac{1}{2}} \frac{1}{\sqrt{c}} (E - F),$$

where

$$r^2 = x^2 + y^2;$$

and if AB be a diameter parallel to r,

$$c = \frac{PB - PA}{PB + PA},$$

and E, F are complete elliptic functions for modulus c;[3]

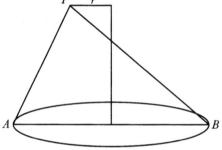

Figure 330,1

also

$$\frac{dV}{dy} = 2y\left(\frac{a}{r}\right)^{\frac{1}{2}} \frac{1}{\sqrt{c}} (E - F).$$

But $\frac{dV}{dz} = w$, where w is the solid angle subtended at P by the circle; that is, the area of the spherical ellipse on a sphere of unit radius cut off by the cone whose vertex is P and base the circle. We have expressions for $\frac{dV}{dx}$ and $\frac{dV}{dy}$. Can $\frac{dV}{dz}$ also be expressed by elliptic functions? and if so, can V itself be so expressed?

I am writing out the theory of circular electric currents, in which these

---

(1) Maxwell's letter of inquiry was read at a meeting of the London Mathematical Society on 11 November 1869.

(2) *Proceedings of the London Mathematical Society*, **3** (1869): 8.

(3) See Number 262 note (3).

quantities occur.[4] The expression $\frac{dV}{dz}$ for an elliptic disc can be found if we know it for a circular one, for the spherical ellipses in the one case are no more complicated than in the other. Can $\frac{dV}{dx}$, or V itself, be found for the elliptic disc?

(4) See the *Treatise*, **2**: 305–7 (§ 701); and Number 341.

REMARKS ON A PAPER BY GEORGE OLDHAM HANLON ON THE *VENA CONTRACTA*[1]

NOVEMBER 1869[2]

From the *Proceedings of the London Mathematical Society*[3]

REMARKS OF MR J. CLERK-MAXWELL ON MR HANLON'S PAPER ON THE VENA CONTRACTA[4]

It appears from this paper that it has been stated, that when a hole is made in one side of a vessel containing water, so as to allow the water to escape, the pressure on the opposite side of the vessel is thereby increased.[5] This statement Mr. Hanlon shows to be erroneous, and asserts that the immediate effect of opening the hole, and allowing motion to take place, is to diminish the pressure in every part of the vessel.

He then shows, by a calculation of the momentum communicated in a unit of time to the fluid which is projected from an orifice in the side of a vessel, that the force acting on it is measured by $\iint \rho v^2 dS$, where ρ is the density, v the velocity at the Vena Contracta where the pressure vanishes, and dS an element of the section of the stream.

Now at the Vena Contracta $v^2 = 2gz$ approximately,[6] where z is the depth, so that the force of propulsion is $F = 2g\rho \iint z dS$; or if $\bar{z}$ is the depth of the centre of gravity of the section S, $F = 2g\rho \bar{z} S$. But at a distance from the

---

(1) G. O. Hanlon, 'The vena contracta', *Proceedings of the London Mathematical Society*, **3** (1869): 4–5.

(2) Hanlon's paper was read to the London Mathematical Society on 11 November 1869; see note (3) and *Nature*, **1** (1869): 91.

(3) *Proceedings of the London Mathematical Society*, **3** (1869): 6–8.

(4) On the term *vena contracta* see Joseph Edleston, *Correspondence of Sir Isaac Newton and Professor Cotes, including Letters of other Eminent Men* (London, 1851): 39n, in comment on Newton's letter to Cotes of 27 March 1710/11. According to Edleston the 'term [was] first used by Jurin, *Philosoph. Transact.* Sept.–Oct. 1722, p. 185... to denote the same thing [as Newton]': 'the water... passes through the hole with a converging motion & thereby grows into a smaller stream after it is past the hole...' (Newton to Cotes, letter of 24 March 1710/11).

(5) Hanlon stated that his paper was written in response to a discussion in *The Engineer* on the hydrodynamics of the 'nozzle ship', the gunboat *The Waterwitch* powered by a water turbine (tested in October 1866). See letters on 'Hydro-propulsion', especially by J. A. L. Airey and R. D. Napier, in *The Engineer* (November 1866 to March 1867).

(6) Following Newton, *Principia* (Book II, Prop. 36). The result was standard in the literature: see W. H. Miller, *The Elements of Hydrostatics and Hydrodynamics* (Cambridge, $_4$1850): 51: 'the velocity of the issuing fluid is equal to the velocity acquired by a heavy body in falling'.

hole, where the velocity is small, the pressure is the hydrostatic pressure $p = g\rho z$.

Let us assume (for an instant) that this is the value of the pressure on every part of the surface of the vessel, in which there is a hole whose section is S', and whose centre of gravity is at a depth $\bar{z}'$. The resultant of the pressures on the sides will be $F' = g\rho\bar{z}'S'$, and this must be equal to F, because action and reaction are equal and opposite. This gives
$$2\bar{z}S = \bar{z}'S'.$$
There is very little difference between $\bar{z}$ and $\bar{z}'$, the depths of the centre of gravity at the hole and at the Vena Contracta. Hence we ought to have $S = \tfrac{1}{2}S'$, or section of Vena Contraction = .5 of the hole.

I am not aware how far the author is original in this method of treating the subject; but it is certainly very clear and intelligible, without the aid of symbols, which is very important in practical matters. Rankine, however (Steam Engine, p. 96), gives $.6zS'$ as the section of the Vena Contracta for round holes;[7] and I have not seen any experimental result as low as $.5S'$.

This arises partly from our having made an erroneous assumption – that the pressure on the sides is the hydrostatic pressure ρgz, whereas it must be diminished by $\tfrac{1}{2}\rho v^2$ wherever there is a velocity v.

Now v will evidently be greatest near the hole, so that the pressure on the side next the hole will be diminished for this reason, as well as by the removal of the stopper of the hole, and the value of F' will be greater than $g\rho\bar{z}'S'$, and therefore S will be greater than $.5S'$.

If the fluid is a perfect liquid originally at rest, it will have a velocity-potential ϕ,[8] and the pressure is given by the equation
$$p = \rho gz - \rho\frac{\delta\phi}{\delta t} = \rho gz - \rho\frac{d\phi}{dt} - \tfrac{1}{2}\rho V^2,$$
where $\dfrac{\delta}{\delta t}$ denotes the rate of change in a moving particle, and $\dfrac{d}{dt}$ denotes rate of change at a point of space. V is the velocity of the fluid.

We must also have at the surface of the vessel $\dfrac{d\phi}{dv} = 0$, where v is the normal to the surface, and ϕ satisfies Laplace's equation[9]
$$\frac{d^2\phi}{dx^2} + \frac{d^2\phi}{dy^2} + \frac{d^2\phi}{dz^2} = 0.$$

---

(7) W. J. Macquorn Rankine, *A Manual of the Steam Engine and other Prime Movers* (London/Glasgow, 1859): 96.

(8) See Number 311 note (6).   (9) See Volume I: 261n.

Now consider the case of a body which conducts electricity – a mass of copper of the same form as the vessel; and let electricity be supplied at the upper surface, and carried off at the point corresponding to the hole, so that the current of electricity entering or escaping is everywhere proportional and parallel to the current of water. Then the electric-potential everywhere will be equal to ϕ, and its value is perfectly definite for a given problem, and problems can be constructed for which the solution can be found by our present methods.[10]

Let ψ be the electric-potential for the copper conductor; then, if the form of the vessel and the motions of the surface remain similar, the velocity-potential $\phi = \psi T$, where T is a function of the time.

If we assume $\psi = 0$ at the free surface, then, since ψ increases along every line of motion,[11] the value of ψ will be positive throughout the vessel, and will have its greatest values at the place of the issuing stream.

Let us first consider the *immediate* effect of opening the hole. In this case we may neglect the square of the velocity; and since at the orifice the pressure becomes zero, we have

$$p = 0 = \rho g \bar{z} - \rho \frac{d\bar{\phi}}{dt},$$

where $\bar{\phi}$ is the value of ϕ at the orifice. If $\bar{\psi}$ is the value of ψ at the orifice, then

$$\bar{\phi} = \bar{\psi} g \bar{z} t;$$

and if ψ is the value of ψ at any other point, then

$$\phi = \psi g \bar{z} t,$$

and

$$p = \rho g z - \rho g \bar{z} \frac{\psi}{\bar{\psi}}.$$

Hence the assertion that the pressure is everywhere diminished is correct, and the amount of diminution is everywhere proportional to ψ, the electric-potential of a conducting mass similar to the water in the vessel, of which the upper surface is maintained at potential zero and the orifice at potential unity, the sides being supposed coated with insulating material.

When the motion has become constant, we may neglect $\frac{d\phi}{dt}$, and we have

$$p = \rho g z - \tfrac{1}{2} \rho V^2,$$

where V is the velocity at any point. At the orifice, $V^2 = 2g\bar{z}$. It appears, therefore, that in this case also the pressure at every point is less than the hydrostatic pressure.

---

(10) On the hydrodynamic analogy for electricity see Number 223, and Volume I: 353–7, 367–9.   (11) See Numbers 223 esp. note (4) and 337.

332

LETTER TO WILLIAM THOMSON

16 NOVEMBER 1869

From the original in the University Library, Cambridge[1]

Glenlair
Dalbeattie
16 Nov 1869

Dear Thomson

Mr Tatlock[2] tells me you want to know about the conductivity of liquids for heat. The last thing on the subject is Prof. F. Guthrie On the Thermal Resistance of Liquids (Proc. RS Jan. 21, 1869).[3] He states in his paper (I do not know if it is printed or to be printed)[4] previous results. His experimental methods seem very good. His chief defect is that he never seems to know what he is going to measure. He works at the Royal Institution and has been so impregnated with radiant heat and otherwise Tyndallized[5] that he describes the specific resistance of a liquid to be the ratio of the quantity of heat *arrested* by the liquid to that arrested by an equal thickness of water.

He states his object to be 'to determine the laws according to which heat travels by conduction through liquids' but he goes to work as if he wanted to find their absorption of radiant heat. The actual phenomena he observes are mainly phenomena of conduction.

He finds that heat gets through a millimeter of water in a minute very much better than any other liquid their resistances being[6]

Water	1	All solutions
Glycerine	3.84	of salts
Acetic acid glacial	8.38	increase
Alcohol	9.08	resistance
Oil of Turpentine	11.75	or diminish
Chloroform	12.10	conductivity
	&c.	

Of course mercury is not in this series. From my recollection of the paper the only results previously obtained were proofs that there is such a thing as true conduction of heat by liquids.

---

(1) ULC Add. MSS 7342, M 107. Previously published in Larmor, 'Origins': 741–2.

(2) John Tatlock, Thomson's assistant and amanuensis; see S. P. Thompson, *The Life of William Thomson Baron Kelvin of Largs*, 2 vols. (London, 1910), **2**: 595.

(3) Frederick Guthrie, 'On the thermal resistance of liquids', *Proc. Roy. Soc.*, **17** (1869): 234–6.

(4) Guthrie's paper was printed in *Phil. Trans.*, **159** (1869): 637–60.

(5) See Numbers 255 and 258.

(6) The values are taken from Guthrie's table of 'specific resistance'.

Perhaps Dr Matthiessen could give you information. He knows what conduction means and he collects the properties of bodies,[7] and he will not tell you what he does not know.

For experiments on steady conduction an iron plate covered with copper on both sides might be useful as a measurer of the flow of heat. The two copper plates to be connected with a galvanometer. The galvanometer having a great resistance compared with the plate, its indications may be trusted to give the mean electromotive force over the plate or the mean flow of heat per square inch. The value of the galvanometer readings must be found by regular calorimetric methods.

The compound plate being a much better conductor than most of the substances to be tried and also probably thinner the differences of temperature in the other bodies may be found by more direct methods of thermometry.

With respect to stress in a medium arising from magnetism

$$\frac{d}{dx}p_{xx} + \frac{d}{dy}p_{yx} + \frac{d}{dz}p_{zx}$$

is the x-force on an element of the medium referred to unit of volume.[8] If in that element there is neither electric current nor magnetization $X = 0$. If there is electric currrent the right expression comes out. If there is magnetization the case is more difficult because of the double def^n of force within a magnet.[9] If there is nothing but Ampère's currents[10] and if these are recognized as currents then all is easy, and

$$X = \alpha\rho - \beta w + \gamma v^{(11)}$$

---

(7) See Number 296 notes (8), (9) and (10).

(8) See the *Treatise*, 2: 256 (§643), and Number 205 esp. note (14).

(9) Thomson's distinction between 'solenoidal' and 'lamellar' distributions of magnetism in his paper 'A mathematical theory of magnetism', *Phil. Trans.*, 141 (1851): 243–85, esp. 269–85 (= *Electrostatics and Magnetism*: 340–404). See the *Treatise*, 2: 31–6 (§§407–16); Numbers 322 note (13) and 353 note (15); and Volume I: 256n, 257n, 260n, 323n.

(10) Ampère's theory of magnets as consisting of molecules within which electric currents circulate: see Numbers 322 note (13) and 410 esp. notes (19) and (26).

(11) Termed one of the 'Equations of Electromagnetic Force' in the *Treatise*, 2: 257 (§643).

(12) See Thomson, 'A mathematical theory of magnetism': 250–6; 'an imaginary magnetic matter...may be conceived to represent the polarity of a magnet of any kind' (on 250).

where $\alpha\,\beta\,\gamma$ are components of magnetic force $u\,v\,w$ are components of currents $\rho =$ density of imaginary magnetic matter[12]

$$4\pi u = \frac{d\gamma}{dy} - \frac{d\beta}{dz}\text{[13]} \quad \&\text{c} \quad 4\pi\rho = \frac{d\alpha}{dx} + \frac{d\beta}{dy} + \frac{d\gamma}{dz}.\text{[14]}$$

Yours truly
J. CLERK MAXWELL

---

(13) Maxwell's equations (E), the 'Equations of Electric Currents', in the *Treatise*, **2**: 231 (§607).

(14) On this expression see the *Treatise*, **2**: 256 (§643).

333

LETTER TO PETER GUTHRIE TAIT

10 DECEMBER 1869

From the original in the University Library, Cambridge[1]

Glenlair
Dalbeattie
10 Dec 1869

D^r T′

I have never attempted to calculate the modifications in the forms of electric stream lines in a conducting plate due to the presence of a magnet of constant strength in as much as I want it but a vain conceit that a magnet has any just title to cause any deviations of the said stream lines from the paths prescribed to them as laid down in the laws of the late Dr G. S. Ohm.[2]

If the magnet can alter the conducting power of the plate either isotropically or in certain directions the stream lines will change. Also if the plate or magnet is free to move, they will move and so produce currents.

But if the magnet does not affect the quality of the plate (See Thomsons Electrodynamic qualities of Metals)[3] then the stream line, me judice, will be unaffected. If they are, glory over me.

If you want to draw the theoretical forms of stream lines and equipotentials in circular or sectorial plates &c I have done a few, & could write out instructions for your youths to do them by means of tracing paper.[4]

You have seen I suppose Kirchhoffs experimental tracing of the equipotential lines on a compound disk one semicircle copper and the other lead.[5]

The electro-kinetic energy of any system of currents is[6]

---

(1) ULC Add. MSS 7655, I, b/15.

(2) Georg Simon Ohm, *Die galvanische Kette, mathematisch bearbeitet* (Berlin, 1827).

(3) William Thomson, 'On the electro-dynamic qualities of metals', *Phil. Trans.*, **146** (1856): 649–751, esp. 736–51 ['Part V'] (= *Math. & Phys. Papers*, **2**: 307–27).

(4) See the *Treatise*, **1**: 239–40 (§§ 194–5) and Fig. XI appended to the volume; and see Number 340. See the paper by Tait's assistant William Robertson Smith, 'On the flow of electricity in conducting surfaces', *Proc. Roy. Soc. Edinb.*, **7** (1870): 79–99 (read 21 February 1870); and the *Treatise*, **1**: 149 (§ 123).

(5) Gustav Kirchhoff, 'Ueber den Durchgang eines elektrischen Stromes durch eine Ebene, insbesondere durch eine kreisförmige', *Ann. Phys.*, **64** (1854): 497–514, esp. 509 and Table V Fig. 3. See the *Treatise*, **1**: 367n (§ 316).

(6) Compare Maxwell's discussion of the theory of electric circuits in the *Treatise*, **2**: 206–8 (§§ 578–9) where he defines the 'Electrokinetic Energy of the system' as 'that part of the kinetic energy of the system which depends on squares and products of the strengths of the electric currents.' See Number 430.

$T = \frac{1}{2}\{L_1 \gamma_1^2 + L_2 \gamma_2^2 + \&c + 2M_{12}\gamma_1\gamma_2 + \&c\}$ where $\gamma_1\, \gamma_2$ are the currents in various conductors and $L\, M\, \&c$ depend on the geometrical arrangement and are of the nature of lines. L_1 depends only on the size & shape of the conductor which carries γ_1 and not on its position. M_{12} depends on the size and shape of the system of two circuits carrying γ_1 & γ_2 &c.

The electromagnetic momentum of a current γ_1 is

$$\xi_1 = \frac{dT}{d\gamma_1} = L_1\gamma_1 + M_{12}\gamma_2 + \&c$$

and if the electromotive force in this circuit is η_1

$$\eta_1 = R_1\gamma_1 + \frac{d\xi_1}{dt}$$

where R_1 is the resistance of the circuit.

If there is no motion of circuits or variation of currents ξ_1 is constant and $\eta_1 = R_1\gamma_1$ or the current when steady is not affected by the presence of other steady currents but is determined by Ohm's Law.

Hence if the stream lines in a conducting plate be drawn when there is no magnet or neighbouring current they will be unaffected when the magnet exists.

For the original lines satisfy Ohm and the conditions of supply & demand, and if there is any change the new system must be the old + a system of reentering streams due to the magnet, which as we have seen does not exist. QED.

I am at the 4th of the 4 parts of my book namely Electrodynamics.[7] I have done the historical and theoretical part (of which you have here a tinkling of the symbols) and am now at Galvanometers and galvanometry[8] but am interrupted by Cambridge Examination.[9] I have still to write out ships magnetism[10] and telegraphy.[11]

I have just revised the paper on Frames and reciprocal figures for the R.S.E.[12] Jenkin has saved me much trouble.[13] I had arranged with W. P. Taylor the independent inventor of the method to give an account of the working of it from a draughtsmanlike point of view and I still expect his

---

(7) See Number 329.

(8) Compare Part IV chapter XV of the *Treatise* (on 'electromagnetic instruments'), 2: 313–34 (§§ 707–29).

(9) Maxwell had been appointed Examiner for the Cambridge Mathematical Tripos in 1870; see *The Cambridge University Calendar for the Year 1870* (Cambridge, 1870): 483.

(10) See the *Treatise*, 2: 70–73 (§ 441).

(11) See the Treatise, 1: 374–87, esp. 383–4 (§ 332).

(12) See Number 334. (13) See Number 334 esp. notes (5) and (8).

paper. But as soon as I have drawn a few pictures I will send you mine which opens up several prospects for an adventurous mathematician as e.g.[14]

If P_1 P_2 are the principal stresses at any point xy of a plane sheet in equilibrium

$$\iint (P_1 + P_2)\, dx\, dy \quad \text{and} \quad \iint P_1 P_2\, dx\, dy$$

depend only on the external forces applied to the edge of the sheet and not on internal strains &c.

Let the resultant force on the edge of the sheet from O to any point P be R (in direction & magnitude) then the 1st integral is the work done on P in going the circuit of the edge, always acted on by R, and the 2nd integral is the area described by R turning on one end as a pivot.

Figure 333,1

Yours
J. C. M.

---

(14) Compare J. Clerk Maxwell, 'On reciprocal figures, frames and diagrams of forces', *Trans. Roy. Soc. Edinb.*, **26** (1870): 1–40, esp. 27–31 (= *Scientific Papers*, **2**: 192–7).

ABSTRACT OF PAPER 'ON RECIPROCAL FIGURES, FRAMES, AND DIAGRAMS OF FORCES'

[17 DECEMBER 1869][1]

From the *Proceedings of the Royal Society of Edinburgh*[2]

ON RECIPROCAL FIGURES, FRAMES, AND DIAGRAMS OF FORCES.

By J. Clerk Maxwell, Esq., F.R.SS.L. & E.[3]

The reciprocal figures treated of in this paper are plane rectilinear figures, such that every line in one figure is perpendicular to the corresponding line in the other, and lines which meet in a point in one figure correspond to lines which form a closed polygon in the other.

By turning one of the figures round 90°, the corresponding lines become parallel, and are more easily recognised. The practical use of these figures depends on the proposition known as the 'Polygon of Forces'. If we suppose one of the reciprocal figures to represent a system of points acted on by tensions or pressures along the lines of the figure, then, if the forces which act along these lines are represented in magnitude, as they are in direction, by the corresponding lines of the other reciprocal figure, every point of the first figure will be in equilibrium. For the forces which act at that point are parallel and proportional to the sides of a polygon formed by the corresponding lines in the other figure.

In all cases, therefore, in which one of the figures represents a frame, or the skeleton of a structure which is in equilibrium under the action of pressures and tensions in its several pieces, the other figure represents a system of forces which would keep the frame in equilibrium; and, if the known data are sufficient to determine these forces, the reciprocal figure may be drawn so as to represent, on a selected scale, the actual values of all these forces.

In this way a practical method of determining the tensions and pressures in structures has been developed. The 'polygon of forces' has been long known. The application to polygonal frames, with a system of forces acting on the angles, and to several other cases, was made by Professor Rankine in his

---

(1) The date the paper was received by the Royal Society of Edinburgh. The paper was read on 7 February 1870: see note (2).

(2) *Proc. Roy. Soc. Edinb.*, **7** (1870): 53–6.

(3) Published in *Trans. Roy. Soc. Edinb.*, **26** (1870): 1–40 (= *Scientific Papers*, **2**: 161–207).

Applied Mechanics.[4] Mr W. P. Taylor, a practical draughtsman,[5] has independently worked out more extensive applications of the method. Starting from Professor Rankine's examples, I taught the method to the class of Applied Mechanics in King's College, London,[6] and published a short account of it in the 'Philosophical Magazine' for April 1864.[7] Professor Fleeming Jenkin, in a paper recently presented to the Society,[8] has fully explained the application of the method to the most important cases occurring in practice, and I believe that it has been found to have three important practical advantages. It is easily taught to any person who can use a ruler and scale. It is quite sufficiently accurate for all ordinary calculations, and is much more rapid than the trigonometrical method. When the figure is drawn the whole process remains visible, so that the accuracy of the drawing of any single line can be afterwards tested; and if any mistake has been made, the figure cannot be completed. Hence the verification of the process is much easier than that of a long series of arithmetical operations, including the use of trigonometric tables.

In the present paper I have endeavoured to develope the idea of reciprocal figures, to show its connection with the idea of reciprocal polars as given in pure mathematics,[9] and to extend it to figures in three dimensions, and to cases in which the stresses, instead of being along certain lines only, are distributed continuously throughout the interior of a solid body. In making this extension of the theory of reciprocal figures, I have been led to see the connection of this theory with that of the very important function introduced into the theory of stress in two dimensions by Mr Airy, in his paper 'On the Strains in the Interior of Beams' (Phil. Trans. 1863).[10]

If a plane sheet is in equilibrium under the action of internal stress of any kind, then a quantity, which we shall call Airy's Function of Stress,[11] can always be found, which has the following properties.

---

(4) W. J. M. Rankine, *A Manual of Applied Mechanics* (London/Glasgow, 1858): 137–40.

(5) See Fleeming Jenkin, 'On the practical application of reciprocal figures to the calculation of strains on framework', *Trans. Roy. Soc. Edinb.*, **25** (1869): 441–7, esp. 441.

(6) Number 203.

(7) J. Clerk Maxwell, 'On reciprocal figures and diagrams of forces', *Phil. Mag.*, ser. 4, **27** (1864): 250–61 (= *Scientific Papers*, **1**: 514–25). See also Number 273.

(8) See note (5).   (9) See Number 273 note (2).

(10) George Biddell Airy, 'On the strains in the interior of beams', *Phil. Trans.*, **153** (1863): 49–79.

(11) See Maxwell's discussion of this function, in his referee's report on Airy's paper: Number 205. See also his papers 'On reciprocal figures, frames, and diagrams of forces': 27–31 (= *Scientific Papers*, **2**: 192–7), and 'On reciprocal diagrams in space, and their relation to Airy's function of stress', *Proceedings of the London Mathematical Society*, **2** (1868): 58–60 (= *Scientific Papers*, **2**: 102–4).

At each point of the sheet let a perpendicular be erected proportional to the function of stress at that point, so that the extremities of such perpendiculars lie in a certain surface, which we may call the surface of stress. In the case of a plane frame the surface of stress is a plane-faced polyhedron, of which the frame is the projection. On another plane, parallel to the sheet, let a perpendicular be erected of height unity, and from the extremity of this perpendicular let a line be drawn normal to the tangent plane at a point of the surface of stress, and meeting the plane at a certain point.

Thus, if points be taken in the plane sheet, corresponding points may be found by this process in the other plane, and if both points are supposed to move, two corresponding lines will be drawn, which have the following property:– The resultant of the whole stress exerted by the part of the sheet on the right hand side of the line on the left hand side, is represented in direction and magnitude by the line joining the extremities of the corresponding line in the other figure. In the case of a plane frame, the corresponding figure is the reciprocal diagram described above.

From this property the whole theory of the distribution of stress in equilibrium in two dimensions may be deduced.

In the most general case of three dimensions, we must use three such functions, and the method becomes cumbrous. I have, however, used these functions in forming equations of equilibrium of elastic solids, in which the stresses are considered as the quantities to be determined, instead of the displacements, as in the ordinary form.

These equations are especially useful in the cases in which we wish to determine the stresses in uniform beams. The distribution of stress in such cases is determined, as in all other cases, by the elastic yielding of the material; but if this yielding is small and the beam uniform, the stress at any point will be the same, whatever be the actual value of the elasticity of the substance.

Hence the coefficients of elasticity disappear from the ultimate value of the stresses.

In this way I have obtained values for the stresses in a beam supported in a specified way, which differ only by small quantities from the values obtained by Mr Airy, by a method involving certain assumptions, which were introduced in order to avoid the consideration of elastic yielding.

335

DRAFTS RELATING TO PART IV OF THE *TREATISE*

circa LATE 1869[1]

From the originals in the University Library, Cambridge[2]

[1] MAGNETIC POTENTIAL OF A LINEAR ELECTRIC CIRCUIT[3]

The magnetic potential at any point of a field of magnetic force is measured by the work which must be done in order to bring a unit magnetic pole from an infinite distance to that point by a path subject to the condition that it shall not pass through a certain finite surface bounded by the circuit and called the diaphragm.

It may be shown from the principle of the conservation of energy that a potential must exist when the magnetic force is due to a permanent magnet. If we explore a limited portion of the field of force by means of a magnet we cannot distinguish between the case in which the force arises from a permanent magnet and that in which it arises from an electric current, the magnet and the current being understood to be outside the region which we explore. We have therefore good reason to believe that the magnetic force arising from electric currents has, at least in singly connected regions of space through which the current does not pass, a magnetic potential.

In the case of a ⟨plane⟩ ⌊circular⌋ circuit the magnetic potential at all points in the plane of the circle outside the circuit is zero. For if the potential at such a point were P then by turning the whole system 180° about the line joining the given point with the centre we shall find that P is now the potential at the point due to the same circuit with the current flowing in the reverse direction. But since every effect of a current is reversed when the current is reversed, the potential must now be $-P$. Hence, since $P = -P$, the only possible value of P is zero.

Any number of contiguous[a] circuits having equal currents flowing round them in the same direction are in all respects equivalent to the circuit which bounds the whole with a current of the same strength flowing round it.

(a) {Maxwell} conterminous.

(1) This date is conjectural, but the MSS were very likely written after the outline of the contents of the *Treatise* (Number 329, and for dating see note (1)), and at about the same time as Number 333.
(2) ULC Add. MSS 7655, V, c/24, 27(b).
(3) ULC Add. MSS 7655, V, c/24. Compare the *Treatise*, 2: 130–2 (§§480–4).

For in the linear conductor which forms the common boundary of two contiguous circuits equal currents are flowing in opposite directions and this is in every respect equivalent to no current at all.

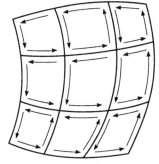

Figure 335,1

Hence the only currents which are not neutralized are those which flow in those parts of the circuits which are not contiguous to other circuits, that is, in the bounding circuit of the whole system.

The effect of a plane circuit at a point whose distance is very great compared with the dimensions of the circuit is proportional to the strength of the current multiplied into the area of the circuit.[4]

For if a number of equal and similar circuits are in the same plane and so near each other that their distances and directions from the given point are sensibly the same the effect of each circuit at the given point will be the same and the effect of the whole system will be proportional to the number of circuits and independent of the mode in which they are arranged.

Hence if the circuits are placed in contact the effect of the circuit which bounds them all will be proportional to its area and independent of its shape.

But we have seen that the effect of a small plane circuit on a distant point depends on its area and not on its shape. Hence the potential due to a small plane area of any form at a distant point in its own plane is zero.

Also since for any plane circuit we may substitute a number of small contiguous circuits in its plane having the same external boundary it follows that the potential due to any plane circuit at any point of the plane outside the circuit is zero.

If one circuit is the projection of another with respect to the given point the two circuits have the same potential at that point.

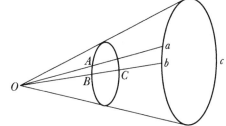

Figure 335,2

For let AB be the two neighbouring points on one circuit and ab the corresponding points of the other then the points $A\,a\,b\,B$ lie in the same plane with O. Hence the potential due to the circuit $A\,a\,b\,B$ at the point O is zero.

Now consider the circuit $a\,b\,c$ together with all the circuits lying in the conical surface of which O is the vertex and bounded by the circuit ABC on the one side and $a\,b\,c$ on the other. These circuits are contiguous and the bounding surface of the system is $a\,b\,c$.

---

(4) See the Treatise, 2: 131 (§482).

The potential at O due to $a\,b\,c$ is therefore equal to the sum of the potentials of all the circuits of the system formed by $A\,B\,C$ and the circuits in the conical surface. But the potential due to those in the conical surface is zero. Hence the potential at O due to $a\,b\,c$ is equal to that due to $A\,B\,C$.

If one of these circuits, say $A\,B\,C$ lies on a spherical surface of radius unity whose centre is O each of the small equal circuits lying on the spherical surface into which it may be divided will be similarly situated with respect to O and the potentials at O due to these circuits will be equal. Hence the potential of the whole circuit at O may be measured by the area of the spherical surface multiplied into the strength of the current.

But the potential due to any circuit is equal to that due to its projection on the spherical surface of radius unity and centre O. Hence the potential at O due to any circuit is equal to the area cut off from the spherical surface of radius unity and centre O by the projection of the circuit with respect to the point O [...].

[2] ON THE CONDUCTION OF ELECTRICITY IN TWO DIMENSIONS[5]

We shall suppose the conduction of electric currents to take place in a thin sheet of conducting matter bounded on both sides by non-conductors. The sheet may be plane or curved and the conductivity may be different at different parts of the sheet or it may be different for different directions at the same point.

Lines of Flow

Let O be any point in the sheet which we may take as origin and let P be any other point and let OP be joined by any curve and let the quantity of electricity which in unit of time crosses the curve OP from left to right be denoted by ϕ.

If any other curve be drawn between O and P and if in the space included between the two curves no electricity be supplied to or removed from the sheet then the quantity of electricity which crosses the second curve must be equal to that which crosses the first in the same time and the value of ϕ will be independent of the form of the curve drawn between O and P, or in other words ϕ is a function of the position of the point P.

Similarly if ϕ' is the value of ϕ corresponding to the point of P' then if a curve PP' be drawn the quantity of electricity which crosses PP' in unit of time from left to right is $\phi' - \phi$.

---

(5) ULC Add. MSS 7655, V, c/27(b). There are preliminary drafts in V, c/27(a). Compare the *Treatise*, **2**: 259–61 (§§647–51).

If a system of lines be drawn on the surface for each of which ϕ is constant and if the consecutive values of ϕ differ by unity (the unit being taken as small as we please) then the system of lines may be called lines of flow and the channels between them unit channels.

If points on the surface are defined by any system of coordinates whose symbols are x and y and if the quantity of electricity which crosses the element dy in unit of time in the direction in which x increases is $u\,dy$ we should have

$$u\,dy = \frac{d\phi}{dy}dy$$

or

$$u = \frac{d\phi}{dy}.$$

If $v\,dx$ is the quantity which crosses dx in the direction in which y increases

$$v = -\frac{d\phi}{dx}.$$

u and v must evidently satisfy the equation of continuity

$$\frac{du}{dx} + \frac{dv}{dy} = 0.$$

u and v may be called the components of the current in the directions x and of y.[6]

If at any point of the surface electricity is conveyed to the sheet or removed from it the function ϕ may have an infinite series of values because the line drawn from O to P may pass any number of times round the point either in the positive or the negative direction, and for each circuit the value of ϕ will be increased or diminished by the quantity of electricity flowing from or to the point in unit of time.

The function ϕ may therefore have an infinite series of values but its differential coefficients, which determine the current at any point have determinate and single values.

Equipotential Lines

Let ψ be the potential of the electricity at any point P of the surface and ψ' the value of ψ at any other point P' then if a wire be made to touch the surface at P and P' it will experience an electromotive force $= \psi - \psi'$.

If ψ and ψ' are equal there will be no electromotive force and no current will be formed in the wire so that by determining the points P' at which the

---

(6) For the hydrodynamical analogy see Volume I: 295–6.

second extremity of the wire must be placed so that there shall be no current we may trace out the equipotential line corresponding to P. If ψ and ψ' are not equal there will be a current which will interfere with the electrical condition of the sheet.

If a system of lines be drawn on the surface for each of which ψ is constant, and if the consecutive values of ψ differ by unity (unity being taken as small as we please), then the system of lines may be called Equipotential Lines and the intervals between them equipotential strata.

If points on the surface are defined by the coordinates x and y then we may define the electromotive force at any point in the direction of x as the electromotive force on the element dx divided by the length of that element. Calling $X\ Y$ the components of the electromotive force at the point (x,y)

$$X = \frac{d\psi}{dx}$$

$$Y = \frac{d\psi}{dy}.$$

Equations of Conduction

At any point of the surface, the components of the electromotive force and those of the electric current are so related that the one pair may be expressed as linear functions of the other.

The most general equations connecting them may be written

$$X = Au + Bv$$
$$Y = Cu + Dv.$$

If we assume a system of rectangular axes x', y', of which the axis of x' makes an angle of θ with that of x where $\tan 2\theta = \dfrac{B+C}{A-D}$ and if we make

$$E^2 = AD - BC \quad \text{and} \quad F^2 = (A-D)^2 + (B+C)^2 \quad \text{and} \quad k^2 = \frac{A+D+F}{A+D-F}$$

and $\sin \chi = \dfrac{C-B}{2E}$ then if we increase the coordinates x' in the ratio k we shall have in the new system if R' is the resultant of X' and Y' and V' that of u' and v' and if the directions of R' and V' are α' & β'

$$R' = EV' \quad \alpha' = \beta' + \chi$$

or the reduced electromotive force has a constant ratio to the reduced current and makes a constant angle χ with it.

The angle χ affords a measure of a rotatory property in the conduction of the medium. The mathematical character of this property has been pointed out by Professor Stokes in his memoir on the conduction of heat in Crystals[7] and by Prof Sir W Thomson in his memoir on Thermodynamics[8] who has shown how to construct a solid having this rotatory property with respect to the connexion between the distribution of heat and the electric currents produced by it.[9]

---

(7) G. G. Stokes, 'On the conduction of heat in crystals', *Camb. & Dubl. Math. J.*, **6** (1851): 215–38 (= *Papers*, **3**: 203–27).

(8) William Thomson, 'On the dynamical theory of heat. Part V. Thermo-electric currents', *Trans. Roy. Soc. Edinb.*, **21** (1854): 123–71, esp. 164–7 (= *Math. & Phys. Papers*, **1**: 232–91).

(9) Compare Maxwell's discussion in 'On Faraday's lines of force', *Trans. Camb. Phil. Soc.*, **10** (1856): 27–83, esp. 39–40 (= *Scientific Papers*, **1**: 171–2); and see Volume I: 360.

336

FROM A LETTER TO KATHERINE MARY CLERK MAXWELL

3 JANUARY 1870

From Campbell and Garnett, *Life of Maxwell*[1]

There is a tradition in Trinity that when I was here I discovered a method of throwing a cat so as not to light on its feet, and that I used to throw cats out of windows. I had to explain that the proper object of research was to find how quick the cat would turn round, and that the proper method was to let the cat drop on a table or bed from about two inches, and that even then the cat lights on her feet.[2]

---

(1) *Life of Maxwell*: 499.

(2) On Maxwell's and Stokes' interest in 'cat-turning' (the motion of the cat being in accordance with the conservation of angular momentum, on which see Volume I: 499–501), see Larmor, *Correspondence*, **1**: 32. The subject was subsequently investigated: see É. J. Marey, 'Des mouvements que certains animaux exécutent pour retomber sur les pieds, lorsqu'ils sont précipités d'un lieu élevé', *Comptes Rendus*, **119** (1894): 714–17; É. Guyou, 'Note relative à la communication de M. Marey', *ibid.*: 717–18; Maurice Lévy, 'Observations sur le principe des aires', *ibid.*: 718–21.

337

REPORT ON A PAPER BY WILLIAM JOHN MACQUORN RANKINE ON FLUID MOTION[1]

2 MARCH 1870

From the original in the Library of the Royal Society, London[2]

REPORT ON PROF^r RANKINES PAPER ON THE MATHEMATICAL THEORY OF STREAM-LINES[3]

A stream line is defined as the line traced by a particle in a current of fluid.[4] It is therefore to be distinguished from what has been elsewhere defined as a 'line of fluid motion', namely a line which coincides throughout its length with the direction of fluid motion at a given instant.[5] In cases of variable motion the lines of fluid motion are different from the stream lines but each stream line at any instant touches one of the lines of fluid motion at that instant. In cases of steady motion which alone are treated of in this paper the two kinds of lines coincide.[6]

The paper begins with a general discussion of stream lines considered as the

---

(1) See also Number 223.

(2) Royal Society, *Referees' Reports*, **7**: 55 *bis*.

(3) W. J. M. Rankine, 'On the mathematical theory of stream-lines, especially those with four foci and upwards', *Phil. Trans.*, **161** (1871): 267–306. The paper was received by the Royal Society on 1 January 1870, with a supplement received on 8 January 1870, and read on 10 February 1870; see the abstract in *Proc. Roy. Soc.*, **18** (1870): 207–9.

(4) As defined by Rankine, 'On the mathematical theory of stream-lines': 267. See also W. J. M. Rankine, 'Summary of the properties of certain stream-lines', *Phil. Mag.*, ser. 4, **28** (1864): 282–8; and his 'Supplement to a paper on stream-lines', *ibid.*, **29** (1865): 25–8. The curves which Rankine here terms 'stream-lines' he had formerly denoted by the term 'water-lines'; see W. J. M. Rankine, 'On plane water-lines in two dimensions', *Phil. Trans.*, **154** (1864): 369–91, and Number 223.

(5) Maxwell had used the term 'lines of fluid motion' in this sense (see note (6)) in his paper 'On Faraday's lines of force', *Trans. Camb. Phil. Soc.*, **10** (1856): 27–83, esp. 30–42 (= *Scientific Papers*, **1**: 160–75). See Volume I: 337–50, 357–61. For the distinction (but with different terminology), see G. G. Stokes, 'Remarks on a paper by Professor Challis, "On the analytical condition of the rectilinear motion of fluids"', *Phil. Mag.*, ser. 3, **21** (1842): 297–300, on 297; 'I shall call the path of a particle of a fluid in space a *line of motion*, and a line traced at a given instant from point to point in the direction of the motion a *line of direction*.'

(6) Compare Maxwell, 'On Faraday's line of force': 31 (= *Scientific Papers*, **1**: 160); 'Lines drawn...that their direction always indicates the direction of fluid motion are called *lines of fluid motion*. If the motion of the fluid be...*steady motion*...these curves will represent the paths of individual particles of the fluid.'

intersections of two series of 'stream-line-surfaces'.[7] If ψ and χ are functions which have constant values for each one of these surfaces and if the consecutive surfaces to these are denoted by $\psi + d\psi$ and $\chi + d\chi$ then these four surfaces will cut off a quadrilateral tube of fluid motion[8] the flow across any section of which is constant throughout its length and is therefore a quantity of the form
$$f(\psi, \chi) \, d\psi \, d\chi.$$

Now any function of ψ and χ is also a stream line function. If therefore we take a new function χ' of ψ and χ such that
$$d\chi' = f(\psi, \chi) \, d\chi$$
then the flow through the tube formed by the intersections of the ψ and χ' surfaces will be simply $d\psi \, d\chi'$.

Whatever be the form of the functions ψ and χ' a case of fluid motion such that the flow through any surface S is represented by the surface integral $\iint d\psi \, d\chi$ extended over the surface is consistent with the incompressibility of the fluid[9] though it may be inconsistent with the dynamics of fluid motion.

In the important class of cases in which a 'velocity potential'[10] exists that is in all cases of irrotational motion the stream line surfaces must be

---

(7) See Rankine, 'On the mathematical theory of stream-lines': 267; 'if the figure of a ship is such that the particles of water glide smoothly over her skin, that figure is a *stream-line* surface'. In a 'Preliminary Report' to the Royal Society's Committee of Papers (Royal Society, *Referees' Reports*, **7**: 55), Stokes criticised this statement: 'Although not expressly stated, it appears to be implied... that the author conceived certain surfaces, but not surfaces in general, to be possible stream-line surfaces... that consequently the investigation of even a very particular class of surfaces which are known to be stream-line surfaces becomes a matter of importance.... Now I contend that the view I have put forward is not correct; that on the contrary the surface of a solid of perfectly arbitrary form... is a stream-line surface... for Nature, as Fresnel remarks, is not embarrassed by difficulties of analysis, and there is nothing to show that a surface, the stream-lines corresponding to which are expressible by an equation of simple form, has an advantage over a surface, the expression of the stream-lines corresponding to which surpasses the power of our analysis.' In a note dated December 1870, appended to this statement in his paper ('On the mathematical theory of stream-lines': 267n), Rankine responded by stating: 'although every surface is a possible stream-line surface, the surface of a ship is not even approximately an actual stream-line surface unless it is such that she does not drag along with her a mass of eddies'.

(8) The term introduced by Maxwell in 'On Faraday's lines of force': 31–5 (= *Scientific Papers*, **1**: 160–5). See Volume I: 338–40. In a note dated June 1871 ('On the mathematical theory of stream-lines': 270n), Rankine referred to Maxwell's term.

(9) Compare Maxwell's non-analytic formulation in 'On Faraday's lines of force': 32–3 (= *Scientific Papers*, **1**: 162–3); and see Volume I: 340.

(10) Helmholtz's term; see his 'Über Integrale der hydrodynamischen Gleichungen, welche den Wirbelbewegungen entsprechen', *Journal für die reine und angewandte Mathematik*, **55** (1858): 25–55, esp. 25: and the translation of the paper (by P. G. Tait) 'On the integrals of the hydrodynamical equations, which express vortex-motion', *Phil. Mag.*, ser. 4, **33** (1867): 485–512, on 485. See Number 311 esp. note (6).

perpendicular to the equipotential surfaces⁽¹¹⁾ the conditions of which are given by the author.

It will be seen from this part of the paper that the general theory of fluid motion is by no means simplified when approached through the theory of stream-line-surfaces. It is in the study of particular cases that these surfaces give us valuable assistance.

The direct problem of finding two systems of stream line surfaces such that the surface of a given ship may be one of them and also such that the relative motion of the water at a distance from the ship is uniform is always capable of a final and single solution, but it generally lies beyond the reach of any known mathematical methods.

Hence we attempt the inverse problem of finding from two given systems of stream line surfaces corresponding to a possible mode of fluid motion what form a ship may have so as to produce this mode of motion in the water.⁽¹²⁾

This problem is comparatively easy and its solution is always capable of expression either in symbols or by diagrams.

By acquiring a knowledge of the different forms of stream-line-surfaces due to different hypotheses as to the nature of the fluid motion and by studying the changes in these forms due to changes in the hypotheses, Prof^r Rankine and those who use his methods hope to be able to design the lines of ships so that the motion of the water near them may be of the kind most favourable to the progress of the ship.

Hence what we have called the inverse problem in hydrodynamics is the leading problem in shipbuilding. The Author then proceeds as in former papers⁽¹³⁾ to show how to draw systems of stream lines in two dimensions and also stream surfaces of revolution in three dimensions.

$\Bigg\{$ With respect to the stream lines in *two* dimensions the most important *theoretical* step has been made by C. Neumann in a paper on the integration of $\frac{d^2\phi}{dx^2}+\frac{d^2\phi}{dy^2}=0$ Crelle 1861.⁽¹⁴⁾ This depends on the theory of Conjugate Functions and their transformations.⁽¹⁵⁾ $\Bigg\}$

---

(11) See Number 223, esp. note (14).

(12) Compare Stokes' comments in his reports on Rankine's paper (notes (7) and (22)).

(13) See Rankine, 'On plane water-lines in two dimensions', and Number 223 esp. note (15); and Rankine, 'Elementary demonstrations of principles relating to stream lines', *The Engineer*, **26** (1868): 285–6.

(14) Carl Neumann, 'Ueber die Integration der partiellen Differential-gleichung: $\frac{\partial^2\phi}{\partial x^2}+\frac{\partial^2\phi}{\partial y^2}=0$', *Journal für die reine und angewandte Mathematik*, **59** (1861): 335–66. See Number 321.

(15) For further discussion see the *Treatise*, **1**: 234–5 (§190); and Number 303 note (3).

I am not aware that any stream lines in 3 dimensions have been investigated except plane stream lines (such as are here given) and the intersections of confocal surfaces of the second order.

In the authors former papers the cases of fluid motion were those compounded of

1st the general motion astern of the whole sea

2nd a motion of divergence from a place in the fore part of the ship

3rd a motion of convergence to a place in the hinder part of the ship.

The ship shapes derived from this hypothesis were named Oogenous Neoids.[16] They were all rather bluff both before and behind and to make them finer other stream lines called Lissoneoids[17] were selected and fastened together in a somewhat discontinuous manner so as to have a sharp angle at both ends.

Now if we wish to construct a case of fluid motion which shall give us a Neoid with sharp ends we must suppose not a single pair of foci of divergence and convergence but a continuous line of foci close to the cutwater, the density along the central line depending on an inverse fractional power of the distance from the point of the cutwater.

From this it will be seen that the foci of most disturbance are very close to the surface of the ship and therefore the suddenness of the disturbance of the water will be greater with an angular end than with one which is rounded.

A result of this kind seems to have been actually obtained by Mr Froude.[18]

This suddenness is avoided by making the internal foci finite in value and at a finite distance from the surface. The Author has used, besides his two original foci, two subsidiary ones before and behind them the effect of which is to give the neoid a longer and a leaner figure near the extremities but to preserve the roundness of the actual extremities.

The shape of the ship is therefore more manageable and by a little more labour which would be willingly undertaken by those who care for shipbuilding any number of foci might be introduced in the places where theory indicates that they would be useful for checking the various wave motions ⟨by⟩ which the power of the engines is wasted. This is pointed out in §19 of the paper.

The author afterwards applies Greens Theorem[19] to the calculation of the

---

(16) See Number 223 note (17).   (17) See Number 223 note (19).

(18) See William Froude's 'explanations' appended to the 'Report of a Committee ... appointed to report on the state of existing knowledge on the stability, propulsion and sea-going qualities of ships...', *Report of the Twenty-ninth Meeting of the British Association for the Advancement of Science* (London, 1870): 10–47, esp. 43–7 and Plate I.

(19) George Green, *An Essay on the Application of Mathematical Analysis to the Theories of Electricity and Magnetism* (Nottingham, 1828): 10; and see *Treatise*, **1**: 108–13 (§100).

energy of the fluid motion. He shows however that for practical purposes the main thing is to prevent the dissipation of energy which is of two kinds.

1st Waves are formed and propagated to a distance carrying off energy depending on their mass and height. This would take place even in a perfect fluid provided the fluid has a free surface.

2nd On account of the viscosity of the fluid rotational motion is set up near the surface and eddies are formed, the energy of which is far greater than that lost by the direct effect of viscosity. These eddies, by Helmholtz' principle,[20] move with the fluid of which they exist, and finally arrange themselves in the wake of the vessel, which is a stream moving behind the vessel, and in the same direction, and such that its central parts move faster than its edges. The author shows that the layer of fluid which is filled with eddies increases in thickness from stem to stern and that $\frac{3}{4}$ of the energy of the wake is in the form of eddies and $\frac{1}{4}$ in that of forward motion. The practical advice to shipbuilders to which the paper leads is

1st to observe the position of the principal waves relatively to an existing ship, and in designing a new one of the same kind to arrange the foci of divergence and convergence so as to check the formation of these waves, or to neutralize them by waves of opposite sign.

2nd To make the variation of velocity of the water in gliding along the water lines as gradual as possible, and thus to reduce to a minimum the formation of eddies.

3rd To deprive, according to Mr Froudes suggestion,[21] the wave as much as possible of its motion so far as this can be done by any arrangement of the propeller. (In screw propellers working in the wake a 'negative slip' has been often observed.)

On the whole I consider the paper a valuable one and worthy of a place in the Transactions, and this chiefly because, in the words of the paper itself, it 'may prove useful in deducing general principles from the data of experiment and observation, and in suggesting plans for further research'.[22]

J. CLERK MAXWELL
Glenlair 2nd March 1870

---

(20) Helmholtz, 'Über Integrale der hydrodynamischen Gleichungen': 33–7; 'On the integrals of the hydrodynamical equations': 491–4.

(21) See Rankine, 'On the mathematical theory of stream-lines': 301.

(22) Rankine, 'On the mathematical theory of stream-lines': 303. In a final report on Rankine's paper, dated 19 January 1871 (Royal Society, *Referees' Reports*, **7**: 56), Stokes wrote: 'I had a little hesitation as to recommending the Committee of papers about this paper. It seems to me that its length is hardly justified by its importance. The first part in which the mathematical reasoning is exact contains little that is new except the following out in detail of

the theoretical motion of a perfect fluid by means of a synthetical solution in which the forms of ships are imitated to a certain extent by curves drawn in accordance with such solution.... The latter part of the paper, into which I have not fully entered, is devoted to a consideration of the effect of waves, i.e. on the resistance. The reasoning in this part of the paper is confessedly probable only and accordingly more or less precarious. To refuse to entertain an investigation on this subject unless it were more exact would be I fear to postpone the question Sine die.... There is no change which I should recommend the Committee to make a condition of printing.'

338

REPORT ON A PAPER BY WILLIAM JOHN MACQUORN RANKINE ON THE THERMODYNAMIC THEORY OF WAVES

26 MARCH 1870

From the original in the Library of the Royal Society, London[1]

REPORT ON PROF^r RANKINES PAPER 'ON THE THERMODYNAMIC THEORY OF WAVES OF FINITE LONGITUDINAL DISTURBANCES'[2]

by J. Clerk Maxwell

In this paper the author investigates the conditions of the propagation of waves of permanent type,[3] and certain properties of the change of type when these conditions are not fulfilled. The method which he has employed differs from the ordinary methods of hydrodynamics with respect to the variables in terms of which the different quantities are expressed.

The velocity of any point of a rigid body is easily conceived and defined. If we suppose a fluid to consist of individual particles it is just as easy to conceive the velocity of any one of them, and if we also assume that the velocity of a particle, instead of being a function of the time, the form of which for different particles is not capable of expression by any single formula, is a continuous function of the coordinates of the particle, and of the time, then we may form the conception of the velocity of a fluid at any point.

But if we have to deal with the flow of heat or of electricity, or even with the flow of fluids composed of molecules in a state of agitation, we have to adopt a totally different conception of the flux. Velocity is measured by the distance described in unit of time but in the case of heat or electricity we have no means of forming any idea of this distance. We therefore measure the flux by the quantity which crosses unit of area in unit of time, passing from the negative to the positive side of the surface.

---

(1) Royal Society, *Referees' Reports*, **7**: 53.

(2) W. J. M. Rankine, 'On the thermodynamic theory of waves of finite longitudinal disturbance', *Phil. Trans.*, **160** (1870): 277–88. The paper was received by the Royal Society on 13 August 1869, with a supplement received on 1 October 1869, and read on 16 December 1869; see *Proc. Roy. Soc.*, **18** (1869): 122, and (abstract) *ibid.*: 80–3.

(3) See Rankine, 'On the thermodynamic theory of waves': 277; 'the word *type* being used to denote the relation between the extent of disturbance at a given instant of a set of particles and their respective undisturbed positions'.

The idea of velocity implies the following a particle in its course. That of flux implies the measurement of the quantity which passes a given surface.

In Prof^r Rankine's paper, the flux through a plane is called the somatic velocity, and, as in the case of waves the plane is supposed to move with the velocity of the wave, and the motion of the fluid is of less consideration, the flux with its sign reversed is called the somatic velocity *of the plane relative to the fluid*.

If the fluid is continuous, the linear velocity of the fluid relative to the plane is the product of the flux by the bulkiness of the fluid. The bulkiness is the inverse of the density, being the volume of unit of mass. In former papers of the author it is called the *volume*,[4] and I think that the word *rarity*, as the strict inverse of density, might be found as convenient as *bulkiness*, just as it is sometimes convenient to consider slowness instead of velocity & resistance instead of conductivity.

The author then considers the propagation of a plane fronted wave of longitudinal displacement, and selects a cylindrical portion of unit of area for examination. A plane is conceived to move through the fluid with somatic velocity m and the position of any other plane is defined by the mass, μ, of fluid between it and the first plane. Everything is then a function of μ and the time.

When the wave is of permanent type, and the first plane moves with the wave-velocity the pressure density &c will be functions of μ only and if we consider two planes both moving with somatic velocity m they will remain at equal distance always.

The author then considers the momentum of the fluid between these planes. The total mass is constant, though the particles are changing. A quantity m of fluid enters the space with a certain velocity, and an equal quantity of it leaves with a certain other velocity. The excess of momentum can only be produced by difference of pressure before and behind. From this consideration an equation is found by elementary reasoning which is a first integral of the ordinary hydrodynamical equation and leads to a determination of the velocity of a wave of permanent type *assuming such a wave to be possible*.

If m is the somatic velocity of the wave p the pressure and s the velocity at any point then

$$m^2 = -\frac{dp}{ds}$$

---

(4) See W. J. M. Rankine, 'On the thermo-dynamic theory of steam engines with dry saturated steam, and its application to practice', *Phil. Trans.*, **149** (1859): 177–92, esp. 182.

and the condition of permanent type is that $\frac{dp}{ds}$ must be constant or that the pressure is a linear function of the volume

$$p = P - m^2(s-S).^{(5)}$$

Now in actual bodies the pressure is a function of the volume and temperature and in the above equation $\frac{dp}{ds}$ means the ratio of the increment of pressure to the increment of volume during the actual changes of pressure and volume which the substance undergoes as the

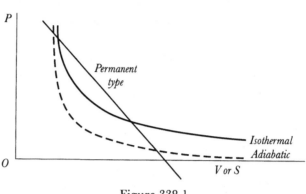

Figure 338,1

wave is propagated through it. In most substances the diagram of volume and pressure gives curves convex to the origin both when the temperature is constant and when there is no communication of heat. For waves of permanent type the line should be straight. Hence in most real cases $\frac{d^2p}{ds^2}$ is positive.

The author therefore endeavours to find under what circumstances $\frac{dp}{ds}$ can be made constant during the propagation of the wave by the communication of heat from the neighbouring parts by conduction.

It appears to me that up to this point the paper is characterized by a degree of simplicity, accuracy and distinctness[6] which is not so well maintained afterwards. The investigation of the condition of permanent type is very original and the different ideas are expressed so as to be readily appropriated by the reader. The ordinary theoretical elastic string, obeying Hookes Law 'Ut Tensio sic Vis'[7] would be, if it could exist, a perfect example of a body transmitting waves of permanent type with constant somatic velocity.

---

(5) See Rankine, 'On the thermodynamic theory of waves': 278; P is the longitudinal pressure, S the 'bulkiness' of the fluid in the undisturbed state.

(6) Reviewing Rankine's paper in a letter to Stokes of 7 March 1870 (Royal Society, *Referees' Reports*, **7**: 51; in Wilson, *Stokes–Kelvin Correspondence*, **2**: 343–5), William Thomson agreed that the 'simple elementary method by which he investigates the condition for sustained uniformity of type is in my opinion very valuable.'

(7) See Volume I: 136n, 160.

But if $\frac{dp}{ds}$ is to be kept constant during the compression or rarefaction[8] by communication of heat from the neighbouring parts of the substance, the heat must pass from hotter to colder parts and whenever this is the case, energy is dissipated and the wave as it goes on loses its energy whether of motion or of elasticity, leaving behind it an increased temperature in the substance.

I am therefore (under correction) of opinion that if the author would work out his theory of permanence of type secured by conduction of heat, he would find that the type is not really permanent unless the substance is left in a different state after the wave has passed it, in which case there must be a constant expenditure of energy by a piston in the tube in keeping up the wave.

The theory of waves in which there is no conduction of heat is of great importance and seems to be given very well arriving at the ordinary result.[9] Prof^r Stokes has shown that in the case of sound-waves the effect of conductivity must be insensible.[10]

The author next considers variation of type.[11]

He considers one plane to move in the undisturbed substance with somatic velocity m and another plane to move in the wave itself with the same somatic velocity so as to include between it and the first plane the constant mass μ.

---

(8) In his letter to Stokes of 7 March 1870 Thomson criticised Rankine's assumption 'that a pulse consisting of a sudden rarefaction as well as a pulse of sudden condensation is of permanent type', arguing that 'the permanence of a pulse of sudden rarefaction is of the same character as the permanence...of unstable equilibrium.' In a note dated 1 August 1870, appended to 'On the thermodynamic theory of waves': 278n, Rankine acknowledges Thomson's correction.

(9) See Rankine, 'On the thermodynamic theory of waves': 282–3, where he derives 'Laplace's well-known law of the propagation of sound'.

(10) G. G. Stokes, 'On a difficulty in the theory of sound', *Phil. Mag.*, ser. 3, **33** (1848): 349–56, esp. 353–6, on the generation of a 'surface of discontinuity' (sudden compression followed by gradual dilatation) by sound waves, a 'queer kind of motion' as he described it in a letter to Lord Rayleigh of 5 June 1877 (Larmor, *Correspondence*, **2**: 103). For Thomson's comments on Stokes' paper see his letter of 7 March 1870 (note (6)).

(11) The material on the variation of type was omitted from the published text of Rankine's paper. In a letter to Stokes of 24 May 1870 (Royal Society, *Referees' Reports*, **7**: 54) Rankine wrote: 'Having considered the reports of Mr Clerk Maxwell and Sir William Thomson on my paper...I have come to the conclusion that it is advisable to *omit* §§ 14 to 19 inclusive, as relating to problems that require further investigation.' Thomson had made some supplementary comments in a letter to Stokes of 9 May 1870 (Royal Society, *Referees' Reports*, **7**: 52; in Wilson, *Stokes–Kelvin Correspondence*, **2**: 345).

The linear distance between the planes being x, if x remains constant the type is constant but if x increases or diminishes while the somatic velocity m is that of a definite part of the wave there is variation of type.

Here again the author considers the mass m which enters the space between the planes with velocity mS and leaves it with velocity $ms - \dfrac{dx}{dt}$ and equates the difference of pressure to the difference of momentum. This was perfectly correct as long as the value of x is supposed to remain constant, but it appears to me that the difference of pressure is the effective cause not only of the difference of momentum of the entering and issuing fluid but of the variations of motion within the space considered.

The velocity at any plane (μ) where the rarity is σ is

$$u = (\sigma - S)m - \frac{dx}{dt}$$

and the momentum of the fluid between the planes is

$$H = \int u\,d\mu = mx - m^2 S - \int_0^\mu \frac{dx}{dt}\,d\mu.$$

What the pressure $p-P$ does in unit of time is to produce a velocity u in the mass m which leaves the second plane *and also* to increase the momentum of the fluid between the planes by $\dfrac{dH}{dt}$. Hence the true equation is

$$p - P = mu + \frac{dH}{dt}$$

$$= m^2(S - \sigma) + m\frac{dx}{dt} + m\frac{dx}{dt} - \int_0^\mu \frac{d^2x}{dt^2}\,d\mu$$

$$p - P = m^2(S - \sigma) + 2m\frac{dx}{dt} - \int_0^\mu \frac{d^2x}{dt^2}\,d\mu.$$

This equation may also be obtained by transforming the ordinary equation

$$\rho\frac{\partial u}{\partial t} + \frac{dp}{dx} = 0 \qquad (12)$$

into

$$\frac{d^2x}{dt^2} - 2m\frac{d^2x}{d\mu\,dt} + m^2\frac{d^2x}{d\mu^2} + \frac{dp}{d\mu} = 0$$

---

(12) See G. G. Stokes, 'On the theories of the internal friction of fluids in motion, and of the equilibrium and motion of elastic solids', *Trans. Camb. Phil. Soc.*, **8** (1845): 287–319, esp. 297 (= *Papers*, **1**: 75–129).

and then increasing with respect to μ from 0 to μ. It differs from equation (42) of Prof Rankines paper by the terms depending on $\frac{dH}{dt}$.

The remarkable result given by the author that the point of maximum density travels with a constant velocity and that the value of this maximum density remains constant is derived from eq^n (42) with others. I am not prepared to say whether the accuracy of this result is affected by the want of accuracy of the equation.

I have not studied the investigations of such waves by the authors mentioned in the supplement,[13] so that I cannot pronounce on the originality of this paper but I consider Prof Rankines mode of treatment very original and especially valuable as presenting a succession of distinct physical conceptions to the mind of the reader during the whole investigation.[14] These conceptions are described in language which is clear enough to the author and to those who have studied his writings, but for the sake of others each new concept should be ushered in with a more distinct statement than is sometimes here given. In particular when the independent variables are changed the change should be clearly stated as when μ is introduced at p. 34.

The investigation of waves of permanent types is well worthy of the Philosophical Transactions.

The merit of the thermodynamical investigation of a possible case of permanent type would be greater if the results were more clearly given when the application of the thermodynamical equations is concluded.

If as I suppose there is an error in eq^n 42 it should be corrected and the result carried on to the end.

J. CLERK MAXWELL

Glenlair, 26th March 1870

---

(13) Papers by S. D. Poisson, Stokes (see note (10)), G. B. Airy, and Samuel Earnshaw are reviewed in the 'Supplement' to Rankine's 'On the thermodynamic theory of waves': 287–8.

(14) See Maxwell's discussion in Chapter 15 'On the propagation of waves' in his *Theory of Heat* (London, 1871): 203–10 (the 'following method of investigating the conditions of the propagation of waves is due to Prof. Rankine').

339
LETTER TO WILLIAM THOMSON
14 APRIL 1870
From the original in the University Library, Cambridge[1]

Glenlair
14 April 1870

Dear Thomson[a]

The first table of dimensions that I know is in Fourier Theorie de Chaleur p 157 and he makes frequent use of it. The dimensions are in length, time, and temperature.[2]

If you define the unit of heat as that which raises unit of volume of the substance in its actual state one degree then in the equation

$$\frac{dv}{dt} = -k\nabla^2 v$$

k is the conductivity with this unit of heat.[3]

But to my question. In an infinite solid heated suddenly at the origin and then left to itself the temperature at a distance r after a time t is

$$v = At^{-\frac{3}{2}} e^{-\frac{r^2}{4kt}} \quad \text{p. 478.}^{(4)}$$

Hence if v_0 is the initial temperature at the point $a\,b\,c$ and v the actual temperature at time t at $x\,y\,z$, distant r from $a\,b\,c$

$$v = \iiint \left(da\,db\,dc\, v_0 \, (kt)^{-\frac{3}{2}} e^{-\frac{r^2}{4kt}} \right).^{(5)}$$

This tells us completely what the state of the infinite solid will be at any future time if we know its initial state. The temperature of every point is the mean of the original temperatures of all the points the weight attributed to each point in taking the mean being $e^{-\frac{r^2}{4kt}}$.

(a) {Thomson} When do you go to Cambridge? Thanks for the diffusion of gases.[6]

(1) ULC Add. MSS 7655, II/36.
(2) Joseph Fourier, *Théorie Analytique de la Chaleur* (Paris, 1822): 157 (§161).
(3) See Fourier, *Théorie Analytique de la Chaleur*: 136 (§142); equation (A), 'l'equation générale... qui est celle de la propagation de la chaleur dans l'intérieur de tous les corps solides'. Here v is the temperature at time t. Maxwell writes $k = K/CD$, where in Fourier's equation (A) K is the conductivity of the body for heat, C the heat capacity per unit mass, and D the density of the body. For Maxwell's discussion of this equation see also the *Treatise*, **1**: 384 (§332), and Number 489.   (4) Fourier, *Théorie Analytique de la Chaleur*: 478 (§376).
(5) Fourier, *Théorie Analytique de la Chaleur*: 479.
(6) Chapter 19 of Maxwell's *Theory of Heat* (London, 1871): 253–60.

This all stands to reason.

Now suppose we have observed the actual state of the infinite solid and wish to deduce its previous state at a time $-t$.

Can we adapt Fouriers solution.

In the formula there is the awkward quantity $(kt)^{-\frac{3}{2}}$ which is objectionable when t is $-^{ve}$. In the method of taking means $e^{\frac{r^2}{4kt}}$ is a very respectable quantity, only it gives the greatest weight to the most distant points and it does this *especially* when t is small,[b] that is just before the time of observation, when if ever,[c] we ought to be able to deduce the previous state from the state of neighbouring points. I have not found any attempt at this inverse problem in Fourier. Has it been done?[d][7] or shown to lead to insuperable difficulties? and if you do not know about it who does? I do not know any (Joseph) Fourierists.[8] He is principally known as having invented Fourier's Theorem the ratio of which to a 3 day problem is an unknown quantity.[9]

Of course if you cut up the distribution of temperature into harmonics, you can work back till the harmonic series becomes divergent. If you invent a function to express the present temperature the divergence usually comes on as soon as you put t negative.[e] It is only when you write down an harmonic series of set purpose that you can avoid this.[10]

It is because you have attended to the historical problem of the conduction of heat that I ask you. Everybody else inclines to the prophetical problem which is much easier.[f]

(b) {Thomson} This is the analytical expression of the impossibility to find a physical antecedent of an arbitrary distribution. See an Essay 'De Caloris Motu per Terrae Corpus' read in the Faculty room of the old College in 1846,[11] and now to be met through all space (if there is no limit to the greatest velocity of an individual molecule of gas) combined with oxygen.

(c) {Thomson] but this is just what cannot be done in a distribution (such as $v = e^{-\frac{r^2}{t}} t^{\frac{1}{2}}$ when $t = 0$) which is essentially initial.

(d) {Thomson} See CMJ Notes on Certain Points in the Theory of Heat or some other equally appropriate & suggestive title, about year 1844.[7]

(e) {Thomson} Hear hear; see CMJ.

(f) {Thomson} because of the irreversibility of dissipation.[12]

(7) In his 'Note on some points in the theory of heat', *Camb. Math. J.*, **4** (1844): 67–72 (= *Math. & Phys. Papers*, **1**: 39–45), Thomson had discussed the problem of negative value assigned 'to the time...[so] the initial state is such as not to be deducible from a previous distribution', leading to a divergent series.

(8) As distinct from disciples of Charles Fourier.

(9) In the Cambridge Mathematical Tripos candidates for Honours sat an examination in which 'the first three days shall be assigned to the more elementary parts of Mathematics and Natural Philosophy'; see the *Cambridge University Calendar for the Year 1869* (Cambridge, 1869): 26.

(10) Maxwell gave a succinct account of the issue in his *Theory of Heat*: 238–45, where he refers to Thomson's 'Note on some points in the theory of heat'; see note (7).

(11) Thomson's Inaugural Dissertation at the University of Glasgow; see S. P. Thompson, *The Life of William Thomson, Baron Kelvin of Largs*, 2 vols. (London, 1910), **1**: 187.

(12) See Number 344; and *Theory of Heat*: 245–8.

I am boiling all this down for my chapter on Conduction with pictures of the diffusion of heat and salts and gases.[13]

The thermal view of an[g] harmonic is a distribution of heat which cools down without altering the ratios of the temperatures of the parts.

To prove that every figure has a fundamental harmonic with a series of higher harmonics in order would be probably a stiff business.[h]

These harmonics die away, the highest most rapidly, and at last, however the body is originally heated (provided the fundamental harmonic is not absent altogether) the distribution approximates to that of the fundamental harmonic.

I have arranged the paraffin between two prisms to determine its refractive index but have not got the angle measured till I have a salt wick going.[14]

I am greatly surprised that Joules combination of levers for magnifying magnetic disturbances does any good.[15] I should have thought that if a microscope is to be used at all there should be no magnification except that done by levers of light which do not get shaken or affected by gravity or viscosity.[16]

Yrs
$\frac{dp}{dt}$[17]

(g) {Thomson} a
(h) {Thomson} Not so very. It was a favourite (unsolved) propos^n of Liouville in 1846 Jan. Feb. March.[18]

(13) Chapter 18, 'On the diffusion of heat by conduction', of the *Theory of Heat*: 233–53.

(14) To determine the relation between the dielectric constant and the index of refraction; for further discussion see Maxwell's letter to Thomson of 21 March 1871 (Number 362). See the *Treatise*, **2**: 388–9 (§§ 788–9) and Volume I: 687n on the significance of this relation for Maxwell's electromagnetic theory of light.

(15) On Joule's dip circle see his paper reported in the *Proceedings of the Literary and Philosophical Society of Manchester*, **8** (1869): 171–3. The axis of the magnetic needle is suspended from two silk filaments, the ends of the thread being supported by the beam of a balance. Nevertheless, Maxwell describes Joule's dip circle in the *Treatise*, where he includes (*Treatise*, **2**: 116, Fig. 18) an elaborated version of the figure which Joule published in his 1869 paper. In a letter to Maxwell (ULC Add. MSS 7655, II/49), which can be dated *c*. 20 June 1871 (from a reference to 'last Saturday June 17') Joule commented that 'Your figure describes the principle of the dip needle exactly'. He went on to describe recent improvements in the design of the instrument, some of which Maxwell incorporated into his account of the dip circle in the *Treatise*, **2**: 115–17 (§463). For Joule's own account (dated 1881) of successive improvements to the dip circle see *The Scientific Papers of James Prescott Joule*, 2 vols. (London, 1884–7), **1**: 577–83.

(16) See Maxwell's proposal for the 'dip needle in the Cambridge Physical Laboratory' in the *Treatise*, **2**: 117 (§463).

(17) Maxwell's thermodynamic *nom de plume* expressed the second law of thermodynamics, taking its form $-dp/dt = $ JCM – from Tait's expression for the law in his *Sketch of Thermodynamics* (Edinburgh, 1868): 91 (§162): 'Hence the second law of thermodynamics may be expressed in

the form $\dfrac{dp/dt}{M} = JC$.' Thus p and t denote pressure and temperature; J the mechanical equivalent of heat ('Joule's equivalent'); M is a coefficient of proportionality, the heat absorbed per unit volume change in an isothermal expansion; and C is a universal function (the 'Carnot function') of the temperature (the reciprocal of the absolute temperature). Tait later explained this usage to Maxwell: see his card of 1 February 1871 (Number 353 note (11)). The subtleties of the signature are fully explained by Martin J. Klein, 'Maxwell, his demon, and the second law of thermodynamics', *American Scientist*, **58** (1970): 84–97, esp. 94–5.

(18) Joseph Liouville, 'Lettres sur diverses questions d'analyse et de physique mathématique concernant l'ellipsoide', *Journal de Mathématiques Pures et Appliquées*, **11** (1846): 217–36, 261–90.

340

LETTER TO JOHN WILLIAM STRUTT

18 MAY 1870

From the original in private possession[1]

Glenlair
Dalbeattie
18 May 1870

Dear Mr Strutt,

I am very much obliged to you for your remarks on the equation of streamlines in which you are right and I have been wrong hitherto.[2]

I remember making out what it should be long ago and copying it when I wanted it instead of doing it again, and I cannot now say whether I made a deliberate error or went wrong in copying. The effect is the same for all that.

The curves $M = $ const are orthogonal to the curves $V = $ const.[3] and in particular

$$\frac{dM}{da} = 2\pi a \frac{dV}{db}$$

and

$$\frac{dM}{db} = -2\pi a \frac{dV}{da}.$$

Hence

$$\frac{dV}{da} = -\frac{1}{2\pi a} \frac{dM}{db}$$

and

$$\frac{dV}{db} = \frac{1}{2\pi a} \frac{dM}{da}.$$

$$\frac{d^2V}{da\,db} = -\frac{1}{2\pi a} \frac{d^2M}{db^2}$$

$$= \frac{1}{2\pi a} \frac{d^2M}{da^2} - \frac{1}{2\pi a^2} \frac{dM}{da}.$$

---

(1) Rayleigh Papers, Terling Place, Terling, Essex.

(2) Compare Number 337 on stream lines. On 10 March 1870 Maxwell's paper 'On the displacement in a case of fluid motion' was read to the London Mathematical Society (see the *Proceedings*, **3** (1870): 82–7 (= *Scientific Papers*, **2**: 208–14)). See Numbers 307 esp. note (9) and 311 for Maxwell's use of the concept of 'stream function' in this paper.

(3) For Helmholtz's discussion see Number 302 note (5). M and V are the velocity potential and stream function, respectively.

Equating these two values of $\dfrac{d^2V}{da\,db}$

$$\frac{d^2M}{da^2}+\frac{d^2M}{db^2}-\frac{1}{a}\frac{dM}{da}=0.$$

To try it, put
$$V=\frac{1}{r}$$

and
$$M=\pi\frac{b}{r}$$

where
$$r^2=a^2+b^2,$$
or
$$V=b \text{ and } M=\pi a^2.$$

I have not got a solution of the case of a plate with a slit in it at one potential and a parallel plate at another but this is my way to get the result.[4]

There are various ways which might do.

For instance we know that if
$$x_1=e^\rho\cos\theta \quad \text{and} \quad y_1=e^\rho\sin\theta$$
then x and y will be conjugate functions with respect to ρ and θ.[5]

Also if $x_2=e^{-\rho}\cos\theta$ and $y_2=e^{-\rho}\sin\theta$.

Whence adding
$$2x_3=(e^\rho+e^{-\rho})\cos\theta \ \&\ 2y_3=(e^\rho-e^{-\rho})\sin\theta.$$

The point (x_3,y_3) is in an ellipse of which the semiaxes are $(e^\rho+e^{-\rho})$ and $(e^\rho-e^{-\rho})$ and in a hyperbola of which the semiaxes are $2a\cos\theta$ & $2a\sin\theta$.

Now let $x_3=e^{\xi/a}\cos\dfrac{\eta}{a}$ and $y_3=e^{\xi/a}\sin\dfrac{\eta}{a}$ then ξ and η will be conjugate functions of ρ and θ.

In particular when $\theta=0$ $\ y_3=0$ and $\eta=0$ or $n\pi a$ $\ \&\ 2e^{\xi/a}=e^\rho+e^{-\rho}$.

When $\theta=\dfrac{\pi}{2}$ $\ x_3=0$ and $\eta=(n+\tfrac{1}{2})\pi a$.

When $\rho=0$ $\ y_3=0$ and $\eta=0$ or $n\pi a$ and $e^{\xi/a}=\cos\theta$.

If we now suppose ρ to be the potential at the point (ξ,η) we shall have $\rho=0$ for the planes $\eta=n\pi$ when ξ is negative but in the same planes when ξ is positive.

$$\frac{\xi}{a}=\log\frac{1}{2}(e^\rho+e^{-\rho}).$$

---

(4) Compare Number 303 on the potential between parallel planes; and the *Treatise*, **1**: 237–48 (§§ 192–202).

(5) See Number 303 note (3).

Hence the equipotential lines are like this (negative values to the right by mistake) turn figure upside down.[6]

At a distance from the ends of the planes when ξ is a large positive quantity

$$\frac{\xi}{a} = \rho - \log_e 2 \text{ nearly}$$

or

$$\rho = \xi + a \log_e 2.$$

But if instead of a thing like a curry comb $\overline{\overline{}}$ we had a plane $|$ then $\rho = \xi$ at a distance.

Hence a thing like a curry comb with a lot of planes cut off by an imaginary plane acts like a plane at a distance $a \log 2$ behind the imaginary plane where the distance between the edges of the planes is πa. The equivalent plane is dotted in the figure.

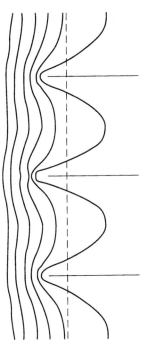

Figure 340,1

Now if we have two opposed planes at a distance b their potentials being 0 and V then if σ is the superficial density $4\pi\sigma = \dfrac{V}{b}$.

If instead of one of the planes we have a set of planes cut off as before the distance between consecutive planes being πa then if b is the distance between the single plane and the edges of the system of planes and σ the mean density on the single plane

$$4\pi\sigma = \frac{V}{b + a\log 2}.$$

Now let A be the area of the plane and let it be opposed to n planes at a distance πa the lengths of the edges being l.

Then $A = n\pi a l$ and the whole charge $= \sigma A = \dfrac{1}{4\pi} \dfrac{V n \pi a l}{b + a \log 2}$.

Now let all the intervals between the planes be filled up except one.

This will certainly not diminish the charge on the sides of the slit though it may increase it. Hence the whole charge is between

$$\frac{1}{4\pi} \frac{VA}{b} \quad \text{and} \quad \frac{1}{4\pi}\left(\frac{n-1}{n}\frac{VA}{b} + \frac{V\pi a l}{b + a\log 2}\right)$$

but probably very nearly the latter even though the slit is not deep.

---

(6) Compare the *Treatise*, **1**: 238–9 (§193) and Fig. XI appended to the volume.

All this supposes b large compared with a. The last expression is if we make

$$\alpha = a\log 2 = (\text{breadth of slit})\frac{\log 2}{\pi}$$

then the charge on the plate of area A bounded by the slit is

$$\frac{V}{4\pi}\left(\frac{A}{b} + \frac{1}{2}\frac{A'-A}{b+\alpha}\right)$$

where A' is the area of the plate together with that of the slit, that is of the aperture in the guard plate. This is the same as if it had been the mean of the areas A and A' provided b is great compared with α.

If you cause a conductor of any form to spin round a magnet and mirror hung up in the axis of spinning you are safe to make the magnet move in the same direction as the conductor both on account of the Earths magnetic induction and on account of the magnet's own induction. See Arago's experiments[7] and the spinning coil Brit Ass Report 1863.[8]

The equations of inductive coil machines must be very interesting.

I am writing all this out of my head which I had carefully emptied of most of these subjects and I have put away my notes so excuse the signs of working in the dark.

Have you tried whether the sudden starting or stopping of a current in a coil has any the least effect in turning the coil in its own plane as it would be turned if the current were of water in a tube.[9]

---

(7) Arago's discovery of the generation of electric currents in a metallic disc rotating in a magnetic field (described in the *Treatise*, **2**: 271–5 (§§668–9)). See François Arago, 'Note concernant les phénomènes magnétiques auxquels le mouvement donne naissance', *Ann. Chim. Phys.*, ser. 2, **32** (1826): 213–23.

(8) See the 'Description of an experimental measurement of electrical resistances, made at King's College' by Maxwell and Jenkin, in the 'Report of the Committee appointed by the British Association on standards of electrical resistance', *Report of the Thirty-third Meeting of the British Association for the Advancement of Science*; held at Newcastle-upon-Tyne in August and September *1863* (London, 1864): 111–76, esp. 163–76. See Numbers 210, 211, 213, 214, 216, 217, 218, 219.

(9) Maxwell had mentioned an experiment on these lines in his letter to Thomson of 10 December 1861 (Volume I: 698). Compare his more detailed discussion in the *Treatise*, **2**: 200–2 (§574), where he concludes that 'no phenomenon of this kind has yet been observed'; and see also Number 430.

If the coil is hung in a horizontal plane you can easily destroy the earths horizontal magnetism by means of magnets.[10]

I remain
Yours truly
J. CLERK MAXWELL

I shall probably be in London by the end of next week.

---

(10) Maxwell makes the same point in the *Treatise*, **2**: 200 (§574).

341

LETTER TO CECIL JAMES MONRO

6 JULY 1870

From the original in the Greater London Record Office[1]

Glenlair
Dalbeattie
July 6 1870

My dear Monro

I was very glad to see your handwriting again and that it was from your old address.[2] My permanent address is as above and I have no other now. My question to the Math Soc.[3] bore fruit in various forms and you have put it very clearly. It would give my mind too great a wrench just now to go into elliptic integrals but I will do so when I come to revise about circular conductors.[4] The area of a spherical ellipse cannot be expressed in terms of *complete* elliptic integrals of the 1st & 2nd kinds only. It may be expressed in complete integrals one of which is of the 3rd kind, and this last may be

---

(1) Greater London Record Office, Acc. 1063/2091. Published (in part) in *Life of Maxwell*: 346–7.

(2) In reply to Monro's letter of 2 June 1870 (GLRO, Acc. 1063/2105); 'I had *Nature* sent me abroad last winter, and I observed in the number for Nov. 18 this question among others propounded in your name to the Mathematical Society, namely whether the solid angle of a cone can be expressed in elliptic integrals. I may have been in some muddle from that time to this, but it seemed to me you must have overlooked a little theorem which I think does the business.... The theorem is that the solid angle of a cone or pyramid is the complement to four right angles of what I will call the total exterior angle, that is, the angle through which an applied plane rolls completely round the figure. This follows at once from the usual form of the value of the area of a spherical polygon: and it has always made me suspect that the solid angle of a cone of the second degree *was* expressible in elliptic integrals. I found in the winter that the expression for the total exterior angle has a great look of an elliptic integral: but I know nothing about elliptic integrals. However, turning over Ellis's Works I find p. 298 that Gudermann had reduced to elliptic integrals the arc of a spherical ellipse; and this settles the matter.... Accordingly on taking it up again I see that the expression for the total exterior angle does easily reduce itself to a linear function of two complete elliptic integrals of the first and third kinds.' Monro is alluding to a passage in R. L. Ellis' 'Report of the recent progress of analysis (theory of the comparison of transcendentals)' in the *Report of the Sixteenth Meeting of the British Association for the Advancement of Science* (London, 1847): 34–90, on 73, reprinted in *The Mathematical and Other Writings of Robert Leslie Ellis, M.A.*, ed. W. Walton (Cambridge, 1863): 238–323, on 298; 'In the fourteenth volume of Crelle's *Journal* (p. 217) M. Gudermann has considered the rectification of the curve called the spherical ellipse, which is one of a class of curves formed by the intersection of a cone of the second order with a sphere. He has shown that its arcs represent an elliptic integral of the third kind.'

(3) Number 330; reported in *Nature*, **1** (1869): 91.

(4) See the *Treatise*, **2**: 299–312 (§§694–706).

expressed in terms of incomplete integrals of the 1st & 2nd kinds. Fortified with this information, which is confirmed by competent authorities and finally by yourself, I can cut the subject short with an easy conscience for I have no scruple about steering clear of tables of double entry, especially when, in all really useful cases convergent series may be used with less trouble, and without any knowledge of elliptic integrals.

On this subject see a short paper on Fluid Displacement in next part of the Math. Soc. Trans. where I give a picture of the stream-lines and the distortion of a transverse line as water flows past a cylinder so.[5]

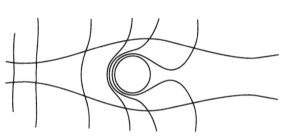

Figure 341,1

Mr. W. Benson, architect 147 Albany Street Regents Park NW told me[6] that you had been writing to Nature[7] and that yours was the only rational statement in a multitudinous correspondence on colours.[8] Mr Benson considers that Aristotle and I have correct views about primary colours. He has written a book with coloured pictures on the science of colour and he shows how to mix colours by means of a prism.[9] He wants to publish an elementary book with easy experiments[10] but gets small encouragement, being supposed an heretic. No other architect in the Architects Society believes him. This is interesting to me as showing the chromatic condition of Architects.

I made a great colour-box in 1862 and worked it in London in 62[11] & 64.[12] I have about 200 equations each year which are reduced but not published. I have set it up here this year and have just got it in working order.

---

(5) See Fig. 1 of Maxwell's paper 'On the displacement in a case of fluid motion', *Proceedings of the London Mathematical Society*, **3** (1870): 82–7 (= *Scientific Papers*, **2**: 208–14).

(6) William Benson to Maxwell, May 1870 (ULC Add. MSS 7655, II/37).

(7) C. J. Monro, 'Correlation of colour and music', *Nature*, **1** (1870): 362–3.

(8) A correspondence initiated by W. F. Barrett, 'Note on the correlation of colour and music', *Nature*, **1** (1870): 286–7. See also *Nature*, **1** (1870): 314, 335, 384–5, 430–1, 557–8, 651–3, and *ibid.*, **2** (1870): 48.

(9) William Benson, *Principles of the Science of Colour concisely stated to aid and promote their useful application to the decorative arts* (London, 1868). There is a copy in Maxwell's library (Cavendish Laboratory, Cambridge).

(10) See Number 359.

(11) See Maxwell's letter to Monro of 18 February 1862 (Volume I: 711); and see Number 202.

(12) See Number 225.

I expect to get some more material and work up the whole together.[13] In particular I want to find any change or evidence of constancy in the eyes of myself & wife during 8 years. I can exhibit the yellow spot[14] to all who have it and all have it except Col. Strange F.R.S.[15] my late father-in law and my wife, whether they be negroes Jews Parsees, Armenians Russians Italians Germans Frenchmen Poles &c. Professor Pole,[16] for instance, has it as strong as me though he is colour blind. Mathison,[17] also colour blind, being fair, had it less strongly marked.

One J. J. Müller in Pogg. Ann. for March & April 1870, examines compound colours and finds the violet without any tendency to red or the red to blue.[18] He also selects a typical green out of the spectrum.[19]

Many thanks for your formula about complementary colours[20] and for

---

(13) See Maxwell's paper 'On colour-vision at different points of the retina' in the *Report of the Fortieth Meeting of the British Association for the Advancement of Science; held at Liverpool in September 1870* (London, 1871), part 2: 40–1 (= *Scientific Papers*, **2**: 230–2).

(14) On the insensitivity of the 'yellow spot' on the retina to greenish-blue light see Volume I: 318, 636.

(15) Lieut. Col. Alexander Strange, FRS 1864; see *Nature*, **13** (1876): 408–9.

(16) William Pole: see Volume I: 632.

(17) William Collings Mathison, Trinity 1834, Tutor 1850–68 (Venn).

(18) J. J. Müller, 'Zur Theorie der Farben', *Ann. Phys.* **139** (1870): 411–31, 593–613, esp. 423–4, where he questions Maxwell's conclusion, in 'On the theory of compound colours, and the relations of the colours of the spectrum', *Phil. Trans.*, **150** (1860): 57–84, on 77–8 (= *Scientific Papers*, **1**: 436), that 'the extreme ends of the spectrum are probably equivalent to mixtures of red and blue'.

(19) Müller, 'Zur Theorie der Farben': 426. Compare Maxwell's choice of 'standard green' in his paper 'On colour vision', *Proceedings of the Royal Institution*, **6** (1870–2): 260–71, esp. 266–7 (= *Scientific Papers*, **2**: 274–5). In a letter to Maxwell of 26 July 1872 (ULC Add. MSS 7655, II/61) J. D. Everett contrasted Maxwell's value with Müller's, and referred disparagingly to Müller's 'mode of experimenting'. This letter, and one of 19 July 1872 (ULC Add. MSS 7655, II/60), were written in connection with Maxwell's review of the proof of the chapter on colour for Everett's translation (with additions) of A. Privat Deschanel, *Elementary Treatise on Natural Philosophy*, 4 parts (London, 1870–2), Part IV: 1004–8.

(20) In his letter of 2 June 1870 (see note (2)) Monro had asked: 'Have you, or has anybody, any further observations than those in your R.S. paper of 1860? The violet region was left so incomplete. At a time when I presumed to meddle with your figures, I hit on what seemed to me a rather curious formula for the relation of complementary colours, namely $(\lambda - L)(L' - \lambda') = M^2$ where λ, λ' are complementary wave-lengths*, and

	L,	L',	M,
for K,	2076,	1842,	77.9
for J,	2132,	1860,	51.2.

* Between 2450 and 2100/, 1825 and 1600.' J and K denote the two observers (Maxwell and his wife Katherine) in Maxwell's paper 'On the theory of compound colours, and the relations of the colours of the spectrum': esp. 69–71, 74–5 (= *Scientific Papers*, **1**: 426–8, 431–2).

your letter in general which I hope may be followed by others. Did you ever get one from me about 4 years ago?

Yours sincerely
J. CLERK MAXWELL

342

REPORT ON A PAPER BY CHARLES BLAND RADCLIFFE[1] ON ANIMAL ELECTRICITY

circa JULY 1870[2]

From the original in the Library of the Royal Society, London[3]

REPORT ON Dr CHARLES BLAND RADCLIFFES PAPER 'RESEARCHES ON ANIMAL ELECTRICITY'[4]

I have in the first place to state, that I have never either made or witnessed any experiments on animal electricity, such as those described in this paper, and that I have not read enough on the subject to be able to form any judgment on the novelty of the doctrines here advanced, or on their consistency with those of other enquirers in the same field.

The experiments, however are so clearly described that I have learnt enough from the paper itself to see something of the state of the subject as it presents itself to the author and to others.[5]

The well known facts that nerves and muscles have certain electrical properties when at rest, and that those are modified when the muscle is in action and that action may be excited by electrical means, are in themselves very interesting from an electrical point of view, and also share in the importance which every phenomenon having a bearing, however remote, on the theory of animal motion must have, both in physics and in physiology.

The first investigation is into the electrical state of a piece of still living nerve or muscle, dissected out of the body and therefore having two sections cut across.

Prof Du Bois Reymond found that if the electrodes of a galvanometer are

---

(1) MD 1851, FRCP 1858 (Boase).

(2) According to the Royal Society's *Register of Papers Received* Radcliffe's paper was referred to Maxwell on 27 June 1870.

(3) Royal Society, *Referees' Reports*, **7**: 49.

(4) Charles Bland Radcliffe, 'Researches on animal electricity' (Royal Society, AP. 52.10). Part I of Radcliffe's paper was received by the Royal Society on 10 March 1870, Part II on 19 May 1870, both parts being read on 16 June 1870; see the abstract in *Proc. Roy. Soc.*, **19** (1870): 22–8. Radcliffe had previously read a paper on the same subject: see his 'Researches in animal electricity', *Proc. Roy. Soc.*, **17** (1869): 377–91.

(5) Radcliffe's paper (see note (4)) fills 100 ms. pages. In his report on the paper (Royal Society, *Referees' Reports*, **7**: 50) William Sharpey noted that 'very many pages of MS are occupied with detailed expositions of well known facts and doctrines in electro-physiology, such as are to be found in most systematic or even elementary treatises'.

put in contact, one with the side of the nerve or muscle and the other with either of its cut extremities a current flows through the coil from the side of the cut extremity, and this goes on for some time, after which the tissue becomes dead.[6]

We shall suppose, though it is not explicitly stated that the electrodes of the galvanometer are of the same metal, say platinum and that the moisture on the ends and on the side of the animal substance is of the same chemical nature. If these conditions are not fulfilled the experiment proves nothing new with respect to animal tissues as the same currents would happen in any moist substance if the fluids or the metals were heterogeneous
but I mention this only to shew that it is important to state the electrical data of an experiment so clearly as to be beyond suspicion and to hint that a little more statement as to the mode of insulating the frogs legs and the galvanometer would be desirable. I shall suppose the method to be that of Du Bois Reymond with electrodes of moist paper.

This experiment clearly shews that, in a nerve or muscle in its normal state, the potential of the outside is positive with respect to that of the inside. This is shown by the current through the galvanometer but Dr Radcliffe has shown it in a more direct manner by means of Sir W. Thomson's quadrant galvanometer.[7]

As far as I can see he has made a decided advance on the statement of Du Bois Reymond with respect to the character of the electrical state of the nerve or muscle by describing it as a state in which each fibre may be compared to a charged Leyden jar (or better a submarine cable) in which the outer coating is positive as regards the inner coating.[8]

This is a much better form of stating the theory than by introducing 'peripolar molecules' but it hardly contains as much as is given by the experiments.[9]

---

(6) Emil Du Bois-Reymond, *Untersuchungen über thierische Electricität*, 2 vols. (Berlin, 1848–9). In 'Researches in animal electricity' (Part I, ff. 1–3) Radcliffe attributed the discovery of the 'nerve-current' and the 'muscle-current' to Du Bois-Reymond.

(7) Read: quadrant electrometer, described in Thomson's 'Report on electrometers and electrostatic measurements', *Report of the Thirty-seventh Meeting of the British Association for the Advancement of Science* (London, 1868): 489–512, on 490–7 and Plate 5 (= *Electrostatics and Magnetism*: 260–309).

(8) Radcliffe maintained that '[Du Bois-Reymond's] nerve current and muscle current... are no more than accidental phenomena... the sheaths of the fibres in nerve and muscle... play the parts of *dielectrics*... the sheath of each fibre acting in fact as a Leyden jar'; 'Researches in animal electricity' (Part I, ff. 9, 14).

(9) See Radcliffe, 'Researches in animal electricity' (Part I, f. 7): 'In order to account for the nerve-current and muscle-current Du Bois-Reymond supposes that the fibre of living nerve and

We find certain currents and certain differences of potential. We infer from these the existence of an electromotive force. We seek for the seat of this electromotive force. We find it in the sheath of the nerve or fibre, for the difference of electrical state is primarily a difference of 'within and without' and the observed difference of 'middle and ends' is only secondary.

How then does the sheath act? Dr Radcliffe supposes it to be like the glass of a Leyden jar, that is, a dielectric and he shows that the nerve substance is sufficiently insulating to act in this way.

He does not explain, however, how the nerve gets charged, or how when discharged through the galvanometer, it becomes constantly recharged, so as to keep up a current for a long time.

The existence of the current through the galvanometer is a proof that the circuit is completed through the sheath of the nerve and that there is here an electromotive force from within to without constantly acting in the normal state of the nerve.[10]

The result of this if the nerve is cut out and insulated is to keep up an exceedingly slow current through the sheath which when it comes to the outer surface creeps along from the middle towards the ends and completes its circuit in the interior. There is therefore a superficial distribution of electrification, positive at the middle, negative at the ends, and this might be tested by a sufficiently delicate proof plane.[11] What is tested by the quadrant electrometer is the difference of potential at different points and this is done without carrying away electricity. The galvanometer tests the very same thing but it cannot do it without carrying off the electricity in a stream.

It may be asked Does the sheath act like a diaphragm between two liquids of different kinds, or in what way is the electromotive force sustained?

I have endeavoured at the risk of introducing errors of my own to make a clear statement of what has been observed, because I think that the author makes use of several expressions which are apt to be misunderstood. 'Free electricity' is one of these and 'Tension' is another. I think 'Tension' in this

---

muscle is made up of an infinite number of what he calls *peri-polar molecules*...which are negatively electrified at the two poles which point to the two ends of the fibre, and positively electrified in the equatoreal interpolar belt which is turned toward the side of the fibre'. See Du Bois-Reymond, *Untersuchungen*, **1**: 680–2. In his report (see note (5)) Sharpey noted however that 'many eminent physiologists who also reject Du Bois Reymond's hypothesis admit the validity of the empirical proof of a current'.

(10) Having seen Maxwell's report Sharpey quotes, in agreement, these last two paragraphs, noting: 'I would add that this hypothesis appears to break down altogether when tested by anatomical facts. It might no doubt be contended with some probability *in the case of a nerve-fibre* that the medullary sheath might act as a dielectric, but the...sheath of a muscular fibre seems utterly unsuited to that end'. (11) See the *Treatise*, **1**: 277–81 (§§ 223–5).

paper always means potential. It is often used in another sense (which I prefer) as the tendency, at any point of an electrified surface, of the electricity to escape by a discharge.[12] I also am afraid that the wording of the paper implies that a piece of nerve, electrified like a Leyden jar, positive on the outside and negative on the inside can have this state of induced charge heightened or relaxed by raising or lowering. The author does not say how the limbs were supported. If, by electrifying them positively, a current from within outwards was set up, this current might act on the internal parts. But if they had been enclosed in brass tubes and if the brass tubes had been electrified so as to raise or lower their potential with that of all that they contained, then whether this operation were slow or sudden, nothing could be known of it to the frog inside from any electrical effect within.

The author attributes the contractions on making and breaking the circuit to the extra-currents which then occur. Volta supposed the contraction on breaking the circuit to be due to an effect like that of the 'hydraulic ram' but Marianini (Dela Rive II 436) showed that this contraction takes place when the circuit is not broken, but the current diverted from the frog by the interposition of a better conductor.[13] This shows that the simple cessation of the current produces contraction. If the good conductor be now removed, so as to throw the current back through the frog, then there will be a true extra-current in the same direction but of greater intensity than the constant current.

He also discusses Electrotonus.[14] When he has shown that the same phenomena occur when a piece of moist silk &c is substituted for the nerve[15] we may as well discontinue our physiological experiments till we have made enough experiments on dead matter to satisfy ourselves as to the nature of the purely electrical part of the phenomenon.

Now if by means of a battery XY a current is produced in a part CD of a linear conductor then if the ends are insulated there will be no currents beyond CD, and if A & B are connected

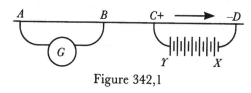

Figure 342,1

(12) See the *Treatise*, 1: 47 (§48).

(13) A. De la Rive, *Traité d'Électricité Théorique et Appliquée*, 3 vols. (Paris, 1854–8), 2: 436. The analogy of the rebounding of a fluid is stated by De la Rive; the paper by Stefano Marianini alluded to is his 'Mémoire sur la secousse...', *Ann. Chim. Phys.*, ser. 2, 40 (1829): 225–56.

(14) See Radcliffe, 'Researches in animal electricity' (Part II, ff. 1–2): 'Under the action of a voltaic current the special electricity and activity of a nerve are strangely modified. The name now given to these strange modifications... is *Electrotonus* – the name which was first applied by their discoverer Prof. Du Bois-Reymond'. See Du Bois-Reymond, *Untersuchungen*, 2: 289.

(15) Radcliffe, 'Researches in animal electricity' (Part II, f. 7).

by a galvanometer which is insulated there will be no current in the coil. But if A or the further part of the galvanometer coil is not well insulated there will be a derived current in G from B to A, and this is the direction of the current, or the variation of current, observed in electrotonus.

But whatever be the true cause of these phenomena, no part of the phenomenon should be stated as a physiological fact about the structure and functions of nerves as nerves[16] till it is clearly established that it is not due to the ordinary electrical properties of the substance experimented on considered as a body having a certain form and electrical resistance and capable of electrolysis and polarization like any other moist conductor.

Towards the end of his paper the author propounds a theory of muscular contraction. He supposes the sheaths of the muscular fibres when at rest to be charged within with negative and without with positive electricity, the attraction of which produces a transverse pressure on the substance of the sheath and this again produces a longitudinal elongation.

There is no doubt that such a charge would produce an effect of this kind on an elastic hollow cylindrical sheath.

But, in the first place, I understand that the appearance of a muscular fibre is that of a series of disks connected by fibrils like the generating lines of a cylinder and that when the fibre is contracted these fibrils are pinched in between every two disks so as to appear like truncated cones. This is not at all similar to the image raised by Dr Radcliffes description.[17]

In the second place the work done by the muscular contraction is indefinitely greater than the energy of the electrical distribution can ever be, so that the moving power of the muscle does not arise from its electrification any more than the moving power of an artificial explosive torpedo arises from the electric spark which explodes it.

In conclusion. The paper was very interesting to me, though by no means satisfactory in an electrical point of view. The only decided novelty seems to be the use of the electrometer. In a physiological point of view I am not qualified to give any opinion.

J. CLERK MAXWELL

---

(16) Contesting Radcliffe's claim that 'electrotonus' was not due to modifications of the nerve current but to 'a charge of free electricity', Sharpey asserted that Radcliffe gave 'no experiments directly proving its nature'.

(17) Sharpey concurred: 'the objection applies which is derived from the anatomical structure of muscle'.

ON THE CHROMATIC EFFECTS OF POLARISED LIGHT ON DOUBLE REFRACTING CRYSTALS:[1] ADDITION TO A PAPER BY FRANCIS DEAS[2]

circa SUMMER 1870[3]

From the *Transactions of the Royal Society of Edinburgh*[4]

[ADDITION TO A MEMOIR BY FRANCIS DEAS]

In Mr Deas' paper a number of interesting experiments are described, in which, by means of a spectroscopic microscope fitted with polarising and analysing prisms, the true nature of the phenomena observed by Brewster, Biot, and others, in plates of selenite, &c.,[5] is made exceedingly intelligible to the understanding, while, at the same time, the eye is satiated with new forms of splendour.

The subject is one to which the attention of experimenters is not so strongly directed as it was fifty years ago; and therefore it is desirable that the remarkably simple methods of observation here described, and the perfection with which the phenomena may be seen by means of modern instruments, should be more generally known.

In the text, the paper appears purely descriptive, without any theoretical application, and the æsthetic beauty of the phenomena might be assumed to be the object of the experiments. But the carefulness of the selection of the experiments and the faithfulness of the description make me think that the author himself looked at what he saw in the light of the theory of double

---

(1) Phenomena discussed by Maxwell in 1848–50; see Volume I: 97–100, 125.

(2) Francis Deas, 'On spectra formed by the passage of polarised light through double refracting crystals', *Trans. Roy. Soc. Edinb.*, **26** (1870): 177–85. A lawyer (LLB Edinburgh 1864) Deas was elected FRSE in 1867; see *Proc. Roy. Soc. Edinb.*, **6** (1867): 70.

(3) The date is conjectural: Deas' paper was read to the Royal Society of Edinburgh on 6 June 1870; see *Proc. Roy. Soc. Edinb.*, **7** (1870): 172–3. But see note (8).

(4) J. Clerk Maxwell, 'Addition to the above paper', *Trans. Roy. Soc. Edinb.*, **26** (1870): 185–8.

(5) David Brewster, 'On the laws of polarisation and double refraction in regularly crystallized bodies', *Phil. Trans.*, **108** (1818): 199–273; J. B. Biot, 'Mémoire sur les lois générales de la double réfraction et de la polarisation, dans les corps régulièrement cristallisés', *Mémoires de l'Académie Royale des Sciences*, **3** (1820): 177–384. The phenomena are described by Brewster in his *A Treatise on Optics* [in Lardner's *Cabinet Cyclopaedia*] (London, 1831): 183–254. See also Jed Z. Buchwald, *The Rise of the Wave Theory of Light* (Chicago/London, 1989): 67–107, 254–6, 368–9, 400–3.

refraction and the interference of light. I, therefore, think that a simple statement of the relation of the visible things here described to the results of theory would greatly increase the value of the paper; for in scientific education the identification of what is observed with what is deduced from theory is of more value than either the process of observation or the process of deduction.

This might be done as follows –

Begin with the plane polarized light, the equations of motion of which are

$$x = c \cos nt \quad y = 0.$$

Now let it pass through a plate of crystal of which the axis is inclined α to the axis of x; and let this crystal produce a retardation whose phase is p in the light polarised in the plane of the axis

$$\text{parallel to axis} \quad x' = c \cos \alpha \cos (nt+p)$$
$$\text{perpendicular to axis} \quad y' = c \sin \alpha \cos nt.$$

Next, let the light fall on an analyser in a plane inclined β to the axis of the crystal. The analysed light will be

$$x'' = c \cos \alpha \cos \beta \cos (nt+p) + c \sin \alpha \sin \beta \cos nt.$$

The intensity of this light will be

$$c^2 \{\cos^2 \alpha \cos^2 \beta + \sin^2 \alpha \sin^2 \beta - 2 \sin \alpha \cos \alpha \sin \beta \cos \beta \cos p\}$$

or

$$\frac{1}{2} c^2 \{1 + \cos 2\alpha \cos 2\beta - \sin 2\alpha \sin 2\beta \cos p\}.$$

We may represent this whole process geometrically as follows –

Let OCO' represent the original polarised light, OCA the angle between the plane of polarisation and the axis of the crystal. The light is resolved into ACA' and DCD'. Now, let a semicircle be drawn with radius OA, and let $OAp = p$ be the phase of retardation; draw pT perpendicular to AO, and draw an ellipse with centre C and touching AO in T and also the other sides of the parallelogram. This ellipse is the path of the light emergent from the crystal. Now let BCB' be the plane

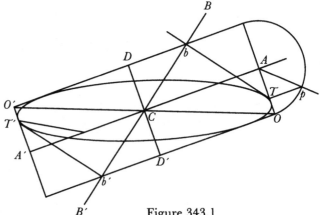

Figure 343,1

of the analyser. Draw $Tb\ T'b'$ tangents to the ellipse perpendicular to BB', then bCb' represents the amplitude of the emergent light.

The *result* of the process may be made still simpler thus:

Draw $CO = c$, in the plane of polarisation, CA parallel to the axis of the crystal, and CB parallel to the analyser. Draw OA perpendicular to CA, AB to CB, and OD to CB, then $CB = c \cos \alpha \cos \beta$, and $BD = c \sin \alpha \sin \beta$; make $DBP = p$, the phase of retardation, and $BP = BD$. Then CP represents the amplitude of the emergent light.

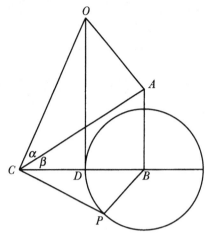

Figure 343,2

The emergent light will be either a maximum or a minimum when $p = 0°$ or $n\pi$.

The minimum will be zero, or blackness, only in the following cases,

1. When $\alpha + \beta = \dfrac{\pi}{2}$ and $p = 0$ or $2n\pi$.

2. When $\alpha - \beta = \dfrac{\pi}{2}$ and $p = 2(n+1)\pi$.

3. When $\alpha = 0$ and $\beta = \dfrac{\pi}{2}$.

4. When $\alpha = \dfrac{\pi}{2}$ and $\beta = 0$.

To compare our results with the experiments, we observe that for a given thickness of the crystal p is a function of the *kind of light*, so that in passing from one end of the spectrum to the other the value of p increases (or diminishes) in a continuous manner. When the film is thick, p will make several entire revolutions within the spectrum. When it is thin, there will be only one or two, or a fraction of a revolution. Take the case of a thick film, then there will be a certain set of black bands when $\beta = \dfrac{\pi}{2} - \alpha$. We may call these No. 1. For these $p = 2n\pi$.

When $\beta = \dfrac{\pi}{2} + \alpha$ there will be another set of black bands, No. 2, intermediate in position to No. 1. For these $p = (2n+1)\pi$.

When $\beta = 0$ or $\frac{\pi}{2}$ the system of bands vanishes.

When $\beta = -\alpha$ the black bands of No. 1 become bright and of maximum intensity.

When $\beta = \alpha$ the black bands of No. 2 become bright and of maximum intensity.

When $\alpha = \frac{\pi}{4}$ all these phenomena are at their greatest distinctness.

In turning the analyser there is simply a dissolution of one system into the other, without motion of the system of bands in the case of a single plate of crystal. But if we place the crystal with its axis inclined 45° to the plane of primitive polarisation, and place above this a film of retardation $\frac{\pi}{2}$ with its axis parallel to the original polarisation, then we have as before for the light emerging from the first crystal,

$$x' = c\frac{1}{\sqrt{2}}\cos(nt+p) \quad y' = c\frac{1}{\sqrt{2}}\cos nt.$$

Resolving these rays in the direction of the axis of the second film, we have

$$x'' = \frac{1}{2}c(\cos(nt+p) + \cos nt)$$

$$y'' = \frac{1}{2}c(\cos(nt+p) - \cos nt),$$

and since x'' is retarded $\frac{\pi}{2}$ it becomes

$$x'' = \frac{1}{2}c(\sin(nt+p) - \sin nt),$$

y'' remaining the same. We may put these values into the form

$$x'' = c\cos\left(nt+\frac{p}{2}\right)\cos\frac{p}{2}$$

$$y'' = c\cos\left(nt+\frac{p}{2}\right)\sin\frac{p}{2}.$$

This shows that after emerging from the circular polarising film the ray is plane-polarised, that the plane of polarisation inclined $\frac{1}{2}p$ to that of primitive polarisation.

If the emergent light is analysed by a dispersion prism, and a Nicol's prism[6] inclined β to the plane of primitive polarisation, there will be black bands (perfectly black) for all colours for which

$$p = 2\beta \quad \text{or} \quad 2\beta + 2n\pi,$$

and as the prism is turned these bands will march forwards in a regular manner across the spectrum.

This very beautiful experiment, in which the phenomena of rotatory polarisation are imitated, is not so well known as it deserves to be. One form of it is due, I believe, to Biot,[7] and another to Wheatstone,[8] but the arrangement here described is by far the most convenient.

When the second plate is thick, then for some points of the spectrum its retardation is $(2n+\frac{1}{2})\pi$. At these points the bands will move forwards when the analyser is turned. At an intermediate set of points the retardation is $(2n-\frac{1}{2})\pi$. At these points the bands will appear to move backwards. At intermediate points the retardation is $n\pi$. At these points the bands will not move, but will become deeper or fainter. I suppose this to be the explanation of the experiment described at p. 181, but the arrangement of the films is not very precisely described.[9]

The experiments with the rings in crystals are very well described, and must be beautiful,[10] but are not so instructive to a beginner as those with the selenite plates. Those, however, who have made out the meaning of the experiments first described have a good right to regale themselves with gorgeous entanglements of colour.

---

(6) See Volume I: 117.

(7) J. B. Biot, 'Mémoire sur les rotations que certaines substances impriment aux axes de polarisation des rayons lumineux', *Mémoires de l'Académie Royale des Sciences*, **2** (1819): 41–136.

(8) Charles Wheatstone, 'Experiments on the successive polarization of light, with the description of a new polarizing apparatus', *Proc. Roy. Soc.*, **19** (1871): 381–9 (read 23 March 1871). In a Royal Institution lecture delivered on 3 February 1871, 'On some experiments on successive polarization of light made by Sir C. Wheatstone', *Proceedings of the Royal Institution of Great Britain*, **6** (1870–2): 205–8, on 205, William Spottiswoode remarked that 'The experiments which formed the subject of this discourse were made by Sir Charles Wheatstone some years ago'. Maxwell's reference to Wheatstone is not therefore inconsistent with the suggested date of Summer 1870 for this text.

(9) Deas, 'On spectra formed by the passage of polarised light': 181; 'a circularly polarising film is interposed between the analyser and the film producing the bands'.

(10) Deas, 'On spectra formed by the passage of polarised light': 182–5; and see Volume I: 99–100.

FRAGMENT OF A DRAFT OF THE 1870 PRESIDENTIAL ADDRESS TO SECTION A OF THE BRITISH ASSOCIATION[1]

circa SUMMER 1870

From the original in the University Library, Cambridge[2]

[ON IRREVERSIBILITY AND ENTROPY]

[...] In the case of the interdiffusion of two different gases, they can be separated again by chemical means,[3] but no natural process can be even thought of which will bring all the individual molecules which are now in the upper part of the room into the upper part again, after they have once been diffused among the lower particles.

This is a case of the irreversible diffusion of material bodies, but the conduction of heat is an example of the diffusion of energy, and it has been pointed out by Sir W. Thomson that this diffusion is not only irreversible, but that it is constantly diminishing that part of the stock of energy which exists in a form capable of being converted into mechanical work.[4] This is Thomsons theory of the irreversible dissipation of energy, and is equivalent to Clausius doctrine of the growth of what he calls Entropy.[5]

The irreversible character of this process is symbolically embodied in Fouriers theory of the conduction of heat, where the formulae themselves indicate a possible solution for all positive values of the time but assume

---

(1) Published in *Nature*, **2** (1870): 419–22, and in the *Report of the Fortieth Meeting of the British Association for the Advancement of Science; held at Liverpool in September 1870* (London, 1871), part 2: 1–9 (= *Scientific Papers*, **2**: 215–29).

(2) ULC Add. MSS 7655, V, h/6. Only fragments of the manuscript are extant: only those folios which differ from the published Address are reproduced here.

(3) Thomas Graham, 'On the absorption and dialytic separation of gases by colloid septa', *Phil. Trans.*, **156** (1866): 399–439. See Number 264.

(4) William Thomson, 'On the dynamical theory of heat, with numerical results deduced from Mr Joule's equivalent of a thermal unit and M. Regnault's observations on steam', *Trans. Roy. Soc. Edinb.*, **20** (1851): 261–88; and Thomson, 'On a universal tendency in nature to the dissipation of mechanical energy', *Proc. Roy. Soc. Edinb.*, **3** (1852): 139–42, esp. 140 (= *Math. & Phys. Papers*, **1**: 174–210, 511–14). Maxwell had first raised the issue in his letter to Thomson of 15 May 1855 (Volume I: 307).

(5) In 1870 Maxwell was still unclear about the concept of entropy. See Number 286 and his discussion in his *Theory of Heat* (London, 1871): 186–8; and Number 483 esp. note (20).

critical values when the time is made zero, and become absurd when the time is assumed to be negative.⁽⁶⁾

The idea which these researches impress on the mind when we follow the natural course of time, is that of an ultimate state of uniform diffusion of energy, which however is not actually reached in any finite time.

But if we reverse the process, and inquire into the former state of things by causing the symbol of time to diminish, we are led up to a state of things which cannot be conceived as the result of any previous state of things, and we find that this critical condition actually existed at an epoch, not in the utmost depths of a past eternity, but separated from the present time by a finite interval.

This idea of a beginning is one which the physical researches of recent times have brought home to us more than any observer of the course of scientific thought in past times would have had reason to expect.⁽⁷⁾[...]

---

(6) See Number 339, esp. note (7).

(7) Compare the *Theory of Heat*: 245–8. See William Thomson, 'On the secular cooling of the earth', *Trans. Roy. Soc. Edinb.*, **23** (1861): 157–70 (= *Math. & Phys. Papers*, **3**: 295–311), Maxwell's source for these remarks.

BRITISH ASSOCIATION PAPER ON HILLS AND DALES

[SEPTEMBER 1870]

From the *Report of the British Association for 1870*[1]

ON HILLS AND DALES[2]

After defining level surfaces and contour-lines on the earth's surface, the author showed that the only measure of the height of a mountain which is mathematically consistent with itself is found by considering the work done in ascending the mountain from a standard station.

By considering a level surface, such as that of the sea, which is supposed gradually to rise by the addition of water from the level of the deepest sea-*bottom* to the *tops* of the highest mountains, he showed that at first there is but one wet region round the deepest bottom. Afterwards other wet regions appear at other bottom points of the surface and continually enlarge. For every new wet region there is a bottom; and when two wet regions coalesce into one there is a point where the surface is level, but neither a top nor a bottom, and this may be called a *Bar*. When a wet region, as the water rises, throws out arms and embraces within it a dry region, there is another level point which may be called a *Pass*. The wet region then becomes cyclic. When the water covers the top of the island thus formed the wet region loses its cyclosis again, and at last, when all the tops are covered, the wet region extends over the whole globe. Hence the number of mountain-tops is equal to the number of passes plus one, and the number of bottoms is equal to the number of bars plus one.

---

(1) *Report of the Fortieth Meeting of the British Association for the Advancement of Science; held at Liverpool in September 1870* (London, 1871), part 2: 17–18.

(2) On 10 March 1870 Maxwell's paper on 'Topographical geometry' was read (by Robert Tucker) to the London Mathematical Society; see the *Proceedings*, **3** (1870): 82, where it is recorded that Arthur Cayley 'made remarks' on the paper. The published version of the paper (of which the present text is, essentially, an abstract), 'On hills and dales', *Phil. Mag.*, ser. 4, **40** (1870): 421–7 (= *Scientific Papers*, **2**: 233–40), is prefixed by a letter (dated 12 October 1870) from Maxwell to the editors of the *Philosophical Magazine*: 'I find that in the greater part of the substance of the following paper I have been anticipated by Professor Cayley, in a memoir "On Contour and Slope Lines", published in the *Philosophical Magazine* in 1859 (S. 4. Vol. XVIII p. 264). An exact knowledge of the first elements of physical geography, however, is so important, and loose notions on the subject are so prevalent, that I have no hesitation in sending you what you, I hope, will have no scruple in rejecting if you think it superfluous after what has been done by Professor Cayley.'

The author then considered lines of slope which are normal to the contour-lines. In general a line of slope is terminated by a top on the one side and by a bottom on the other. At a pass or a bar, however, there is a singularity. Two lines of slope can be drawn through this stationary point; one of these is terminated by two tops and is a line of watershed, the other is terminated by two bottoms and is a line of watercourse. The watershed intersects the watercourse at right angles.

If we consider all the watersheds which meet at the same mountain-top, each of these will reach a pass or a bar. The watercourses, which also pass through these points, form a closed boundary, which is that of the region occupied by all the lines of slope which meet at the mountain-top. This region round the mountain is called a Hill.

In the same way there is a system of watersheds forming the boundary of a region called a Dale, within which all the lines of slope run to the same bottom.

The whole surface of the earth may be divided into Hills, the number of these being the same as that of their Tops.

By an independent division, the whole surface may be divided into Dales, each Dale having a different Bottom.

Besides this, we may, by superposing these divisions, consider the earth as divided into Slopes, each slope being bounded by two watersheds and two watercourses, and being named from the top and the bottom between which all its lines of slope run.

The number of Slopes is shown to be equal to the total number of Tops, Bottoms, Passes, and Bars minus two.[3]

---

(3) Compare Number 317.

346

LETTER TO PETER GUTHRIE TAIT

7 NOVEMBER 1870

From the original in the University Library, Cambridge[1]

Glenlair
Dalbeattie
Nov 7 1870

Dear Tait

$$\nabla = i\frac{d}{dx} + j\frac{d}{dy} + k\frac{d}{dz}.\quad^{(2)}$$

What do you call this? Atled? I want to get a name or names for the result of it on scalar or vector functions of the vector of a point.

Here are some rough hewn names.[3] Will you, like a good Divinity shape their ends properly so as to make them stick.

(1) The result of ∇ applied to a scalar function might be called the slope of the function. Lamé would call it the differential parameter,[4] but the thing itself is a vector, now slope is a vector word, whereas parameter has, to say the least, a scalar sound.

2 If the original function is a vector then ∇ applied to it may give two parts. The scalar part I would call the Convergence of the vector function and the vector part I would call the twist of the vector function.[5]

---

(1) ULC Add. MSS 7655, I, b/16. Previously published in Knott, *Life of Tait*: 143–4.

(2) See P. G. Tait, *An Elementary Treatise on Quaternions* (Oxford, 1867): 221, 267; and Tait, 'Formulae connected with small continuous displacements of the particles of a medium', *Proc. Roy. Soc. Edinb.*, **4** (1862): 617–23, esp. 618; i, j, k are unit vectors at right angles to each other, which Tait (*Quaternions*: 46–7) terms 'quadrantal versors'. Maxwell had discussed Hamilton's '*characteristic of operation*' ∇ in his letter to Tait of 11 December 1867 (Number 277). See William Rowan Hamilton, *Lectures on Quaternions: containing a Systematic Statement of a New Mathematical Method* (Dublin, 1853): 610 (§620); and also W. R. Hamilton, 'On quaternions; or on a new system of imaginaries in algebra', *Phil. Mag.*, ser. 3, **31** (1847): 278–93, esp. 291.

(3) See Number 347; and Maxwell's discussion of quaternions in his essay 'On the mathematical classification of physical quantities', *Proceedings of the London Mathematical Society*, **3** (1871): 224–32 (= *Scientific Papers*, **2**: 257–66).

(4) Gabriel Lamé, *Leçons sur les Coordonnées Curvilignes et leurs Divers Applications* (Paris, 1859): 6; and see Number 277 note (18).

(5) Hamilton's terms 'scalar' and 'vector' are used by Tait in his *Quaternions*: 49, where he gives a definition: 'a quaternion, in general, may be decomposed into the sum of two parts, one numerical, the other a vector. Hamilton calls them the SCALAR, and the VECTOR, and denotes them respectively by the letters S and V prefixed to the expression for the quaternion'. See also Number 347.

(Here the word twist has nothing to do with a screw or helix. If the words *turn* or *version* would do they would be better than twist for twist suggests a screw.)

Twirl is free from the screw notion and is sufficiently racy. Perhaps it is too dynamical for pure mathematicians so for Cayleys sake I might say Curl (after the fashion of Scroll).

Hence the effect of ∇ on a scalar function is to give the slope of that scalar and its effect on a vector function is to give the convergence and the twirl of that vector.

The result of ∇^2 [6] applied to any function may be called the concentration of that function because it indicates the mode in which the value of the function at a given point exceeds (in the Hamiltonian sense) the average value of the function in a little spherical surface drawn round it.

Now if σ be a vector function of ρ and F a scalar function of ρ [7]

∇F is the slope of F

$V\nabla . \nabla F$ is the twirl of the slope which is necessarily zero

$S\nabla . \nabla F = \nabla^2 F$ is the convergence of the slope, which is the concentration of F.

Also $S\nabla\sigma$ is the convergence of σ

$V\nabla\sigma$ is the twirl of σ. [8]

Now the convergence being a scalar if we operate on it with ∇ we find that it has a slope but no twirl.

The twirl of σ is a vector function which has no convergence but only a twirl.

Hence $\nabla^2\sigma$, the concentration of σ is the slope of the convergence of σ together with the twirl of the twirl of σ & $\therefore$ the sum of two vectors.

What I want is to ascertain from you if there are any better names for these things, or if these names are inconsistent with anything in Quaternions, for I am unlearned in quaternion idioms and may make solecisms.

I want phrases of this kind to make statements in electromagnetism and I do not wish to expose either myself to the contempt of the initiated, or Quaternions to the scorn of the profane.

Yours truly
J. CLERK MAXWELL

(6) See Number 277.

(7) On the use of the symbols S and V see note (5).

(8) For these applications of Hamilton's operator ∇ see Tait, *Quaternions*: 267–8. See Maxwell, 'On the mathematical classification of physical quantities': 230–2 (= *Scientific Papers*, **2**: 263–6) and the *Treatise*, **1**: 28–9 (§25) where he develops the argument.

347

MANUSCRIPT ON THE APPLICATION OF QUATERNIONS TO ELECTROMAGNETISM

NOVEMBER 1870[1]

From the original in the University Library, Cambridge[2]

ON THE APPLICATION OF THE IDEAS OF THE CALCULUS OF QUATERNIONS TO ELECTROMAGNETIC PHENOMENA[3]

The invention of the Calculus of Quaternions by Hamilton is a step towards the knowledge of quantities related to space which can only be compared for its importance with the invention of triple coordinates by Descartes.[4]

The limited use which has up to the present time been made of Quaternions must be attributed partly to the repugnance of most mature minds to new methods involving the expenditure of thought and partly to the hitherto undeveloped state of the mathematical investigations in which their peculiar power is most apparent.

The ideas of the calculus of quaternions may be distinguished from its operations and methods. I propose at present to shew how these ideas may be applied to our subject without entering on the operations and methods of the Calculus.

The quantities treated of in the calculus of quaternions are of two essentially distinct kinds Scalars and Vectors.[5] A Scalar quantity is one which does not involve direction. The Mass of a body, the quantity of electricity in a body the potential at a point are instances of scalar quantities.

A Vector quantity is one which has direction as well as magnitude and is such that a reversal of its direction reverses its sign. The typical quantity of this kind is the displacement of a point which is represented by a line drawn from its original to its final position.

The velocity of a body, the force acting on it an electric current, the magnetization of a particle of iron are instances of vector quantities.

There are other quantities which have reference to direction which are not vector quantities. Stresses and Strains are examples of these. These quantities

---

(1) See Number 348.   (2) ULC Add. MSS 7655, V, c/15.

(3) Compare Maxwell's essay 'On the mathematical classification of physical quantities', *Proceedings of the London Mathematical Society*, **3** (1871): 224–32 (= *Scientific Papers*, **2**: 257–66), read on 9 March 1871, where these quaternion arguments are developed. See also the *Treatise*, **1**: 27–9 (§§25–6).

(4) See also Number 485.   (5) See Number 346 note (5).

may be turned through two right angles without altering their value. They may be called [linear and vector functions of a vector.][6]

The symbol of a vector is understood to express its direction as well as its magnitude. This is the fundamental idea of the calculus of quaternions. When the symbol of a vector is put before us, we must conceive a quantity definite in direction and magnitude. The single symbol implies as much as the three components of the quantity do in the Cartesian or any other coordinate system. But though the single symbol implies all this, it does not and cannot express it numerically for three numerical equations are required to express a directed quantity.

The calculus of quaternions is not therefore like the Cartesian geometry a method of applying the science of number to the investigation of space, it is a calculus founded on the independent investigation of space and in which several of the rules relating to operations with numbers are not applicable.

The sum of two vectors is a vector which is the resultant, in the mechanical sense, of the two vectors.

Thus if OA and OB are two vectors

$$OA + OB = OC$$

and $$OA - OB = BA.$$

The product of two vectors is a quantity consisting of a scalar and a vector part. The scalar part of the product of OA and OB is $OA.OB \cos AOB$.

The vector part of $OA.OB$ is a vector perpendicular to the plane of the paper drawn downwards

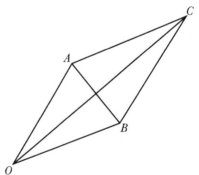

Figure 347,1

and is equal to $OA.OB \sin AOB$

or to the area of the parallelogram formed on OA and OB.

For instance, if OA represents a force and OB the displacement of a body acted on by the force then the work done by the displacement is a quantity which has no direction and is therefore scalar. In fact it is the scalar part of $OA.OB$ which is written

$$S.(OA.OB) = OA.OB \cos AOB.$$

The moment of the force OA acting at B about the origin O is a quantity whose direction is that of the axis through O about which the moment is taken, that is, the perpendicular to the plane of OA and OB drawn upwards.

---

(6) As in the *Treatise*, **1**: 10 (§12). Space in the MS.

It is therefore a vector quantity and in this case its value is the vector part of the product of OA and OB which is written

$$V.(OA.OB) = OA.OB \sin AOB.$$

The position of a point in space is generally expressed by the vector, ρ, drawn from the origin to that point and any quantity whose value depends on the position of the point is said to be a function of ρ.

Thus the potential of a point is a scalar function of ρ, and the resultant force at a point is a vector function of ρ.

Since scalar quantities are of the same kind as those expressed by the symbols we have been in the habit of using we shall retain the same symbols to express them.

For vector quantities Hamilton uses Greek letters but since in electromagnetism we have a large number of different vector quantities we shall express them by German capitals. All such symbols must be understood to have direction as well as magnitude.

Vector Functions of the Electromagnetic Field[7]

$\mathfrak{A}$ = Electromagnetic Momentum
$\mathfrak{B}$ = Magnetic Force
$\mathfrak{C}$ = Electric Current (Total)
$\mathfrak{D}$ = Electric Displacement
$\mathfrak{E}$ = Electromotive Force
$\mathfrak{F}$ = Mechanical Force
$\mathfrak{G}$ = Velocity
$\mathfrak{H}$ = Magnetization
$\mathfrak{I}$ = Magnetic Induction
$\mathfrak{K}$ = Conduction current

As examples of Addition we have

$$\mathfrak{I} = \mathfrak{B} + 4\pi\mathfrak{H}$$

or the magnetic induction is the resultant of the magnetic force and 4π times the magnetization.[8]

We have also

$$\mathfrak{C} = \mathfrak{K} + \dot{\mathfrak{D}}$$

---

(7) See the *Treatise*, 2: 236–7 (§618) for a list of 'principal vectors', which differs from the present list. In the *Treatise* Maxwell writes $\mathfrak{B}$ for magnetic induction $\mathfrak{H}$ for magnetic force, and $\mathfrak{I}$ for intensity of magnetisation.

(8) See the *Treatise* 2: 238 (§619) where he writes $\mathfrak{B} = \mathfrak{H} + 4\pi\mathfrak{I}$ (see note (7)). He follows this usage in Number 353, see esp. note (15).

or the total electric current is the resultant of the current of conduction and the rate of variation of the electric displacement.[9]

The symbol ∇ placed before a function of the vector ρ denotes that the operation denoted by

$$\nabla = i\frac{d}{dx} + j\frac{d}{dy} + k\frac{d}{dz} \quad *^{(10)}$$

is to be performed on the function, $i\,j\,k$ being three unit vectors at right angles to each other.

We shall first consider the effect of ∇ on f a scalar function of ρ

$$\nabla f = i\frac{df}{dx} + j\frac{df}{dy} + k\frac{df}{dz}.$$

The interpretation of this equation is that ∇f is a vector, the components of which are $\frac{df}{dx}$ in the direction of x, $\frac{df}{dy}$ in that of y and $\frac{df}{dz}$ in that of z.

For instance if f is the electric potential of a point then $-\nabla f$ represents in direction and magnitude the resultant electromotive force at the point due to the variation of the potential from point to point in space. I shall call ∇f the *slope* of the scalar function f.[11] Lamé† uses the term Differential Parameter[12] but neither the term itself nor the mode in which Lamé uses it indicates that the quantity referred to has direction as well as magnitude. I have used the word slope for want of a better to express the vector which indicates at any point the rate of variation of a scalar quantity with the variation of position in space. The slope is measured in the direction in which the scalar increases most rapidly and its length indicates this rate.

Let us next examine the effect of ∇ upon a vector function of ρ, for instance

$$\sigma = i\xi + j\eta + k\zeta.$$

Performing the operation and remembering the Quaternion rules for the multiplication of $i\,j$ and k we find that the result consists of two parts. The scalar part is

$$S\nabla\sigma = -\left(\frac{d\xi}{dx} + \frac{d\eta}{dy} + \frac{d\zeta}{dz}\right)$$

---

* See Taits Quaternions §364[10]   † Fonctions Inverses[12]

---

(9) See the *Treatise*, 2: 238 (§619).

(10) P. G. Tait, *An Elementary Treatise on Quaternions* (Oxford, 1867): 267–8.

(11) Compare Maxwell's discussion in his essay 'On the mathematical classification of physical quantities': 230–2 (= *Scientific Papers*, 2: 263–6).

(12) Gabriel Lamé, *Leçons sur les Fonctions Inverses Transcendantes et les Surfaces Isothermes* (Paris, 1857): 2, where he uses the symbol Δ_2 for ∇^2; see Number 277. Lamé had used the expression '*paramètres differentiels*' in his *Leçons sur les Coordonnées Curvilignes*: 6; see Number 346 note (4).

and the vector part is

$$V\nabla\sigma = i\left(\frac{d\zeta}{dy}-\frac{d\eta}{dz}\right)+j\left(\frac{d\xi}{dz}-\frac{d\zeta}{dx}\right)+k\left(\frac{d\eta}{dx}-\frac{d\xi}{dy}\right).\quad{}^{(13)}$$

Here ξ η and ζ are the rectangular components of the vector function. If we suppose σ to represent the velocity of a fluid then $S\nabla\sigma$ represents the rate at which the motion of the fluid converges to a given point. I propose therefore to call $S\nabla\sigma$ the *convergence* of the vector σ.

If σ_0 is the value of σ at a given point then if $V\nabla\sigma$ is positive the vector $\sigma-\sigma_0$ near the point will be directed more towards the point than from it hence the propriety of the term convergence.

The vector part of $\nabla\sigma$ or $V\nabla\sigma$ is indicated by its three components. If σ is the velocity of a fluid then $V\nabla\sigma$ is the rotation of the particles of the fluid, the direction of this vector being the axis of rotation drawn in such a direction that the rotation appears to an eye looking in the direction of the axis to be opposite to the hands of a watch.

I propose to call $V\nabla\sigma$ the *curl* of the function σ. It might be called rotation, version, twist or twirl but all these names have motion implied in them so that I prefer the word curl which has not hitherto been used in any other mathematical sense.

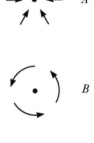

Figure 347,2

At A we have an illustration of convergence without curl, at B of curl without convergence and at C of curl combined with convergence.

If σ represent the velocity of an incompressible liquid, the convergence of σ is zero.

If σ represent the resultant force of any system of attracting points then the curl of σ is zero.

If we now take as the original vector function ∇f or the slope of the scalar function f and perform on it the operation ∇ we shall find

$$\nabla^2 f = S\nabla.\nabla f$$
for
$$V\nabla.\nabla f = 0.$$

This may be shown symbolically by performing the operation ∇ on itself.

---

(13) Compare Maxwell's statement of these quaternion expressions in the *Treatise*, **1**: 28 (§25), and see Tait, *Quaternions*: 268–9. Compare also Tait, 'On Green's and other allied theorems', *Trans. Roy. Soc. Edinb.*, **26** (1870): 69–84, esp. 79, where the expressions for $S\nabla\sigma$ and $V\nabla\sigma$ are given in the form as stated by Maxwell here.

This result is
$$\nabla^2 = -\left(\frac{d^2}{dx^2}+\frac{d^2}{dy^2}+\frac{d^2}{dz^2}\right). \quad (14)$$

Hence ∇^2 is a scalar operation and the result of it on any function is scalar or vector as the original function is scalar or vector. Hence $\nabla^2 f$ is a scalar since f is so and $\nabla^2 \sigma$ is a vector since σ is so.

If round any point we draw a small sphere whose radius is r then if q is any function whatever
$$q_0 - \frac{3}{4\pi r^3}\Sigma\, q\, dv = \frac{r^2}{10}\nabla^2 q$$

where q_0 is the value of q at the centre and the integration is extended over the sphere. In other words the value of q at the centre exceeds the average value of q in the sphere by $\frac{r^2}{10}\nabla^2 q$.

I propose to call $\nabla^2 q$ the *concentration* of q at a point in space because it indicates the excess of the value of q at that point over its mean value in the immediate neighbourhood of the point.

If q is a scalar function the meaning of its mean value is well known. If q is a vector function its mean value is a vector which must be found by the rules for integrating vector functions and the excess of q_0 above this value is also a vector.

Hence we get the following results.
$$\nabla^2 f = S\,.\,\nabla\,.\,V\nabla f$$

The concentration of a scalar function is also scalar and it is the convergence of the slope of that scalar.
$$\nabla^2 \sigma = V\nabla S\nabla\sigma + V\nabla V\nabla\sigma$$

The concentration of a vector function is a vector and it is the sum of two vectors, one of which is the slope of the convergence of the vector and the other is the curl of the curl of the vector.

We also have
$$V\nabla\,.\,\nabla f = 0$$
or the slope of a scalar has no curl
$$S\nabla V\nabla\sigma$$
or the curl of a vector has no convergence.

It may also be shown that every vector function without curl is the slope of

---

(14) Tait, *Quaternions*: 267; W. R. Hamilton, *Lectures on Quaternions* (Dublin, 1853): 611 (§620). See the *Treatise*, **1**: 29 (§26) where Maxwell notes that ∇^2 is 'an operator occurring in all parts of Physics, which we may refer to as Laplace's Operator'.

some scalar, and that every vector function without convergence is the curl of some vector and that every vector function may be represented as the slope of a certain scalar together with the curl of a certain vector.

348

LETTER TO PETER GUTHRIE TAIT

14 NOVEMBER 1870

From the original in the University Library, Cambridge[1]

Glenlair
14 Nov 1870

D^r T'

I return you Smith's letter.[2] If Cadmus had required to use ∇ and had consulted the Phoenician professors about a name for it there can be no question that Nabla[3] would have been chosen on the א ב ג principle.

It is plain that Hamilton's ∇ derives itself with all its congeners from Leibnitz' d which has become consecrated to differentiation along with $D\ \partial\ \delta\ \jmath$ &c and a name derived from its shape is hardly the thing.

With regard to my dabbling in Hamilton I want to leaven my book with Hamiltonian ideas without casting the operations into a Hamiltonian form for which neither I nor, I think, the public are ripe.

Now the value of Hamiltons idea of a Vector is unspeakable and so are those of the addition and multiplication of vectors. I consider the form into which he put these ideas, such as the names of Tensor Versor, Quaternion[4] &c important and useful but subject to the approval of the mathematical world. As for the particular symbols, Roman Greek small or capital erect or inverted these should be preserved only for the sake of consistency.

For instance if you have 7 or 8 kinds of vectors in one problem one might use – say German Capitals to distinguish them from the scalar quantities in the same problem.

The names which I sent you were not for ∇ but the results of ∇. I shall send you presently what I have written, which though it is in the form of a chapter of my book is not to be put in but to assist in leavening the rest.[5] I shall take

---

(1) ULC Add. MSS 7655, I, b/17. Published in extract in Knott, *Life of Tait*: 144.

(2) William Robertson Smith, Tait's assistant at Edinburgh University 1868, Professor of Hebrew at the Free Church Aberdeen 1870 (*DNB*). See Knott, *Life of Tait*: 143, 171, 291–2.

(3) An Assyrian harp. Hence Maxwell's dedication of his poem, written in Edinburgh in September 1871 at the British Association meeting, to Tait as the 'Chief Musician upon Nabla'. See *Life of Maxwell*: 634–6; and Knott, *Life of Tait*: 172–3, a version which includes the Hebrew superscription added by Robertson Smith to Maxwell's autograph original (ULC Add. MSS 7655, V, 1/3).

(4) See P. G. Tait, *An Elementary Treatise on Quaternions* (Oxford, 1867): 33; 'it appears that a quaternion...may itself be decomposed into two factors...the *stretching* factor...is called the TENSOR...[and the] *turning* factor...is called the VERSOR.'

(5) See Number 347.

the learned Auctor and the grim Tortor into my serious consideration though Tortor has a helical smack which is distasteful to me but poison to T.

As for T'''[6] who took his Bain[7] to gnaw in the Alps[8] along with the Farbenlehre he cured his distress by applying to the Sortes Bainales. Send his lecture.[9]

I have had no Nablody from you since the motion of a rigid body[10] and will be thankful for it and the lecture which Smith refers to.[11]

Here is something for Sang.[12]

If a heavy particle move on a smooth sphere radius a so that the difference of height at its highest and lowest point is $2c$ then if a circle of radius a be placed so that its highest and lowest points are at the same levels as those of the path of the particle

namely $b+c$ and $b-c$

and if (as is necessary) the height above the mean point (b) to which the velocity in the sphere is due be

$$\frac{b^2+c^2-a^2}{2b}$$

and that in the circle

$$\frac{b^2-c^2+a^2}{2b}$$

then the bodies if started at the same level will preserve equal heights.

From this I get that if an infinite number of such bodies were moving in a

---

(6) John Tyndall.

(7) Alexander Bain, *Logic*, 2 vols. (London, 1870).

(8) Tyndall had recently published an essay on 'Climbing in search of the sky', *Fortnightly Review*, **13** (1870): 1–15.

(9) In his lecture on the 'Scientific use of the imagination', presented at the meeting of the British Association at Liverpool on 16 September 1870 (which Maxwell had attended: see Numbers 344 and 345), Tyndall had commented critically on Goethe's *Farbenlehre* and Bain's *Logic*. The lecture was published, and subsequently reprinted in Tyndall's *Essays on the Use and Limit of Imagination in Science* (London, 1870): 13–51 (see esp. 13–14).

(10) P. G. Tait, 'On the rotation of a rigid body about a fixed axis', *Trans. Roy. Soc. Edinb.*, **25** (1869): 261–303, where Tait had employed quaternion notation.

(11) Part of an address Tait had delivered to the University of Edinburgh was published as 'Energy, and Prof. Bain's Logic' in *Nature*, **3** (1870): 89–90. Tait trounced Bain's use of the expression 'convertibility of *force*' in his *Logic*, **2**: 30–1.

(12) Edward Sang, 'On the motion of a heavy body along the circumference of a circle', *Trans. Roy. Soc. Edinb.*, **24** (1867): 59–71; Sang, 'Additional note on the motion of a heavy body along the circumference of a circle', *Trans. Roy. Soc. Edinb.*, **26** (1870): 449–57, read 6 February 1871; see *Proc. Roy. Soc. Edinb.*, **7** (1871): 361–5.

sphere then if a small force came to act on them the centre of gravity of the lot would be neither raised nor lowered.

Yours
J.C.M.

The prop is the same in form for a body of two equal axes of inertia moving about a point fixed in the third.

349

LETTER TO JOHN HUTTON BALFOUR[1]

28 NOVEMBER 1870

From a holograph copy by Peter Guthrie Tait in the University Library, Cambridge[2]

G[lenlair]
D[albeattie]
28/11/70

(a) Dr Prof Balfour

I do not presume to inform an officer of the Society with respect to its recent awards. I saw that T[ait] had got the K[eith] Prize which is or ought to be known to the public.[3] I have not yet got a copy of the reasons for w^h it was awarded, so if I coincide with them it does not arise from imitation.

The question seems to be What is T′ good for? Now I think him good 1st for writing a book on Q[uaternions],[4] and for being himself a living example of a man who has got the Q mind directly from H[amilton]. I am unable to predict the whole consequences of this fact because besides knowing Q T′ has a most vigorous mind & is well able to express himself especially in writing, and no one can tell whether he may not yet be able to cause the Q ideas to overflow all their math. symbols & to become embodied in ordinary language so as to give their form to the thoughts of all mankind.

I look forward to the time when the idea of the relation of two vectors will be as familiar to the popular mind as the rule of 3 & when the fact that $ij = -ji$[5] will be introduced into hustings' speeches as a telling illustration. Why not? We have had arithmetical & geometrical series, and lots of old scraps of Math used in speeches.

Nevertheless I do not recommend some of T′'s math papers to be read as

---

(a) {Tait} Balfour having asked Maxwell to write something which could be read at a meeting of R.S.E. when I was to get the Keith medal was mystified as follows.

(1) General Secretary of the Royal Society of Edinburgh; see *Proc. Roy. Soc. Edinb.*, **7** (1870): 231.

(2) ULC Add. MSS 7655, II/38. First published in Knott, *Life of Tait*: 149–50, where Tait's abbreviations are expanded.

(3) The letter was apparently written in connection with David Milne Home's address (as Vice-President of the Royal Society of Edinburgh) on 5 December 1870. See *Proc. Roy. Soc. Edinb.*, **7** (1870): 232–307, esp. 234–5, where Milne Home eulogises Tait for the award of the Society's Keith Prize (as announced on 20 December 1869: see *Proc. Roy. Soc. Edinb.*, **7** (1869): 33), and quotes a letter from William Thomson to Balfour, presumably solicited (along with the Maxwell letter reproduced here) as evidence of Tait's contributions to science.

(4) P. G. Tait, *An Elementary Treatise on Quaternions* (Oxford, 1867).

(5) Hamilton's abandonment of the commutative law of multiplication in quaternion algebra. See Tait, *Quaternions*: 46–7; and on the unit vectors i and j see Number 346 note (2).

an address to the Soc^y, ore rotundo. That on Rotation$^{(6)}$ is very powerful, but the last one on Green's and other allied theorems$^{(7)}$ is really great.

The work of math^{ns} is of two kinds, one is counting, the other is thinking. Now these two operations help each other very much but in a great many investigations the counting is such long & such hard work, that the math^n girds himself to it as if he had contracted for a heavy job and thinks no more that day. Now T' is the man to enable him to do it by thinking, a nobler though more expensive occupation, and in a way by w^h he will not make so many mistakes as if he had pages of $=^{ns}$ to work out.

I have said nothing of his book on Heat,$^{(8)}$ because though it is the clearest thing of the sort, it is not so thoroughly imbued with his personality as his Q. works. In this however I am probably entirely mistaken, so I advise you to ask T' himself who I have no doubt could hit off the thing much better than any one.

I remain
Yours truly
J. CLERK MAXWELL

(6) P. G. Tait, 'On the rotation of a rigid body about a fixed axis', *Trans. Roy. Soc. Edinb.*, **25** (1869): 261–303, the paper for which Tait was awarded the Keith Prize; see *Proc. Roy. Soc. Edinb.*, **7** (1869): 33.

(7) P. G. Tait, 'On Green's and other allied theorems', *Trans. Roy. Soc. Edinb.*, **26** (1870): 69–84.

(8) P. G. Tait, *Sketch of Thermodynamics* (Edinburgh, 1868).

350

LETTER TO JOHN WILLIAM STRUTT

6 DECEMBER 1870

From the original in private possession[1]

Glenlair
Dec 6 1870

I send you my paper on viscosity of gases.[2] The value for air was tested by new experiments the year after and found not to need correction.[3]

Dear Strutt

If this world is a purely dynamical system and if you accurately reverse the motion of every particle of it at the same instant then all things will happen backwards till the beginning of things the rain drops will collect themselves from the ground and fly up to the clouds &c &c and men will see all their friends passing from the grave to the cradle till we ourselves become the reverse of born, whatever that is. We shall then speak of the impossibility of knowing about the past except by analogies taken from the future & so on.[4]

The possibility of executing this experiment is doubtful but I do not think that it requires such a feat to upset the 2nd law of Thermodynamics.

For if there is any truth in the dynamical theory of gases the different molecules in a gas at uniform temperature are moving with very different velocities. Put such a gas into a vessel with two compartments and make a small hole in the wall about the right size to let one molecule through. Provide a lid or stopper for this hole and appoint a doorkeeper, very intelligent and exceedingly quick, with microscopic eyes but still an essentially finite being.

Figure 350,1

Whenever he sees a molecule of great velocity coming against the door

---

(1) Rayleigh Papers, Terling Place, Terling, Essex. Previously published (in part) in R. J. Strutt, *John William Strutt, Third Baron Rayleigh* (London, 1924): 47–8.

(2) See Number 252.   (3) See Number 260.

(4) For discussion of time-reversal see Number 286 esp. note (12). Compare the discussion by William Thomson, 'The kinetic theory of the dissipation of energy', *Nature*, **9** (1874): 441–4 (= *Math. & Phys. Papers*, **5**: 11–20); if 'the motion of every particle in the universe were precisely reversed at any instant, the course of nature would be simply reversed for ever after... if also the materialistic hypothesis of life were true, living creatures would grow backwards, with conscious knowledge of the future, but no memory of the past, and would become again unborn'. See Thomson's comment on time-reversal appended to Maxwell's letter to Tait of 11 December 1867 (Number 277).

from A into B he is to let it through, but if the molecule happens to be going slow he is to keep the door shut. He is also to let slow molecules pass from B to A but not fast ones. (This may be done if necessary by another doorkeeper at a second door.) Of course he must be quick for the molecules are continually changing both their courses and their velocities.

In this way the temperature of B may be raised and that of A lowered without any expenditure of work, but only by the intelligent action of a mere guiding agent (like a pointsman on a railway with perfectly acting switches who should send the express along one line and the goods along another).

I do not see why even intelligence might not be dispensed with and the thing be made self-acting.[5]

Moral The 2nd law of Thermodynamics has the same degree of truth as the statement that if you throw a tumblerful of water into the sea you cannot get the same tumblerful of water out again.[6]

Many thanks for your two papers.[7] The electromagnetic one has just come in time for me as I am at that part of the subject. Have you seen Helmholtz on the Equations of Motion of Electricity in conductors at rest.[8] It is a very powerful paper.

I have been doing Webers theories of magnetic and diamagnetic induction.[9] There are some mistakes in integration[10] but the theory of moveable magnetic molecules is of great use in explaining phenomena especially all about magnetization demagnetization and remagnetization.

Yours truly
J. CLERK MAXWELL

I have improved my book by means of 3 of your suggestions.[11]

1   Wrong sign in an equation about M.[12]

---

(5) See Number 277 for the first version of this argument.

(6) See Number 287 for the first statement of this point.

(7) J. W. Strutt, 'On an electromagnetic experiment', *Phil. Mag.*, ser. 4, **39** (1870): 428–35; and Strutt, 'Remarks on a paper by Dr. Sondhauss', *ibid.*, **40** (1870): 211–17.

(8) Hermann Helmholtz, 'Ueber die Bewegungsgleichungen der Elektricität für ruhende leitende Körper', *Journal für die reine und angewandte Mathematik*, **72** (1870): 57–128.

(9) See the *Treatise*, 2: 74–87 (§§442–8) and 418–25 (§§832–45); and Numbers 278 and 295.

(10) See the *Treatise*, 2: 78n (§443); and Number 411 esp. note (4).

(11) In Strutt's paper 'On some electromagnetic phenomena considered in connexion with the dynamical theory', *Phil. Mag.*, ser. 4, **38** (1869): 1–15. Compare the 'Theory of electric circuits' in the *Treatise*, 2: 206–10 (§§578–84).

(12) The 'coefficient of mutual induction' between two circuits. See Strutt, 'On some electromagnetic phenomena': 6, and the *Treatise*, 2: 209–10 (§582–4); and see Number 430.

2 ⌊discussion of⌋ Terms of kinetic energy involving products of currents and ordinary velocities.[13]

3 Magnetization as a test of maximum current and as a cause of anomalies in galvanometry.[14]

If therefore any more occur to you and you send me them I shall be thankful.

APPENDIX: FROM THE MANUSCRIPT OF THE *THEORY OF HEAT*

circa LATE 1870[15]

From the original in the University Library, Cambridge[16]

[1] [LIMITATION OF THE SECOND LAW OF THERMODYNAMICS][17]

Before I conclude I wish to direct attention to an aspect of the molecular theory which deserves consideration.

---

(13) See Strutt, 'On some electromagnetic phenomena': 6–7, and the *Treatise*, **2**: 206–9 (§§ 578–81); and see Numbers 333 and 430.

(14) See Strutt, 'On some electromagnetic phenomena': 8–9. On galvanometry, see a card (postmarked 11 January 1871) from William Thomson to Maxwell: 'Adjust R till contact at K makes no change in deflec^n of galvan^r needle. This determines G, the resistance of galv^r coil $a:b::R:G$. Do you know this plan? It is too absurdly obvious yet for years I had never known how to find the resist^{ce} of a galv^r coil simply from one self deflection, & without knowing the resistance of the battery. / Interchange battery & galv^r, and you have Mance's method for resistance of battery.' (ULC Add. MSS 7655, I, a/6). Henry Mance's paper, on a 'Method of measuring the resistance of a conductor or of a battery, or of a telegraph-line influenced by unknown earth-currents, from a single deflection of a galvanometer of unknown resistance', *Proc. Roy. Soc.* **19** (1871): 248–52, was communicated by Thomson to the Royal Society (recorded as received 12 January 1871). Mance's paper, and Thomson's paper on a 'Modification of Wheatstone's bridge to find the resistance of a galvanometer-coil from a single deflection of its own needle', *Proc. Roy. Soc.*, **19** (1871): 253, repeating the contents of his card to Maxwell, were read to the Royal Society on 19 January 1871. Maxwell gave an account of Thomson's and Mance's methods, for the determination of the resistance of a galvanometer and a battery, in the *Treatise*, **1**: 410–13 (§§ 356–7).

Figure 350,2

(15) It is apparent that Maxwell was well advanced in writing the *Theory of Heat* by April 1870 (see Number 339); that he had abandoned work on the *Treatise* at that time (see Number 341); and that in December 1870 he wrote to J. W. Strutt developing the argument here reproduced from the final folios of the manuscript of the *Theory of Heat*.

(16) ULC Add. MSS 7655, IV, 1 (last 5 ff.).

(17) Compare the *Theory of Heat* (London, 1871): 308–9.

One of the best established facts in thermodynamics is that it is impossible in a system enclosed in an envelope which permits neither change of volume nor passage of heat, in which the temperature and pressure is everywhere the same, to produce any inequality of temperature or of pressure without the expenditure of work. This is the second law of Thermodynamics[18] and it is undoubtedly true as long as we can deal with bodies only in mass and have no power of perceiving or handling the separate molecules of which they are made up. But if we conceive a being whose faculties are so sharpened[19] that he can follow every molecule in its course, such a being whose attributes are still as essentially finite as our own would be able to do what is at present impossible to us.

For we have seen that the molecules of a mass, say, of air at uniform temperature and pressure are moving with velocities by no means uniform though the mean velocity of any great number of them arbitrarily selected is almost exactly uniform.

Now let us suppose that a vessel full of air of uniform temperature and pressure is divided into two portions A and B by a division in which there is a large hole. Over this hole is placed a sliding plate pierced with a single hole so small that only one molecule can get through at a time.

This sliding plate the mass of which may be supposed excessively small is placed in charge of a being whose senses are so acute that he can see every molecule of the air, at least when it is near the hole and he is instructed that whenever a molecule of division A is approaching the hole with more than the mean velocity he is to shift the plate so as to let it pass through to division B but when a molecule is coming slowly in the same direction he is to arrange so that it strikes the plate and does not get through the hole.

In the same way he is to allow slow molecules to pass from B to A and to refuse a passage to fast molecules in the same direction.

The result will be that the mean velocity of the molecules in division B will be increased and that of those in division A diminished by the mere sliding of the plate without any expenditure of work.

It follows that the second law of thermodynamics is no longer true if we suppose an intelligent and active being able to perform the operations with the sliding piece which we have just described.

This is only one of the instances in which conclusions which we have drawn from our experience of bodies consisting of an immense number of molecules may be found not to be applicable to the more delicate observations and experiments which we may suppose made by one who can perceive and handle the individual molecules which we deal with only in large masses.

---

(18) See Number 277 notes (9) and (10).   (19) See note (5).

In dealing with masses of matter while we do not perceive the individual molecules we are compelled to adopt what I have described as the statistical method of calculation and to abandon the strict dynamical method in which we follow every motion by the calculus.[20]

It would be interesting to enquire how far those ideas about the nature and methods of science which have been derived from examples of scientific investigation in which the dynamical method is followed are applicable to our actual knowledge of concrete things which as we have seen is of an essentially statistical nature because no one has yet discovered any practical method of tracing the path of a molecule or of identifying it at different times.

I do not think however that the perfect identity which we observe between different portions of the same kind of matter can be explained on the statistical principle of the stability of the averages of large numbers of quantities each of which may differ from the mean.

For if of the molecules of some substance such as hydrogen some were of greater mass than others, we have the means of producing a separation between molecules of different kinds and in this way we should be able to produce two kinds of hydrogen one of which would be somewhat denser than the other. As this cannot be done, we must admit that the equality which we assert to exist between the molecules of hydrogen applies to each individual molecule and not merely to the average of groups of millions of molecules.

[2] [NATURE AND ORIGIN OF MOLECULES][21]

We have thus been led by our study of visible things to a theory that they are made up of a finite number of parts or molecules each of which has a definite mass and possesses other properties. The molecules of the same substance are all exactly alike but different from those of other substances. There is not a regular gradation in the mass of molecules from that of hydrogen which is the least of those known to us to that of   [22] but they all fall into a limited number of classes or species the individuals of each species being exactly similar to each other and no intermediate links are found to connect one species with another by a uniform gradation.

We are here reminded of the speculations concerning the relations between the species of living things. Here also we find that the individuals are naturally grouped into species and that intermediate links between the species are wanting. But in each species variations occur and there is a

---

(20) See the *Theory of Heat*: 288; and Number 478 §6.
(21) Compare the *Theory of Heat*: 310–12.   (22) The published text reads: bismuth.

perpetual generation and destruction of the individuals of which the species consist.

Hence it is possible to frame a theory to account for the present state of things by means of generation variation and discriminative destruction.

In the case of the molecules however each individual is permanent there is no generation or destruction and no variation or rather difference between the individuals of each species.

Hence the kind of speculation with which we have become so familiar under the name of theories of evolution is quite inapplicable to the case of molecules.

It is true that Des Cartes whose inventiveness knew no bounds has given a theory of the evolution of molecules. He supposed that the molecules with which the heavens are nearly filled have received a spherical form from the long continued grinding of their projecting parts so that like marbles in a mill they have 'rubbed each others angles down'.[23] The result of this attrition forms the finest kind of molecules with which the interstices of the globular molecules are filled. But besides these he describes another elongated kind of molecules, the *particula striata* which have received their form from their often threading the interstice between three spheres in contact. They have thus acquired three longitudinal ridges and since some of them during their passage are rotating on their axes these ridges are not parallel to the axis but are twisted like threads of a screw. By means of these little screws he most ingeniously explains the phenomenon of magnetism.[24]

We cannot understand Des Cartes without bearing in mind that he recognizes no property in matter except extension so that he confounds matter with the space which it occupies. ⟨He is therefore full of error with respect to all kinetic properties depending on mass.⟩[25] His opinions therefore about the mutual action of bodies and the parts of bodies whether in motion or at rest are exceedingly strange and in contrast with the perfection of his geometry.

But it is evident that his molecules are very different from ours. His seem to be produced by some general break up of his solid space and to be ground down in the course of ages and though their relative magnitude is in some degree determinate there is nothing to determine the absolute magnitude of any of them.

Our molecules on the other hand are unalterable by any of the processes

---

(23) R. Descartes, *Principia Philosophiæ* (Amsterdam, 1644): 93; 'quod alicujus corporis anguli sic atterantur' (Pars Tertia, Prop. XLVIII).

(24) Descartes, *Principia Philosophiæ*: 266–78 (Pars Quarta).

(25) Compare Maxwell's comment in Number 377 para 7.

which go on in the present state of things and every individual of each species is of exactly the same magnitude as though they had all been cast in the same mould like bullets and not merely selected and grouped according to their size like small shot.

The individuals of each species also agree in the nature of the light which they emit, that is in their natural periods of vibration. They are therefore like tuning forks all tuned to concert pitch or like watches regulated to solar time.[26]

In speculating on the cause of this equality we are debarred from imagining any cause of equalization on account of the immutability of each individual molecule. It is difficult to conceive of selection and elimination of intermediate varieties for where can these eliminated molecules have gone to if as we have reason to believe the hydrogen &c of the fixed stars is composed of molecules identical in all respect with our own.

The time required to eliminate from the whole of the universe visible to us every molecule whose mass differs from that of our so called elements by processes similar to Grahams method of dialysis[27] which are the only methods we can conceive of at present would exceed the utmost limits ever demanded by evolutionists as many times as these exceed the period of vibration of a molecule.

But if we suppose the molecules to be made at all or if we suppose them to consist of something previously made why should we expect any irregularity to exist among them. If they are as we believe the only material things which still remain in the precise condition in which they first began to exist why should we not rather look for some indication of that spirit of order our scientific confidence in which is never shaken by the difficulty we experience in tracing it in the complex arrangements of visible things, and of which our moral estimation is shown in all our attempts to think and speak the truth and to ascertain the exact principles of distributive justice.

---

(26) Compare the concluding remarks of Maxwell's discourse on 'Molecules', *Nature*, **8** (1873): 437–41 (= *Scientific Papers*, **2**: 361–78).

(27) Thomas Graham, 'On the absorption and dialytic separation of gases by colloid septa', *Phil. Trans.*, **156** (1866): 399–439. See Number 264.

= 351 =

LETTER TO GEORGE GABRIEL STOKES

11 JANUARY 1871

From the original in the University Library, Cambridge[1]

Glenlair
Dalbeattie
11 Jan 1871

My dear Stokes

I received the copy of the Adams Prize Essay[2] some time ago, and have been gradually getting into the subject.

Did not you set the theorem about the surface integral

$$\left(\left(\frac{d\gamma}{dy} - \frac{d\beta}{dz}\right)dy\,dz + \ldots + \right)$$

over a surface bounded by the curve s being equal to

$$\left(\alpha \frac{dx}{ds} + \beta \frac{dy}{ds} + \gamma \frac{dz}{ds}\right)ds.\text{[3]}$$

I have had some difficulty in tracing the history of this theorem.[4] Can you tell me anything about it.

Yours truly
J. CLERK MAXWELL

I hope you saw the eclipse well.[5]

---

(1) ULC Add. MSS 7656, M 428. First published in Larmor, *Correspondence*, 2: 31.

(2) According to the 'Book of Minutes relating to The Adams Prize, kept by the Plumian Professor [James Challis]' (Cambridge Observatory): '1869 Feb. 11, Professor Cayley was appointed Adams Prize adjudicator from the nomination of Downing College, and 1869 Feb. 15, Mr J. C. Maxwell was appointed adjudicator from the nomination of St. Catharine's College. Prize to be adjudged in 1871.' A further note states: '1869 March 15, Adams Prize subject agreed upon in the Lent Term of 1869, to be adjudged in 1871. / A determination of the circumstances under which discontinuity of any kind presents itself in the solution of a problem of maximum or minimum in the Calculus of Variations, and applications to particular instances. / ⁂ It is expected that the discussion of the instances should be exemplified as far as possible geometrically, and that attention be especially directed to cases of real or supposed failure of the Calculus.' Challis subsequently recorded the award of the prize: '1871 April 4, the Adams Prize was adjudged to Mr Todhunter M.A. of St John's College (Subject, *Discontinuity in Calculus of Variations*, proposed in Lent Term of 1869).'

(3) The theorem, known as 'Stokes' theorem', first stated by William Thomson in a letter to Stokes of 2 July 1850 (ULC Add. MSS 7656, K 39; printed in Wilson, *Stokes–Kelvin Correspondence*, 1: 97), was published by Stokes in his Smith's Prize examination of 1854, where Maxwell was placed equal Smith's Prizeman; see Number 366 note (3) and Volume I: 257–8n. The terms and form in which Maxwell describes the theorem here follow its statement by Thomson and Tait, *Natural Philosophy*: 124 (§ 190j).   (4) See also Number 366.

(5) The total eclipse of the sun on 22 December 1870; see *Proc. Roy. Soc.*, **19** (1870–1): 123, 290.

352

DRAFT LETTER TO PETER GUTHRIE TAIT[1]

23 JANUARY 1871

From the original in the University Library, Cambridge[2]

Ardhallow
Dunoon
Jan 23 1871

D^r T'

Still harping on that Nabla![3]

The present Nablody is on ∇^{-1}.[4]

Let us first consider all space and then particular regions.

We know that the equation $\nabla^2 \xi = x$

with the condition $\xi = 0$ at ∞ has no solution

but
$$\xi = \frac{1}{4\pi} \iiint \frac{x}{r} d(\text{volume}) \qquad \text{(over all space)}.$$

This is true whether x be a scalar or a vector and ξ is scalar or vector according as x is.

Hence if σ is a vector function we can express σ as $\sigma = \nabla \tau$ by finding τ from the equation $\nabla^2 \tau = \nabla \sigma$.

Now $\nabla \sigma$ is partly scalar ($= m$) and partly vector ($= \alpha$). Let P be the potential of m and $L\,M\,N$ the constituents of vector potential[5] of α then τ is expressed by an equation of the form

$$\tau = P + iL + jM + kN.$$

See Stokes on Dynamical Theory of Diffraction Camb Trans 1849 or 50.[6]

This can be done only in one way, that is, P, L, M, N are all determinate quantities vanishing at ∞.

Now for the present question.[7]

---

(1) A preliminary version of Number 353, but possibly sent to Tait.

(2) ULC Add. MSS 7655, I, b/19.

(3) The operator ∇; see Number 348 note (3).

(4) As discussed by Tait in his paper 'On Green's and other allied theorems', *Trans. Roy. Soc. Edinb.*, **26** (1870): 69–84, esp. 73–4.

(5) See also the *Treatise*, **2**: 27–8, 236 (§§405, 617) on the vector potential.

(6) G. G. Stokes, 'On the dynamical theory of diffraction', *Trans. Camb. Phil. Soc.*, **9** (1849): 1–62, esp. 6–10 (= *Papers*, **2**: 243–327).

(7) As discussed by Tait in his paper 'On some quaternion integrals', *Proc. Roy. Soc. Edinb.*, **7** (1870): 318–20 (read 19 December 1870).

If σ is a vector function and if within the region $\sum$
$$S\nabla\sigma = 0^{(8)}$$
then it is possible to find a vector function τ such that within the region $\sum$, $\sigma = V\nabla\tau$.

The only case in which this is not possible is when $\sum$ is a periphractic region[9] enclosing a region $\sum'$, in which $S\nabla\sigma$ is finite for then for a closed surface within $\sum$ but surrounding this region $\sum'$

$$\iint S.Vv\sigma\,ds = M \text{ instead of } 0.$$

This is the reason why it is impossible to express τ as an integral derived from the density as the potential is derived except by some such dodge as the following.

Let $P = \dfrac{1}{r}$ be the potential of a unit at the origin, then if we make

$$F = 0$$
$$G = \frac{d}{dz}\int P\,dx = \frac{xz}{r(y^2+z^2)}$$
$$H = -\frac{d}{dy}\int P\,dx = -\frac{xy}{r(y^2+z^2)}$$

then the vector $\tau = iF + jG + kH$ is such that $V.\nabla\tau = \nabla P$.

Now what is the reason of our having to adopt such an unsymmetrical form to express a thing derived from $P = \dfrac{1}{r}$. Because though $\nabla^2 P = 0$ in the whole periphractic region surrounding the origin, $\iint SUv\nabla P\,ds$ is not zero but 4π for any closed surface surrounding the origin but $\iint SUvV\nabla\tau^{(10)}$ *must* be zero for every closed surface so that if $V\nabla\tau = \nabla P$ throughout the region $\sum$ that region

---

(8) The solenoidal condition: see the *Treatise*, **1**: 21, 28 (§20, 25) and Number 396 note (8). See also Numbers 322 note (13) and 353 note (15).

(9) See Maxwell, *Treatise*, **1**: 17 (§18); 'When a region encloses within itself other regions, it is called a Periphractic region.' J. B. Listing had used the term 'Periphraxis' in his 'Der Census räumlicher Complexe', *Abhandlung der Math. Classe der Königlichen Gesellschaft der Wissenschaften zu Göttingen*, **10** (1861): 97–182, esp. 135–6, 168–170, 182, with the same meaning: 'Eigenschaft einer Fläche oder eines Raumes, wenn sie allseitig zusammenhängen und einen Complex oder Complextheil rings umhüllen.' This definition was included by Maxwell in his transcription of the definitions of terms which Listing appended to his paper (ULC Add. MSS 7655, V, c/40).

(10) Read: $\iint SUvV\nabla\tau\,ds$. U is the 'versor': see Number 353 note (9).

cannot be periphractic enclosing the origin. There must be a discontinuity somewhere and we have chosen to make it by boring a hole along the negative part of the axis of x. Along the line it is not true that $V\nabla\tau = \nabla P$.

Of course by integrating F, G, H and taking in all the elements of mass we might concoct a value of τ more or less satisfactory, but it is simply impossible to construct τ so as to be valid for the whole region surrounding a point at which is placed a finite mass. If however there is a region $\sum'$ in which the algebraic sum of the masses is zero, then we may deal with it as with a magnet whose components of magnetization at any point are A, B, C. If we then make

$$F = \iiint \frac{C(y'-y) - B(z'-z)}{r^3} dx\, dy\, dz$$

$$G = \iiint \frac{A(z'-z) - C(x'-x)}{r^3} dx\, dy\, dz$$

$$H = \iiint \frac{B(x'-x) - A(y'-y)}{r^3} dx\, dy\, dz$$

or if

$$\tau = iF + jG + kH$$

$$\mathfrak{J} = iA + jB + kC^{(11)}$$

$$\rho' - \rho = i(x'-x) + j(y'-y) + k(z'-z)$$

$$\tau = \iiint \frac{V.\mathfrak{J}(\rho'-\rho)}{r^3}.$$

We have also

$$P = \iiint \frac{A(x'-x) + B(y'-y) + C(z'-z)}{r^3}$$

and $\quad V\nabla\tau = \nabla P.$

If within any closed surface $\nabla^2 P = 0$ then it is always possible and in one way only to find a function P' vanishing at ∞ for which, outside the surface, $\nabla^2 P = 0$ and for which, at the surface

$$SU\nu\nabla P = SU\nu\nabla P'.$$

Then if the surface is a magnetic shell of strength $P-P'$ at every point, the potentials P & P' will be those of the shell.

Also if the surface is a conducting sheet for which $P-P'$ is the stream function the magnetic potentials will still be P and P'.

---

(11) Maxwell now uses $\mathfrak{J}$ for the intensity of magnetisation. Compare Number 347 esp. note (7).

353
LETTER TO PETER GUTHRIE TAIT[1]

23 JANUARY 1871

From the original in the University Library, Cambridge[2]

| this week only |

Ardhallow
Dunoon
Jan 23 1871

D^r T'

Still harping on that Nabla?

You will find in Stokes on the Dynamical Theory of Diffraction[3] something of what you want, this at least which I quote from memory.

1 For all space – your eq^n

$$\nabla \sigma = \nabla^2 (\tau + v)$$

where σ is given and τ & v are to vanish at ∞ gives but one solution for τ and for v the first derived by integration from $V\nabla\sigma$ and the second from $S\nabla\sigma$ by the potential method and we then get the result in the form

$$\sigma = V\nabla\tau + \nabla v$$

(because as Helmholtz has shown (Wirbelbewegung) $S\nabla\tau = 0$).[4] All this is as old as 1850 at least. See Stokes.

Now we leave all space and consider a region $\sum$ within which $\nabla^2 P = 0$ and therefore ∇P has no convergence. Now if a vector function has no convergence it ought to be capable of being represented as the curl of a vector function[5] or there ought to be a vector σ such that

$$V\nabla\sigma = \nabla P.$$

The simplest case to begin with is of course the potential due to unit of mass at the origin. Find σ and τ for that case! The difficulty arises from the fact that the region in which $\nabla^2 P = 0$ is here periphractic and surrounds completely the origin where this is not true. If we draw a closed surface

---

(1) Compare Number 352.

(2) ULC Add. MSS 7655, V, b/18. Published in part in Knott, *Life of Tait*: 145–7.

(3) G. G. Stokes, 'On the dynamical theory of diffraction', *Trans. Camb. Phil. Soc.*, **9** (1849): 1–62, esp. 6–10 (= *Papers*, **2**: 243–327).

(4) Hermann Helmholtz, 'On the integrals of the hydrodynamical equations, which express vortex-motion', *Phil. Mag.*, ser. 4, **33** (1867): 485–512, esp. 495.

(5) On the terms 'convergence' and 'curl' see Numbers 346 and 347.

including the origin then

$$\iint SU\nu\nabla P\,ds = 4\pi$$

whereas $\iint SU\nu V\nabla\sigma^{(6)} = 0$, *necessarily.*[7]

Hence to make it impossible for the region Σ to include the origin we must get rid of periphraxy by drawing a line from the origin to ∞ and defining the region Σ so as not to interfere with this line.

We may then write p for $\dfrac{1}{r}$ and

$$P = -\int_0^\infty S\nabla p\,d\rho = p$$

$$\sigma = \int_0^\infty V\nabla p\,d\rho.$$

If we suppose the line to be in the axis of x this gives

$$\sigma = i(0) + j\frac{xz}{r(y^2+z^2)} - k\frac{xy}{r(y^2+z^2)}$$

an exceedingly ugly form for a thing derived from so symmetrical a beginning.

But this cannot be avoided if the algebraic sum of the masses is finite.

If it is 0 we may treat it as magnetic matter.

If in a region Σ' in which there is magnetization the intensity of magnetization be

$$\mathfrak{J} = iA + jB + kC$$

and if $p = \dfrac{1}{r}$ where r is the distance between $x\,y\,z$ and $x'y'z'$ then

$$P = \iiint \frac{A(x'-x) + B(y'-y) + C(z'-z)}{r^3}\,dx'\,dy'\,dz'$$

$$= \iiint S\mathfrak{J}\nabla p\,d\varsigma'$$

or

$$= -\iiint \frac{1}{r}\left(\frac{dA}{dx} + \frac{dB}{dy} + \frac{dC}{dz}\right)dx'\,dy'\,dz'$$

$$= -\iiint pS\nabla\mathfrak{J}\,d\varsigma'.$$

---

(6) See Number 352 note (10); and on 'Periphraxis' see Number 352 note (9).

(7) See P. G. Tait, 'On some quaternion integrals', *Proc. Roy. Soc. Edinb.*, **7** (1870): 318–20.

Also $\sigma = iF + jG + kH$

where $F = \iiint \dfrac{C(y'-y) - B(z'-z)}{r^3} dx'\, dy'\, dz'$ &c

or $\sigma = \iiint V \mathfrak{J} \nabla p\, d\varsigma'.$

All this occurs in passing from the old theory of magnetism to the electromagnetic.

I have put down a lot of imitations of your jargon mainly that you may check me in any solecism. I think if you are making a new edition of 4nions [8] you should give prominence to the rules defining the extent of the application of symbols such as $V, S, T, U, K,$[9] &c which are consecrated letters, not to be used for profane purposes.

The use of dots and brackets should also be defined so as to know how far the virtue of an operator extends.

Here is another view of your case.[10]

Let S be a region within which $\nabla^2 P = 0$ and let P' be a function vanishing at ∞ and having $\nabla^2 P' = 0$ outside S & such that at the surface
$$SU\nu\nabla P = SU\nu\nabla P'.$$

It is well known that there is only one solution for P'.

Now let $P - P' = 4\pi\phi$ at the surface S.

Then $P = \iint \dfrac{\phi}{r^3} SU\nu . r\, ds$

and $\sigma = \iint \dfrac{\phi}{r^3} VU\nu . r\, ds.$

Another expression for the components of σ is

$$F = \iint \dfrac{\phi}{r^2} dr\, dx \quad G = \iint \dfrac{\phi}{r^2} dr\, dy \quad H = \iint \dfrac{\phi}{r^2} dr\, dz$$

the integrations being taken over the surface S and the independent variables being r and *one* of the coordinates $x\ y$ or z.

What do you make of this?

---

(8) P. G. Tait, *An Elementary Treatise on Quaternions* (Oxford, 1867).

(9) V and S are the 'vector' and 'scalar' parts of a quaternion; T and U the 'tensor' ('stretching' factor) and 'versor' ('turning' factor); and Kq denotes the 'conjugate' of a quaternion q, which 'has the same tensor, plane, and angle, only the angle is taken the reverse way'. See Tait, *Quaternions*: 49, 33, 35; and see Numbers 346 note (5) and 348 note (4).

(10) See Tait, 'On some quaternion integrals': 319–20.

You say that the constituents of τ are potentials with densities $\dfrac{1}{4\pi}\dfrac{dP}{dx}$ &c. Well then take $P = \dfrac{1}{r}$ & $\dfrac{dP}{dx} = -\dfrac{x}{r^3}$ &c then the constituents of τ will be $\dfrac{1}{8\pi}\dfrac{x}{r}$ &c

or
$$8\pi\tau = i\frac{x}{r} + j\frac{y}{r} + k\frac{z}{r}$$

and
$$\nabla\tau = \frac{1}{4\pi}\frac{1}{r} = P \quad \text{a scalar.}$$

In fact whatever scalar form P be if $\nabla^2\tau = \nabla P$ $\nabla\tau = P$ a pure scalar.[11] Multiply this by $d\rho$ (a pure vector) and you get a pure vector $d\rho\,\nabla\tau = d\rho\,P$. Hence your expression[12]

$$S\int V(d\rho\,\nabla)\,\tau = S\int d\rho\,P = 0$$

because if it is anything it is the integral of a vector multiplied by a scalar and that is a pure vector and the scalar part of it is 0.

I suppose this is nonsense arising from our being barbarians to one another. Will you therefore be so kind as to give me a code by which I may interpret the symbols $V\,d\rho\,\nabla$ that is to say, tell me what these symbols, thus arranged, ask me to do.

Helmholtz as you will see goes in for

$$\nabla^2\Psi = -2\frac{dP}{dt}$$

where P is the electrostatic potential. [13]

---

(11) In his reply dated 1 February 1871 Tait wrote: 'Dr J. C. M. [= dp/dt (T's Thermodyn^{cs} §162)] / You say – "of whatever scalar form P be, if $\nabla^2\tau = \nabla P$, then $\nabla\tau = P$." I fear not, and with this falls your inferences. Would it were so simple! But in reality it leads $S.\nabla\tau = 0$. / Try your hand at *this*. If $U\nu$ be the unit normal vector at any point of a non-closed surface, and σ any vector, $\iint V.U.\nu\nabla^2\sigma ds = \int V(\nabla d\rho\nabla)\,\sigma$ / where the first extends over the surface, the second round its edge. When am I to see the MSS of the curls of the slopes &c &c. Y^{rs} ℊ.' (ULC Add. MSS 7655, I, a/7). For Maxwell's thermodynamic signature $dp/dt = $ J.C.M. see Number 339 note (16). The example Tait gives Maxwell is discussed in his 'On some quaternion integrals': 320, and for Maxwell's reply see Number 356. Tait's signature ℊ is a compact monogram giving all three initials P.G.T.; see Knott, *Life of Tait*: 92n.

(12) Tait, 'On some quaternion integrals': 320.

(13) Hermann Helmholtz, 'Ueber die Bewegungsgleichungen der Elektricität für ruhende leitende Körper', *Journal für die reine und angewandte Mathematik*, **72** (1870): 57–128, esp. 79, where Ψ is the potential of dP/dt. Maxwell made notes on Helmholtz's paper (ULC Add. MSS 7655, V, c/23), noting this expression.

Note – the vector σ as determined above is such that $S\nabla\sigma = 0$ so that we may truly say $\nabla\sigma = \nabla P$.

In electromagnetism P is the magnetic potential and ∇P is the magnetic force outside the magnet or inside it in a hollow tube whose sides are parallel to the magnetization,

$$\nabla\sigma = \nabla P \quad \text{outside but inside}$$
$$\nabla\sigma = \nabla P + 4\pi \mathfrak{J}$$

where $\mathfrak{J}$ is the magnetization.[14] $\nabla\sigma$ is the magnetic force in a crevasse $\perp \mathfrak{J}$.[15]

I have not been able to make much of your τ. I coloured some diagrams of lines of force Blue & red but I must study the Astronomer to define the magnetic tints and softness. Sir W. Hamilton (Edin^h) was partial to redintegration,[16] an operation you should get a symbol for. Among other scientific expressions I would direct your attention to the salutary influence of Demon-stration and Deter-mination, and to two acids recently studied, Periodic and Gallery Thronic acids. The 1st you will find use for. The 2nd is for the Ld High Commissioner.

Yours J. C. M.

(14) See Number 352 esp. note (11).

(15) The expression above may be written $\mathfrak{B} = \mathfrak{H} + 4\pi\mathfrak{J}$ (see the *Treatise*, 2: 238 (§619)), and expresses the relation between magnetic induction ($\mathfrak{B}$) and magnetic force ($\mathfrak{H}$); see the *Treatise*, 2: 22–4 (§§397–400). Maxwell here reformulates Thomson's distinction between 'lamellar' and 'solenoidal' distributions of magnetism (see Number 322 note (13)) into a distinction between the 'flux' of magnetic induction and magnetic force. In his 'A mathematical theory of magnetism', *Phil. Trans.*, **141** (1851): 243–85, esp. 275, 277 (= *Electrostatics and Magnetism*: 340–404) Thomson had represented a solenoidal distribution of magnetism by 'the force at a point in an infinitely small crevass tangential to the lines of magnetization'; while in a lamellar distribution the magnetic force 'at a point in an infinitely small crevass perpendicular to the lines of magnetization' differs from the force in a tangential crevass by a term 'equal to the product of 4π into the intensity of the magnetization'.

(16) Sir William Hamilton, *Lectures on Metaphysics and Logic*, ed. H. L. Mansel and J. Veitch, 4 vols. (Edinburgh/London, 1859–60), **2**: 238; 'the law of Redintegration or Totality.... Those thoughts suggest each other which had previously constituted parts of the same entire or total act of cognition.'

354

REPORT ON A PAPER BY JOHN WILLIAM STRUTT ON THE THEORY OF RESONANCE

31 JANUARY 1871

From the original in private possession[1]

REPORT ON A PAPER 'ON THE THEORY OF RESONANCE' BY THE HON. J. W. STRUTT[2]

The resonators here considered are supposed to be cavities in a rigid and fixed body communicating with the atmosphere through holes or necks and the resonance is of a period such that the wave length of the sound is considerably greater than four times the greatest dimension of the cavity.

The energy of the system may be separated into the kinetic and the potential energy and in this case the kinetic energy may be regarded as residing in the air close to the hole or in the neck of the resonator while the potential energy resides in the air which fills the whole cavity.

Of course this can never be strictly true for there must be variations in the density of the air in the neck and also motion of the air in the cavity, but it may be shown that the smaller the dimensions of the cavity compared with the wave length of its resonance the more nearly may the air in the neck be regarded as moving without change of density and the air in the cavity be regarded as acting like a spring.

We have therefore two questions to study, the motion of a fluid of constant density passing from a vessel into another or into infinite space through a hole or neck the transverse dimensions of which are small compared with those of either vessel.

In this case it may be shown that the motion in the parts of the vessels distant from the neck is very small and that the whole motion depends on the variation of one variable and may be expressed in terms of the quantity of fluid which, since a given epoch has passed through the neck in the positive direction.

If this quantity be called X then the total strength of the current through the neck at a given instant is $\dot{X}$ and if there is but one neck the kinetic energy of the motion is

$$\tfrac{1}{2} A \dot{X}^2$$

---

(1) Rayleigh Papers, Terling Place, Terling, Essex.
(2) J. W. Strutt, 'On the theory of resonance', *Phil. Trans.*, **161** (1871): 77–118. The paper was received by the Royal Society on 2 July 1870 and read on 24 November 1870; see *Proc. Roy. Soc.*, **19** (1870): 106–7.

where A is a constant depending on the shape of the neck and the density of the fluid. In the generalized language of dynamics A is the Moment of Inertia of the neck or channel. The calculation of this quantity in different cases is one of the principal theoretical results of this paper.

If X represents the volume of fluid we may write

$$A = \frac{\rho}{c} \quad \text{where } \rho \text{ is the density and } c \text{ is a linear quantity.}$$ [3]

The momentum of the motion is $\frac{\rho}{c}\dot{X}$ and the force which produces it is $\frac{\rho}{c}\ddot{X}$ since c and ρ are independent of X. This quantity is simply the difference of hydrostatic pressure in the communicating vessels.

Much use is made in the paper of the analogy between the case of such a tube and that of an electrical conductor.[4] If the conductor is of the same shape as the neck and connects two large conducting bodies of the same substance then if X is the quantity of electricity which passes through the conductor $\dot{X}$ will be the strength of the current and $R\dot{X}^2$ will be the dynamical value of the heat generated by friction in unit of time. Also $R\dot{X}$ will be the difference of potentials of the two bodies. Hence cæteris paribus, c is a quantity proportional to the conductivity of the neck.

In fact in the electrical case c is the side of a cube of the same material as the conductor which has the same resistance.

In the hydrodynamical case it is the side of a cube of the same density as the fluid such that the same difference of hydrostatic pressure on two opposite sides will produce the transfer of matter through a fixed plane.[5]

It is in the calculation of this important quantity that the author in my opinion has shown the greatest ability. It is in the approximate solution of problems of which we cannot obtain an exact solution that the mathematician displays the power of judicious selection and adaptation of means to ends which he seldom is credited with by the outer world. In the present case the author has shown how to calculate two quantities one of which is certainly greater and the other certainly less than the quantity to be found and by a sufficiently careful adjustment of the conditions chosen these two quantities may be made to approximate, from opposite sides, to the true value.

As the analogy of the conductor of electricity is perfect and as the author

---

(3) The quantity c depends on the form of the necks of resonators; see Strutt, 'On the theory of resonance': 78.

(4) See Strutt, 'On the theory of resonance': 81, where the analogy is based on 'the motion of an incompressible fluid' (Maxwell's analogy: see Volume I: 337–50, 357–61).

(5) Strutt, 'On the theory of resonance': 78, 81.

has mixed the two analogous cases in his sketch I shall state his method in the electrical form.

(1) If the conductivity of any portion of a conductor is increased the conductivity of the whole is increased and if the conductivity of any portion is diminished that of the whole is diminished.

(2) If an infinitely thin sheet of any form drawn in a conductor is made perfectly conducting, the conductivity of the conductor will be increased unless the sheet coincides with an equipotential surface, in which case the conductivity of the conductor will remain the same.

Hence the true conductivity is less than that due to any arrangement of perfectly conducting sheets in the body except that in which the sheets are equipotential surfaces.

(3) If the sheet be made a perfect non-conductor it will diminish the conductivity of the body unless the sheet coincides with a surface of flow in the natural state of the body in which case it will not affect the conductivity.

If therefore we calculate the conductivity on two suppositions in the first of which a series of perfectly conducting surfaces is made to intersect the conductor while in the second the current is constrained by tubes of flow then we know that the first value is greater and the second less than the truth unless the surfaces and tubes are chosen to coincide with the equipotential surfaces and lines of flow.[6]

The nearer the forms of the surfaces are to these forms the nearer will the two values approach the truth and since the truth is a minimum of the first value and a maximum of the second small variations in the forms of the surfaces will not affect it.

If F is the function which is constant for each perfectly conducting surface and V its potential then the distance between two consecutive surfaces is $-\dfrac{dF}{\nabla F}$ where $\nabla = i\dfrac{d}{dx} + j\dfrac{d}{dy} + k\dfrac{d}{dz}$ [7] and the total current is

$$C = \iint \nabla F \, dS \cdot \dfrac{dV}{dF}$$

where dS is an element of the surface $F = $ const and the integration is extended over the whole of this surface which belongs to the conductor.

Hence
$$\dfrac{V}{C} = \int \dfrac{dF}{\iint \nabla F \, dS} \quad (8)$$

---

(6) Strutt, 'On the theory of resonance': 98–110. On his use of extremal conditions see Number 355 note (3).

(7) See Number 346 esp. note (2).   (8) See Strutt, 'On the theory of resonance': 109.

and $\frac{V}{C}$ is the resistance of the conductor $\frac{C}{V}$ being the conductivity. The value of the conductivity thus found is certainly not smaller than the truth.[9]

Next let two systems of surfaces of flow ψ_1 and ψ_2 be drawn in the conductor so as to guide the current in lines not differing much from the true lines of flow. If dC be the current flowing in the tube formed by the interaction of $\psi_1, \psi_2\ \psi_1+d\psi_1, \psi_2+d\psi_2$ the intensity of the current is given in velocity and direction by the quaternion expression

$$\frac{dC}{d\psi_1 d\psi_2} V(\nabla\psi_1 \nabla\psi_2)$$

(where V denotes the operation of finding the vector of the product which follows).[10]

The resistance of the tube is

$$\frac{1}{d\psi_1 d\psi_2}\int ds\, V(\nabla\psi_1 \nabla\psi_2)$$

where ds is an element of the length of the tube.

The conductivity of the conductor formed of the system of tubes is

$$\iint \frac{d\psi_1 d\psi_2}{\int ds\, V(\nabla\psi_1 \nabla\psi_2)}$$

and this is certainly not greater than the true conductivity.

In the case of figures of revolution we put $\psi_2 = \phi$ the angle measured round the axis and the result becomes that in the paper.

The application of this method to finding quantities respectively greater and less than the conductivity of a conductor in the form of a figure of revolution whose sides are inclined to the axis at an angle which never becomes great is one of the most important results of the paper.[11]

The determination of the correction where the section suddenly becomes very great is also important.

In the calculation of this correction the investigation of the potential on itself, of a disk whose density is $1 + \mu r^2$ where r is the distance from the centre might I think be simplified thus.[12]

Begin by finding the potential at the edge of such a disk of radius a. Take

---

(9) Compare the *Treatise*, **1**: 353–6 (§306), where Maxwell acknowledges his use of Strutt's method.   (10) See Numbers 346 and 347.

(11) Strutt, 'On the theory of resonance': 108–10.

(12) Strutt added a footnote incorporating Maxwell's discussion of this case; see 'On the theory of resonance': 102–3n.

polar coordinates (ρ, θ) the pole being at the edge, then
$$r^2 = \rho^2 - 2\rho a \cos\theta + a^2$$
and
$$V = \iint (1+\mu)(\rho^2 - 2\rho a \cos\theta + a^2)\, d\theta\, dr$$
the limits of r being 0 and $2a\cos\theta$ and those of θ $-\dfrac{\pi}{2}$ and $+\dfrac{\pi}{2}$.

We get at once
$$V = 4a + \frac{20}{9}\mu a^3.$$

Now let us cut off a strip of breadth da from the edge of this disk.
The mass of this strip is $2\pi a(1+\mu a^2)\, da$.
The work done in carrying this strip off to infinity is
$$2\pi a\, da(1+\mu a^2)\left(4a + \frac{20}{9}\mu a^3\right).$$

If we gradually pare the disk down to nothing and carry all the parings to ∞ we find for the total work by integrating with respect to a from a to 0
$$\frac{8\pi}{3}\left(a^3 + \frac{14}{15}\mu a^5 + \frac{5}{21}\mu^2 a^7\right).$$

The potential of the disk on itself in the sense in which this expression is used in the paper is twice this quantity. I think there is less chance of numerical errors if we follow this method of calculation than in the method of the paper, especially if we wish to take in higher powers of r^2 in the expression for the density, as the path of approximation indicates.

I have spoken of these investigations as if they related to the conductivity for electricity because in the acoustical application even the accurate solution of this question is only an approximation to the truth and because in the present state of experimental science the resistance of a conductor can be determined with far greater accuracy than the pitch of a resonance. By means of mercury a conductor of uniform conductivity may be obtained of any required form and since the forms here discussed terminate in large masses, the electrodes may be made so large that no error of imperfect contact can occur.

In the experiments described, the pitch of the resonance was generally lower than that calculated.[13] Is it possible that any part of this difference is due to a yielding of the walls of the cavity.[14] When the resonator is a thin

---

(13) Strutt, 'On the theory of resonance': 110–18.

(14) In revising his paper for publication Strutt added a discussion (acknowledging Maxwell's suggestion) of the effect of deficient rigidity of the envelope, finding that this would have no sensible effect. See 'On the theory of resonance': 87–8.

glass flask the motions of the sides may be felt by the hand and the author mentions this fact. Any want of rigidity in the sides will diminish the apparent elasticity and so lower the pitch of the resonance. Of course the viscosity of the air in the neck has the same tendency but its effect is probably small.

The method adopted by the author of producing the sound independently of the resonator is better than the common method of blowing over the orifice and so introducing rapid motion probable change of temperature and certain change of density into the part of the apparatus where we have originally supposed no motion but the ebb and flow of the resonance.

When the exciting sound is produced by the voice, the resonator responds to the proper pitch and produces an effect which reacts on the voice in a more marked way than it is distinguished by the ear. See p. 7 of the experimental part.[15]

I have not read any of the works cited by the author[16] so I take his word for his originality in the acoustics and for what he has found accomplished. I think however that besides the very valuable method of approximation by two limits already mentioned the paper in its physical aspect has merits which render it suitable for the Philosophical Transactions.[17]

J. CLERK MAXWELL
31 Jan 1871

P.S. I find that if at p 27[18] instead of assuming a stream function ψ, we use this function merely to split up the conductor into tubes of flow, and then determine the conductivity of the conductor as the sum of the conductivities of the tubes, we obtain for the lower limit of the conductivity[19]

$$\frac{\pi}{\int \frac{1}{y^2}\overline{\left|\frac{dy}{dx}\right|}^2 dx} \log \left\{ \frac{1 + \int \frac{1}{y^2}\overline{\left|\frac{dy}{dx}\right|}^2 dx}{\int \frac{1}{y^2} dx} \right\}^{[20]}$$

---

(15) Strutt, 'On the theory of resonance': 112.

(16) These include Hermann Helmholtz, 'Theorie der Luftschwingungen in Röhren mit offenen Enden', *Journal für die reine und angewandte Mathematik*, **58** (1859): 1–72.

(17) In a letter to Stokes of 20 January 1871 (Royal Society, *Referees' Reports*, 7: 138) R. B. Clifton stated that: 'Mr Strutt's treatment of these questions appears to me to differ from all similar investigations which have come under my notice, and to be applicable to a more extended class of problems than that of which solutions have hitherto been attempted.'

(18) Strutt, 'On the theory of resonance': 105–6.

(19) Read: upper limit. See Number 355 esp. note (6).

(20) y is the radius of the conductor. See Strutt, 'On the theory of resonance': 105–6.

and this value, owing to there being less constraint, is a little nearer to the truth than the value in the paper, as is easily shown by expansion of the logarithm.[21]

---

(21) See Number 355.

355

LETTER TO JOHN WILLIAM STRUTT

4 FEBRUARY 1871

From the original in private possession[1]

Ardhallow
Dunoon
Feb 4 1871

Dear Strutt

Your letter was forwarded to me here and as I expected to be at home before this I put off answering till now. I shall be at Glenlair by the 8th, I expect.

Your method of determining two quantities, one of which is certainly greater and the other certainly less than the resistance is a most valuable one and as far as I know it is original.[2] I have translated it into electrical language for my book.[3]

If
$$Q_1 = \iiint \frac{1}{\alpha^2}(a^2+b^2+c^2)\,dx\,dy\,dz$$

where
$$\frac{da}{dx}+\frac{db}{dy}+\frac{dc}{dz} = 0$$

and where $\quad la+mb+nc = q$

is given for every point of a closed surface (of course with the condition $\iint q\,dS = 0$) then Q_1 is an absolute and unique minimum when

$$a = -\alpha^2\frac{dV}{dx} \quad b = -\alpha^2\frac{dV}{dy} \quad c = -\alpha^2\frac{dV}{dz}$$

where V is some function of $x\,y\,z$.[4]

---

(1) Rayleigh Papers, Terling Place, Terling, Essex.   (2) See Number 354.

(3) See the *Treatise*, **1**: 115–118 (§102), where he acknowledges Strutt's paper 'On the theory of resonance', *Phil. Trans.*, **161** (1871): 77–118 as suggesting his method. Strutt had based his theoretical argument on the treatment of extremal conditions which determine the bounding surface of fluids in Thomson and Tait, *Natural Philosophy*: 229–30, which was itself based on William Thomson's paper 'Notes on hydrodynamics. V. On the vis-viva of a liquid in motion', *Camb. & Dubl. Math. J.*, **4** (1849): 90–4 (= *Math. & Phys. Papers*, **1**: 107–12), where Thomson had applied energy conditions to the analysis of the motion of an incompressible fluid enclosed within a flexible and extensible envelope. See Number 427 note (3) and also Thomson's paper 'Theorems with reference to the solution of certain partial differential equations', *Camb. & Dubl. Math. J.*, **3** (1848): 84–7 (= *Math. & Phys. Papers*, **1**: 93–6) and the *Treatise*, **1**: 103–7 (§98) for the general statement of the theorem Maxwell terms 'Thomson's theorem', now generally known (following Riemann) as 'Dirichlet's principle'.

(4) Compare Maxwell's discussion of the 'Superior limit of the coefficients of potential' in the

If the system is so arranged that q is a linear function of some quantity C then V will also be a linear function of C and we may write $C = KV$ and $Q_1 = \frac{1}{2}CV = \frac{1}{2}KV^2$.

Now if Q_1' be a value of Q_1 found from a wrong distribution of $a\ b\ c$

$$Q_1' > Q_1 \quad \text{and} \quad K < \frac{2Q_1'}{V^2}.$$

Again if
$$Q_2 = \iiint \alpha^2 \left(\overline{\frac{dV}{dx}}^2 + \overline{\frac{dV}{dy}}^2 + \overline{\frac{dV}{dz}}^2 \right) dx\,dy\,dz$$

where V is given $= V_1$, V_2 at certain surfaces S_1, S_2 and at other points of the surface

$$l\frac{dV}{dx} + m\frac{dV}{dy} + n\frac{dV}{dz} = 0$$

Q_2 is a minimum when

$$\frac{d}{dx}\alpha^2\frac{dV}{dx} + \frac{d}{dy}\alpha^2\frac{dV}{dy} + \frac{d}{dz}\alpha^2\frac{dV}{dz} = 0.^{(5)}$$

If
$$C = \iint \alpha^2 \left(l\frac{dV}{dx} + m\frac{dV}{dy} + n\frac{dV}{dz} \right) dS_1$$
$$Q_2 = \tfrac{1}{2}\sum CV = \tfrac{1}{2}RC^2.$$

Hence if Q_2' is the result of an arbitrary form given to V

$$R < \frac{2Q_2'}{C^2}.$$

But in cases where S_1 and S_2 are the only conducting surfaces $KR = 1$ so that $R > \dfrac{V^2}{2Q_1}$.

Your value $\dfrac{1}{\pi} \int \dfrac{dx}{y^2} \left\{ 1 + \dfrac{1}{2}\overline{\dfrac{dy}{dx}}^2 \right\}^{(6)}$ may be made smaller thus.

You first cut your conductor into layers by the function $\psi^{(7)}$ and assume that the current in each layer is the same.[8] If instead of this assumption you

---

Treatise, **1**: 117 (§102), establishing the unique minimum value of the energy quantity Q within a region bounded by a surface S, the quantities a, b, c being subject to the equation of continuity, and l, m, n being the direction-cosines of the normal.

(5) Compare Maxwell's account of the 'Method of approximating to the values of coefficients of capacity, &c.' in the *Treatise*, **1**: 115 (§102).

(6) See Strutt, 'On the theory of resonance': 106. Strutt's expression for the upper limit of the conductivity; his expression for the lower limit is $\int dx/\pi y^2$, where y is the radius of the conductor.

(7) The stream function.   (8) See Strutt, 'On the theory of resonance': 104.

treat the several layers as independent conductors, having the same difference of potential at the ends you will find for the conductivity of the system

$$\frac{\pi}{\int \overline{\left|\frac{1}{y^2}\frac{dy}{dx}\right|^2} dx} \log_e \left(\frac{1 + \int \overline{\left|\frac{1}{y^2}\frac{dy}{dx}\right|^2} dx}{\int \frac{1}{y^2} dx} \right)$$

As there is less constraint here than in your supposition the conductivity is greater and the resistance less, but the resistance is still greater than the true resistance when there is no constraint.[9]

With respect to colour boxes.

I have had so much trouble with bisulphide of carbon owing to its sensitiveness to change of temperature that I will have no more to do with it.[10]

Mr Huggins showed me beautiful compound prisms by Grubb[11] which give a large field and great dispersion. If I have time I mean to try something of this kind.

Figure 355,1

The system of reflexion is very convenient with respect to compactness. It is very necessary however to be able to clean the surfaces well as the surface from which the light finally emerges is exposed to the full light which enters the box. A large lens in front of or close behind the slits would be an improvement for the reason you state. It may be made out of thick plate glass $6\frac{1}{2}$ inches aperture for 15/ at least that was the charge for one which answered me very well though not achromatic.

The only thing to be attended to about the lens near the prisms is the pair of reflected images which must be arranged so as not to be in that part of the field where the two kinds of light are in contact. If they are inconvenient you can stop them out by cutting out a card properly and setting it up in the box.

---

(9) See also Number 354. In his reply of 14 February 1871 (see Number 358 note (6)) Strutt acknowledged: 'I believe the new limit you give for the resistance of a conductor of rev^n is different from any in my paper & closer, but it is nearly a year since my paper was written so that I hardly remember.'

(10) For Maxwell's use of a carbon bisulphide prism in his 1862 colour box see Volume I: 711. These prisms were used for spectroscopy, being of great dispersive power. In his paper 'Description of a train of eleven sulphide-of-carbon prisms arranged for spectrum analysis', *Proc. Roy. Soc.*, **13** (1864): 183–5, J. P. Gassiot states a difference of refractive index for extreme spectral rays as 0.077 for carbon bisulphide as compared with 0.026 for flint glass (values cited from Brewster's *Optics*). In his reply of 14 February 1871 Strutt wrote: 'Thanks for your hints about colour boxes w^h will be very useful.... I had myself experienced the inconvenience of bisulphide of carbon.'

(11) The Dublin opticians and instrument-makers Thomas Grubb & Son; see Larmor, *Correspondence*, **1**: 203–7.

If you are quite sure of the angle of your broken mirror, you can silver one of those very obtuse prisms which are used for interference.

Silver is better than quicksilver and is not liable to go wrong. I have not tried silver as an exposed surface but only the surface of contact of silver & glass. My original slits were pieces of brass made to slide on a frame with shutters of cardboard and silk hinges behind. Of course they were often not perpendicular to the scale which was divided both above and below. My present slits are bounded by pieces of sheet brass like [Fig. 355, 4]. There are six, which slide in a broad channel in the frame. The jaws of the slits are all in one plane. I made it in card in 1853 but I despaired of getting anyone to make it in brass till 1863 when Miller who came to Becker from White of Glasgow made it very well. It was a troublesome piece of work. The adjustments can be made outside the box. For a reflecting box I would not recommend it only I should prefer the plane slips made so as not to break your nails when you try to slide them.

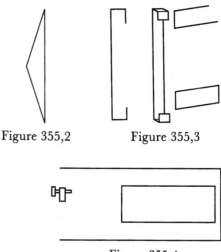

Figure 355,2   Figure 355,3

Figure 355,4

Can you compare the resonance of a hollow india rubber ball with a similar ball of glass. The want of rigidity must lower the pitch.

I have been trying large tin foot warmers and flasks with thin sides but I have nothing to compare them with except a piano which is certainly flat and the thick sided things I have tried give an uncertain answer except when made to speak themselves.[12]

Yours truly
J. CLERK MAXWELL

---

(12) In his reply of 14 February 1871 (see note (9)) Strutt responded: 'Do you refer to resonators communicating with external air by holes, or necks? I could calculate the pitch of the *inertia* if the elastic case could be neglected so that a simple relation would hold between the volume & pressure inside. / A moderator globe makes a good resonator. A piece of rubber tubing (French is best & if of suitable diam will stay in the ear without being held) forms communication between ear & interior. Covering one hole lowers pitch about a fifth. I can determine by resonance the note of almost anything down to a jam pot to about a $\frac{1}{4}$ of a semitone, but that requires practice.'

356
POSTCARD TO PETER GUTHRIE TAIT
14 FEBRUARY 1871
From the original in the University Library, Cambridge[1]

[Glenlair
Dalbeattie]

D^r T'[2] You must explain the laws of the operators V & S. I suppose $VS = 0 = SV$, $VV = 1$, $SS = 1$, ∇ is a mere operator like $\frac{d}{dx}$, of dimensions -1 in length. What is $\int V.(Vd\rho\nabla)\sigma$ compared with $\int V(d\rho.\nabla\sigma)$?

Have you been introduced to Virial and Ergal? Ergal is an old Friend = Potential of a system on itself or $\sum m_1 m_2 \phi_{12}$. Virial is

$$\sum m_1 m_2 r_{12} \frac{d\phi_{12}}{dr_{12}}.$$ [3]

He appears in $\frac{dp}{dt}$ on Reciprocal Figures &c p13 near bottom.[4]

Clausius is now working along with these eminent artistes at the 2nd law of $\Theta\Delta^{cs}$,[5] but as far as I see they have not yet furnished him with the dynamical

---

(1) ULC Add. MSS 7655, I, b/20.

(2) In reply to Tait's postcard of 1 February 1871: see Number 353 note (11).

(3) The concepts of 'virial' and 'ergal' were introduced by Rudolf Clausius in his paper 'Ueber einen auf die Wärme anwendbaren mechanischen Satz', *Ann. Phys.*, **141** (1870): 124–30; (trans.) 'On a mechanical theorem applicable to heat', *Phil. Mag.*, ser. 4, **40** (1870): 122–7. 'Virial...from the Latin word *vis* (force)' is the mean value of the magnitude $\frac{1}{2}\sum r\phi(r)$, where $\phi(r)$ is the force between two mass points at a distance r. Clausius terms the 'magnitude whose differential represents the negative value of the work, from the Greek word ἔργον (work), the *ergal* of the system'. He concludes that: '(1) the sum of the *vis viva* and the ergal is constant. (2) the mean *vis viva* is equal to the virial.'

(4) On Maxwell's signature dp/dt see Number 339 note (17). He is referring to his paper 'On reciprocal figures, frames, and diagrams of forces', *Trans. Roy. Soc. Edinb.*, **26** (1870): 1–40, esp. 13 (= *Scientific Papers*, **2**: 175–6); 'Theorem. In any system of points in equilibrium in a plane under the action of repulsions and attractions, the sum of the products of each attraction multiplied by the distance of the points between which it acts, is equal to the sum of the products of the repulsion multiplied each by the distance of the points between which it acts.'

(5) Rudolf Clausius, 'Ueber die Zurückführung des zweiten Hauptsatzes der mechanischen Wärmetheorie auf allegemeine mechanische Principien', *Ann. Phys.*, **142** (1871): 433–61; first published in *Sitzungsberichte der Niederrheinischen Gesellschaft für Natur- und Heilkunde* (1870): 167–89.

condition of the equilibrium of temperature. This is got by the celebrated principle of Assumption and Resumption.

Pray read line 3 on opposite side after the Lion & Unicorn.[6]

$$\text{Yrs } \frac{dp}{dt}^{[7]}$$

(6) Printed on the post card under the Royal crest is the legend: 'The address only to be written on this side'. Addressing his card to Maxwell at Glenlair, Tait had added: 'Forward if necessary'. The post office had thereupon stamped 'Contrary to regulations' on the card. Tait misunderstood Maxwell's chiding: see note (7).

(7) In his reply of 17 February 1871 (ULC Add. MSS 7655, I, a/8) Tait wrote: 'D^r dp/dt. In verity $VS = 0 = SV$, but also of a truth $VV = \underline{V}$ and not $= 1$; also $SS = \underline{S}$. / $\int V(V . dp\nabla) \sigma = \int (dp \, S . \nabla \sigma - \nabla S \sigma dp)$ but our friend / $\int V(dp\nabla\sigma) = \int (dp \, S . \nabla \sigma - \nabla S \sigma dp + S(dp\nabla) \, \sigma)$. In each case ∇ applies to σ only not to dp. / Is not 'Argal' used in the preparations for the 'Burial' scene of the fiancée of the Prince of Denmark. Perhaps C. has designs extending even further than Schleswig. But whatever they are they are bosh. The true thing was given by Newton, though he didn't know it. Yours ♋. P.S. 3rd line after Unicorn was University. I fail utterly to take the joke.' On 'argal' (a corruption of 'ergo') see Shakespeare, *Hamlet*, Act V, 1:*l*. 21 (*OED*). Tait alludes to the Prussian annexation of the Danish duchies of Schleswig and Holstein.

357

DRAFT LETTER TO EDWARD WILLIAM BLORE[1]

15 FEBRUARY 1871

From the original in the University Library, Cambridge[2]

Glenlair
Dalbeattie
Feb 15 1871

My dear Blore[3]

Though I feel much interest in the proposed chair of Experimental Physics I had no intention of applying for it when I got your letter, and I have none now unless I come to see that I can do some good by it.

---

(1) Trinity 1848, Fellow 1853 (Venn).

(2) ULC Add. MSS 7655, II/39. Published (in part) in *Life of Maxwell*: 350.

(3) In a letter of 13 February 1871, addressed from Trinity College, Cambridge (ULC Add. MSS 7655, II/38A), Blore wrote: 'My dear Maxwell / Our Professorship of Experimental Physics is now founded & though the Salary is not magnificent (£500 a year) yet there is a general wish in the University that this branch of Science should be supported in a way creditable to the University. The Duke of Devonshire has undertaken the expense of the building & Apparatus, & it remains for us that we should find the Professor. Many residents of influence are desirous that you should occupy the post hoping that in your hands this University would hold a leading place in this department. It has, I believe, been ascertained that Sir W. Thomson would not accept the Professorship. I mention this in case you should wish to avoid the possibility of coming into the field against him. Should you be willing to stand, as I hope, I & many others will exert our influence to secure your election. / Believe me / Yours very truly / E. W. Blore'.

The post was advertised on 14 February 1871: 'The Vice-Chancellor hereby gives notice that the election of a Professor of Experimental Physics will take place in the Senate House on Wednesday, March 8, at One o'Clock in the Afternoon. / The Electors are the persons whose names are on the Electoral Roll of the University. / The Vice-Chancellor and Proctors will receive the votes from One to half-past Two o'Clock, when the Vice-Chancellor will declare the Election.' (ULC, CUR, 39, 33 (13); and *Cambridge University Reporter* (15 February 1871): 188).

Stokes (the Lucasian Professor) wrote to Maxwell on 16 February 1871: 'My dear Maxwell, / The election of the new physical professor is fixed for March 8. Are you coming forward? If, as I hope, you are, I think you would most likely be elected. If you are not it would be desirable to let your friends know at once that good men may not be prevented from coming forward by thinking that you are doing so. / Yours sincerely / G. G. Stokes / Pray let it be known without delay be your decision what it may. / Sir William Thomson will not come forward.' (ULC Add. MSS 7655, II/40).

In a letter of 14 February 1871 J. W. Strutt wrote to Maxwell (see Number 358 note (6)): 'When I came here last Friday I found every one talking about the new professorship and hoping that you would come. Thomson it seems has definitely declined, and there is a danger that some resident may get promises unless a proper candidate is seen in the field. There is no one here in the least fit for the post. What is wanted by most who know anything about it is not so much a lecturer as a mathematician who has actual experience in experimenting, & who might direct the

Can you tell me anything of the nature and duties of the Professor.⁽⁴⁾

Is he a University Professor or does he derive his origin from Trinity or any other College or from the Chancellor or other munificent person.

Who appoints him and is the appointment for life or during pleasure?

For how many terms a year is he expected to reside & lecture?

Are the pupils to have facilities for doing experimental work, that is to say is there to be a room where things may be kept as they are from one day to another and not be required to be cleared off at the end of the days work?

I suppose that the supply of pupils is neither encouraged nor checked by any University regulation.

Who are the other candidates?

I am sorry Sir W. Thomson has declined to stand.⁽⁵⁾ He has had practical

---

energies of the younger Fellows & bachelors into a proper channel. There must be many who w^d be willing to work under a competent man & who while learning themselves w^d materially assist him. There w^d I am told be every disposition on the part of authorities to help the new Professor. I hope you may be induced to come; if not I can't imagine who it is to be. / Do not trouble yourself to answer me about this, as I believe others have written to you about it.'

(4) In a letter of 18 February 1871 (ULC Add. MSS 7655, II/41) Stokes wrote: 'My dear Maxwell / The duties of the Professor of Experimental Physics to be appointed on March 9 are to reside 18 weeks at least in Term time in each academical year; to give at least one course of lectures in each of two terms and not fewer than 40 lectures in the year. His scheme of lectures to be subject to the approval of the board of Mathematical Studies. He is subject to the regulations of the statute for Sir Thos Adams's professorship and certain other professorships in common but this contains details which would not influence your choice. / I only returned from London in time for a late dinner so I take no time in writing to you. / The attendants at the lecture would probably consist mainly / 1. of those who take some branch of physics for one of their subjects i.e. the subjects which they "take in" for the math^l tripos when the new regulations come into force. / 2. Of Poll men who take one of these branches of physics for the subject of their "special" exam^n. / 3. Of Natural Sciences Tripos men. / One of the first duties of the new Professor [...]'. The second sheet of the letter is missing: but see Stokes' letter of 14 March 1871 (Number 358 note (11)) for his account of the duties of the professor. The terms of the professorship as stated by Stokes had been published as the 'Regulations for the Professorship of Experimental Physics', *Cambridge University Reporter* (8 February 1871): 175.

(5) For the circumstances see S. P. Thompson, *The Life of William Thomson Baron Kelvin of Largs*, 2 vols. (London, 1910), 1: 558–66. Maxwell decided to stand for election to the professorship within the week. On 23 February 1871 Stokes wrote again: 'My dear Maxwell / I am glad you have decided to come forward. / As the election rests with the electoral roll, a rather numerous body, I think it would be well that you should print a circular concerning your intention to come forward and direct it to be sent to the members of the electoral roll. If it be generally known that you stand I think it probable there will be no other candidate, but the body is rather numerous to inform otherwise than by a circular. If you have written to many perhaps they will make it sufficiently known. I will help when I return to Cambridge. / Yours sincerely / G. G. Stokes' (ULC Add. MSS 7655, II/42). On 24 February 1871 Blore issued a notice on

experience in teaching experimental work, and his experimental corps have turned out very good work.

I have no experience of this kind and I have seen very little of the somewhat similar arrangements of a class of real practical chemistry. The class of physical investigations which might be undertaken with the help of men of Cambridge education and which would be creditable to the University demand, in general, a considerable amount of dull labour which may or may not be attractive to the pupils.

Maxwell's behalf (ULC, CUR, 39, 33 (14); and *Cambridge University Reporter* (1 March 1871): 219). Maxwell was duly elected on 8 March: see the *Reporter* (15 March 1871): 247. In a letter to Stokes of 3 March 1871 (ULC Add. MSS 7656, K 173; printed in Wilson, *Stokes–Kelvin Correspondence*, **2**: 352–4), William Thomson wrote: 'I am very glad Maxwell is standing for the Professorship'.

358

LETTER TO JOHN WILLIAM STRUTT

15 MARCH 1871

From the original in private possession[1]

Glenlair
Dalbeattie
15 March 1871

I hear Monro has been corresponding with you[2] wh: is a good thing. Benson has published a *little* book called Manual of Colour (Chapman & Hall).[3] It is I think an advance on the big book.[4]

Dear Strutt

I am to lecture on colours at the Royal Institution on the 24th.[5] If you care to go and are not a member I have tickets to spare. I have been so busy with the lecture that I have fallen back with correspondence. I have yours of S. Valentine's Day.[6]

Prisms of 60° would do very well.[7] I happened to have a pair of prisms of 45° when I made a reflecting box. The only disadvantages of a large angle are greater loss of light by reflexion and narrower field of view for the same length of side of prism.

I have received your paper on sky blue.[8] For experiments of the kind mentioned there (which you do not describe)[9] I should think the simplest

---

(1) Rayleigh Papers, Terling Place, Terling, Essex.

(2) On colour vision, as Monro informed Maxwell in his letter of 3 March 1871 (see Number 359 note (2)). Monro wrote to Strutt on 5 and 27 February 1871 (Rayleigh Papers, Terling); and see J. W. Strutt, 'Some experiments on colour', *Nature*, **3** (1871): 234–7.

(3) As he informed Maxwell in a letter of 13 March 1871 (ULC Add. MSS 7655, II/43). See William Benson, *Manual of the Science of Colour* (London, 1871). See Maxwell's comments in 'On colour vision', *Proceedings of the Royal Institution*, **6** (1872): 260–71, esp. 264 (= *Scientific Papers*, **2**: 272).

(4) See Number 341 note (9). (5) See Number 360 notes (1) and (2).

(6) J. W. Strutt to Maxwell, 14 February 1871 (typed copy in the Rayleigh Papers, Terling Place; printed in R. J. Strutt, *John William Strutt, Third Baron Rayleigh* (London, 1924): 48–9), written in reply to Number 355: see Number 355 notes (9), (10) and (12), and Number 357 note (3).

(7) In response to Strutt's query in his letter of 14 February 1871: see Number 355 note (10).

(8) Strutt enclosed a copy of his paper, published in the February 1871 number of the *Philosophical Magazine*, with his letter of 14 February 1871; see J. W. Strutt, 'On the light from the sky, its polarization and colour', *Phil. Mag.*, ser. 4, **41** (1871): 107–20. See Number 359.

(9) Strutt, 'On the light from the sky': 113–14. Strutt described his apparatus by which a 'comparison was made between sky light and that of the sun diffused through white paper', in

method would be to use the sky blue light to form a spectrum to be observed in the ordinary way and to allow the light to be compared with it (say sun light from white paper) to form a spectrum through the same slit or a continuation of it of different breadth and to polarize the white light in a plane to be varied at pleasure.

You observe both spectra through a fixed Nicols prism as analyzer and turn the polariser till you get equality of light at a particular point of the spectrum.

In this way you could analyse the blue colour of both portions of sky light that polarized in the plane of the Sun and that polarized in the perp. plane.

Of course you place your analyzer so $\langle \rangle$ with its long diameter parallel to the edges of your prisms, so as to destroy as little transmitted light as you can.

All this depends very much on the question whether you can more easily get a slit with a variable breadth capable of exact measurement or a beam of constant light polarized in a variable plane.

My eyes are almost blinded by the snow and the sun on it so that I write at random.

Many thanks for your good wishes with respect to the new professorship.[10] I always looked forward to it with much interest tempered with some anxiety when it was merely to be erected in the University. I now take your good wishes as personal to myself and my anxiety has developed into responsibility.

I hope you will be in Cambridge occasionally for it will need a good deal of effort to make Exp. Physics bite into our University system which is so continuous and complete without it.[11]

---

a supplement to his paper 'On the light from the sky, its polarization and colour', *Phil. Mag.*, ser. 4, **41** (1871): 274–9, esp. 278–9.

(10) See Strutt's letter of 14 February 1871: see Number 357 note (3).

(11) Following Maxwell's election on 8 March (see Number 357 note (5)), Stokes wrote to him on 14 March 1871 (ULC Add. MSS 7655, II/44): 'My dear Maxwell, / The principal duty, I take it, of the new professor in the first instance will be to give his advice as to the construction of the proposed physical laboratory & museum, and as to the expenditure of the sum which the University will lay out in establishing a collection of physical instruments. I take for granted that no one will expect you to lecture next Easter Term. I don't recollect whether the residence required is distributed – so much in the Mich^s term & so much in the Lent and Easter terms – or merely left personal, so much in the year, but I can ascertain when I return to Cambridge. / The Syndicate appointed to consider the site &c &c of the proposed physical laboratory has only just been appointed. I should suppose it would be generally felt that you ought to be added to it. / I am afraid you will find a good deal of difficulty in getting a house in Cambridge. The supply is hardly equal to the demand. / Yours sincerely / G. G. Stokes / I return to Cambridge this evening.' Maxwell was appointed to the Syndicate on 16 March 1871 (ULC, CUR, 39, 33 (16)).

To wrench the mind from symbols and even from experiments on paper to concrete apparatus is very trying at first, though it is quite possible to get fascinated with a course of observation as soon as we have forgotten all about the scientific part of it.

If we succeed too well, and corrupt the minds of youth, till they observe vibrations and deflexions and become Senior Op.s instead of Wranglers,[12] we may bring the whole University and all the parents about our ears.

Yours truly
J. CLERK MAXWELL

---

(12) Candidates for honours in the Mathematical Tripos were graded (in descending order) as Wranglers, Senior Optimes and Junior Optimes.

359
LETTER TO CECIL JAMES MONRO
15 MARCH 1871
From the original in the Greater London Record Office[1]

Glenlair
Dalbeattie
15 March 1871

Dear Monro[2]

I have been so busy writing a sermon on Colour and Tyndalizing my imagination up to the lecture point[3] that along with other business I have had no leisure to write to any one.

I think a good deal may be learned from the *names* of colours, not about colours, of course, but about names and I think it is remarkable that the rhematic instinct has been so much more active, at least in modern times, on the less refrangible side of primary green ($\lambda = 510 \times 10^{-9}$ mètre).[4]

I am not up in ancient colours, but my recollection of the interpretations of the lexicographers is of considerable confusion of hues between red and yellow and rather more discrimination on the blue side. Qu. If this is true, has the red sensation become better developed since those days? Benson has a new book Chapman & Hall 1871 called 'Manual of Colour'.[5]

I think it is a great improvement on the Quarto,[6] both in size and quality. It is the size of this paper I write on.

I have not asked you if you wish to go to sermon on Colour for I do not

---

(1) Greater London Record Office, Acc. 1063/2092. Previously published in *Life of Maxwell*: 379–81.

(2) In reply to Monro's letters of 3 March 1871 (Greater London Record Office, Acc. 1063/2106, 2109b, 2109c; reproduced in part in *Life of Maxwell*: 376–9), and 9 March 1871 (Greater London Record Office, Acc. 1063/2107).

(3) For his Royal Institution lecture 'On colour vision' on 24 March 1871: see Number 360 notes (1) and (2).

(4) In response to Monro's remark, in his letter of 3 March (see note (2)) on the 'insane trick of reasoning about colours *as identified by their names*'. See Monro's reply in his letter of 21 March 1871 (Number 363 notes (3) and (4)). The word 'rhematic' is defined by the *OED* as meaning 'pertaining to the formation of words', where Maxwell's usage (as quoted in the *Life of Maxwell*) is the second example quoted. The first usage cited is by Friedrich Max Müller in his essay (of 1856) on 'Comparative mythology' in his *Chips from a German Workshop*, 2 (London, 1867): 9; '[The] period to which we must assign the first beginnings of a free and simply agglutinative grammar...we call it the Rhematic Period.' In the essay on 'Comparative mythology' Max Müller outlined his theory of the origin of mythology in words originally descriptive of the sun. Maxwell was familiar with Max Müller's solar theory (see Number 449).

(5) See Number 358 note (3).   (6) See Number 341 note (9).

think the R. I. a good place to go to of nights even for strong men. I have however some tickets to spare.

The peculiarity of our space[7] is that of its three dimensions none is before or after another. As is x so is y and so is z.

If you have 4 dimensions this becomes a puzzle for first if three of them are in our space then which three. Also if we lived in space of m dimensions but were only capable of thinking n of them then 1st which n? 2nd If so things would happen requiring the rest to explain them and so we should either be stultified or made wiser.

I am quite sure that the kind of continuity which has 4 dimensions all coequal is not to be discovered by merely generalizing Cartesian space equations. (I dont mean by Cartesian space that which Spinosa worked from Extension the one essential property of matter, and Quiet the best glue to stick bodies together.)[8]

---

(7) In his letter of 3 March (see note (2)) Monro had asked: 'Could you tell me where I could find anything about geometry, of any number of dimensions more than 3, in a form intelligible to moderate capacities? Don't refer me to Helmholtz's article in the *Academy*. What stumps me is this. Take four. Is *ijkl* to be $= -1$ or not? If yes, operate upon l; the $ij k = l$, therefore *ijk* is not $= -1$ (for whatever l may be, it is not the scalar -1), therefore space of three dimensions in space of four dimensions is not *our* space of three dimensions, which they who talk, as Riemann and, more hypothetically, Helmholtz do, of our moving (in four dimensions) into regions where our space (of three dimensions) is *curved* – necessarily assume it to be. On the other hand if *ijkl* is not $= -1$, but $= -l$, (so that space of three dimensions in space of four dimensions may be our space of three dimensions, & *ijk* may be $= -1$,) then in the first place, space of three dimensions does not stand to space of four in the same relation in which space of two stands to space of three, and secondly in particular, the dimension l stands in a relation to the other three peculiar to itself. This cannot be intended by those who speak of geometry of four dimensions. / In either case there is no reason that I can see for calling it "geometry". The formal relations are not analogous; the metaphor does not hold. But *something* is meant by calling it geometry; – Riemann expressly distinguishes between the properties necessary to a multiplicity of three variables and the additional properties which belong to space. I don't know whether you will throw over Riemann; but Cayley, as I see by a recent *Nature*, speaks of geometry of m dimensions as a conception useful to aid the imagination. Very good; to this it may be no objection that space of more than three dimensions is out of all experience; but it is an objection, if the conception is not merely inexperiencible but self contradiction. Such I make it out to be as above, by an argument which at any rate imposes on myself.' (This part of Monro's letter is not reproduced in the *Life of Maxwell*: see note (2)). See Arthur Cayley, 'On abstract geometry', *Proc. Roy. Soc.*, **18** (1869): 122–3 (= *Nature*, **1** (1870): 294). Monro was referring to Helmholtz's paper on 'The axioms of geometry', *The Academy*, **1** (1870): 128–31. For Maxwell's comments on Riemann's non-Euclidean geometry see his letter to Tait of 11 November 1874 (to be published in Volume III; reproduced in facsimile in P. M. Harman, *Energy, Force and Matter* (Cambridge, 1982: 96).

(8) In a letter of 10 September 1871 (Greater London Record Office, Acc. 1063/2109a; reproduced in large part in *Life of Maxwell*: 382–3), Monro responded: 'Looking at your old

I think it was Jacob Steiner who considered the final cause of space to be the suggestion of new forms of continuity.⁽⁹⁾

I hope you will continue to trail clouds of glory after you and tropical air and be as it were a climate to yourself. I am glad to see you occasionally in Nature.⁽¹⁰⁾ I shall be in London for a few days next week, address Athenæum Club.

I think Strutt on sky blue is very good.⁽¹¹⁾ It settles Clausius vesicular theory.⁽¹²⁾

> for putting all his words together
> 'tis 3 blue beans in 1 blue bladder.
>
> Mat. Prior⁽¹³⁾

The exp. phys at Cambridge is not built yet but we are going to try.⁽¹⁴⁾

The desideratum is to set a Don and a Freshman to observe & register (say) the vibrations of a magnet together, or the Don to turn a winch & the Freshman to observe and govern him.

Yours sincerely
J. CLERK MAXWELL

letter again, I don't quite see the force of either of your objections to space of more than three dimensions. First you ask, if we can think some of the dimensions and not others, then *which*? Surely one might answer that depends, – depends namely on your circumstances, on circumstances which in your circumstances you cannot expect to judge of.... So, now, the missing dimension or dimensions, if any, might be determined by circumstances which we could not tell unless we knew all about the said dimension or dimensions. In my *ijkl* argument I fancied I had found actual contradiction in the laws of combination, but I was guilty of the old mistake of using symbols without making up my mind what they meant.'

(9) Possibly suggested by the preliminary discussion in *Jacob Steiner's Vorlesungen über synthetische Geometrie. Zweiter Teil. Die Theorie der Kegelschnitte, gestützt auf projektivische Eigenschaften*, ed. Heinrich Schröter (Leipzig, 1867): 1–3.

(10) See C. J. Monro, 'On the colour yellow', *Nature*, **3** (1871): 246.

(11) J. W. Strutt, 'On the light from the sky, its polarization and colour', *Phil. Mag.*, ser. 4, **41** (1871): 107–20, esp. 111; 'When light is scattered by particles which are very small compared with any of the wave-lengths, the ratio of the amplitudes of the vibrations of the scattered and incident light varies inversely as the square of the wave-length, and the intensity of the lights themselves as the inverse fourth power.' See Number 358.

(12) Rudolf Clausius, 'Ueber die Lichtzerstreung in der Atmosphäre und ueber die Intensität des durch die Atmosphäre reflectirten Sonnenlichts', *Ann. Phys.*, **72** (1847): 294–314; Clausius, 'Ueber die Natur derjenigen Bestandtheile der Erdatmosphäre, durch welche die Lichtreflexion in derselben bewirkt wird', *ibid.*, **76** (1849): 161–88; Clausius, 'Ueber die Blaue Farbe des Himmels und die Morgen – und Abendröthe', *ibid.*: 188–95. In the subsequently published supplement to his paper 'On the light from the sky, its polarization and colour', *Phil. Mag.*, ser. 4, **41** (1871): 274–9, Strutt critically reviewed Clausius' theory that the light of the sky was due to reflection from water bubbles.

(13) Matthew Prior, 'Alma', Canto I, *ll.* 28–9 (the 'Cambridge wits' on Aristotle).

(14) In his letter of 9 March 1871 (see note (2)) Monro had congratulated Maxwell on his appointment: 'I am very glad to see they have elected you at Cambridge.'

I shall be happy to propose you as a member of the Math Society if you agree. £1 per ann I think but I compound. I will see about the Proceedings.[15]

---

(15) In his letter of 9 March 1871 (see note (2)) Monro had asked: 'Can the outer world obtain the *Proceedings of the London Mathematical Society*? and where? & what does it cost?'. In a letter of 21 March 1871 (Greater London Record Office, Acc. 1063/2108) Monro replied: 'I think I may as well ask you to propose me, as you offer to do, as a member of the Mathematical Society: – and I hereby do ask you.' Monro was proposed for election on 13 April and elected on 11 May 1871; see *Proceedings*, **3** (1871): 233, 266.

360
DRAFTS ON COLOUR BLINDNESS[1]
circa MARCH 1871[2]
From the originals in the University Library, Cambridge[3]

[COLOUR BLINDNESS]

[1][4] But the most valuable evidence which we have as to the true nature of colour vision is furnished by the colour blind.

I have not hitherto said anything about the evidence as to colour vision given us by a very important class of witnesses – the colour blind. One of the most celebrated cases of this peculiarity of vision is that of Dr Dalton, the founder of the Atomic Theory in Chemistry. The scarlet gown, the symbol of the dignity of Doctor when conferred on him by the University of Oxford appeared to the Quaker philosopher as a sober drab. Sir John Herschel in a letter written to Dalton in 1832[5] was the first to explain the true nature of colour blindness. It arises simply from the absence of one of the three primary colour sensations. In all cases actually observed it is the sensation which we call red which is absent. The other two sensations which we call green and blue appear to be the same to the colour blind as to those who have perfect vision. Hence Sir John Herschel proposed to call the vision of such persons dichromic as dependent on two primary colours, whereas ordinary vision is trichromic, depending on three primary colours.[6] Dichromic vision is also called Daltonism from the most celebrated instance of its occurrence[7] but, the late Dr George Wilson very properly protested against such an unworthy use of Daltons name as if his most memorable characteristic had been a defect of vision. Daltonism can only mean an adherence to Dalton's atomic theory not an inability to distinguish colours.[8]

A Daltonian must be one who can see what Dalton pointed out to us about the constitution of bodies, not one who like Dalton cannot perceive Red.

---

(1) See J. Clerk Maxwell, 'On colour vision', *Proceedings of the Royal Institution of Great Britain*, **6** (1872): 260–71 (= *Scientific Papers*, **2**: 267–79).

(2) The lecture was read on 24 March 1871: see note (1) and Numbers 358 and 359.

(3) ULC Add. MSS 7655, V, b/12.

(4) Compare Maxwell, 'On colour vision': 269–70 (= *Scientific Papers*, **2**: 277–8).

(5) John Herschel to Dalton, 20 May 1833, in W. C. Henry, *Memoirs of the Life and Scientific Researches of John Dalton* (London, 1854): 25–7.

(6) See Herschel's letter to Dalton in Henry, *John Dalton*: 26; and compare Volume I: 654–6.

(7) See Volume I: 245n.

(8) George Wilson, *Researches on Colour-Blindness* (Edinburgh, 1855): 161; 'Daltonism *should* signify the Doctrine of Indivisible Chemical Atoms; and a Daltonian, a believer in such.'

[2] [...Colour blind people can perceive the extreme end of the spectrum which we call red, though it appears much][9] darker to the colour blind than to us but it is not invisible to them. Hence we are obliged to deduce the nature of the missing sensation by calculation as we cannot find any part of the spectrum which represents it.

It appears from calculation that the sensation which we must henceforth consider as the true primary red is a colour not unlike the extreme red of the spectrum but deeper in hue.

All the colours between the red end of the spectrum and primary green require the same quantity of blue to render them equivalent to the standard white as seen by the colour blind. Hence all these colours are to their eyes identical in hue, the only difference between the appearance of the different parts of this portion of the spectrum being in brightness.

If, then, we call Primary Red the sensation which we have in addition to those which are experienced by the colour blind all the colours between primary green and the extreme red of the spectrum are compounded of primary red and primary green in various proportions. The extreme red of the spectrum is itself capable of exciting the green sensation but in a very small degree.

It is probable therefore that by gazing for some time at a green light and then suddenly turning our eyes to the red of the spectrum beyond C we shall experience a sensation which is almost exactly the primary red.[10]

---

(9) As in Maxwell, 'On colour vision': 269 (= *Scientific Papers*, **2**: 277).
(10) Compare Maxwell's discussion of colour blindness in 1860; see Volume I: 649–56.

361

FROM A LETTER TO KATHERINE MARY CLERK MAXWELL

20 MARCH 1871

From Campbell and Garnett, *Life of Maxwell*[1]

[London]
20 March 1871

There are two parties about the professorship. One wants popular lectures, and the other cares more for experimental work. I think there should be a gradation – popular lectures and rough experiments for the masses; real experiments for real students; and laborious experiments for first-rate men like Trotter[2] and Stuart[3] and Strutt.[4]

---

(1) *Life of Maxwell*: 381.

(2) Coutts Trotter, Trinity 1855, Fellow 1861, College Lecturer in Physics 1869–84; his career was devoted to University administration (Venn). See his letter to Maxwell of 20 April [1871] (ULC Add. MSS 7655, II/46) on R. B. Clifton's Oxford physical laboratory, and on the Syndicate appointed to oversee the construction of the Cambridge laboratory (see Number 358 note (11)). Trotter informed Maxwell: 'I have just returned from Oxford. Clifton's building seems to me as far as I can judge very convenient.... There is no doubt much to be said for natural selection but will not the struggle for existence between the men who want their rooms darkened and the men who want their rooms light the men who want to move about magnets and the men who want to observe galvanometers be unduly severe. Anent architects... I hope it will not be a great swell from London, there is I take it no one who is likely to have the faintest idea of what is wanted from a physical laboratory and the only chance of a convenient building seems to be the getting of some one who will not be above taking hints as to the arrangements....'.

(3) James Stuart, Trinity 1862, Professor of Mechanism 1875 (Venn).

(4) See Number 358.

362

LETTER TO WILLIAM THOMSON

21 MARCH 1871

From the original in the University Library, Cambridge[1]

Athenæum
21 March 1871

Dear Thomson[a]

Thanks for your card. I must put Tait right. His modesty is such that he speaks as a mere mouthpiece of Hamilton when the inspiration, if any, is of the kind which allows the almost immodified manifestation of the personality of the writer.[2]

I am going to Cambridge on Saturday to discuss the Adams prize subjects and I believe you are to set some.[3] Can you inspire me a little if you are not to be there yourself so as to get a physical subject this time.[4] We had the

---

(a) {Thomson} Please return to Sir W. Thomson The College Glasgow.[5]

(1) ULC Add. MSS 7655, II/45. Previously published in A. T. Fuller, 'James Clerk Maxwell's Cambridge manuscripts: extracts relating to control and stability – VI', *International Journal of Control*, **43** (1986): 1135–68, esp. 1164–5.

(2) See also Number 349.

(3) The 'Book of Minutes relating to the Adams Prize, kept by the Plumian Professor [James Challis]' records that: 'At the congregation on Thursday March 16th, 1871, Sir William Thomson, LL.D., of St. Peter's College, on the nomination of St. Peter's College, and Professor J. Clerk Maxwell of Trinity College, on the nomination of Trinity College were appointed examiners for the Adams Prize to be adjudged in 1873.' (Cambridge Observatory Archive).

(4) The 'Book of Minutes' (see note (3)) records: '1871 March 27, the following Adams Prize subject, to be adjudged in 1873 was agreed upon: / *A Dissertation on the effect of the Tides in altering the length of the day.* / ** it is required that the amount of alteration be connected, at least by approximate considerations, with quantities known by observation or experiment, and that an attempt be made to calculate it strictly either by employing directly the general equations of Hydrodynamics, or by assuming the height and time of Tide all over the earth to be known. The dissertation may include a discussion of the evidence of a retardation of the earth's rotation derived from astronomical theory and observation. / (The meeting was held at Pembroke College Lodge, and was attended by Profrs. Challis & Maxwell. Profr. Sir William Thomson was not present, but had signified his assent to the choice of subject.)' A subsequent undated note records that: 'No exercises were sent in for the Prize to be adjudged in 1873.' The determination of the tidal retardation of the earth's rotation had been discussed by Thomson in his 1866 Rede Lecture at Cambridge; see his paper 'On the observations and calculations required to find the tidal retardation of the earth's rotation', *Phil. Mag.*, ser. 4, **31** (1866): 533–7 (= *Math. & Phys. Papers,* **3**: 337–41). Thomson was currently a member of the British Association Committee on tidal observations; see S. P. Thompson, *The Life of William Thomson, Baron Kelvin of Largs*, 2 vols. (London, 1910), **1**: 581; **2**: 611, 619.

(5) Thomson probably forwarded Maxwell's letter to Challis for consideration at the meeting

Calculus of Variations last time.⁽⁶⁾ One essay is in 5 vols quarto, not unintelligible and very elaborate but has no examples of the kind of discontinuity which first occurred to me. eg Suppose the velocity of travelling up a road is some power of the cosine of the inclination, make the quickest road to the top of a hemispherical hill.⁽⁷⁾ Here the result (a pure diff calc affair) is a road of constant slope till the slope of the hill is equal to that slope and then an arc of a great arch to the top. The reason is that the three roots of an equation coalesce and the line of slope from being a line of maximum slowness of ascent becomes a line of maximum speed.

I believe you have a question about stability. Here was the form in which I put it before but if we can fuse any good points together I think it will be carried.

In the motion of a connected system a particular case is defined by the eq^{ns}

$$F_1 = \text{const} \quad F_2 = \text{const} \quad \&c$$

F_1 F_2 being functions of the variable coordinates. If this motion receives a slight instantaneous disturbance determine the character and periodicity (if periodic) of the subsequent motion discussing the properties of dynamical stability and the relations of kinetic foci by means of well chosen examples of progressive complexity.

---

of the Adams Prize examiners on Monday 27 March: see note (4). The parts of the letter not concerned with Adams Prize problems have a line drawn through them by Thomson.

(6) Maxwell was currently serving as an examiner for the Adams Prize for 1871; see his letter to Stokes of 11 January 1871 (Number 351, esp. note (2)).

(7) There is a draft of the problem in a notebook (ULC Add. MSS 7655, V, k/9, f. 21ᵛ). This draft may be dated (see Number 300 esp. note (3)) probably to summer 1868: 'If the velocity of a carriage is proportional to the nth power of the cosine of the inclination of the road determine the angle of quickest ascent and show that the road of quickest ascent up a hemispherical hill consists of an epicycloid and an arc of a great circle. If $\tan \alpha = \sqrt{\dfrac{1}{n}}$ the epicycloid is formed by a great circle rolling on a circle rad α.' Maxwell subsequently set the problem for the 1873 Mathematical Tripos: see Number 436. In his discussion of the problem in his paper 'On a problem in the calculus of variations in which the solution is discontinuous', *Proc. Camb. Phil. Soc.*, **2** (1873): 294–5 (= *Scientific Papers*, **2**: 310), he states that the problem 'was set as an example of discontinuity introduced into a problem in a way somewhat different from any of those discussed in Mr Todhunter's essay.... In the problem now before us there is no discontinuity in the statement'. He is alluding to Isaac Todhunter, *Researches in the Calculus of Variations, principally on the Theory of Discontinuous Solutions: An Essay to which the Adams Prize was awarded in the University of Cambridge in 1871* (London 1871).

2

An exposition of the doctrine of the distribution of errors in fallible observations special attention being paid to the application of the method to determine the proper choice of the form and dimensions of apparatus and other variable magnitudes in an experiment in order to deduce from the results the least fallible value of the quantity to be determined.

3

A statement of the principles of the Calculus of Quaternions in which every operation is explained in connexion with the physical meaning of some of its applications.

4

A discussion of the cases in which theorems applicable to the space within a region bounded by a single surface of simple continuity require modification when applied to a region bounded by more than one surface or by one or more cyclic surfaces.

An exposition (consisting of explanations &c) of Maupertuis principle of Least Action and of Hamiltons principle of Varying action with examples.

Will you if you have time also give me some notion about what you think is wanted for material accommodation for exp. physics at Cambridge.[8]

Lecture room *taken for granted*.

Place to stow away apparatus d°.

Large room with tables &c for beginners at experiments, gas & water laid on &c.

A smaller place or places for advanced experimenters to work at experiments which require to be left for days or weeks standing.

A place on the ground floor with solid foundations for things requiring to be steady.

Access to the roof for atmospheric electricity.

A place with good ventilation to set up Groves or Bunsens batteries[9] without sending fumes into the apparatus.

---

(8) See also Number 364.

(9) See the *Treatise*, **1**: 326–8 (§272); and Number 289 note (12) on Grove's cell. Bunsen's cell was like Grove's, with the platinum plate replaced by porous carbon.

A good Clock in a quiet place founded on masonry, electric connexion from this to other clocks to be used in the expts and from these connexion to machines for making sparks, marks on paper, &c.

A well constructed oven, heated by gas to get up a uniform high temperature in large things.

A gas engine (if we can get it) to drive apparatus, if not, the University crew in good training in four relays of two, or two of four according to the nature of the exp^t.

We should get from the B.A. some of their apparatus for the Standard committee. In particular the spinning coil$^{(10)}$ and the great electrodynamometer.$^{(11)}$ If not we must have a large coil made and measured with the utmost precision to be used as a standard to compare others with by putting the latter inside and concentric and dividing the current till there is a null deflexion.

I shall discuss the small apparatus with you another time.

Will you send me in a week to Glenlair (after 1st April) half an ounce of the paraffin of which the sp ind capacity is 1.977$^{(12)}$ that I may find its index of refraction.$^{(13)}$ Observe 1.96 is the square of 1.4.$^{(14)}$ I suppose it is too opaque

(10) Used for experiments on standards of electrical resistance: see Number 210 note (2).

(11) Described in the *Treatise*, **2**: 330–1 (§725); and see Number 416 esp. note (3).

(12) The value for the dielectric constant of paraffin obtained by J. C. Gibson and T. Barclay, 'Measurement of specific inductive capacity of dielectrics, in the Physical Laboratory of the University of Glasgow', *Phil. Trans.*, **161** (1871): 573–83. The paper was received on 23 November 1870 and read on 2 February 1871.

(13) Maxwell mentioned this experiment – intended to test his prediction from his electromagnetic theory of light that 'the dielectric capacity of a transparent medium should be equal to the square of its index of refraction' (*Treatise*, **2**: 388 (§788)) – in his letter to Thomson of 14 April 1870 (Number 339). He had first stated this relation in his letter to Faraday of 19 October 1861 (Volume I: 686–7), and in 'On physical lines of force. Part III', *Phil. Mag.*, ser. 4, **23** (1862): 12–24, on 22–3 (= *Scientific Papers*, **1**: 500–1).

(14) In the *Treatise*, **2**: 388 (§789) he cites an experimental value of 1.422 for the index of refraction of paraffin, indicating only an approximate agreement with theory. 'At the same time, I think that the agreement of the numbers is such that if no greater discrepancy were found between the numbers derived from the optical and electrical properties of a considerable number of substances, we should be warranted in concluding that the square root of K, though it may not be the complete expression for the index of refraction, is at least the most important term in it.' Ludwig Boltzmann subsequently provided evidence for Maxwell's theoretical argument; see Boltzmann, 'Über die Verschiedenheit der Dielekricitätsconstante des krystallisirten Schwefels nach verschiedenen Richtungen', *Wiener Berichte*, **70**, Abtheilung II (1874): 342–66. See Volume I: 687n.

to make a prism of but with sodium light I expect to find its index by sticking it on the side of a prism and finding when total reflexion begins.

I am to lecture on colour on Friday at the R.I. & to rehearse tomorrow.(15)

Yours truly
J. CLERK MAXWELL

(15) Maxwell delivered his Royal Institution lecture 'On colour vision' on Friday, 24 March 1871; see Number 360 notes (1) and (2).

363

FROM A LETTER TO KATHERINE MARY CLERK MAXWELL

22 MARCH 1871

From Campbell and Garnett, *Life of Maxwell*[1]

Athenæum
22 March 1871

I also got a first-rate letter from Monro about colour, and the Arab words for it (I suppose he studied them in Algeria).[2] They call horses of a smutty yellow colour 'green'. The 'pale' horse in Revelation is generally transcribed green elsewhere, the word being applied to grass, etc.[3] But the three green things in the Arabic dictionary are 'gold, wine, and meat', which is a very hard saying.[4]

---

(1) *Life of Maxwell*: 382.

(2) C. J. Monro to Maxwell, 21 March 1871 (Greater London Record Office, Acc. 1063/2108; the main part of the letter is reproduced in *Life of Maxwell*: 381–2).

(3) Monro wrote: 'You know the 'pale' horse of the Apocalypse (vi. 8) well that is $\chi\lambda\omega\rho\acute{o}\varsigma$ which is usually 'green' you know....The Arabic for green...is akhdár...But $\chi\lambda\omega\rho\acute{o}\varsigma$ and akhdár too are certainly the colour of chlorophyll'.

(4) Monro wrote: 'according to dictionaries "the three greens" in Arabic are "gold wine and meat"...'. Compare A. I. Sabra's note on terms for 'green' in the Arabic and Latin versions of Alhazen's *Optics*. See *The Optics of Ibn Al-Haytham. Books I–III. On Direct Vision*, trans. A. I. Sabra, 2 vols. (London, 1989), **2**: 40–4, esp. 41; '*akhdar/viridis* = green. Three shades of green are mentioned: *akhdar zar'ī/viridis segetalis* = fresh green, apparently the colour of fresh vegetation...*akhdar zinjārī/viridis myrti* (*sic*) = rust-green; *akhdar fustuqī/viridis levistici* = pistachio-green.'

364

PLANS FOR THE PHYSICAL LABORATORY
circa MARCH 1871[1]

From the original in the Cavendish Laboratory[2]

PHYSICAL LABORATORY

Cast iron hollow bricks built into the walls at intervals.
Every third joist of the ceiling 3 inches deeper so as to project beyond the plaster.
No hot water pipes in the end of the building where the magnetic room is.
Windows of lecture room to the lane only.
Shutters with pasteboard pannels painted black to draw all at once.
Loft above the lecture room for diagrams &c.
All gas & water pipes to be exposed everywhere.
All cocks to be on vertical portions of the pipe.
Flues from the principal chimneys to be carried to the battery closets, the lecture table &c. Gas and water and electrodes in the lecture table to be below the level and to be covered with square brass traps.

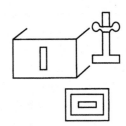

Figure 364,1

Figure 364,2

⌐ dry electrical room
  long loft in back with 2 traps.
  Clarkes Potentiometer[3]
  Microfarad.[4] ⌐

Comparator for comparing lengths.
Pair of microscopes sliding on a bar.
Dividing instrument.
Spherometer.

---

(1) See Number 365.
(2) Maxwell notebook, Museum of the Cavendish Laboratory, Cambridge (photocopy in ULC Add. MSS 7655, V, n/1).
(3) See Number 415 esp. note (5).
(4) 10^{-13} absolute units of capacity; see Fleeming Jenkin, *Electricity and Magnetism* (London, 1873): 159; and see also Numbers 415 and 420 esp. note (8).

Cathetometer.⁽⁵⁾
Theodolite.
Balance large and small standard.

Rough balances and ⊢———⊣ in every room.

Weights   British & metrical.
Astronomical Clock with electric connexions.
Common clocks in connexion in every room.
Experimental clocks in connexion.
Frame for swinging pendulums.
Vacuum case for d°.
Helmholtzs chronographic pendulum.⁽⁶⁾
Foucaults pendulum⁽⁷⁾ in Tower.
Jenkin's Governor.⁽⁸⁾
Chronograph?

---

(5) An instrument for measuring differences in level. In his note book (see note (2)) Maxwell jotted down a reference to a cathetometer described by Quincke; see G. Quincke, 'Ueber die Capillaritätsconstanten des Quecksilbers', *Ann. Phys.*, **105** (1858): 1–48, esp. 12–18 and Plate I.

(6) See Hermann Helmholtz, 'On the methods of measuring very small portions of time, and their application to physiological purposes', *Phil. Mag.*, ser. 4, **6** (1853): 313–25, esp. 315–17.

(7) Léon Foucault, 'Sur une nouvelle démonstration expérimentale du mouvement de la terre, fondée sur la fixité du plan de rotation', *Comptes Rendus*, **35** (1852): 421–4; Foucault, 'Sur les phénomènes d'orientation des corps tournant entraînés, par un axe fixe à la surface de la terre', *ibid.*: 424–7.

(8) See Number 219 esp. note (8).

365

POSTCARD TO WILLIAM THOMSON

30 MARCH 1871

From the original in the National Library of Scotland, Edinburgh[1]

[Glenlair]

What time between the 4th & 11 or outside the latter limit would do to see you in Glasgow about the Laboratory. I will send you a plan along with a paper on the size of molecules by Loschschmidt of Vienna.[2] Consider especially whether a water turbine to drive a magneto electric engine would be preferable to Grove.[a][3] I mean to have a water engine. I am to look after you and Clifton.[4] Where is Helmholtz? Berlin or Heidelberg.[5]
(Address Glenlair)

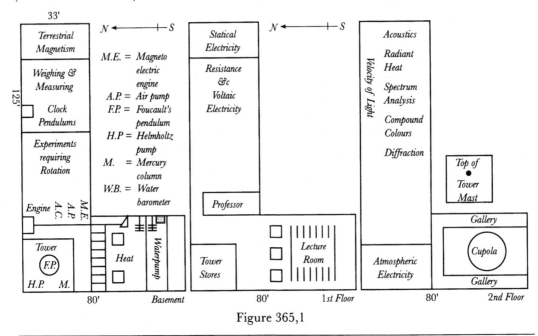

Figure 365,1

(a) {Thomson} might be so / but certainly not preferable to a Porous-cell-less Daniel[6]

(1) National Library of Scotland, MS. 1004 f. 40. Published in facsimile in C. W. F. Everitt, 'Maxwell's scientific creativity', in *Springs of Scientific Creativity: Essays on Founders of Modern Science*, ed. R. Aris, H. T. Davis and R. H. Stuewer (Minneapolis, 1983): 89.

(2) Joseph Loschmidt, 'Zur Grösse der Luftmolecüle', *Wiener Berichte*, **52**, Abtheilung II (1865): 395–413. On Thomson's interest see Number 377 esp. note (34).

(3) A Grove battery: see Number 289 note (12).

(4) Robert Bellamy Clifton, Professor of Experimental Philosophy at Oxford (Venn). A copy of the plans of the Oxford Physical Laboratory is preserved in ULC Add. MSS 7655, V, j/1.

(5) Helmholtz had accepted the professorship of physics at Berlin in December 1870; see Leo

Koenigsberger, *Hermann von Helmholtz*, 3 vols. (Braunschweig, 1902–3), **2**: 186. In answer to Maxwell's query Tait responded in a card of 31 March 1871 (ULC Add. MSS 7655, I, a/9): 'D^r dp/dt. / H^2's address is now Königinn Augusta Str. 45 Berlin. / Did you get the proofs of your book and a letter I sent to the Athenaeum? Y^{rs} ☤.' Tait refers to the proofs of Maxwell's *Theory of Heat* (London, 1871). See Numbers 366, 367, 372, 373 and 374.

(6) See Thomson's paper 'On a constant form of Daniell's battery', *Proc. Roy. Soc.*, **19** (1871): 253–9, read 19 January 1871. Maxwell describes Thomson's form of Daniell's battery in the *Treatise*, **1**: 327–8 (§272).

POSTCARD TO PETER GUTHRIE TAIT

4 APRIL 1871

From the original in the Cavendish Laboratory[1]

[Glenlair]

D^r T'. Proofs &c come to hand.[2] Corrections thankfully received and honour given to whom honour is due. But the history of

$$\iint \left\{ l\left(\frac{dZ}{dy} - \frac{dY}{dz}\right) + m\left(\frac{dX}{dz} - \frac{dZ}{dx}\right) + n\left(\frac{dY}{dx} - \frac{dX}{dy}\right) \right\} dS = \int \left(X\frac{dx}{ds} + Y\frac{dy}{ds} + Z\frac{dz}{ds} \right) ds$$

ascends (at least) to Stokes Smiths Prize paper 1854 and it was then not altogether new to yours truly.[3] Do you know its previous history? Poisson?[4] on light???[5]

Any suggestions about physical laboratories thankfully received. Present notion is – Avoid smooth plastered walls & ceilings where no wood can be found for the thread of your screw, but introduce freely wooden pillasters and beams in ceiling not plastered over.

---

(1) Museum of the Cavendish Laboratory, Cambridge (photocopy in ULC Add. MSS 7655, I, b/21).

(2) Proofs of the *Theory of Heat*: see Number 365 note (5).

(3) The terms and form in which Maxwell writes 'Stokes' theorem' follow Stokes' statement of the theorem in his Smith's Prize examination of February 1854, where Maxwell was placed equal Smith's Prizeman; see *The Cambridge University Calendar for the Year 1854* (Cambridge, 1854): 415 (= Stokes, *Papers*, **5**: 320). See also Maxwell's similar discussion of the theorem in the *Treatise*, **1**: 25–7 (§24); and compare Number 351.

(4) Theorems relating surface and volume integrals are stated by S. D. Poisson, 'Mémoire sur la théorie du magnétisme', *Mémoires de l'Académie Royale des Sciences de l'Institut de France*, **5** (1826): 247–338, esp. 294–6; in his 'Mémoire sur la théorie du magnétisme en mouvement', *ibid.*, **6** (1827): 441–570, esp. 455–8; and in his 'Mémoire sur l'équilibre et les mouvements des corps élastiques', *ibid.*, **8** (1829): 357–570, 623–7. See J. J. Cross, 'Integral theorems in Cambridge mathematical physics, 1830–55', in *Wranglers and Physicists*, ed. P. M. Harman (Manchester, 1985): 112–48, esp. 118–21.

(5) In his reply of 5 April 1871 (ULC Add. MSS 7655, I, a/10) Tait wrote: '17 Drummond place, Edin^h/O dp/dt, See above, and don't send cards meant for me to T. As to $\iint SU\nu\nabla\sigma\, ds = \int S\sigma\, d\rho$ I really thought it due to T and first published by the Archiepiscopal pair. I am glad you took my remonstrance about *my* thunder in good part as I felt some difficulty in making it – but it was for ∇ alone that I took to Q originally, and it has always been my endeavour to work it out. The paper of w^h I sent you a Proc. Abstract will contribute an immense deal more to its development. As to Laboratories, come here on y^r way from Glasgow, and you will see my poor make-shifts, and learn my *address* practically. T'.' Following Tait's statement of Stokes' theorem in quaternion form, see Maxwell's similar statement of the theorem in the *Treatise*, **1**: 28 (§25). The 'Archiepiscopal pair' were Thomson and Tait, whose names were those of the Archbishops

What about magneto electric engines as against Grove's battery?[6] There is to be a spinning room on ground floor for stirring water, spinning coils &c with driving gear & governor, and chronoscope.[7]

$$\text{Yrs } \frac{dp}{dt}$$

---

of York and Canterbury (William Thomson and Archibald Campbell Tait). On Stokes' theorem see Thomson and Tait, *Natural Philosophy*: 124, and Number 351 note (3). For Tait's 'thunder' see his cards of 1 and 17 February 1871 (Numbers 353 note (11) and 356 note (7)). The paper to which Tait alludes is his 'On some quaternion integrals', *Proc. Roy. Soc. Edinb.*, **7** (1870): 318–20; and see Numbers 352, 353 and 356 for Maxwell's discussion, and Number 362 for his comments to Thomson.

(6) See Number 365.   (7) See Number 364.

367

POSTCARD TO PETER GUTHRIE TAIT

3 MAY 1871

From the original in the University Library, Cambridge[1]

[Cambridge]

O T'. Proofs sent May^{2nd}. Pray return to Athenæum quam prox. Have you had pp. 32–48 from T yet. I want your views on it too. If you agree with pp 1–32 I shall have them printed off finally.[2] I have been at the Clarendon & they are to go a head.[3] They need to! I had no time to get to see your fixings[4] so I must conceive them in my mind till August. Clifton has had terrible work and has done it well.[5] Now he is a Plumber, now a Scene shifter and Property man, now a Bricklayer &c through all the trades mentioned by the learned Martinus Scriblerus.[6]

---

(1) ULC Add. MSS 7655, I, b/22.

(2) Proofs of the *Theory of Heat*: see Number 365 note (5).

(3) On 10 May 1871 Maxwell signed a contract with the Delegates of the Clarendon Press, Oxford (copy in ULC Add. MSS 8812/159) for the publication of the *Treatise*. He had already discussed publication with Bartholomew Price, the Secretary to the Delegates. In a letter of 4 January 1871 (ULC Add. MSS 7656, P 659) Price had stated that: 'I am pleased to hear that you are so far on with the work that we may begin printing. Our rule here is, to obtain an order from the Delegates for that purpose; and when I apply for it, as I shall do in a few days, I shall be expected to lay before them as full details as possible. Will you therefore now give me an estimate, as near as you can, of the number of pages of the book'.

(4) Tait's Edinburgh laboratory: see Number 366 note (5).

(5) See Number 365 note (4). Maxwell sketched the plan of R. B. Clifton's 'Oxford Physical Laboratory' in his notebook (Museum of the Cavendish Laboratory, Cambridge; photocopy in ULC Add. MSS 7655, V, n/1).

(6) The 'Memoirs of Martinus Scriblerus', a satirical work written mainly by John Arbuthnot, and published in the second volume of Pope's prose works in 1741.

368

POSTCARD TO PETER GUTHRIE TAIT
8 MAY 1871
From the original in the University Library, Cambridge[1]

[London]

O T′. I am desolated! I am like the Ninevites! Which is my right hand? Am I perverted?[2] a mere man in a mirror, walking in a vain show? What saith the Master of Quaternions? i to the South j to the West and k to the Heavens above. See Lectures §65 κ, τ, λ.[3] Lay hold of one of these and turn screw wise and you rotate $+$. To this agree the words of my text. But what say T and T′ §234. They are perverted. If a man at Dublin finds a watch, he lays it on the ground with its face up, and its hands go round from S to W and he says This is $+$ rotation about an axis looking upwards. If the watch goes to Edin^h or Glasgow T′ or T carefully lays it down on its face, and after observing the gold case he utters the remarkable aid to memory contained in §234 of the book.[4] Please put me out of suspense by a note to 15 Upper Baker Street, N.W. I must get hold of the Math. Society and get a consensus of the craft.[5]

Tell me order of integration too.[6]

Yrs $\frac{dp}{dt}$

a mere chest of drawers

---

(1) ULC Add. MSS 7655, I, b/23.

(2) See Numbers 370 and 371. 'Perversion' also had the meaning: 'change to error in religious belief' (*OED*).

(3) William Rowan Hamilton, *Lectures on Quaternions* (Dublin, 1853): 59 (§65); 'let i, j, k, denote three straight lines *equally long*, but differently directed; let it be also supposed that these different directions are *rectangular* each to each; and... let us conceive that these directions of i, j, k, are respectively *southward*, *westward*, and *upward* (in the present or in some other part of the northern hemisphere of the earth); so that i and j are both horizontal, but k is a vertical line.'

(4) Thomson and Tait's discussion of the direction of a couple in *Natural Philosophy*: 173 (§234); 'Hold a watch with its centre at the point of reference, and with its plane parallel to the plane of the couple. Then, according as the motion of the hands is contrary to, or along with the direction in which the couple tends to turn, draw the axis of the couple through the face or through the back of the watch. It will be found that a couple is completely represented by its axis'.

(5) See Number 370.

(6) In his reply dated 9 May 1871 (ULC Add. MSS 7655, I, a/11) Tait wrote: 'O dp/dt, the system $i = S, j = W, k = Z$ is that of H, and was of course adopted by me in Q^{ns} so as to avoid perplexing readers of H & T′. If a new ed^n be ever called for, I shall take $i = E, j = N, k = Z$ w^h is T & T′ §234. The reason for the latter is that, *from our northern latitudes*, unscrewing represents Earth's rotation & rev^n Sun's rotation & planets' rev^n &c and is therefore the *natural physical* $+$ rotation. T′ told T at the time that §234 was confusing. T answered, "all the better, it

will fix it in the reader's mind"!!! T′ did n't see it, but consented. As to $\int$, I have always done this $\int_x \int_y \int_z Q\, dx\, dy\, dz$; – but I know that many say that it is better to do $\int_z \int_y \int_x Q\, dx\, dy\, dz$. This is more matter of taste than of agreement with nature. That trout indeed is "wondrous bad" enough to drive the eater mad, For 'tis but concentrated flea – Flea – smaller animalculae. These feed on spores & deadly germs, With which their stomachs come to terms; Think Edinburgh Pharisee, How kindly such will take to thee! Y^{rs} ☊.' On Tait's *Elementary Treatise on Quaternions* see Number 370 note (3); and on 'Pharisee' see Number 371 note (8).

369

POSTCARD TO PETER GUTHRIE TAIT

11 MAY 1871

From the original in the University Library, Cambridge[1]

[London]

O T'![2] Are not Vitreous and Boreal $+^{ve}$ Resinous and Austral $-ve$. Is not from Copper to Zinc through the wire $+^{ve}$ and from the Arctic to the Antarctic regions on the earths surface $+^{ve}$ ie the line NS on a compass needle indicates the $+$ direction of magnetic force. But if a current runs round a horizontal circuit withershins, E N W S it becomes $=$ a magnetic shell austral face up, boreal down and a needle within stands $\boxed{\begin{array}{c}N\\S\end{array}}$. Hence if we draw x to E and y to N we must draw z down. If we point in succession to $x\,y$ and z we describe a cone anticlock wise. If we move along any axis and revolve positively we describe a left handed screw. The Master of the Quaternions[3] and the Censor of Space[4] are at one on this point. I am going to consult the Math. Soc. tonight.[5] Hirst's[6] notion was that of T & T'. If I am convinced I will be converted and remodel all my book and all my contrivances for remembering these directions. But it will take one or two of us to settle the hash of the M of Q. and the C of S. The new P.R.S[7] must be involved by all that is red and all that is blue. If I find a watch I will pin it to the North star and it will indicate which way the world goes round to all northerners.[8]

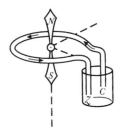

Figure 369,1

15 Upper Baker Street NW $\dfrac{dp}{dt}$

---

(1) ULC Add. MSS 7655, I, b/24.

(2) In reply to Tait's card of 9 May 1871 (Number 368 note (6)).

(3) William Rowan Hamilton: see Number 368.

(4) Johann Benedict Listing: see Number 370, a pun on his 'Census räumlicher Complexe' (1861).   (5) See Number 370.

(6) Thomas Archer Hirst, Professor of Mathematics at University College London until 1870, who had a special interest in geometry (*DNB*); see Number 370.

(7) George Biddell Airy was elected President of the Royal Society on 30 November 1871; see *Proc. Roy. Soc.*, **20** (1871): 57.

(8) In his reply of 13 May 1871 (ULC Add. MSS 7655, I, a/12) Tait wrote: 'O *dp/dt*. What saith Trigonometry (& Geometry of Two dimensions) to the point at issue? – Surely

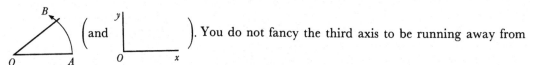. You do not fancy the third axis to be running away from you? Eh? Catton has started a *mixture* of picoline, carbolic acid &^{c} whose composition (not molecular arrangement) is that of wool, and with it he manures (guano-wise) the backs of his 70,000 sheep! We call it a farm-a-cutical process. ΛΩΦP. I have got a dodge for making a battery which can give but $\frac{1}{20}$ inch of voltaic arc give an inch of the same, and a spectroscope of perfectly unlimited dispersion made of *one* piece of glass. Also conical refractions of both kinds made a *class* experiment for 200 gaping spectators. Who is the Censor of Space? Census räumlicher Complexe? Y^{rs} ♌. P.S. For further information consult M^{rs} T' and Mrs A. C-B at the Langham next week early.' Tait is referring to the wife of Alexander Crum Brown (see Number 478 note (12)); and to the chemist Alfred Catton.

QUESTION TO THE LONDON MATHEMATICAL SOCIETY ON SPATIAL RELATIONS

11 MAY 1871

From the *Proceedings of the London Mathematical Society*[1]

Prof. Clerk Maxwell asked for information from the members as to the convention established among Mathematicians, with respect to the relation between the positive direction of motion along any axis, and the positive direction of rotation round it. In Sir W. R. Hamilton's lectures on Quaternions, the coordinate axes are drawn x to South, y to West, and z upwards.[2] The same system is adopted in Prof. Tait's Quaternions,[3] and in Listing's 'Vorstudien zur Topologie'.[4] The positive directions of translation and of rotation are thus connected in a left-handed screw, or the tendril of the hop.

On the other hand, in Thomson's and Tait's Natural Philosophy, §234, the relations are defined with reference to a watch,[5] and lead to the opposite system, symbolized by an ordinary or right-handed screw, or the tendril of the vine.[6] If the actual rotation of the earth from West to East be taken

---

(1) *Proceedings of the London Mathematical Society*, **3** (1871): 279–80.

(2) W. R. Hamilton, *Lectures on Quaternions* (Dublin, 1853): 59; see Number 368 note (3).

(3) P. G. Tait, *An Elementary Treatise on Quaternions* (Oxford, 1867): 43.

(4) Johann Benedict Listing, 'Vorstudien zur Topologie', in *Göttinger Studien. 1847. Erste Abtheilung: Mathematische und naturwissenschaftliche Abhandlungen* (Göttingen, 1847): 811–75, esp. 818.

(5) See Number 368 note (4).

(6) In the *Treatise*, **1**: 24n (§23) Maxwell notes that: 'Professor W. H. Miller has suggested to me that as the tendrils of the vine are right-handed screws and those of the hop left-handed, the two systems of relations in space might be called those of the vine and the hop respectively.' Maxwell had presumably consulted William Hallowes Miller, whose *A Treatise on Crystallography* (Cambridge, 1839) is cited by Listing in his 'Vorstudien zur Topologie': 875 with reference to a brief discussion of crystal symmetry. In his discussion of 'Helikoide oder Wendellinie', specifically of 'rechtswendig oder dexiotrop' and 'linkswendig oder laeotrop', Listing referred to the direction of tendrils in botany; see his 'Vorstudien zur Topologie': 838–50. In a report of the discussion, 'Right-handed v. left-handed', *Journal of Botany, British and Foreign*, **9** (1871): 216, Robert Tucker (Secretary of the London Mathematical Society) remarked that: '[Maxwell] refers to Linnæus ('Philosophia Botanica', 1757, p. 39), where, speaking of the trunk, he says, "Caulis...spiraliter ascendens...*Sinistrorsum* (secundum solem vulgo: Humulus, Lonicera, Tamus. *Dextrorsum*) contra motum solis vulgo: Convolvulus, Phaseolus" etc. Mr. Maxwell states also that De Candolle was the first botanist who, in 1827, has decided otherwise, and that many botanists have been led astray and perverted by him.' These comments were not included in the published report in the London Mathematical Society's *Proceedings*. The Linnæus text here cited is quoted (though with some differences in transcription) by Listing, 'Vorstudien zur Topologie':

positive, the direction of the earth's axis from South to North is positive in this system. In pure mathematics little inconvenience is felt from this want of uniformity; but in astronomy, electro-magnetics, and all physical sciences, it is of the greatest importance that one or other system should be specified and persevered in. The relation between the one system and the other is the same as that between an object and its reflected image, and the operation of passing from one to the other has been called by Listing *Perversion*.[7]

Sir W. Thomson and Dr. Hirst[8] stated the arguments in favour of the right-handed system, derived from the motion of the earth and planets and the convention that North is to be reckoned positive, and also from the practice of Mathematicians, in drawing x to the right-hand and y upwards on the plane of the black board, and z towards the spectator. No arguments in favour of the opposite system being given, the right-handed system, symbolized by a corkscrew or the tendril of the vine, was adopted by the Society.

APPENDIX: NOTE ON SPATIAL RELATIONS

11 MAY 1871

From the original in the Cavendish Laboratory[9]

System of the Vine adopted May 11, 1871, by the L.M.S.
Vitreous electricity is $+$.
Austral magnetism is $+$.

---

845. These differences suggest that Maxwell had also consulted Linnæus' *Philosophia Botanica* (Stockholm, 1751/Vienna, 1755): 39. It would seem likely that Listing's paper was also the source from which the reference to the alternative directional convention, which had been proposed by A. P. de Candolle in his *Organographie Végétale* (Paris, 1827): 156, was drawn; see Listing, 'Vorstudien zur Topologie': 848. For discussion of Maxwell's reported comment on De Candolle see H. F. Hance, 'Right-handed v. left-handed', *Journal of Botany*, **9** (1871): 333–4. In the *Treatise*, **1**: 24n (§23) Maxwell notes that: 'The system of the vine, which we adopt, is that of Linnæus, and of screw-makers in all civilized countries except Japan. De Candolle was the first who called the hop-tendril right-handed, and in this he is followed by Listing, and by most writers on the rotatory polarization of light'.

(7) Listing, 'Vorstudien zur Topologie': 830; 'so dürfte es zweckmässig sein, den Fall einer halben Umdrehung, wodurch sich zwei Dimensionen zugleich umkehren, eine *Inversion* oder *Umkehrung* schlechthin, den Fall einer einzigen Dimensionsumkehrung aber eine *Perversion* oder Verkehrung zu nennen, und im dritten Falle also, wo alle drei Dimensionen umgekehrt sind, den Körper als *verkehrt und umgekehrt zugleich* anzusehen.' See the *Treatise*, **1**: 24 (§23).

(8) See Number 369 note (6).

(9) Notebook, Museum of the Cavendish Laboratory, Cambridge (photocopy in ULC Add. MSS 7655, V, n/1).

Appendix: note on spatial relations, 11 May 1871 643

The end of a magnet which points N is +.
Terrestrial magnetic force is towards the N.
Magnetization is from the S end to the N end of magnet.
⌞internal⌟ Magnetization of the Earth is from N to South.
Electric current. Copper→wire→Zinc→acid→[10]
System of Hop in Hamiltons Lectures §65–71.

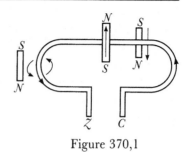

Figure 370,1

---

(10) Compare the figure in 'On physical lines of force. Part II', *Phil. Mag.*, ser. 4, **21** (1861), Plate V, Fig. 1 (= *Scientific Papers*, **1**: Plate VIII, Fig. 1, facing 488); and see Figure 385, 1.

371

POSTCARD TO PETER GUTHRIE TAIT

12 MAY 1871

From the original in the University Library, Cambridge[1]

[London]

art 23[2] In this treatise, the motions of translation along any axis and of rotation round that axis will be assumed to be of the same sign when they are related to each other in the same way as the motions of translation and rotation of a right handed screw. For instance if the actual motion of rotation of the earth from W to E is taken + the direction from the S pole to the N. pole will be taken +.

If a man walks in the positive direction, the + rotation is upwards on the left and downwards on the right.

This is the right handed definition of directions and is adopted in this treatise and in T & T'.[3] The opposite system is adopted in H and T'^{s} Q$^{s\,[4]}$ and in Listing.[5] If we confound the one with the other, every figure will become *perverted* (a phrase of L denoting an effect similar to that of reflexion in a mirror.[6] | O T' I am perverted by T & the L.M.S last night.[7] Will this do?[8] Tell me that I may print.[9]

$$\text{Y}^{rs}\ \frac{dp}{dt}$$

---

(1) ULC Add. MSS 7655, I, b/25.
(2) See the *Treatise*, **1**: 24 (§23).
(3) See Number 368 note (4).
(4) See Numbers 368 note (3) and 370 note (3).
(5) See Number 370 note (4).
(6) See Number 370 esp. note (7).
(7) See Number 370.

(8) Referring to his card of 13 May 1871 (Number 369 note (8)) in his reply of 14 May 1871 (ULC Add. MSS 7655, I, a/13), Tait there wrote: 'O dp/dt, Though I sent you a P.C. last night y^{rs} rec^d this morning induces me to send another. You are now O.K., and only for the sake of criticism do I permit myself to add the following. The words "this treatise" occur *twice*; "the (linear) direction from the S to N pole". "If a man walk (forwards) in the"..."a wheel (City Arab style) to right is +". / Happy to receive, along with so illustrious a pervert, the whole L.M.S. What a haul! Surely it will now dominate the world of math. & phys. / Have to lecture R.S.E. (is F.R.S.E. = Pharisee?) on Monday on Spectrum Analysis. *Two* carts to take batteries &c down to their rooms. Awful bore. Y^{rs} ♄'. On 15 May 1871 Tait delivered an 'Address on spectrum analysis' to the Royal Society of Edinburgh; see *Proc. Roy. Soc. Edinb.*, **7** (1871): 455–61.

(9) Maxwell took note of Tait's emendations in revising this draft of *Treatise* §23.

372

POSTCARD TO PETER GUTHRIE TAIT

25 MAY 1871

From the original in the University Library, Cambridge[1]

[London]

O T'. Can you tell me the tale of the Florentine thermometers, one of which is in your Apparatus room having glass beads for degrees? Who made them? at what date? Were any ancient observations made with them which have been translated into modern degrees since the discovery of the instrument. When were they lost? Who discovered them again & when? Who wished they had been discovered? Who gave one to the Edin^h Nat Phil. Is there anything in print about it? Information sent to $\frac{dp}{dt}$ will receive due attention.[2]

Again! Who is the author of the theorem

$$\iint S.\nabla \frac{1}{\rho} Uvds = 4\pi$$ or 0 according as a closed surface encloses the origin or not. It is Gauss or Stokes? I mean in its Cartesian form.[3]

To conclude. Is $Xdx + Ydy + Zdz$ in certain cases, a *complete, exact total* or what else? differential. Which is the correct word.[4]

Lastly I thank you and praise you for turning me from the system of the hop to that of the vine. I have perverted the whole of electromagnetics to suit.[5] When you send me my proofs I will send you correct cards of the book. But tell me about the thermometers at once if you can.

$$\frac{dp}{dt}$$

---

(1) ULC Add. MSS 7655, I, b/26. (2) For the *Theory of Heat*. See Number 374.
(3) On Gauss' theorem see Number 374, esp. note (5).
(4) Compare *Treatise*, **1**: 14 (§16), where Maxwell discusses line-integrals, and uses the word 'exact' differential.
(5) See Numbers 370 and 371.

373

POSTCARD TO PETER GUTHRIE TAIT

27 MAY 1871

From the original in the University Library, Cambridge[1]

[London]

O T'. It was you who taught me to revere the name of Jacques Alexandre César Charles.[2] Since then I have endeavored to discover his excellence. He invented the Charlière[3] and went up in it. He also wrote many papers one of these is Essai sur les moyens d'etablir entre les thermomètres une comparabilité &c 1787. Ac. Sc.[4] This is the only thermal paper of his but there is nothing in it about the laws of expansion of gases, but many other excellent obs^{ns}. I cannot find in Verdet anything about him, at least in the book I sought in,[5] so Charles must look to those laurels with which, according to the late Lord Byron, he rhymes.[6]

Well done conical refraction!![7] Carnots Geometry of Position[8] is like

---

(1) ULC Add. MSS 7655, I, b/27.

(2) See Maxwell's letter to Tait of July 1868 (Number 296 esp. note (19)); and see also Number 382 note (9). See the *Theory of Heat* (London, 1871): 29–30n.

(3) A hydrogen balloon, in which Charles ascended on 1 December 1783.

(4) J. A. C. Charles, 'Essai sur les moyens d'établir entre les thermomètres une comparabilité, sinon exacte, au moins plus approchée que celle qu'on a obtenue jusqu'a présent', *Mémoires de l'Académie Royale des Sciences* (année 1787): 567–82, a reference Maxwell recorded in a notebook (King's College London Archives, Maxwell Papers, Notebook (3)).

(5) Possibly: Émile Verdet, *Cours de Physique professé à l'École Polytechnique*, 2 vols. (Paris, 1868–9), of which there is a copy in Maxwell's library (Cavendish Laboratory, Cambridge). In his reply of 1 June 1871 Tait repeated the source he had cited in his *Sketch of Thermodynamics* for his discussion of 'Charles' law': 'O dp/dt, I sent you today your proofs with a good deal of irreverent pencil scoring thereon. Good *may* perhaps come of it, but I was toothachy & inclined to be severe. / See Note E to Verdet's "Leçons de Chimie et de Physique" apropos of Chawles. / Give me a good empirical formula for temperature along a bar when things have reached a steady state. Forbes takes $\log t = \log A + \dfrac{Bx}{1-Cx}$, but I find not this nor $t = Ae^{px} + Be^{qx}$ at all good. Y^{rs} ♄.' (ULC Add. MSS 7655, I, a/14). See 'Note E' to É. Verdet, *Théorie Mécanique de la Chaleur*, 2 vols. (Paris, 1868–72), **1**: cviii–cix, on the 'loi de Charles'. For Forbes' formula see Part II of his 'Experimental inquiry into the laws of the conduction of heat in bars, and into the conducting power of wrought iron', *Trans. Roy. Soc. Edinb.*, **24** (1865): 73–110, on 83–4. For further discussion of 'Charles' law' see Tait's card of 7 June 1871 (Number 375 note (2)).

(6) See Number 296 esp. note (21).

(7) See Tait's card of 13 May 1871 (Number 369 note (8)).

(8) L. N. M. Carnot, *Géométrie de Position* (Paris, 1803).

Chasles Superior ditto.⁽⁹⁾ Mine is that which Gauss calls Geometria Situs as opposed to G. Magnitudinis.⁽¹⁰⁾

(9) Michel Chasles, *Traité de Géométrie Supérieure* (Paris, 1852).

(10) Maxwell is alluding to Gauss' comments on 'Geometria Situs' and 'Geometria Magnitudinis' in a note published in his *Werke*, **5**: 605 (see Number 276 note (8)). The distinction is between topology and projective geometry.

374

POSTCARD TO PETER GUTHRIE TAIT

27 MAY 1871

From the original in the University Library, Cambridge[1]

[London]

O T'. Many thanks for your information &c.[2] It has been the means of giving me the chance of getting Babbages Florentine Thermometer for Cambridge.[3] NB. Libri says that Père Rinieri / Raineri / Reinerius / Renieri / Reinieri made obs^{ns} 5 times a day for 16 years with these thermometers at the convent degli Angeli. He died 1647. Hence thermometers existed in 1631. They were made by Giuseppe Moriani called 'Il Gonfia' Freezing pt. = 13°.5. Accademia del Cimento began 18 June 1657 & was suppressed in 1667. Therm found by Antinori 1829 and described by Guglielmo Brutus Icilius Timoleon Libri Carucci dalla Sommaja Ann de Ch XLV (1830).[4]

The theorem I wished a father for is that in T + T' §492.[5] I have yet to

---

(1) ULC Add. MSS 7655, I, b/28.

(2) See Number 372 for Maxwell's query about the 'Florentine thermometers'.

(3) In his first annual report on the 'Cavendish Laboratory', published in the *Cambridge University Reporter* (27 April 1875): 352–4, on 354, Maxwell recorded that a 'Thermometer found by Antinori in the repositories of the Accademia del Cimento' in Florence had been presented to the Laboratory 'by the late C. Babbage F.R.S.' In his reply to Maxwell's query, Tait may have drawn attention to Charles Babbage in connection with the Florentine thermometer. In his *Reflections on the Decline of Science in England* (London, 1830): 182, Babbage had referred to a Florentine thermometer and a paper on it by Libri (see note (4)), to which Maxwell here makes reference. A similar thermometer had been presented to the Royal Society on 3 February 1870: 'Among the Presents received was a Thermometer, presented by Mr Augustus de Morgan, which had been made in Florence in the seventeenth century. It was one of a collection discovered in the Museo Fisico of Florence in 1829, which had belonged to the Accademia del Cimento' (*Proc. Roy. Soc.*, **18** (1870): 183–4). In a manuscript jotting (Notebook, Museum of the Cavendish Laboratory, Cambridge; copy in ULC Add. MSS 7655, V, n/1) Maxwell noted that the thermometer had been 'Presented to R.S. by De Morgan Feb. 3 1870'.

(4) G. Libri, 'Mémoire sur la détermination de l'échelle du thermomètre de l'Académie del Cimento', *Ann. Chim. Phys.*, ser. 2, **45** (1830): 354–61; and compare Maxwell, *Theory of Heat* (London, 1871): 34.

(5) See Number 372, and Thomson and Tait, *Natural Philosophy*: 372 (§492); 'Let S be any closed surface, and let O be a point, either external or internal, where a mass m, of matter is collected. Let N be the component of the attraction of m in the direction of the normal drawn inwards from any point P, of S. Then, if $d\sigma$ denotes an element of S, and $\iint$ integration over the whole of it, $\iint N d\sigma = 4\pi m$, or $= 0$, according as O is internal or external.' The theorem is stated

learn the rudiments of Q^{ns}. I send you pp 1–17 to keep & pp. 65–80 to annotate.[6] I shall be at 15 Upper Baker Street till we have settled with the D. of Devonshire about our plans.[7] I am brewing details still but the principal features are now in rough plans. I mean to try and settle the Ohm again.

$$\frac{dp}{dt}$$

by C. F. Gauss in his 'Allgemeine Lehrsätze in Beziehung auf die im verkehrten Verhältnisse des Quadrats der Entfernung wirkenden Anziehungs-und Abstossungs-Kräfte', in *Resultate aus den Beobachtungen des magnetischen Vereins in Jahre 1839*, ed. C. F. Gauss and W. Weber (Leipzig, 1840): 1–51, see esp. §23; reprinted in Gauss, *Werke*, **5** (Göttingen, 1867): 197–242, esp. 225–6 for the theorem; and trans. in *Scientific Memoirs*, ed. R. Taylor, **3** (London, 1843): 153–96, esp. 180–81.

(6) Of the *Theory of Heat*.

(7) According to a letter of 1 June 1871 from the Duke of Devonshire to the Vice-Chancellor of Cambridge University, John Power (ULC, V. C. Corr. I. 2/5), Maxwell, together with the architect William Milner Fawcett and the Vice-Chancellor, was to meet the Duke at Devonshire House, London on 8 June.

375

POSTCARD TO PETER GUTHRIE TAIT

3 JUNE 1871

From the original in the University Library, Cambridge[1]

[London]

$$V = 2\pi\sigma\frac{a}{p}\Big(\Psi(a+p) - \Psi(a-p)\Big).$$

V const. for all values of p less than a. To find Ψ.

Put $\Psi(r) = Cr + \chi(r)$ then if $V = 4\pi\sigma aC$, $\chi(a+p) = \chi(a-p)$.

Since this is true for various values of a as well as of p, $(a+p)$ is independent of $(a-p)$ and $\chi(r)$ must be zero or a constant.

Hence
$$\Psi(r) = Cr + B$$
$$\Psi'(r) = C = rf(r)$$

and potential $= ef(r) = e\dfrac{C}{r}$ $\therefore C =$ unity & $V = 4\pi\sigma a$.

There are no infinite series here. On the other hand there are no excursions into the region of homogeneous solid spheres.[2]

---

(1) ULC Add. MSS 7655, I, b/29.

(2) Tait's reply of 5 June 1871 (ULC Add. MSS 7655, I, a/15) establishes the context, and reference to his paper 'On an expression for the potential of a surface-distribution, and on the operator $T\nabla = \sqrt{(d/dx)^2 + (d/dy)^2 + (d/dz)^2}$', *Proc. Roy. Soc. Edinb.*, **7** (1871): 503–6 (read 20 May 1871): 'O dp/dt Neat but *not* correct, as you will see by what follows. Let fr/r be potential function, e distance of point from centre of shell a, r the dist^{ce} of an element $(2\pi a^2\rho\,\delta a\sin\theta\,\delta\theta)$ from the point. Then $r\,dr = ae\sin\theta\,d\theta$ & potential $V = \dfrac{2\pi\rho a\,\delta a}{e}\displaystyle\int_{a-e}^{a+e} f(r)\,dr$./MULTIPLY BY e & DIFF^{te} WITH RESPECT TO IT./Then $V = 2\pi\rho a\,\delta a\,\{f(a+e) + f(a-e)\}$. Diff^{te} again $0 = f'(a-e) - f'(a-e)$. When, as a & e are independent, $f'r = C$, $fr/r = C + C'/r$. Your method gives the C' only, and is therefore obviously *incomplete*, to say the least. But what can one expect from a follower of Pratt, and a dealer in infinite series? There is no difficulty in extending the solid sphere affair to this case. Y^{rs} ୯. McVillain has refused to publish T' on Thermody^{es}. It remains for you to render it *essential* in Cambs.' In a subsequent card of 7 June 1871 (ULC Add. MSS 7655, I, a/16) Tait made further reference to the issue, and responded to a missing card of Maxwell's on 'Charles' law' (on which see Number 373 esp. note (5)): 'O dp/dt, I rel*ay* simply on Verdet's Note E, but your quotation bears me out, and I think it desirable to give G.L. merely equivalent volumes (w^h is high claim, but) which, x'cpt where you and C are concerned don't much appear in D.T.H. Many thanks for the paper from L.M.S. with its—iteration of T''s services. Surely, after such ramming, the charge must have been got home! I gave the R.S.E. at its last meeting a quat. proof of the $1/T\rho$ potential for constancy inside *any* closed surface *with proper distribution of matter thereon*. The method also shows what the proper &^{c} is. Here is a theorem w^h I beg you to ponder & report on. If $\Theta\theta = V.\eta\phi\eta$ (Θ scalar, θ & η vectors) then $H\eta = V.\theta\phi\theta$. This is easily proved. Now suppose η be

15 U B St till Θursday,⁽³⁾ then Glenlair

$\frac{dp}{dt}$

determined by $\frac{d\eta}{dt} = V.\eta\phi\eta$, is θ given by $\frac{d\theta}{dt} = V.\theta\phi\theta$? I never heard of the Dark Blue, but would be obliged to you for a perusal of the Sylvestrian Ode. Y^{rs}♋. / T went to Lisbon in the L.R. a fortnight ago. Dew in London on Friday.' In his *Theory of Heat* (London, 1871): 295–7 Maxwell gave an account of Gay-Lussac's 'law of volumes', that 'in the case of gases the volumes of the combining quantities of different gases always stand in a simple ratio to each other', and of the 'law of the equal dilatation of gases discovered by Charles'. Gay-Lussac had questioned Charles' claims (but in this was not followed by Verdet, Tait and Maxwell) in his 'Recherches sur la dilatation des gaz et des vapeurs', *Annales de Chimie*, **43** (1802): 137–75, esp. 157–8. In a notebook entry (Cavendish Laboratory, Cambridge; copy in ULC Add. MSS 7655, V, n/1) Maxwell did however transcribe Gay-Lussac's comments denying Charles' claims: 'Il me parait donc qu'on ne peut conclure de ces expériences la vraie dilatation des gaz'. The 'L.M.S.' paper Tait alludes to is Maxwell's 'On the mathematical classification of physical quantities', *Proceedings of the London Mathematical Society*, **3** (1871): 224–32, esp. 230–32 (= *Scientific Papers*, **2**: 263–6) on Tait's work on quaternions.

(3) It had been arranged that Maxwell should meet the Duke of Devonshire in London on Thursday 8 June 1871; see Number 374 note (7).

376

POSTCARD TO PETER GUTHRIE TAIT

14 JUNE 1871

From the original in the University Library, Cambridge[1]

Glenlair 14 June 1871

O T'. I send you sheet 2 to nabble at.[2] I expect a clean copy soon but I have no other at present. I also send you sheet 6 which I have not been able to correct yet, and I hope to do so in a day or two, but I am not able yet, having been at 106 °F on Sunday & in bed since. Dont be afraid of my card for I have no spots and am perfectly well today. Case of febricula, $MgSO_4$ &c. Probably from working 9 days a week in London. I think you should make a supplementary book on Quaternions explaining the true principles of dots and brackets and defining the limits of the sway of symbols as the Spaniards define the end of an interrogation or we that of a quotation. Behold the Sylvestrian Sonnet.[3]

Tasso to Eleonora

Calm, pure & mirroring the blue above
    To whom comminglingly my life's streams flow,
    Making that one which many seemed but now,
Thou art the sum and ocean of my love!
What though my soul rebellious pulses prove:
    These are the gnats that o'er the surface play,

---

(1) ULC Add. MSS 7655, I, b/30.

(2) Proofs of the *Treatise*; see Number 367. This card was written in reply to Tait's cards of 7 June 1871 (Number 375 note (2)), and of 13 June 1871 (ULC Add. MSS 7655, I, a/17) where he wrote: 'O dp/dt, I wait impatiently for a spare copy of your proof-sheet N° 2; upon which I wish to try my ∇-Math. during the vacation. The first sight I got of it led me to the theorem (of awful import) $\epsilon^{-S.\sigma\nabla}f(\rho) = f(\rho+\sigma)$. / Also $\iiint (\epsilon^{-S\sigma\nabla}-1)Qd\varsigma = -\iiint (S\sigma\nabla - \frac{1}{1.2}(S\sigma\nabla)^2 + ...)Qd\varsigma$. / Suppose the integration extended through a sphere, centre ρ & rad. r, the right side becomes $= 0 - \frac{vr^2}{10}\nabla^2 Q + \&^c$ where v is vol. of sphere. This gives your *concentration* theorem. But there are still better fish in this new sea, several of which have already risen. Y^{rs} ᛏ.' Tait discussed these quaternion theorems in his paper 'On some quaternion transformations', *Proc. Roy. Soc. Edinb.*, **7** (1871): 501–3 (read 20 May 1871). On Maxwell's 'concentration theorem' see Number 347, a result published in his essay 'On the mathematical classification of physical quantities', *Proceedings of the London Mathematical Society*, **3** (1871): 224–32, esp. 231 (= *Scientific Papers*, **2**: 264).

(3) In response to Tait's request for J. J. Sylvester's poem in his card of 7 June 1871 (Number 375 note (2)).

The fleeting colours painted on the spray;
They cannot in its depths the ocean move.
In the Elysium of thy love I dwell,
    And at its lucid fountain in thine eyes
    Immortal longings of the soul allay,
    Vainly thy pride's dissembling lips devise
How best the dear conclusion to repel,
    The silent message of those orbs unsay.

MANUSCRIPT ON THE HISTORY OF THE KINETIC THEORY OF GASES: NOTES FOR WILLIAM THOMSON[1]

circa SUMMER 1871[2]

From the original in the University Library, Glasgow[3]

KINETIC THEORY OF GASES[4]

1 Democritus see Lucretius. 2 Lucretius. α Bodies are composed of a finite number of indivisible but invisible parts. β These parts are in constant motion even when the motion of the body in mass is not perceived. γ the direction of this motion is *downward* and sensibly but not mathematically uniform. This is a strong point with Lucretius and the weak point of his theory. δ irregularity of the deflexions of the atoms introduced to account for free will &c. This is very important in T. L. Carus.

---

(1) In a post card (post mark: 'Edinburgh June 17, 71'), William Thomson wrote with reference to his forthcoming Presidential Address to the British Association; see the *Report of the Forty-first Meeting of the British Association for the Advancement of Science; held at Edinburgh in August 1871* (London, 1872): lxxxiv–cv, esp. xciii–xcv for his account of gas theory. 'O *dp.dt*. Where is the Address you undertook to write? It should be in the printers hands soon, so please don't delay longer. Send it to Athenaeum Club London posting not later than next Wednesday. It must be *complete* (for press) on Dynamical Theory of gases, Diffusion & all who worked meritoriously on it, whether experimentally or theoretically and *their merits carefully weighed*. This last is de rigeur. Include also everything that occurs to you. Don't omit H^2, on Gauss & Ampère &c. (Neumaniac anticipatory potentials may in pity be spared, but)? Weber's formulae for mutual force? Be explicit, and don't be misled by anything I have said above. If anything else occurs to you don't omit it. I am in London Wed. Thurs. & Frid. and sleep on board LR 5 nights of every week. So don't omit to keep me informed. T' joins me in the hope that the $MgSO_4$ sufficed.' Tait appended: 'After the above lucid statement of everything, I have nothing to add. My question was, If together they give a parabola, will they separately.♀' (ULC Add. MSS 7655, I, a/19). Tait's question referred to his card of 14 June 1871 on thermo-electricity: see Number 378 note (11).   (2) See note (1).

(3) Glasgow University Library, Kelvin Papers, M 23. First published by H. T. Bernstein, 'J. Clerk Maxwell on the kinetic theory of gases', *Isis*, **54** (1963): 206–15, on 210–15.

(4) In 1860 and again in 1867 Maxwell referred to his theory as 'the dynamical theory of gases'; see notes (16) and (30). For this usage see especially his letter to Stokes of 18 December 1866 (Number 266). Compare the definitions of 'dynamics' and 'kinetics' in Thomson and Tait's *Natural Philosophy*: vi; 'we employ the term *Dynamics* in its true sense as the science which treats of the action of *force*, whether it maintains relative rest, or produces acceleration of relative motion. The two corresponding divisions of Dynamics are thus conveniently entitled *Statics* and *Kinetics*.'

Lib II, 284

>Quare in seminibus quoque idem fateare necesse est
>Esse aliam præter plagas et pondera causam
>Motibus, unde hæc est nobis innata potestas:
>De nihilo quoniam fieri nil posse videmus,
>Pondus enim prohibet, ne plagis omnia fiant,
>Externa quasi vi: sed ne mens ipsa necessum
>Intestinum habeat cunctis in rebus agendis;
>Et devicta quasi cogatur ferre patique:
>*Id facit exiguum clinamen principiorum*
>*Nec regione loci certa, nec tempore certo.*[5]

3 Catena of upholders of intestine motion in hot bodies. Bacon Newton Boyle Cavendish &c.

4 Dan. Bernoulli, not very definite but stated the theory of pressure produced by impact.[6]

5 Lesage of Geneva wrote an essay Lucrèce Newtonien[7] deducing gravity from the impact of ultramundane corpuscles going *in all directions* and maintaining that if Lucretius had possessed half the mathematical skill of this contemporary Euclid of Alexandria he would have carried physical science far beyond the stage to which Newton advanced it. Lesage himself would have made a more important contribution to science, if, before calculating the results of the impact of his corpuscles, he had studied the few sentences in which Newton demonstrates the true laws of impact.

6 Pierre Prevost of Geneva (author of theory of Exchanges) published another treatise of Lesage and one of his own[8] in which he ascribes the pressure of gases to the impact of their molecules against the sides of the vessel, but introduces the ultramundane corpuscles to maintain the motion of gaseous molecules.

---

(5) *Titi Lucreti Cari De Rerum Natura Libri Sex*, ed. and trans. H. A. J. Munro, 2 vols. (Cambridge, ₂1866), **1**: 93–4 (Book II, 284–93); 'Wherefore in seeds too you must admit the same, admit that besides blows and weights there is another cause of motions, from which this power of free action has been begotten in us, since we can see that nothing can come from nothing. For weight forbids that all things be done by blows through as it were an outward force; but that the mind itself does not feel an internal necessity in all its actions and is not as it were overmastered and compelled to bear and put up with this, is caused by a minute swerving of first-beginnings at no fixed part of space and no fixed time.' (*ibid.*, **2**: 35). On the swerve of Lucretian atoms see also Numbers 257 esp. note (10), and 439 esp. note (19).

(6) Daniel Bernoulli, *Hydrodynamica, sive de Viribus et Motibus Fluidorum Commentarii* (Strasbourg, 1738): 200–2.

(7) G. L. Le Sage, 'Lucrèce Newtonien', *Nouveaux Mémoires de l'Académie des Sciences et Belles-Lettres de Berlin*, (1782): 404–32; and in Pierre Prevost, *Notice de la Vie et des Écrits de George-Louis Lesage de Genève* (Geneva, 1805): 561–604.

(8) *Deux Traités de Physique Mécanique* publiés par Pierre Prevost (Geneva/Paris, 1818).

7 Herapath in his Mathematical Physics 1847 gives still more extensive applications of the theory – to gases flowing out of small holes, diffusing through each other &c. I think the notion of temperature being as the square of the velocity is his but he makes the 'true temperature' the square root of what we call absolute temperature. This is a mere definition. He also gives −480 °F or −491 °F as the 'point of absolute cold'.[9]

It is remarkable that Lesage and Herapath should have independently fallen into similar errors about the impact of bodies,[10] these errors being I believe unknown in the text books of their day. The only source from which these errors might have been derived is the Principia of Descartes.[11]

8 Joule in 1848 calculated with great exactness the velocity of the molecules of hydrogen and subjected the theory to the test of experiment.[12]

9 In 1856 Dr Krönig directed attention to the kinetic theory of gases and showed how the gaseous laws may be deduced from the impact of perfectly elastic molecules.[13] His conceptions of the arrangements and motions of the molecules are deficient in generality.

10 The great development of the theory is due to Clausius.[14]

- α The arrangement of the molecules at any instant is perfectly general.
- β The impacts of the molecules against each other are taken fully into account.
- γ The relation between their diameter, the number in a given space and the mean length of path is determined.
- δ Mathematical methods are introduced for dealing *statistically* with immense numbers of molecules by arranging them in groups according to their directions velocities &c.

---

(9) John Herapath, *Mathematical Physics; or the Mathematical Principles of Natural Philosophy: with a Development of the Causes of Heat, Gaseous Elasticity, Gravitation, and other Great Phenomena of Nature*, 2 vols. (London, 1847), **1**: 243–5, 282–5, and 249.

(10) Herapath, *Mathematical Physics*, **1**: 8–11.

(11) René Descartes, *Principia Philosophiæ* (Amsterdam, 1644), Pars Secunda.

(12) James Prescott Joule, 'Some remarks on heat, and the constitution of elastic fluids', *Memoirs of the Literary and Philosophical Society of Manchester*, **9** (1851): 107–14 (read 3 October 1848); and in *Phil. Mag.*, ser. 4, **14** (1857): 211–16.

(13) August Krönig, 'Grundzuge einer Theorie der Gase', *Ann. Phys.*, **99** (1856): 315–22.

(14) Rudolf Clausius, 'Ueber die Art der Bewegung welche wir Wärme nennen', *Ann. Phys.*, **100** (1857): 353–80; (trans.) 'On the kind of motion which we call heat', *Phil. Mag.*, ser. 4, **14** (1857): 108–27; and Clausius, 'Ueber die mittlere Länge der Wege, welche bei der Molecularbewegung gasförmiger Körper von den einzelnen Molecülen zurückgelegt werden; nebst einigen anderen Bemerkungen über die mechanische Wärmetheorie', *Ann. Phys.*, **105** (1858): 239–58; (trans.) 'On the mean length of the paths described by the separate molecules of gaseous bodies on the occurrence of molecular motion: together with some other remarks upon the mechanical theory of heat', *Phil. Mag.*, ser. 4, **17** (1859): 81–91.

ε The slowness of diffusion is accounted for, and steps taken towards a complete theory.

ζ Theory of evaporation and maximum density of vapours.

η Theory of the change of partners among the molecules of compound bodies and the theory of electrolytic conduction under the smallest electromotive force, &c &c.[15]

θ Internal energy of molecules.

11 Maxwell 1860.[16] α Clausius assumed the velocities of the molecules equal. (This is no essential part of his theory but may be regarded as a trial assumption.) Maxwell showed that the velocities range through all values, being distributed according to the same law which prevails in the distribution of errors of observation and in general in all cases in which a general uniformity exists in the mass amidst apparent irregularity in individual cases.

β When there are two or more kinds of molecules acting on one another by impact the average *vis viva* ⌊kinetic energy⌋ of a molecule is the same whatever its mass. Hence follows the dynamical interpretation of
1 Gay Lussacs law of equivalent volumes of gases[17]
2 Dulong & Petits law of specific heats of gases.[18]
I claim N° 1 but am willing to distribute as regards N° 2.

γ Theory of Internal Friction of gases and calculation of the mean length of path of the molecules from Stokes theory[19] of Bailys pendulum expts.[20]

δ Development of Clausius theory of diffusion with errors and failures and a deduction of length of path from Grahams expts.[21]

---

(15) R. Clausius, 'Ueber die Electricitätsleitung in Elektrolyten', *Ann. Phys.*, **101** (1857): 338–60; (trans.) 'On the conduction of electricity in electrolytes', *Phil. Mag.*, ser. 4, **15** (1858): 94–109. See Number 478.

(16) J. C. Maxwell, 'Illustrations of the dynamical theory of gases', *Phil. Mag.*, ser. 4, **19** (1860): 19–32; *ibid.*, **20** (1860): 21–37 (= *Scientific Papers*, **1**: 377–409).

(17) On 'Avogadro's hypothesis' and the law of equivalent volumes see Number 259 notes (13) and (14).

(18) A. T. Petit and P. L. Dulong, 'Sur quelques points importants de la théorie de la chaleur', *Ann. Chim. Phys.*, ser. 2, **10** (1819): 395–413, esp. 405. For Maxwell's discussion of 'the law of Dulong and Petit' that 'the specific heat is inversely as the specific gravity', see his lecture to the Chemical Society of 18 February 1875, 'On the dynamical evidence of the molecular constitution of bodies', *Nature*, **11** (1875): 357–9, 374–7, esp. 375 (= *Scientific Papers*, **2**: 432).

(19) G. G. Stokes, 'On the effect of the internal friction of fluids on the motion of pendulums', *Trans. Camb. Phil. Soc.*, **9**, part 2 (1851): [8]–[106] (= *Papers*, **3**: 1–136).

(20) Francis Baily, 'On the correction of a pendulum for the reduction to a vacuum: together with remarks on some anomalies observed in pendulum experiments', *Phil. Trans.*, **122** (1832): 399–492.

(21) Thomas Graham, 'A short account of experimental researches on the diffusion of gases

ε   Theory of conduction of heat in gases, obvious, probably due to ever so many people, but comparison of conductivity of air and lead (erroneous) is my own.[22]

12   Clausius made objection N° 1 to an integration founded on his theory of uniform velocity of molecules.[23] (This is the first commitment of Clausius to such a theory.) As he was sure to be converted & I was lazy I said 0.[24] Objections N° 2 &c to theory of diffusion and conduction were well founded and in his paper on Conduction Clausius greatly advanced the methods of treatment,[25] and caused me to go through the subject still in the old style but improved.   (Not published)[26]

13   Oscar Emil Meyer made extensive experiments on internal friction[27] and in 1865 made a more extensive theory of friction of gases,[28] still on Maxwells framework.

14   Maxwell in 1865 made experiments on viscosity of gases proving that it is independent of the pressure and proportional to absolute temperature, and that the ratios of the viscosity of air, carbonic acid and hydrogen agree with those given by Graham.[29]

In 1866 he published a revised theory of gases in which the molecules are

---

through each other, and their separation by mechanical means', *Quarterley Journal of Science*, **20** (1829): 74–83. Graham's experimental data on gaseous diffusion was cited by Herapath, *Mathematical Physics*, **2**: 24–5.

(22) Maxwell had compared the conductivities of air and copper in 'Illustrations of the dynamical theory of gases. Part II', *Phil. Mag.*, **20** (1860): 32–3 (= *Scientific Papers*, **1**: 404–5), using an incorrect value for the conductivity of copper given by W. J. M. Rankine, *A Manual of the Steam Engine and other Prime Movers* (London/Glasgow, 1859): 259, which did not correctly reduce the value to English measure, and using a number which relates to one hour as the unit of time as though it was calculated for one second. He gave a corrected calculation, acknowledging Clausius' result – in his 'Ueber die Wärmeleitung gasförmiger Körper', *Ann. Phys.*, **115** (1862): 1–56, esp. 54 – that 'lead should conduct heat 1400 times better than air', in his paper 'On the dynamical theory of gases', *Phil. Trans.*, **157** (1867): 49–88, on 88 (= *Scientific Papers*, **2**: 77).

(23) Rudolf Clausius, 'On the dynamical theory of gases', *Phil. Mag.*, ser. 4, **19** (1860): 434–6.

(24) See Number 207 §4 and note (13), and Number 284.

(25) Rudolf Clausius, 'Ueber die Wärmeleitung gasförmiger Körper'; (trans.) 'On the conduction of heat by gases', *Phil. Mag.*, ser. 4, **23** (1862): 417–35, 512–34.

(26) Number 207.

(27) O. E. Meyer, 'Ueber die Reibung der Flüssigkeiten', *Ann. Phys.*, **113** (1861): 55–86, 193–228, 383–425.

(28) O. E. Meyer, 'Ueber die innere Reibung der Gase', *Ann. Phys.*, **125** (1865): 177–209, 401–20, 564–99.

(29) J. Clerk Maxwell, 'On the viscosity or internal friction of air and other gases', *Phil. Trans.*, **156** (1866): 249–68 (= *Scientific Papers*, **2**: 1–25). See Number 252.

not regarded as hard elastic spheres but as acting on one another at various distances[30] so as to produce an effect similar to that of a repulsive force varying inversely as the square[31] of the distance. Mathematical methods altered and systematized.

15   Prof. J Loschmidt of Vienna 12 Oct 1865 communicated to the Imp. Acad of Vienna a speculation on the size of the molecules of air deduced from Clausius relation between the mean path, the diameter and the number in unit of volume combined with an estimate of the volume occupied by the molecules themselves from a consideration of the volumes of various substances in the liquid state.

Diameter of a molecule of air one millionth of a millimetre.[32]

16   Stoney in 1868 independently made an estimate of the same kind founded on the same data and leading to a similar result.[33]

17   W. Thomsons stereoscopic view of the same thing from several different directions.[34]

18   Loschmidt 1870 describes expts on diffusion of pairs of gases much more accurate than those of Graham.[35]

19   Gustav Hansemann of Eupen publishes 1871 'Die Atome und ihre Bewegungen, ein Versuch Zur Verallgeimeinerung der Krönig-Clausius'schen Theorie der Gase' pp. 191 and ranging from elastic spheres to the formation of the Tast-Geschmacks-und Geruchs-Organen and general theory of life intellect and intellectual progress.[36] But I only got this as a gift from the author a week ago and I have not looked it in the mouth yet.

I hope to see & hear you at Edinburgh.[37] The printers are rather slow

---

(30) Maxwell, 'On the dynamical theory of gases', *Phil. Trans.*, **157** (1867): 49–88 (= *Scientific Papers*, **2**: 26–78). See Number 263.   (31) Read: fifth power.

(32) Joseph Loschmidt, 'Zur Grösse der Luftmolecüle', *Wiener Berichte*, **52**, Abtheilung II (1865): 395–413.

(33) George Johnstone Stoney, 'The internal motions of gases compared with the motions of waves of light', *Phil. Mag.*, ser. 4, **36** (1868): 132–41.

(34) William Thomson, 'The size of atoms', *Nature*, **1** (1870): 551–3 (= *Math. & Phys. Papers*, **5**: 289–96). See also Thomson's reference to establishing 'a definite limit for the sizes of atoms' in a letter to James Prescott Joule published in extract in *Proceedings of the Literary and Philosophical Society of Manchester*, **2** (1862): 176–8 (= *Electrostatics and Magnetism*: 317–18); and Maxwell's letter to Thomson of 17 December 1861 (Volume I: 702).

(35) Joseph Loschmidt, 'Experimental-Untersuchungen über die Diffusion von Gasen ohne poröse Scheidewände' *Wiener Berichte*, **61**, Abtheilung II (1870): 367–80; *ibid.*, **62**, Abtheilung II (1870): 468–78. See Number 470.

(36) Gustav Hansemann, *Die Atome und ihre Bewegungen. Ein Versuch zur Verallgemeinerung der Krönig-Clausius'schen Theorie der Gase* (Cologne/Leipzig, 1871).

(37) At the meeting of the British Association for the Advancement of Science; see note (1).

about Electricity and I have given up sending you proofs till you have served as an Ass.⁽³⁸⁾ Tait has been very useful about it. You should let the world know that the true source of mathematical methods applicable to physics is to be found in the Proceedings of the Edinburgh F.R.S.E.'s.

The volume- surface- and line-integrals of vectors and quaternions and their properties as in the course of being worked out by T' is worth all that is going on in other seats of learning.⁽³⁹⁾

Have you got anything about Sir B. Brodie⁽⁴⁰⁾ or do you leave that to the Chemists?⁽⁴¹⁾ They have no right to it. Did you get my letters and proofs at the Athenæum? I want to know if I may publish Ts theorem as I have printed it.⁽⁴²⁾

Yours $\frac{dp}{dt}$

---

(38) See note (1).

(39) Especially: P. G. Tait, 'On Green's and other allied theorems', *Trans. Roy. Soc. Edinb.*, **26** (1870): 69–84.

(40) Benjamin Collins Brodie, 'The calculus of chemical operations; being a method for the investigation, by means of symbols, of the laws of the distribution of weight in chemical change. Part I. On the construction of chemical symbols', *Phil. Trans.*, **156** (1866): 781–859.

(41) See Number 270.

(42) On 'Thomson's theorem' see the *Treatise*, **1**: 103–7 (§98) and Number 355 note (3).

378

LETTER TO CHARLES WILLIAM SIEMENS[1]

23 JUNE 1871

From a photocopy of the original in the University Library, Cambridge[2]

Glenlair
Dalbeattie
23 June 1871

My dear Sir

After our conversation in May I put a very short statement of your method of measuring temperatures by electric resistance[3] in the little book on heat which I am doing for Longman.[4] Of course there is no room there for matter belonging properly to electricity. But I wish to give a better account of your researches on resistance at high temperatures in my book on electricity in the chapter on the properties of metals as regards resistance.[5] I have read the abstract of your Bakerian Lecture[6] but I suppose the complete paper will not be out for some time, and I was unfortunately not in London when it was read.

It would be a great benefit to my book and to me if you could give me the values which you have obtained for the coefficients of your formula

$$R = \alpha T^{\frac{1}{2}} + \beta T + \gamma$$

in the case of platinum or any other metal.[7] The existence of the term in $T^{\frac{1}{2}}$ if it is established as a real fact and not merely as an expression of the slower rate of increase of resistance at high temperatures is of great importance. One result is that T cannot be negative or R would be impossible so that the position of absolute zero may be deduced by this method.

I think that if part of the resistance is proportional to the velocity of the molecules we may conclude that it depends on this velocity. But I find that in the theory of gases conduction of heat, and diffusion go on faster at high

---

(1) Wilhelm Siemens (brother of Werner Siemens), engineer, FRS 1862 (*DNB*).

(2) Courtesy of the English Electric Company: copy in ULC Add. MSS 7655, III, a. First published in *A Collection of Letters to Sir Charles William Siemens 1823–1883* (London, 1953): 23–4.

(3) As described in his Bakerian Lecture read to the Royal Society on 27 April 1871; see Charles William Siemens, 'On the increase of electrical resistance in conductors with rise of temperature, and its application to the measure of ordinary and furnace temperatures; also on a simple method of measuring electrical resistances', *Proc. Roy. Soc.*, **19** (1871): 443–5.

(4) See Maxwell's description of Siemens' work in his *Theory of Heat* (London, 1871): 52–4.

(5) See the *Treatise*, **1**: 416–17 (§360).

(6) In *Proc. Roy. Soc.*; see note (3).

(7) Maxwell gives values for platinum, copper and iron in the *Treatise* §360.

temperatures$^{(8)}$ and we know that the resistance of electrolytes and of most dielectrics diminishes as the temperature rises so that in these bodies I would expect the term in $T^{\frac{1}{2}}$ to appear in the formula for conductivity, not in that for resistance. The metals we know are different and their conductivity both for heat and for electricity diminishes as the temperature rises but I know of no satisfactory explanation of this.

Can you tell me if gas coke increases or diminishes in resistance as the temperature rises. Hockin told me that Selenium increases like the metals.$^{(9)}$ Are there any other non metallic bodies which do so?

Have you seen Tait's results about the electromotive force of thermoelectric circuits.$^{(10)}$ He finds the formula

$$E = A(T_1 - T_2)\{T_0 - \tfrac{1}{2}(T_1 + T_2)\}$$

is true for several combinations

T_1 = temperature of hot junction
T_2 =   cold
T_0 = temperature at which the metals are neutral to one another
A a constant for the pair of metals.$^{(11)}$

---

(8) See Number 263.

(9) See a letter from Charles Hockin to Maxwell of 11 March 1870 (ULC Add. MSS 7655, II/34): 'For selenium in the crystalline form the lowest resistance I have obtained is 600 units per metre cube at 100 °C altering exactly one per cent for each degree (increasing with temperature)'. See the *Treatise*, **1**: 418 (§362) where Maxwell gives this value. Hockin also includes data for gutta percha: 'equivalent to 3.53×10^{12} units for the resistance of a piece of gutta percha a metre every way in dimensions... I reckon it to increase 20 times in resistance between 24° & 0 °C'; data which Maxwell records in the *Treatise*, **1**: 423 (§368). Hockin also reported that he had 'had an opportunity of verifying the fact that I had heard before that it is not until some hours after the gutta percha has taken its temperature that the resistance alters to its final value. This is very curious'. Maxwell acknowledges this observation in *Treatise* §368.

(10) P. G. Tait, 'On thermo-electricity', *Proc. Roy. Soc. Edinb.*, **7** (1870): 308–11.

(11) See the *Treatise*, **1**: 305–6 (§254). In a card of 14 June 1871 (ULC Add. MSS 7655, I, a/18) Tait addressed the following query to Maxwell: 'O dp/dt You are aware that I think I have proved that in a Thermo-electric circuit the electromotive force $E = A(t-t_1)\left(t_0 - \dfrac{t+t_1}{2}\right)$ t & t_1 are absolute temp^{res} of hot & cold junction, and t_0 the neutral point. Would you consider it a complete proof of the truth of this, if I drop thermometers altogether (the air ther^r being horribly unwieldy) and, plotting from *two separate* circuits with junctions at the same temperature find the curve representing the relation between E & E' to be also (in every case and however highly the heating is carried) a parabola, as it should be if the above equation be correct? An early answer requested. Y^{rs} ☊.' Tait amplified his query in a note appended to Thomson's card of 17 June 1871 (Number 377 note (1)), and gave further clarification in a card of 20 June

Of course this formula tells us nothing about absolute zero because the sum of the coefficients of the temperatures in such factors are zero. I mention this because along with your result about resistance it helps to clear up the electric properties of metals, and perhaps you do not see the Edinburgh Proceedings.

Yours very truly
J. CLERK MAXWELL

I should be glad of any suggestions on pp 51–53 of the proof I send you.[12]

1871 (ULC Add. MSS 7655, I, a/20): 'O dp/dt I fear my hasty scribble on T's post-card was not very intelligible. Behold then the process:– $(\xi-\eta)^2 = 4(f-f')(f'\xi-f\eta)$ may be written $\sqrt{f^2-\xi} - \sqrt{f'^2-\eta} = \pm(f-f')$ ξ & η depend each on temp^{re}, *not* on one another. Hence if we write $\sqrt{f^2-\xi} = \pm(\tau\pm f)$ we have also $\sqrt{f'^2-\eta} = \pm(\tau\pm f')$. These are $\xi = \tau(2f-\tau)$ & $\eta = \tau(2f'-\tau)$. Hence, if ξ gives a parabola in terms of absolute temp^{re}, τ must be a linear function of abs. temp. N'est ce pas? Respondez-Vite! ୨.' Tait discussed the issue in his 'Relation between corresponding ordinates of two parabolas', *Proc. Roy. Soc. Edinb.*, **7** (1871): 499–500 (read 20 May 1871).

(12) See note (4).

379

LETTER TO JOHN WILLIAM STRUTT

8 AND 10 JULY 1871

From the original in private possession[1]

Glenlair
Dalbeattie
8 July 1871
10th July. Papers received[2]

Dear Strutt

I have received your letter dated 'Fourth of July Day'. I wish you all joy in the new state of things, and I hope that on the 19th the number of individuals existing will be so far diminished and the number of dualities increased.[3]

With regard to the laboratory, the word denotes a place to work at experiments and connotes a place full of articles not wanted at present and liable to noxious fumes. Hence, especially if you use nitric acid, a corner should be consecrated to it and a pipe or flue constructed to carry the fumes up the nearest chimney.

If you have more than one window and all on one wall, the space between

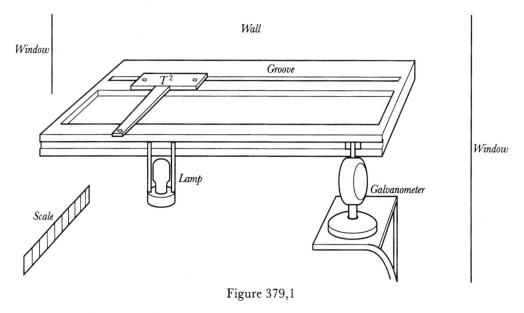

Figure 379,1

---

(1) Rayleigh Papers, Terling Place, Terling, Essex.
(2) See note (5).
(3) The occasion of Strutt's marriage to Evelyn Balfour; see R. J. Strutt, *John William Strutt, Third Baron Rayleigh* (London, 1924): 57.

two windows is probably the best to erect a reflecting galvanometer à la Thomson.[4]

About $7\frac{1}{2}$ feet (according to your height) from the ground fasten a frame of wood the length of the flat part of the wall and say 2 feet broad to hang things from. On one of the long sides is a groove of section ▭. The other side is planed flat.

To support anything so as to be free only to move in one direction parallel to itself place it on a stand (a T square) having 3 legs with hemispherical (not conical) feet. ⊔ Two of these feet slide in the groove thus ▭ on the principle of the round peg in the triangular hole. The other leg is a little shorter and slides on the flat board. This is Thomson's (and a good) plan for securing one degree of freedom. No carpenter will believe this till he is converted.

In front of the wooden frame hang a curtain rod and have 2 dark or black curtains which may be drawn to meet. They need not hang down more than 3 or 4 feet. Thus you have a darkish but easily accessible tent.

You hang the lamp a little above your head fix the galvanometer on a bracket at a height so that you can see it well and your scale at the proper place, which will be at a good height to read when standing in the tent. To adjust the height of the scale fasten it at right angles to a vertical bar which slides *easily* in two mortise holes. Place a vertical bar one on each side of the scale so as to bend the scale slightly concave. The friction of

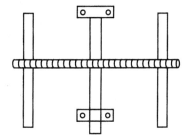

Figure 379,2

this arrangement will keep the scale from sliding down, and the absence of carpenters tight fittings will make it easily adjustable. A concave scale is a decided advantage especially (of course) one concentric with the mirror.

It is difficult to imagine exactly your condition. I have put down what happened to be in my head. For Optics you want shutters and I think shop shutters the best type (old style of shop do.) with a bar at the top of the window to push them under and a ledge below to rest them on. For a table I prefer a few tressels (masons horses) and a plank or two pretty thick with a selection of screw nails with self entering points, rather of the long and thin

---

(4) On Thomson's mirror galvanometer, see S. P. Thompson, *The Life of William Thomson Baron Kelvin of Largs*, 2 vols. (London, 1910), **1**: 347–9, 355. See also Number 399 note (7), and G. Green and J. T. Lloyd, *Kelvin's Instruments and the Kelvin Museum* (Glasgow, 1970): 30–1.

kind. Have the frames of your lenses &c with wooden bottoms with holes to screw them on the planks.

I have not got your papers yet.[5] I do not consider that I am done with you yet as regards the Phys. Lab.[6] I am glad to see Clifford going in for a chair in London instead of poking in rotten trees for South American beetles and fevers.[7] I have drawn the lines of force and equipotential surface for a single and a double tangent galvanometer.[8]

Yours truly
J. CLERK MAXWELL

APPENDIX: FROM A LETTER OF REFERENCE FOR WILLIAM KINGDON CLIFFORD

circa JULY 1871

From Clifford, *Lectures and Essays*[9]

The peculiarity of Mr. Clifford's researches, which in my opinion points him out as the right man for a chair of mathematical science, is that they tend not to the elaboration of abstruse theorems by ingenious calculations, but to the elucidation of scientific ideas by the concentration upon them of clear and steady thought. The pupils of such a teacher not only obtain clearer views of the subject taught, but are encouraged to cultivate in themselves that power of thought which is so liable to be neglected amidst the appliances of education.

---

(5) Possibly: J. W. Strutt, 'On the light from the sky, its polarization and colour', *Phil. Mag.*, ser. 4, **41** (1871): 274–9; Strutt, 'On the scattering of light by small particles', *ibid.*: 447–54 (published in the April and June numbers of the *Philosophical Magazine*).

(6) See Number 358.

(7) W. K. Clifford had been a member of the Eclipse Expedition in 1870; and in 1871 was appointed Professor of Applied Mathematics at University College, London (Venn; *DNB*).

(8) See Figs. XVIII and XIX in the *Treatise*, **2**; and the *Treatise*, **2**: 307, 318–19 (§§ 702, 713).

(9) Quoted by Frederick Pollock in his 'Introduction' to *Lectures and Essays by the Late William Kingdon Clifford*, ed. Frederick Pollock and Leslie Stephen, 2 vols. (London, 1879), **1**: 14.

380

POSTCARD TO PETER GUTHRIE TAIT

13 JULY 1871

From the original in the University Library, Cambridge[1]

[Glenlair]

O T′[2] Total ignorance of H[3] and imperfect remembrance of T′ in Trans RSE[4] caused $\frac{dp}{dt}$ to suppose that H in his optical studies had made the statement in the form of a germ which T′ hatched.[5] I now perceive that T′ sat on his own egg, but as his cackle about it was very subdued compared with some other incubators, I was not aware of its origin when I spoke to B.A.[6] When I examined hastily H on Rays I expected to find far more than was there. But the good of H is not in what he has done but in the work (not near half done) which he makes other people do. But to understand him, you should look him up, and go through all kinds of sciences, then you go back to him and he tells you a wrinkle. I have done lines of force and = pot^{ls} of double tangent galv^{rs} in a diagram, showing the large uniform field. Is T still in London?[a]

(a) {Tait} Send back to T′.

(1) ULC Add. MSS 7655, I, b/31. Previously published in Knott, *Life of Tait*: 99–100.

(2) Written in reply to Tait's postcard of 9 July 1871 (ULC Add. MSS 7655, I, a/21): '$\bar{y}$ O dp/dt did'st though say, to the B.A. last year that "H discovered that to every brachistochrone problem there corresponds one of free motion"? Pray give me the reference, for I thought T′ had some little credit in the business, & your remark would annihilate it in very great measure.⌾'.

(3) William Rowan Hamilton, 'Theory of systems of rays', *Transactions of the Royal Irish Academy*, **15** (1827): 69–174; *ibid.*, **16** part 1 (1830): 2–62; *ibid.*, **16** part 2 (1831): 93–125; *ibid.*, **17** (1832): 1–144.

(4) P. G. Tait, 'On the application of Hamilton's characteristic function to special cases of constraint', *Trans. Roy. Soc. Edinb.*, **24** (1865): 147–66.

(5) Tait and Maxwell had however discussed the subject in 1865: see Maxwell's letter to Tait of 17 June 1865 (Number 249, esp. note (2)).

(6) Published in the *Report of the Fortieth Meeting of the British Association for the Advancement of Science; held at Liverpool in September 1870* (London, 1871), part 2: 1–9, on 8 (= *Scientific Papers*, **2**: 228).

LETTER TO JAMES THOMSON

13 JULY 1871

From the original in the Library of The Queen's University, Belfast[1]

Glenlair
Dalbeattie
13 July 1871

Dear Sir

In a book on heat which I am in the midst of,[2] I have given a short account of Dr Andrews researches,[3] about which we had some conversation at Glasgow. I have since heard his lecture at the Royal Institution[4] and seen a little of the phenomena.

My account of the facts and theories is therefore derived partly from Andrews and partly from you and is considerably modified in the process of boiling down. I should like to hear from you if the proof I send gives a fair account of what Andrews and you have done and more particularly if you have told me anything in confidence that you have not yet published mark it out.[5] I hope however that you will publish some of what you told me[6] for the speculation seemed of the fertile kind.

Sir William's relations between capillarity, curvature and pressure of

---

(1) James Thomson Papers, MS. 13/22a, The Queen's University of Belfast Library.

(2) J. Clerk Maxwell, *Theory of Heat* (London, 1871). In a letter to Maxwell of 20 June 1871 (ULC Add. MSS 7655, II/48), the publisher, William Longman, wrote: 'I am glad to hear from my friend Goodeve that your Treatise on Heat is, in his opinion, a perfect model of what such a book ought to be. He is so much pleased with it that he is most anxious that you should make up your mind to contribute further to the series by committing yourself to undertake the writing of the Preliminary Discourse, and he advised me to take the opportunity of your enjoying a pleasant comparative holiday in the country to disturb it by suggesting your devoting a part of it to this noble object. I should be very glad to find that you considered this a timely suggestion and were not greatly disgusted my disturbing your tranquillity.' On Thomas Minchin Goodeve see Volume I: 29, 30, 662n. Maxwell did not contribute further to the Longman series of 'Textbooks on Science'.

(3) Andrews' discovery of the continuity of the liquid and gaseous states of matter; and of the critical point of temperature above which these states could not be distinguished. See Thomas Andrews, 'On the continuity of the gaseous and liquid states of matter', *Phil. Trans.*, **159** (1869): 575–90.

(4) Thomas Andrews, On the gaseous and liquid states of matter', *Proceedings of the Royal Institution of Great Britain*, **6** (1872): 356–64; read 2 June 1871.

(5) For Thomson's response see his letter of 21 July 1871 (Number 382 note (2)).

(6) See James Thomson, 'Considerations on the abrupt changes at boiling or condensing in reference to the continuity of the fluid state of matter', *Proc. Roy. Soc.*, **20** (1871): 1–8.

vapour⁽⁷⁾ seem to me to be connected with the retardation of boiling and of condensation.[8]

The next difficulty is What determines the true boiling temperature of the steam which is found to be so constant?[9]

If I do not hear from you in 10 days I shall suppose you are not at home and use my own discretion.

Remember me kindly to Mrs Thomson and believe me

Yours very truly
J. CLERK MAXWELL

Shall you be at Edinburgh at the B.A.?[10]

---

(7) William Thomson, 'On the equilibrium of vapour at a curved surface of liquid', *Proc. Roy. Soc. Edinb.*, **7** (1870): 63–8.

(8) Compare Maxwell, *Theory of Heat*: 267–8.

(9) See Thomson's letter of 21 July 1871 (Number 382 note (2)); and Maxwell, *Theory of Heat*: 124–6.

(10) See Number 382 note (5).

= 382 =

LETTER TO JAMES THOMSON

24 JULY 1871

From the original in the Library of The Queen's University, Belfast[1]

Glenlair
Dalbeattie
24 July 1871

My dear Thomson
    Many thanks for your letters corrections and papers.[2] Pray give my

---

(1) James Thomson Papers, MS 13/22c, The Queen's University of Belfast Library.

(2) In reply to Maxwell's letter of 13 July 1871 (Number 381) Thomson wrote on 21 July 1871 (copy in the Thomson Papers, MS 13/22b): 'My dear Maxwell / I have been a little longer of writing to you than I hoped, having been away from home for two long days on a survey & much engaged at home on another day or two. / In the proof sheets which you sent me & which I now return, there are a few sentences which I think would require a little amendment as I think a few of them scarcely attribute to Dr Andrews the credit which is due to him for the revolution he has brought about in people's views in general on the relations of the gaseous & liquid states of matter. / I think in justice to him as well as to make the historical allusions in your book correct in reference to this matter it ought to be stated that it was Dr Andrews who showed that the liquid & gaseous states are continuous & that to him is due the true explanation of Caynard de la Tour's experiment. In your proofs I have inserted a few proposed alterations as suggestions for your consideration, but of course with the intention that you should do whatever you will think right & suitable yourself. / Then as to the passages relating to my suggestion (pages 122 & 123), I think you will find on consideration that what you have written will not hold good altogether. I think it is *not* possible for the substance at the pressure indicated by B to pass into the gaseous state & that if the liquid is in contact with its vapour at this pressure it is *really found that the liquid will not* begin to pass into the gaseous state. On the contrary I think under the circumstances stated it will all go down to the liquid state. / Again:– If there be any drops of liquid in the vessel when the pressure is that belonging to D & H, I think condensation will *not* now begin but on the contrary all the liquid will evaporate into the gaseous state. Then in respect to the question in your letter where you say "The next difficulty is:– *What determines the true boiling temperature of the steam which is found to be so constant?*" I will answer rather a corresponding question which is quite to the same effect but suits better to the diagram before us in which the vertical ordinates represent pressures, and the horizontal ones represent volumes:– *What determines the true boiling pressures of the steam which is found to be so constant for any given temperature?* I reply:– There is just one intermediate point of pressure between the pressure at F and the pressure at D, at which the liquid and its gas can be present together in contact with one another; and that is the boiling, or rather evaporating or condensing pressure, for the temperature to which the curve belongs. In using the name boiling pressure here we must understand not the very uncertain and variable pressure at which bubbles would form themselves in a continuous liquid when the boiling takes

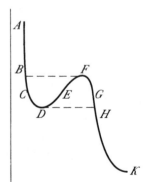

Figure 382,1

thanks to Dr Andrews for his lecture.$^{(3)}$ I have not had time to digest all you have sent. May I keep your copy of the R.S. paper$^{(4)}$ till I see you in Edinburgh?$^{(5)}$ You are certainly right that there is a definite pressure at which evaporation takes place at a given temperature (putting aside capillary phenomena). But I never could see what that pressure must be with reference to your continuous curve.$^{(6)}$ I think, however, that the following method determines it.

place with bumping; but the absolutely definite pressure at which the liquid and its gas can be present together in contact with each other when either evaporation or condensation may be going on, or no change either way may be taking place. / I think there is no "*lingering*" in the liquid nor in the gaseous condition, when the two conditions of the same substance are present together, and the pressure is being altered while the temperature is fixed (or equally when the temperature is altered while pressure is fixed). / I enclose to you a manuscript copy of my paper recently sent to the Royal Society on this subject & which I presume will very soon be published in the *Proceedings*. I suppose it will be published before your book will come out; & I think if you w^d wish to refer to it as a published paper permission may easily be obtained to do so or information as to the date or page at which it will appear in the Proceedings may easily be obtained by applying to the Secretaries of the Royal Society either Prof. Stokes Lensfield Cottage Cambridge or to Walter White Esq. Royal Society Burlington House London. You might write if you wish. / I sent to you by this post a report of Dr Andrews's lecture at the Royal Institution at which I think you say you were present; & also I send you a copy of "Nature" containing an article abridged from an essay by me giving an account of Dr Andrews's researches & conclusions. / Mrs Thomson and I hope to be at the Brit. Assoc. and hope to see you there & with kind regards I am / Yours truly / James Thomson.'

Thomson's Royal Society paper (see note (4)) was received on 4 July 1871, and read on 16 November 1871. The experiments by Charles Cagniard-Latour referred to were reported in his 'Exposé de quelques résultats obtenus par l'action combinée de la chaleur et de la compression sur certains liquides tels que l'eau, l'alcool', *Ann. Chim. Phys.*, ser. 2, **21** (1822): 127–32, 178–82; and his 'Sur les effets qu'on obtient par l'application simultanée de la chaleur et de la compression à certains liquides', *ibid.*, **22** (1823): 410–15. These experiments had established the basis for Andrews' research; see his 'On the continuity of the gaseous and liquid states of matter', *Phil. Trans.*, **159** (1869): 575–90, esp. 575. This paper, the Bakerian Lecture for 1869, was described in an essay by James Thomson, 'The continuity of the gaseous and liquid states of matter', *Nature*, **2** (1870): 278–81.

(3) Thomas Andrews, 'On the gaseous and liquid states of matter', *Proceedings of the Royal Institution of Great Britain*, **6** (1872): 356–64.

(4) James Thomson, 'Considerations on the abrupt changes at boiling or condensing in reference to the continuity of the fluid state of matter', *Proc. Roy. Soc.*, **20** (1871): 1–8.

(5) At the meeting of the British Association where Thomson read a paper (summarising his ideas) 'Speculations on the continuity of the fluid state of matter, and on relations between the gaseous, the liquid, and the solid states', *Report of the Forty-first Meeting of the British Association for the Advancement of Science; held at Edinburgh in August 1871* (London, 1872), part 2: 30–3.

(6) See Thomson's figure (Figure 382,1) in his letter of 21 July 1871. Andrews had obtained curves that included a straight segment parallel to the axis of volume; see his 'On the continuity of the gaseous and liquid states of matter': 583. In his 'Considerations on the abrupt changes of

For given value of p the pressure and θ the absolute temperature let there be three values of v, the volume

v_1 the liquid volume
v_2 the unstable volume
v_3 the gaseous volume
$\Big\}$ for unit of mass

Let x be the mass of the liquid
y ——————— gas
$x+y = $ const.

Let $\phi_1\ \phi_2\ \phi_3$ be Rankines thermodynamic function[7] for the 3 states.

Figure 382,2

In general, if v and ϕ be made to vary
the work done by the fluid is $p\,dv$
the heat absorbed measured dynamically $\theta\,d\phi$
Energy developed or emitted $\quad p\,dv - \theta\,d\phi$.

Hence if any variation takes place in the mixed mass of liquid and gas

$$\text{Energy emitted} = x(p_1\,dv_1 - \theta_1\,d\phi_1) + y(p_3\,dv_3 - \theta_3\,d\phi_3).$$

If the variation arises from a change of pressure dp while the temperature θ remains the same then p & θ are the same throughout the expression

$$\text{and energy} = dp.x\left(p\frac{dv_1}{dp} - \theta\frac{d\phi_1}{dp}\right) + y\left(p\frac{dv_3}{dp} - \theta\frac{d\phi_3}{dp}\right)$$

θ being constant in the differentiation.

Next let x vary then $dx + dy = 0$
and the energy emitted is

$$dp\,dx\left\{p\frac{dv_1}{dp} - \theta\frac{d\phi_1}{dp} - \left(p\frac{dv_3}{dp} - \theta\frac{d\phi_3}{dp}\right)\right\}.$$

Now x will tend to increase or condensation will occur when this quantity is positive and to diminish, indicating evaporation when it is negative. Hence

---

boiling or condensing': 2, Thomson argued for 'theoretical continuity', as represented by the isothermal curve in Figure 382,1, which shows a maximum and minimum. Compare Maxwell's discussion in his *Theory of Heat* (London, 1871): 124–6, where he reproduces Thomson's figure: 'the isothermal curves for temperatures below the critical temperature are only apparently, and not really, discontinuous'.

(7) W. J. M. Rankine, 'On the geometrical representation of the expansive action of heat, and the theory of thermo-dynamic engines', *Phil. Trans.*, **144** (1854): 115–75, esp. 126. As Maxwell subsequently grasped (see Number 483, esp. note (18)), 'The entropy of Clausius...is only Rankine's Thermodynamic function'.

the equilibrium of vapour and liquid occurs when

$$p\frac{dv}{dp} - \theta\frac{d\phi}{dp} \qquad (A)$$

is the same for the liquid and the gaseous states.

But by thermodynamics $\dfrac{d\phi}{dp} = -\dfrac{dv}{d\theta}$ [8]

so that we may write the expression

$$p\frac{dv}{dp}_{(\theta\,\text{const})} + \theta\frac{dv}{d\theta}_{(p\,\text{const})}. \qquad (B)$$

Here $-\dfrac{dv}{dp}_{(\theta\,\text{const})}$ denotes the compressibility of unit of mass at constant temperature and $\dfrac{dv}{d\theta}_p$ the dilatability of unit of mass at constant pressure. The expression (B) must be the same for the liquid & the gas at the point of equilibrium.

Take the case of steam. Suppose it obeys Boyle & Charles[9] in the gaseous state

then $\dfrac{pv}{\theta}$ is constant and $p\dfrac{dv}{dp} + v\dfrac{dv}{d\theta} = 0$.

In the liquid state therefore $p\dfrac{dv}{dp} + \theta\dfrac{dv}{d\theta} = 0$.

In fact both these terms are very small and of opposite signs, but the second is the largest in most cases. Hence for the vapour $p\dfrac{dv}{dp} + \theta\dfrac{dv}{d\theta}$ is positive. We know that the compressibility is greater than that given by Boyle's law. Hence, à fortiori the dilatation at constant pressure must be greater than that given by Charles' law. In fact the dilatation of superheated vapour is much greater than that of permanent gases.

---

(8) Maxwell's *First Thermodynamic Relation*, $\dfrac{dv}{d\theta}_{(p\,\text{const})} = -\dfrac{d\phi}{dp}_{(\theta\,\text{const})}$; see his *Theory of Heat*: 165, 167n.

(9) See Maxwell's statement in his *Theory of Heat*: 29–30; the 'law of Charles... the volume of a gas under constant pressure expands when raised from the freezing to the boiling temperature by the same fraction of itself, whatever be the nature of the gas.' See Numbers 373 esp. note (5) and 375 note (2).

We may also write the expression (**B**)
$$\frac{dv}{dp}_{(\theta\,\text{const})}\left(p - \theta\frac{dp}{d\theta}_{(v\,\text{const})}\right)$$

or still more simply $\frac{dE}{dp}_{(\theta\,\text{const})}$.

This condition determines the value of p at which the liquid & its vapour can coexist

so that the condition is

$$\frac{d}{dp}(E_1 - E_3) = 0$$

or $E_3 - E_1$ is a maximum for the given value of the temperature where E_3 and E_1 denote the intrinsic energy of unit of mass of the gas and the liquid at the same temperature and pressure.[10]

I have made use of writing to you in order to get this matter into shape as I am very busy at present about electricity so I was by no means clear about the matter when I began writing. I now see that E_1 the intrinsic energy is the best thing to look at. In a perfect gas it is constant for the same temperature whatever be the pressure, and is proportional to the temperature. In an incompressible liquid it is independent of the pressure and is proportional to the temperature and the specific heat.

In real liquids the part depending on the temperature is still commonly greater than that depending on pressure.

I think that this leads to a method of determining, from a complete knowledge of the continuous isothermal curve and the consecutive isothermal curves, the points of those curves which correspond to the state of equilibrium between the liquid and its vapour, and shows that I was wrong in supposing that there would be anything indefinite about it.

Have you stated anything about this in the paper you are going to print?

I remain
Yours very truly
J. CLERK MAXWELL

(10) Maxwell states this conclusion in his *Theory of Heat*: 125. This establishes the condition determining the pressure at which gas and liquid can co-exist at equilibrium, the condition which determines the position of the line *CG* in Thomson's figure (Figure 382,1). Maxwell subsequently revised this conclusion, in his lecture 'On the dynamical evidence of the molecular constitution of bodies', *Journal of the Chemical Society*, **13** (1875): 493–508, esp. 496–7 (= *Scientific Papers*, **2**: 424–6).

383

NOTE FOR WILLIAM THOMSON AND PETER GUTHRIE TAIT[1]

LATE AUGUST 1871[2]

From the original in the University Library, Edinburgh[3]

[Glenlair]

Art 391 of $\frac{dp}{dt}$ boiled down[4]

$$\sum x' dm = lM \quad \sum y' dm = mM \quad \sum z' dm = nM$$
$$\sum x'^2 dm = A \quad \sum y'^2 dm = B \quad \sum z'^2 dm = C$$
$$\sum y'z' dm = P \quad \sum z'x' dm = Q \quad \sum x'y' dm = R.$$

Expansion of V in spherical harmonix

$$\sum U_0 \, dm = 0$$

$$\sum U_1 \, dm = M \frac{lx + my + nz}{r^3}$$

$$\sum U_2 \, dm = \frac{x^2(2A-B-C) - y^2(2B-C-A) + z^2(2C-A-B) + 6(Pyz + Qzx + Rxy)}{2r^5}$$

make the axis of x in the direction of $l\ m\ n$ then
Place the origin where

$$x = \frac{2A-B-C}{4M} \quad y = \frac{R}{M} \quad z = \frac{Q}{M}.$$

---

(1) This note was occasioned by a letter from Thomson to Tait of 21 August 1871 (Edinburgh University Library, Dc.2.76[16] folios 12–16), and is written on the *verso* of Thomson's letter which Tait forwarded to Maxwell. Thomson wrote: 'D^r T' I have at last got to the reprint of electrical papers, and in doing Math. Th. of Magnetism §§8–13 have been forced to bring to an issue the long impending question what is *the* magnetic axis of a magnet and what is its proper centre. Maxwell is (?) sure (?) to have it in his book [here Maxwell appends: "See Art 391 to which please refer. dp/dt"] so this is a race and you as Sec RSE are bound to see fair play.' Thomson then gives a statement (which is slightly revised in the text, dated September 1871, published in his *Electrostatics and Magnetism*: 367–70) of his theory of the magnetic axis of a magnet. After giving an account of this theory in his letter to Tait Thomson adds: 'I shall wait to see if the bait takes'. Maxwell responded by giving an abstract of his own version of the problem, intended, as Thomson had surmised, for the *Treatise*.

(2) See note (1).

(3) Edinburgh University Library, Dc.2.76[16] folio 16 *verso*.

(4) Compare the *Treatise*, **2**: 17–19 (§§391–2), where the argument has been slightly revised.

Then turn about the axis of x till P vanishes and the third term of V becomes
$$\frac{(y^2-z^2)(3B-C)}{4r^5}.$$

The spherical surface integral of the square of the third term is a minimum when the centre is the centre of the magnet thus found.

The axis of x drawn *through this centre* is The axis of the magnet and those of y & z as drawn above are the secondary axes.

$A\;B\;C$ correspond to moments of inertia
$P\;Q\;R$ to products of inertia
but $A\;B\;C$ are not necessarily $+^{ve}$.

The total mass $= 0$ and the centre of gravity is at ∞ in the direction of the axis.

O T'. Send back my proofs and let the work proceed.[5]

---

(5) Proof sheets of §§145–150 of the *Treatise* (on spherical harmonics) are postmarked (returned to Oxford) 1 September 1871 (ULC Add. MSS 7655, IV/2).

384

POSTCARD TO PETER GUTHRIE TAIT

5 SEPTEMBER 1871

From the original in the University Library, Cambridge[1]

[Glenlair]

O T'. A complete set of the figs I to XII[2] given to T' at N. P.[3] Class room. Only one set in my possession at present. Spherical Harmonics first written in 1867[4] but worked up from T & T' when that work appeared[5] and since.

Have you a short and good way to find $\iint (\vartheta_i^{(s)})^2 \, dS$?[6] If so make it known at 1^{ce}[7] that I may bag it lawfully as T' 4^{nion} path to harmonic analysis.

$$\frac{K.N.}{T.} = \frac{P.^{epper}D.^{not}}{\text{no means}}$$

$$\frac{dp}{dt}$$

---

(1) ULC Add. MSS 7655, I, b/32. Previously published (in part) in Knott, *Life of Tait*: 100.
(2) For the *Treatise*.   (3) Natural Philosophy.
(4) See Maxwell's letter to Tait of 11 December 1867 (Number 277).
(5) Thomson and Tait, *Natural Philosophy*: 140–60.
(6) The quantity $\vartheta_i^{(s)}$ is a function of the spherical coordinate, θ, where i and s denote the poles of the harmonic function, and dS is the element of the surface. See Thomson and Tait, *Natural Philosophy*: 149; and for Maxwell's solution see Number 387.

(7) Maxwell's further work on spherical harmonics for the *Treatise* in the autumn of 1871 (see Numbers 387 and 388) may have been encouraged by papers read by W. K. Clifford and William Thomson at the British Association meeting in Edinburgh in August 1871, to which he makes reference in the *Treatise*, **1**: 171 (§138). See W. K. Clifford, 'On a canonical form of spherical harmonics', and W. Thomson, 'On the general canonical form of a spherical harmonic of the nth order', in the *Report of the Forty-first Meeting of the British Association* (London, 1872), part 2: 10, 25–6.

NOTE FOR FLEEMING JENKIN ON THE THEORY OF ELECTRIC CIRCUITS

circa SEPTEMBER 1871[1]

From the original in the University Library, Cambridge[2]

[ELECTRICAL CIRCUITS AND LINES OF FORCE]

The mutual mechanical action of electric currents was discovered by Ampère,[3] who determined the mathematical form of the law of this action by an investigation which is one of the most brilliant illustrations of scientific method.[4] We shall find it, however more convenient to employ the method of Faraday, in which the action is defined with reference to the lines of magnetic force.

Lines of Force[5]

Every electric current is a closed circuit. The action of this current on magnets or other currents in its neighbourhood is identical with that of a magnetic shell, uniformly magnetized normal to its surface and bounded by the circuit formed by the current.

The lines of magnetic force due to the current are also closed curves each of which passes through the electric circuit and returns outside the circuit thus.[6]

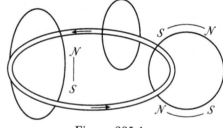

Figure 385,1

When a considerable length of the circuit is straight, the lines of magnetic force near it are circles and the amount of the force is

$$2\frac{C}{r}$$

where C is the current and r the distance from it.

---

(1) This date is conjectural. The text may well relate to the annotation on the proof of Jenkin's *Electricity and Magnetism* (London, 1873) published as an appendix *infra*: see note (10). The argument itself suggests a date after June 1871: see note (8).

(2) ULC Add. MSS 7655, II/239 (from the Jenkin papers).

(3) A. M. Ampère, 'Mémoire sur la théorie mathématique des phénomènes électrodynamiques uniquement déduite de l'éxpérience', *Mémoires de l'Académie Royale des Sciences*, **6** (1827): 175–388.

(4) Compare Maxwell's remarks in the *Treatise*, **2**: 162 (§528), where he describes Ampère as 'the "Newton of electricity"'.   (5) Compare the *Treatise*, **2**: 140–1 (§§493–5).

(6) On Figure 385,1 see Number 370 esp. note (10).

The forms of the lines of magnetic force are more complicated in other cases but they can be drawn when the current is circular.

Action on a moveable portion of a conductor carrying a current[7]

Any moveable portion of a conductor carrying an electric current (which may be the same current as the acting current) is acted on by an electromagnetic force which tends to move it in a direction depending on two things, its own direction and that of the magnetic force.

Draw from any point two straight lines, the first representing in magnitude and direction the strength of the current in the moveable wire, while the second represents in direction and magnitude the magnetic force at the place. The electromagnetic force on unit length of the wire is perpendicular to the plane of these two lines and is represented in magnitude by the parallelogram which they contain.

To determine which way this force acts place a corkscrew perpendicular to this parallelogram and turn it from the direction of the electric current to the direction in which the end marked N of a compass needle would point. The screw will then move in the direction of the force.[8]

From this it is easy to see that if a circuit has a long straight portion like a telegraph wire it will attract a conductor parallel to itself if the current in the conductor is in the same direction as in the telegraph wire and will repel it if the two currents are in opposite directions.

All these actions are summed up in Faraday's law that any moveable part of the second circuit tends to move so as to increase the number of the lines of magnetic force due to the first circuit which are embraced by the second.[9]

(a)

(a) {Jenkin} J. Clerk Maxwell.

(7) Compare the *Treatise*, **2**: 135–6 (§489).
(8) See Numbers 370 and 371 for Maxwell's adoption of the analogy of a corkscrew: 'A common corkscrew may be used as a material symbol of the same relation' (*Treatise*, **1**: 24n (§23)). Compare Jenkin's discussion of the corkscrew rule in his *Electricity and Magnetism*: 148.
(9) See the *Treatise*, **2**: 175 (§541).

APPENDIX: ANNOTATION ON PROOF OF JENKIN'S ELECTRICITY AND MAGNETISM[10]

circa SEPTEMBER 1871[11]

From the original in the University Library, Cambridge[12]

GENERAL ANNOTATION

Electrification a condition of bodies to be described. This may be measured. The quantity on which it depends is called Electricity. When electrified conductors are connected by a wire a transfer of electrification takes place. That which determines the direction of the transfer is the relative Potential of the two conductors. Define equal, higher & lower as applied to Potential. You may afterwards define the exact *measurement* of Potential by the work done on the test charge, but get the notion of Potential in before §7[13] or you are in danger of beginning with loose and even erroneous expressions. It is quite as easy for a beginner to understand 'potential' as to understand 'electrical state' which is vague or 'electrification' which is wrong.[14]

---

(10) Fleeming Jenkin's text *Electricity and Magnetism* was published by Longmans in 1873. This first set of proofs (pp. 1–48) is dated 22 August 1871 by the printer. Jenkin wrote to Maxwell on 28 October 1871 (ULC Add. MSS 7655, II/51) acknowledging receipt of the annotated proofs, sending a second set (pp. 49–64) for comment, and returning the first set for reference. See also Number 450.

(11) See note (10).   (12) ULC Add. MSS 7655, V, c/41.

(13) In §7 of his *Electricity and Magnetism*: 7–8, Jenkin discusses the production of positive and negative electricity from rubbed glass and resin, respectively.

(14) Maxwell does however use the term 'electrification' in the *Treatise*, **1**: 30–2 (§§27–9).

386

LETTER TO PETER GUTHRIE TAIT

19 OCTOBER 1871

From the original in the University Library, Cambridge[1]

Ardhallow
Dunoon
19/10/71

O T'

I send you prooves.[2] As I have not engraved copies of all the figures I enclose some of the originals.

T (W & J)[3] & H²[4] are becalmed in the Hebrides. I got a post card from Gair lock Ross shire which enticed me to Greenock at 4 in the morning on Friday. I enjoyed my own society there till 4 in the afternoon of Saturday. I thought I saw L. R.[5] creeping up by Gourock last night (Monday).

Can you tell me anything about John Hunter M.A. Prof^r &c.[6]

I only know him as the man who charges charcoal with bad smells.[7] Would he be a good demonstrator at Cambridge? I have no doubt that a man who could occlude a fishy fume in a burnt stick could also floor a demon which I suppose to be the essential part of the office. But I doubt if our laboratory would be sufficiently absorbent to occlude so volatile a spirit, for he seems to have improved the shining hour in every laboratory under heaven.

I have written to Cambridge to know my powers of appointing an exorcist and what form of ordination is required.

Hitherto I consider that we would be the better of a man who has seen many professors and known their manners rather than one who represents simply the continuity of University life.

Yrs
$\frac{dp}{dt}$

---

(1) ULC Add. MSS 7655, I, b/33.

(2) Proof sheets of §§ 150–56 of the *Treatise* are stamped 28 September 1871 by the Clarendon Press (ULC Add. MSS 7655, IV/2)   (3) William and James Thomson.

(4) Helmholtz.   (5) William Thomson's yacht the *Lalla Rookh*.

(6) John Hunter, formerly assistant to Thomas Andrews at Queen's College, Belfast, had been professor of mathematics and natural philosophy at King's College, Windsor, Nova Scotia, 1870–71, but had resigned due to ill-health and returned to Britain in autumn 1871. See *Proc. Roy. Soc. Edinb.*, **8** (1875): 322–4.

(7) John Hunter, 'On the absorption of vapours by charcoal', *Journal of the Chemical Society*, ser. 2, **3** (1865): 285–90; *ibid.*, **5** (1867): 160–4; *ibid.*, **6** (1868): 186–92; *ibid.*, **8** (1870): 73–4.

387

POSTCARD TO PETER GUTHRIE TAIT

23 OCTOBER 1871

From the original in the University Library, Cambridge[1]

[London]

O T'! R.U. AT 'OME? $\iint \mathrm{Spharc}^2 dS$ was done in the most general form in 1867.[2] I have now bagged ξ & η from T & T'[3] and done the numerical value of $\iint (Y_i^{(s)})^2 dS$[4] in 4 lines, thus verifying T + T''s value of $\iint (\vartheta_i^{(s)})^2 dS$.[5]

Your plan[6] seems indep^t of T + T' or of me. Publish!

I am busy supplying the physical necessities of scientific life. Address 11 Scroope Terrace, Cambridge. Prooves have got as far as grooves, corrugated plates, gratings and guard-rings.[7] If you have time for criticism they shall be sent.

$$\iint (Y_i^{(s)})^2 dS = \frac{8\pi a^2}{2i+1} \frac{\lfloor i+s \lfloor i-s}{2^{2s} \lfloor i \lfloor i}$$[8]

except when $s = 0$ when $\iint (Q_i)^2 dS = \frac{4\pi a^2}{2i+1}$.[9]

Hence $\int_{-1}^{+1} (\vartheta_i^{(s)})^2 d\mu = \frac{2}{2i+1} \frac{2^{2s} \lfloor i-s \lfloor s \lfloor s}{\lfloor i+s}$ without exception.[10]

Y^{rs} $\frac{dp}{dt}$

---

(1) ULC Add. MSS 7655, I, b/34. Previously published (in part) in Knott, *Life of Tait*: 100, and in facsimile in C. W. F. Everitt, *James Clerk Maxwell* (New York, 1975): 26.

(2) See Number 384.

(3) In their discussion of spherical harmonics (*Natural Philosophy*: 148) Thomson and Tait had used imaginary coordinates ξ and η, where $\xi = x + \sqrt{-1}y$ and $\eta = x - \sqrt{-1}y$. See the *Treatise*, **1**: 164 (§132).

(4) $Y_i^{(s)}$ is the surface harmonic, i and s denoting its axes, dS the element of surface.

(5) Thomson and Tait, *Natural Philosophy*: 149; and see Number 384.

(6) P. G. Tait, 'Note on spherical harmonics', *Proc. Roy. Soc. Edinb.*, **7** (1871): 589–96. See Number 388. (7) See the *Treatise*, **1**: 240–53 (§§196–206).

(8) The value of the surface integral (taken over the surface S of a sphere of radius a) of the square of a surface harmonic $Y_i^{(s)}$ of the symmetrical system, where $i-s$ poles are placed at one point and the remaining s poles at equal distance round one half of the equator. See the *Treatise*, **1**: 163, 174 (§§132, 141). Maxwell uses the symbol $\lfloor$ for factorial: see Numbers 389 and 390.

(9) When all the poles are concentrated at the pole of the sphere, the harmonic becomes a zonal harmonic (Q_i) for which $s = 0$. See the *Treatise*, **1**: 163 (§132).

(10) See the *Treatise*, **1**: 173–4 (§141), where μ denotes $\cos\theta$, where θ is the spherical coordinate.

388

LETTER TO PETER GUTHRIE TAIT

2 NOVEMBER 1871

From the original in the University Library, Cambridge[1]

11 Scroope Terrace
Cambridge
2 Nov 1871

O T'

Your notes have ravished me. An interest in $\Sigma\phi\alpha\rho\xi$ being revived[2] this is exactly what is wanted for a quantitative or computative discussion of the symmetrical system considered as depending only on certain symbols i and s.[3]

It seems to have little or nothing to do with your 4 nionic reduction which is of course indep^t of a selected axis.

My method is also indep^t of a selected axis but does not seem equivalent to your 4 nion reduction which goes by steps.[4]

Murphy is not at all bad in his way and affords a very good specimen of a Caius man working a calculation.[5]

How is it that $\Sigma\phi\alpha\rho\xi$ can be worked only at Caius? See Murphy Green[6] O'Brien[7] Pratt.[8] When I examined here the only men who could do figure of the earth were mild Caius men. All the rest were Prattists if anything.

---

(1) ULC Add. MSS 7655, I, b/35. Previously published (in part) in Knott, *Life of Tait*: 100–1.

(2) See Tait's paper, 'Note on spherical harmonics', *Proc. Roy. Soc. Edinb.*, **7** (1871): 589–96; here $\Sigma\phi\alpha\rho\xi$ = 'Spharx'.

(3) See Number 387 esp. note (8).

(4) See Tait's reply of 10 November 1871 (Number 389 note (14)).

(5) Robert Murphy, Caius 1825, third wrangler 1829, Fellow 1829 (Venn). For Murphy's discussion of Laplace coefficients see his *Elementary Principles of the Theories of Electricity, Heat and Molecular Actions. Part I. On Electricity* (Cambridge, 1833): 3–24 ('Preliminary propositions').

(6) George Green, Caius 1832, fourth wrangler 1837, Fellow 1839 (Venn). Green made extensive use of the Laplace coefficients; see especially his 'Mathematical investigations concerning the laws of the equilibrium of fluids analogous to the electric fluid, with other similar researches', *Trans. Camb. Phil. Soc.*, **5** (1833): 1–63 (= *The Mathematical Papers of the Late George Green*, ed. N. M. Ferrers (London, 1871): 119–83), on which see Number 310 esp. note (3).

(7) Matthew O'Brien, Caius 1834, third wrangler 1838, Fellow 1840 (Venn). See his text *Mathematical Tracts. Part I. On Laplace's Coefficients, the Figure of the Earth, the Motion of a Rigid Body about its Center of Gravity, and Precession and Nutation* (Cambridge, 1840).

(8) John Henry Pratt, Caius 1829, third wrangler 1833, Fellow 1836 (Venn). See his text *The Mathematical Tracts. Part I. On Laplace's Coefficients, the Figure of the Earth, the Motion of a Rigid Body Architecture, but chiefly to the Theory of Universal Gravitation* (Cambridge, $_2$1845): 159–75.

I think a very little mortar would make a desirable edifice out of your article.

In selecting the absolute value of the constant coefft of a harmonic we may go on one of several principles. Mine is to differentiate $\dfrac{1}{r}$ i times with respect to i directions which may be coincident or not,[9] and then divide by $\lfloor i$ and multiply by r^{i+1}.[10]

If they coincide we get Q_i.[11]

If $i-s$[12] coincide with the axis of symmetry and s are at intervals of $\dfrac{\pi}{s}$ round the equator we get a symmetrical system containing $s\phi$.

This is $Y_i^{(s)} = 2^x \dfrac{\lfloor i-s}{2^s \lfloor i} \sin^s \theta \dfrac{d^s Q_i}{d\mu^s} \cos(s\phi + \alpha)$

except when $s = 0$ when $2^x = 1$.[13]

Your $\Theta_i^{(s)}$[14] is $\sin^s \theta \dfrac{d^s Q_i}{d\mu} \cos(s\phi + \alpha)$.

That of $T + T'$[15] is yours multiplied by $\dfrac{2^i \lfloor i \lfloor i-s}{\lfloor 2i}$

and has the coefft of μ^{i-s} equal to 1.

$T + T'$'s $\dfrac{\vartheta_i^{(s)}}{\sin^s \theta}$ is $= 1$ when $\mu = 1$.[16]

$\vartheta_i^{(s)} =$ your $\Theta_i^s \times 2^s \dfrac{\lfloor i-s \lfloor s}{\lfloor i+s}$.[17]

The great thing is to avoid confusion. I rather think your value is the best to impress on the mind.

It lies between it and $\vartheta_i^{(s)}$ which has a certain claim.

The diggings in Σφαρξ are very rich and a judicious man might get up a capital book for Cambridge, in which the wranglers would lade themselves with thick clay till they become blind to the concrete.

---

(9) See Number 281 and the *Treatise*, **1**: 162 (§131).
(10) See the *Treatise*, **1**: 160 (§130). Maxwell uses the symbol $\lfloor$ for factorial: see Numbers 389 and 390.
(11) See Number 387 note (9).   (12) See Number 387 note (8).
(13) See the *Treatise*, **1**: 164 (§132); for the spherical coordinates θ and ϕ and for μ and $Y_i^{(s)}$ see Number 387 notes (4) and (10).   (14) In his 'Note on spherical harmonics'.
(15) Thomson and Tait, *Natural Philosophy*: 149.
(16) For $\vartheta_i^{(s)}$ see Number 384 note (6).   (17) See Number 387.

But try and do the 4^{nions}. The unbelievers are rampant. They say 'show me something done by 4^{nions} which has not been done by old plans. At the best it must rank with abbreviated notation'.

You should reply to this, no doubt you will. But the virtue of the 4^{nions} lies not so much as yet in solving hard questions as in enabling us to see the meaning of the question and of its solution, instead of setting up the question in $x\,y\,z$, sending it to the analytical engine and when the solution is sent home translating it back from $x\,y\,z$ so that it may appear as A, B, C to the vulgar.

There appears to be a desire for thermodynamics in these regions more than I expected, but there are some very good men to be found.

You will observe a tendency to bosch in this letter which pray xqs as I have been reading an ill assorted lot of books till I cannot correct prooves.

Yours truly
$\frac{dp}{dt}$

In (6)[18] divide by $(1-\mu^2)^s$ and then differentiate the equ^{n} after (13) with respect to μ and you get a result the same as if you put $s+1$ for s and $\theta^{(s+1)}$ for $\frac{d\theta^{(s)}}{d\mu}$. Hence if $\theta^{(s+1)} = C\frac{d\theta^{(s)}}{d\mu}$, this is a solution. But $\theta^{(0)} = Q_i$. Q.E.D.

Eq^{n} to begin with.

$$\left\{i(i+1) - s(s+1)\right\}\theta_i^{(s)} - 2(s+1)\mu\frac{d\theta_i^{(s)}}{d\mu} + (1-\mu^2)\frac{d^2\theta_i^{(s)}}{d\mu^2} = 0.$$

---

(18) Of Tait's paper 'Note on spherical harmonics': 593.

POSTCARD TO PETER GUTHRIE TAIT

7 NOVEMBER 1871

From the original in the University Library, Cambridge[1]

[Cambridge]

Laplace is a very clever fellow. Liv III, chap. II.[2]

O T′ Weber has reason.[3] His force has a potential[4] which involves the square of the relative velocity.[5] Hence in any cyclic operation no work is spent or gained. So Conservation is conserved. But Helmholtz has shown (Crelle = ^{ns} of electric motion)[6] that it is possible (by Webers Law) to produce in a material particle carrying electricity an infinite velocity in a finite space and finite time and it appears from the formula that forthwith it is hurled with this ∞ velocity into a region where by the formula the velocity is $\sqrt{-1}$.[7]

---

(1) ULC Add. MSS 7655, I, b/36. Previously published in facsimile in P. M. Harman, *Energy, Force, and Matter* (Cambridge, 1982): 96. See Plate XV.

(2) Laplace's discussion of the Laplace coefficients in Book III chapter 2 ('Développement en série, des attractions des sphéroides quelconques') of his *Traité de Mécanique Céleste*, 5 vols. (Paris, An VII [1799]–1825), **2**: 25–49 (= *Oeuvres Complètes de Laplace*, 14 vols. (Paris, 1878–1912), **2**: 24–52).

(3) Maxwell now recognises that Helmholtz's argument in *Über die Erhaltung der Kraft*, which he had himself supported (see Number 284 note (13)), that Weber's electrodynamic force law was inconsistent with energy conservation, is invalid. Compare his discussion in the *Treatise*, **2**: 429–30 (§§852–3) where he explains Weber's argument.

(4) As Weber had established in 1848. See Wilhelm Weber, 'Elektrodynamische Maassbestimmungen', *Ann. Phys.*, **73** (1848): 193–240, esp. 229 (= *Wilhelm Weber's Werke*, 6 vols. (Berlin, 1892–4), **3**: 215–54).

(5) Wilhelm Weber, 'Ueber einen einfachen Ausspruch des allgemeinen Grundgesetzes der elektrischen Wirkung', *Ann. Phys.*, **136** (1869): 485–9 (= *Werke*, **4**: 243–6). Weber obtains the formula $\frac{ee'}{r}\left[1-\frac{1}{c^2}\left(\frac{dr}{dt}\right)^2\right]$ for the potential between two moving particles of charge e, e' at a distance r from each other, where c is a limiting velocity of the electric masses.

(6) Hermann Helmholtz, 'Ueber die Bewegungsgleichungen der Elektricität für ruhende leitende Körper', *Journal für die reine und angewandte Mathematik*, **72** (1870): 57–128, esp. 63–4.

(7) Helmholtz states: 'Aber es widerspricht in so fern, als zwei elektrische Theilchen, die sich nach diesem Gesetze bewegen und mit endlicher Geschwindigkeit beginnen, in endlicher Entfernung von einander unendliche lebendige Kraft erreichen und also eine unendlich grosse Arbeit leisten können' ('Ueber die Bewegungsgleichungen der Elektricität': 63). Maxwell states this conclusion in the *Treatise*, **2**: 430 (§854).

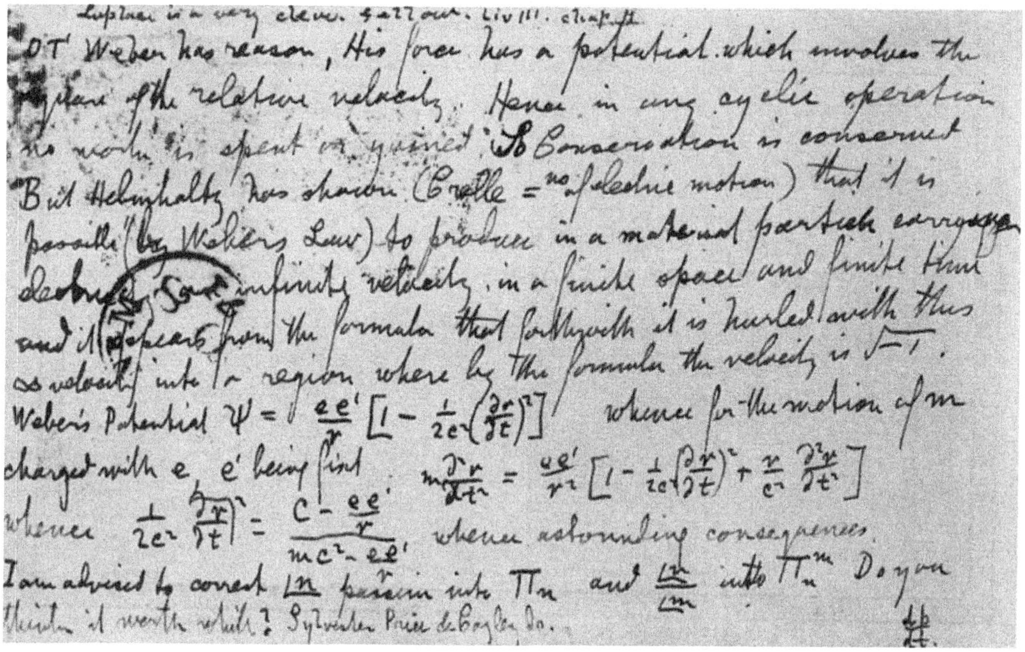

Plate XV. Maxwell's postcard to Peter Guthrie Tait of 7 November 1871 (Number 389).

Weber's Potential $\psi = \frac{ee'}{r}\left[1 - \frac{1}{2c^2}\left(\frac{\partial r}{\partial t}\right)^2\right]$ (8) whence for the motion of m charged with e, e' being fixt

$$m\frac{\partial^2 r}{\partial t^2} = \frac{ee'}{r^2}\left[1 - \frac{1}{2c^2}\left(\frac{\partial r}{\partial t}\right)^2 + \frac{r}{c^2}\frac{\partial^2 r}{\partial t^2}\right]^{(9)}$$

whence $\dfrac{1}{2c^2}\overline{\dfrac{\partial r}{\partial t}\Big|}^2 = \dfrac{C - \dfrac{ee'}{r}}{mc^2 - \dfrac{ee'}{r}}$ (10) whence astounding consequences.[11]

I am advised to correct $\underline{|n}$ passim into Π_n and $\dfrac{\underline{|n}}{\underline{|m}}$ into Π_n^m.[12] Do you think it worth while? Sylvester Price[13] & Cayley do.[14]

$\dfrac{dp}{dt}$

---

(8) But compare Weber's formula (see note (5)), as correctly cited by Helmholtz, 'Ueber die Bewegungsgleichungen der Elektricität': 64n.

(9) In his 'Ueber die Bewegungsgleichungen der Elektricität': 63 Helmholtz gives Weber's electrodynamic force law in the form $m\dfrac{d^2r}{dt^2} = \dfrac{ee'}{r^2}\left[1 - \dfrac{1}{c^2}\left(\dfrac{dr}{dt}\right)^2 + \dfrac{2r}{c^2}\dfrac{d^2r}{dt^2}\right]$, where m is the mass of the electric particle e, again correctly following Weber's own statement of the law in his paper 'Elektrodynamische Maassbestimmungen, insbesondere Widerstandsmessungen', *Abhandlungen der Königlichen Sächsischen Gesellschaft der Wissenschaften, math.-phys. Klasse*, **1** (1852): 199–381, on 268 (= *Werke*, **3**: 301–471).

(10) Following Helmholtz, 'Ueber die Bewegungsgleichungen der Elektricität': 64. Multiplying the force law by dr/dt and integrating, Helmholtz obtains $\dfrac{m}{2}\left(\dfrac{dr}{dt}\right)^2 = C - \dfrac{ee'}{r} + \dfrac{ee'}{rc^2}\left(\dfrac{dr}{dt}\right)^2$ (where C is the constant of integration), and hence $\dfrac{1}{c^2}\left(\dfrac{dr}{dt}\right)^2 = \dfrac{C - (ee'/r)}{\frac{1}{2}mc^2 - (ee'/r)}$.

(11) Helmholtz concludes: 'Ist $ee'/r > \frac{1}{2}mc^2 > C$ so ist $(dr/dt)^2$ positiv und grösser als c^2, also dr/dt reell. Ist letzteres selbst positiv, so wird r wachsen, bis $ee'/r = \frac{1}{2}mc^2$, dann wird dr/dt unendlich gross. Dasselbe wird geschehen, wenn in Anfange $C > \frac{1}{2}mc^2 > ee'/r$ und dr/dt negativ ist.' ('Ueber die Bewegungsgleichungen der Elektricität': 64).

(12) Tait had used the symbol $\underline{|n}$ for n-factorial, writing '$1.2.3....n = \underline{|n}$' in his paper 'On the law of the frequency of error', *Trans. Roy. Soc. Edinb.*, **24** (1865): 139–45, on 141. For further discussion of these symbols see Number 390, esp. notes (3) and (4).

(13) Bartholomew Price: see Number 367 note (3).

(14) In his reply (to Numbers 388 and 389) dated 10 November 1871 (ULC Add. MSS 7655, I, a/22), Tait made further reference to his 'Note on spherical harmonics', presented to the Royal Society of Edinburgh on 18 December 1871 (see Number 388 note (2)): 'O dp/dt 'ηρ αρ

μωρ Σφαρξ. Let $\sqrt{1+2\mu h+h^2} = 1+hy$, $h/\sqrt{} = h\, dy/d\mu$. But

$$y = \mu + h\frac{1-y^2}{2} = \mu + h\frac{1-\mu^2}{2} + \frac{h}{1.2}\frac{d}{d\mu}\left(\frac{1-\mu^2}{2}\right)^2 + \ldots,$$

$$\therefore Q_i = (-)^i\left(\frac{d}{d\mu}\right)^i\left(\frac{1-\mu^2}{2}\right)^i.$$

This is *not* Potato? The complete integral of $i(i+1)q_i + \frac{d}{d\mu}\left(\overline{1-\mu^2}\frac{dq_i}{d\mu}\right) = 0$ is $q_i = CQ_i\int\frac{d\mu}{(1-\mu^2)Q_i^2}$; and if Q_i be expressed in terms of q_i, we have $S_i = P_iQ_i$ where $\frac{d^2P_i}{dq_i^2} + Q_i^4\frac{d^2P_i}{d\phi^2} = 0$. This at once *suggests* $P_i = \Sigma_0^i A_s\Theta_i^{(s)}\cos(s\phi+\alpha_s)$. The 4^{ns} are going on, but the essential asymmetry bothers them as they are not naturally lopsided. $V_i = r^{i+1}S\alpha_1\nabla S\alpha_2\nabla S\alpha_3\nabla \ldots S\alpha_i\nabla\frac{C}{r}$ where the operator may be written $S.(\alpha_1\nabla\alpha_2\nabla\ldots\alpha_i\nabla)$ – a *very* curious result. At any rate $\iint(V_i)^2 ds = \frac{2^{i+2}\pi}{\underline{|2i+1}}a^{2i+2}\Sigma_0^{2i}(_sV_0^2)$!!!

By all means make $\underline{|i} = \Pi_i$, if Cayley & Sylvester wish it – Price is the opposite of priceless in this matter. Why not take Euler's formula $\underline{|n} = \Gamma(n+1)$? ℘.'

390

POSTCARD TO WILLIAM THOMSON

7 NOVEMBER 1871

From the original in the University Library, Cambridge[1]

[Cambridge]

Pray return sheet M (p 161–176) with remarks if possible.[2](a)(b) I am requested to extirpate the Johnian symbol $\lfloor i$[3] and to adopt the Gaussian Π_i.[4] I had used $\lfloor i$ as a mere abbreviation for $1.\,2\ldots i$,[5] not as a definite integral which has this value when i is integral. I send you slip as far as 64 which annotate at your convenience & return. You will see the Electrometers there.[6]

Laplace[7] has a clear view of the Biaxial harmonic.[8] T′ has an excellent discussion[9] of Q_i[10] and $\vartheta_i^{(s)}$[11] and their relations deduced from their definitions and not from their expansions as Murphy does.[12] Murphy is very clever, but not easily appreciated by the beginner. We are beginning θermodynamics.[13]

$$\frac{dp}{dt}$$

(a) {Thomson} (done) T Nov 9/71

(b) {Thomson} I thought it very good if it was it you sent me. Can I do more just now in the matter?

(1) ULC Add. MSS 7655, II/52. Previously published (in part) in Knott, *Life of Tait*: 102.

(2) *Treatise* §§ 130–44.

(3) In referring thus to the symbol $\lfloor i$ for the i-factorial Maxwell probably has Isaac Todhunter (St John's 1844, senior wrangler 1848, Fellow 1849 (Venn)) in mind. On his use of the symbol '$\lfloor n \ldots$ for the product $1.2,\ldots n$' see Todhunter, *A History of the Mathematical Theory of Probability* (Cambridge/London, 1865): ix.

(4) Carl Friedrich Gauss, 'Disquisitiones generales circa seriem infinitam', *Commentationes Societas Regiae Scientiarum Gottingensis Recentiores*, **2** (1812): on 26 (= Gauss, *Werke*, 3 (Göttingen, 1866): 125–62, on 146); where Gauss writes '$\Pi z = 1.2.3.\ldots z$'.

(5) See Numbers 387 and 388, a usage he retained in the *Treatise*.

(6) See the *Treatise*, **1**: 263–80 (§§ 214–25).

(7) See Number 389 note (2).

(8) A term used by Thomson and Tait, *Natural Philosophy*: 157.

(9) See Number 388 note (2).   (10) See Number 387 note (9).

(11) See Number 384 note (6).   (12) See Number 388 esp. note (5).

(13) In his Cambridge lectures on 'Heat': see *Cambridge University Reporter* (October 18, 1871): 16.

391

LETTER TO ROBERT DUNDAS CAY

23 NOVEMBER 1871

From the original in the Library of Peterhouse, Cambridge[1]

11 Scroope Terrace
Cambridge
23 Nov 1871

My dear Uncle Robert

I enclose Receipt for £56.17/ .[2]

We are sorry that you have had such a severe attack of Bronchitis but we hope you are now getting better.

We have been very busy getting settled here and are not quite done yet with the settling. We have had severe cold weather which has been very trying for my wife. Our most important business is attending solemn feasts from 7 to 10 p.m. graced by the presence of not less than two Masters of Colleges and ornamented with a selection of Doctors of Divinity and filled up with Masters of Arts and their wives. To arrange these dignitaries a diligent study of the Calendar is required. In due time we shall have to draw up a scheme of their positions round our table so as to avoid any errors of precedence.

The minor amusements of lecturing &c go on without disturbance. Next term building will commence.[3]

With kind regards from self & wife.

Your aff^t nephew
J. CLERK MAXWELL

---

(1) Peterhouse, Maxwell MSS (32).   (2) See Volume I: 682n.
(3) See Number 397.

392

REPORTED COMMENTS ON THE STRAINS OF AN IRON STRUCTURE

5 DECEMBER 1871[1]

From the *Proceedings of the Institution of Civil Engineers*[2]

[DISCUSSION OF A PAPER BY WILLIAM BELL][3]

Professor J. Clerk Maxwell observed, through the Secretary,[4] that if the Author of the Paper could prove that his method of measuring the strains on comparatively small portions, as 50 inches,[5] of an iron structure was practicable, it would be a most valuable means of testing the accuracy of engineering calculations; and a careful examination of the marks before and after the erection, and again a year or two afterwards, would enable an opinion to be formed, as to the security of the structure itself, and as to the behaviour of iron under long-continued strains.[6] Experiments were confined so exclusively to longitudinal stress, that instances of yielding to different kinds of combined stress, such as occurred in structures, must be very useful. For example, there was no evidence to show how the value of the greatest safe vertical pressure or tension would be modified if one, or two, horizontal pressures or tensions coexisted with it. Probably two horizontal pressures would increase the power of supporting a vertical pressure. A thorough discussion of the experiments of M. Tresca on lead might give some information as to that material, which, however, was not much used by Engineers. Nevertheless, a perusal of Tresca's 'Sur l'écoulement des corps solides'*[7] might be interesting to practical men, as it bore on the theory of punching and wire-drawing.

* *Vide* 'Mémoire sur l'écoulement des corps solides soumis à des fortes pressions. Par H. Tresca. Comptes rendus hebdomadaires des Séances de l'Académie des Sciences, 1864'. Tome lix, p. 754 *et seq.*[7]

---

(1) See note (3).

(2) *Minutes of Proceedings of the Institution of Civil Engineers; with Abstracts of the Discussions*, **33** (1871): 130–1.

(3) William Bell, 'On the stresses of rigid arches, continuous beams, and curved structures', *Minutes of Proceedings of the Institution of Civil Engineers*, **33** (1871): 58–126, read 5 December 1871.

(4) James Forrest. (5) Bell, 'On the stresses of rigid arches': 124–6.

(6) In response, Bell observed that 'there were as yet no experiments to show the minimum distance between the marks, which would give reliable information as to the state of strain on the metal...'; *ibid.*: 158–9.

(7) H. Tresca, 'Mémoire sur l'écoulement des corps solides soumis à des fortes pressions', *Comptes Rendus*, **59** (1864): 754–8.

POSTCARD TO PETER GUTHRIE TAIT

7 DECEMBER 1871

From the original in the University Library, Cambridge[1]

[Cambridge]

Find $\int_0^\pi \int_0^{2\pi} \int_{9\text{Dec}1871}^{1\text{Feb}1872} \left\{Q_0 + 3Q_1 + \ldots + (2i+1)Q_i + \&c\right\} \frac{1}{4\pi} \frac{d}{d\sigma} \frac{dp}{dt} \cos\lambda \, d\tau \, dl \, d\lambda$

where the pole of the zonal harmonics is at $\lambda = 55°.1'$N, $l = 3°.38'$W.[2]

Compare T's equ^{ns} derived from 2nd law of $\Theta\Delta^{cs}$[3] with Edlunds expts on Peltier effect Phil Mag 1871.[4]

Peltier effect (ratios)[5]		Thermoelectric E.M.F. for 10 °C diff.[6]
Bismuth–Copper	141.3	78.47 – Why so small?[7]
Argentan[8]–copper	15.57	24.17
Platinum–copper	5.37	8.30
Copper–iron	17.83	24.93

(1) ULC Add. MSS 7655, I, b/37.

(2) The latitude and longitude of Glenlair: see Number 292.

(3) William Thomson, 'On the dynamical theory of heat. Part V. Thermo-electric currents', *Trans. Roy. Soc. Edinb.*, **21** (1854): 123–71, esp. 133–45 (= *Math. & Phys. Papers*, **1**: 232–91). See also Number 322.

(4) E. Edlund, 'On the electromotive force on the contact of different metals', *Phil. Mag.*, ser. 4, **41** (1871): 18–29.

(5) As given by Edlund, 'On the electromotive force on the contact of different metals': 25.

(6) As given by Edlund, 'On the electromotive force on the contact of different metals': 28.

(7) Thomson responded to Maxwell's query in a card dated 4 January 1872 (ULC Add. MSS 7655, I, a/24): 'T 2 dp/dt / the el. m. f.^{ce} of a thermo-elect circuit belongs to the whole circuit not to either junction alone. See waterpipe analogy Proc RSE 1851 (if the Secretaries have correctly reported the whole proceedings of the meeting). The more we understand of the potential, pressure, &^{c} of electricity in metals the more perfect is the analogy. You are welcome to the thermo O^t copper zinc air I have done with it years ago till I come back to it again. Oil of turpentine (as dry as you can get) and melted paraffin may be substituted for the air. I am doing so not very successfully now, and did so many times & years back. You said that Clausius made proportionality of current to external EMF in electrolysis which was what I objected to. / I have no doubt of the diffusion theory of currents through electrolytes in infin. EMF. /25 years ago I did not

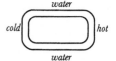

Figure 393,1. If mean temp^{re} > 4°

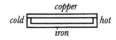

Figure 393,2. If mean temp^{re} > 289°

Motto for an abuse of vortex atoms
δῖνος βασιλεύει τον Δί' εξεληλακώς.⁽⁹⁾

know that $\iint f(x,y)\,dx\,dy$ is absurd. / The current is against hands of a watch. / Can you come on Frid. or Sat. or if not, when?' The paper Thomson refers to is his paper 'On a mechanical theory of thermo-electric currents', *Proc. Roy. Soc. Edinb.*, **3** (1851): 91–8 (= *Math. & Phys. Papers*, **1**: 316–23), where there is no mention of the analogy to which he alludes. Thomson had published the analogy in his 'On the dynamical theory of heat. Part V': 147. See also Number 428 esp. note (10).

(8) An alloy of nickel, copper and zinc (German silver); see Henry Watts, *A Dictionary of Chemistry*, 5 vols. (London, 1863–9), **1**: 356, and **2**: 51.

(9) Aristophanes, *The Clouds*, 1471. See *The Clouds of Aristophanes* [trans. B. B. Rogers] (Oxford, 1852): 125; 'Young Vortex reigns, and he has turned out Zeus'.

394

POSTCARD TO PETER GUTHRIE TAIT

12 DECEMBER 1871

From the original in the University Library, Cambridge[1]

[Glenlair]

O T'. The neutral pt[2] as depending on sp.h of E^y[3] is a T' thing and should be expressed in terms of T'. Do any such terms exist besides Lab. notes P.RSE 1870–71 p308?[4] If so, send them. I have of course got the relation[5]

$$T_{ab} = \frac{k_a T_a - k_b T_b}{k_a - k_b}$$

where k_a k_b are the sp. h. in 2 metals[6] and T_a T_b the neutral pts with respect to a standard metal (Standard metal should have $k = 0$ if possible (which it is)). Pray send what may be described as the very words of T'.[7]

$$\frac{dp}{dt}$$

---

(1) ULC Add. MSS 7655, I, b/38.

(2) The temperature at which pairs of metals in a thermo-electric circuit are neutral to each other. See William Thomson, 'On the dynamical theory of heat. Part V. Thermo-electric currents', *Trans. Roy. Soc. Edinb.*, **21** (1854): 123–71, esp. 145.

(3) Thomson's term 'specific heat of electricity'; see his 'Thermo-electric currents': 146.

(4) P. G. Tait, 'On thermo-electricity', *Proc. Roy. Soc. Edinb.*, **7** (1870): 308–11.

(5) But see Number 396.   (6) But see Number 401.

(7) See Number 396 esp. note (2).

395

DRAFT OF PAPER 'ON THE GEOMETRICAL MEAN DISTANCE OF TWO FIGURES ON A PLANE'[1]

circa DECEMBER 1871[2]

From the original in the University Library, Cambridge[3]

ON THE GEOMETRICAL MEAN DISTANCE OF TWO PLANE FIGURES[4]

The following method of treating the mutual induction of two conductors is useful in the case of coils.

Let there be two conductors such that the transverse section of the two conductors is a figure of the same form at all parts of the length of the conductors and let the dimensions of this double section be small compared with the radius of curvature of the axis of either conductor. It is required to find the distance at which two linear conductors must be placed from each other having the same form of axis as the actual conductors so that the coefficient of the mutual induction of the linear conductors may be equal to that of the two given conductors.

The coefficient of mutual induction of two linear conductors which are everywhere equidistant depends on the logarithm of their distance.[5] Hence what we have to find is the arithmetical mean of the logarithms of the distances between every pair of filaments one in each conductor and this is the logarithm of the distance required.

In other words the distance required is the geometrical mean of the distances between every pair of filaments, one in each conductor.

Hence, when the form and relative position of the transverse sections of the two conductors are given, we have only to solve the geometrical problem of finding the geometrical mean of the distances between pairs of points one in each of two plane figures, the points being understood to be uniformly distributed in each figure.

The following are some of the results of this method of finding what we may call the geometrical mean distance.

---

(1) *Trans. Roy. Soc. Edinb.*, **26** (1872): 729–33 (= *Scientific Papers*, **2**: 280–5), read 15 January 1872 (see *Proc. Roy. Soc. Edinb.*, **7** (1872): 613). Proofs are in ULC Add. MSS 7655, V, c/17.

(2) See Maxwell's letter to P. G. Tait of 21 December 1871 (Number 396).

(3) ULC Add. MSS 7655, V, c/16.

(4) See also the *Treatise*, **2**: 294–8 (§§ 691–3).

(5) See the *Treatise*, **2**: 289 (§ 685).

Let the section of the first conductor be a thin circular ring and that of the other a point, then the geometrical mean distance of the point from the ring is equal to its distance from the centre of the ring when the point is outside the ring, and equal to the radius of the ring when the point is inside the ring.

If the sections of both conductors are thin circular rings then if each ring is outside the other the mean distance is the distance of their centres, but if the one is within the other their mean distance is the radius of the greater.

If the sections of both conductors are circular areas, or rings bounded by concentric circles and if each is outside the other then their mean distance is the distance of their centres.

If however the one is wholly within the other and if a_1 and a_2 are the outer and inner radii of the outer ring, and R the mean distance required then

$$\log R = \frac{a_1^2 \log a_1 - a_2^2 \log a_2}{a_1^2 - a_2^2} - \frac{1}{2}.$$

It appears from this that R is independent of the form of the section of the conductor which is within the tubular conductor.

It is not necessary that the two figures should be different in order to determine their mean distance for we may find the geometrical mean of the distance between all pairs of points of the same figure.

In the case of a circular area of radius a this mean distance is R where $\log R = \log a - \frac{1}{4}$.

In the case of a ring bounded by two concentric circles of radii a_1 and a_2, a_1 being the greater

$$\log R = \log a_1 - \frac{a_2^4}{(a_1^2 - a_2^2)^2} \log \frac{a_1}{a_2} + \frac{1}{4} \frac{3a_2^2 - a_1^2}{a_1^2 - a_2^2}.$$

When the ring is very thin R becomes equal to a_1.

If the section of the first conductor is the line AB and that of the second the point O such that OA is perpendicular to AB and $AOB = \theta$

$$\log R = \log OB + \frac{\theta}{\tan \theta} - 1.$$

The mean distance of BC from O is R where

$$\log R = \frac{AC \log OC - AB \log OB + \widehat{BOC} \cdot OA}{BC} - 1.$$

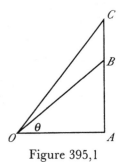

Figure 395,1

If R is the geometrical mean of the distances of every pair of points on a straight line from each other the length of the line being a

$$\log R = \log a - \frac{3}{2}.$$

If R is the geometrical mean of the distances of every pair of points one in each of two lines AB and CD lying in the same straight line then

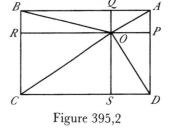

Figure 395,2

$2AB.CD \log R$
$= AD^2 \log AD + BC^2 \log BC - AC^2 \log AC$
$\quad - BD^2 \log BD - 3AB.CD.$

If R is the geometrical mean of the distances of every point of the rectangle $ABCD$ from the point O

$$2AB.AD \log R = 2OP.OQ \log OA + 2OQ.OR \log OB$$
$$+ 2OR.OS \log OC + 2OS.OP \log OD$$
$$+ \widehat{BOA}.OP^2 + \widehat{AOB}.OQ^2 + \widehat{BOC}.OR^2$$
$$+ \widehat{COD}.OS^2 - 3AB.AD.$$

If the point O is one of the angles of a rectangle whose sides are a and b and diagonal $r = \sqrt{a^2 + b^2}$

$$\log R = \log r + \frac{1}{2}\frac{a}{b}\tan^{-1}\frac{b}{a} + \frac{1}{2}\frac{b}{a}\tan^{-1}\frac{a}{b} - \frac{3}{2}.$$

When $a = b$ $\quad \log R = \log a + \frac{1}{2}\log 2 + \frac{\pi}{2} - \frac{3}{2}$
$\qquad = \log a + 0.4273699.$

If R is the geometrical mean of the distances of every pair of points of this rectangle

$$\log R = \log r - \frac{1}{6}\frac{a^2}{b^2}\log\frac{r}{a} - \frac{1}{6}\frac{b^2}{a^2}\log\frac{r}{b}$$
$$+ \frac{2}{3}\frac{a}{b}\tan^{-1}\frac{b}{a} + \frac{2}{3}\frac{b}{a}\tan^{-1}\frac{a}{b} - \frac{25}{12}.$$

When $a = b$ $\quad \log R = \log a + \frac{1}{3}\log 2 + \frac{\pi}{3} - \frac{25}{12}$
$\qquad = \log a - 0.8050866.$

In terms of logarithms to base 10 we have, when

$b = a$	$\log_{10}\frac{R}{a} = \overline{1}.6503553$	$\frac{R}{a} = 0.44705$	$\log_{\epsilon}\frac{R}{a} = -0.8050866$
$b = 2a$	$\log_{10}\frac{R}{a} = \overline{1}.92648$	$\frac{R}{a} = 0.84427$	$\log_{\epsilon}\frac{R}{a} = -0.39954$
$b = 3a$	$\log_{10}\frac{R}{a} = \overline{1}.95163$	$\frac{R}{a} = 0.89461$	$\log_{\epsilon}\frac{R}{a} = -0.11138$
$b = 4a$	$\log_{10}\frac{R}{a} = \overline{1}.96183$	$\frac{R}{a} = 0.91587$	$\log_{\epsilon}\frac{R}{a} = -0.08789$
$b = 3x\ \ a = 2x$	$\log_{10}\frac{R}{x} = 0.05194$	$\frac{R}{x} = 1.1271$	$\log_{\epsilon}\frac{R}{x} = +0.11960$
$b = 4x\ \ a = 3x$	$\log_{10}\frac{R}{x} = 0.19443$	$\frac{R}{x} = 1.5647$	$\log_{\epsilon}\frac{R}{x} = +0.44770$

If two squares have a side common to both the geometrical mean distance of pairs of points one in each square is $0.99401a$ where a is the side of the square.

If the two squares are placed so as to have one angle in contact and their diagonals in a straight line, the geometrical mean distance is $1.0011d$ where d is the diagonal.

Hence for squares at greater distances we may consider the geometrical mean distance as the distance between their centres of gravity without introducing more than one thousandth part of error.

396

LETTER TO PETER GUTHRIE TAIT

21 DECEMBER 1871

From the original in the University Library, Cambridge[1]

Glenlair
21 Dec 1871

O. T.

Am I right in supposing the following to be a graphic representation of your $\Theta.H.$ theory.[2]

Let $k_a\ k_b\ k_c$ be sp. h. of η in metals $a\,b\,c$.[3] From pure thermoelectric experiments we can determine the difference $k_a - k_b$ in absolute measure, and from Thomsons much more precarious direct experiments[4] we may make a shot at the ratio $k_a : k_b$ say in iron & copper in which k_a and k_b are of opposite signs and one of them is small. Hence the absolute values can be ascertained roughly and the differences very approximately.

In this way draw Thomson's figure[5] as on last page. (If you reject Thomson absolute determinations of sp h the figure simply gets a little loose in the joints.)

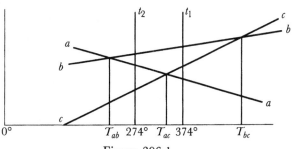

Figure 396,1

Then the Π_{ab}eltier effect at temperature t is the parallelogram whose base is the intercept of the ordinate between the lines a and b and whose height is up to temperature 0°.

The electromotive force for junctions at t_1 and t_2 is the area intercepted between the ordinates t_1 & t_2 and the lines aa and bb. (Remember signs if t_1 & t_2 are on opposite sides of t_{ab}.)

---

(1) ULC Add. MSS 7655, I, b/39. Published in extract in Knott, *Life of Tait*: 150.

(2) See P. G. Tait, 'On thermo-electricity', *Proc. Roy. Soc. Edinb.*, **7** (1871): 597–602, read 18 December 1871.

(3) See Number 394 esp. note (3).

(4) William Thomson, 'On the electro-dynamic qualities of metals', *Phil. Trans.*, **146** (1856): 649–751, esp. 649–709 (= *Math. & Phys. Papers*, **2**: 189–327, esp. 189–266).

(5) Thomson, 'On the electro-dynamic qualities of metals': 708; and also Thomson, 'On the dynamical theory of heat. Part V. Thermo-electric currents', *Trans. Roy. Soc. Edinb.*, **21** (1854): 123–71, esp. 146 (= *Math. & Phys. Papers*, **1**: 232–91).

Also by property of straight lines
$$(k_b - k_c) T_{bc} + (k_c - k_a) T_{ca} + (k_a - k_b) T_{ab} = 0$$
a relation between the neutral pts.[6]

Would the R.S.E. care for a short statement of the importance of a knowledge of the Geometrical Mean Distance of Two Figures in the same plane (which may be identical)?[7] Of course this means the geometric mean of all the distances between points in the figures, the points being scattered with uniform density.

The Harmonic mean distance of any two bodies is of course still more important in itself but it happens not to be wanted so much.

The Geometric ditto is the thing for coils of wire &c &c.

The Harmonic for ordinary attractions.

If so I will send you it before the 15th Jan.

Pray let me know soon about the thermoelectricity as it is your thing and I am improving the statement of it as per your note.

Impress on T that $\frac{d^2}{dx^2} + \frac{d^2}{dy^2} + \frac{d^2}{dz^2} = -\nabla^2$ and not $+\nabla^2$ as he vainly asserts is now commonly believed among us.

Also how much better and easier he would have done his solenoidal and lamellar business[8] if in addition to what we know is in him he had had, say 20 years ago, Q_s^n to hunt for Cartesians instead of vice versâ. The one is a flaming sword which turns every way; the other is a ram pushing westward and northward and (downward?).

What we want a Council to determine is the true doctrine of brackets and dots and the limits of the jurisdiction of operators.

$$\frac{\partial p}{\partial \theta}$$

Thanks for prooves. I send you more just received.

---

(6) See the *Treatise*, **1**: 306 (§254) for a statement of the argument.

(7) See Number 395 esp. note (1).

(8) On Thomson's discussion of 'solenoidal' and 'lamellar' distributions of magnetism see Numbers 322 note (13) and 353 note (15). Maxwell has in mind his discussion of the effect of ∇ on a vector function σ, terming the scalar part $S\nabla\sigma$ *convergence* and the vector part $V\nabla\sigma$ *curl* (see Number 347 and the *Treatise*, **1**: 28 (§25)). $S\nabla\sigma = 0$ and $V\nabla\sigma = 0$ are solenoidal and lamellar distributions, respectively.

397

LETTER TO WILLIAM MILNER FAWCETT[1]

1 JANUARY 1872

From the original in private possession[2]

Glenlair
Dalbeattie
1 Jan 1872

My dear Sir

Professor Clifton seems to find his white wall useful to him.[3] I do not know myself what the expense of plastering would be. I think a moveable white screen would be sufficient as most of the work will be done by diagrams or on a black board.

I quite agree with you that it is better to have the ceiling of wood instead of plaster.

I have been settling the positions of the stone blocks in the lower floor and of the tables above and also of the holes through the floors for suspension of instruments below. I shall send you plans of these things[4] as soon as I have got them finished. Wishing you a happy New Year

I am
Yours very truly
J. CLERK MAXWELL

---

(1) Jesus 1855; the architect of the Cavendish Laboratory (Venn), the likely addressee. See Number 374 note (6).

(2) Collection of Sydney Ross, donated to the James Clerk Maxwell Foundation, Edinburgh.

(3) In the Oxford laboratory: see Number 365 note (4).

(4) Compare Maxwell's sketch in his card to Thomson of 30 March 1871 (Number 365).

398

POSTCARD TO PETER GUTHRIE TAIT
1 JANUARY 1872
From the original in the University Library, Cambridge[1]

[Glenlair]

O T′ Art thou a Sec. of the F.R.S.E's and knowest not Vol XXIV pt I N° VII, p59[2] where you will see your problem[3] solved. You may state N° 2 thus. Two equal circles have the same horizontal lowest tangent (or if you like stand at different inclinations on the same horizontal plane one vertical, the other inclined) particles are projected at the same instant from the lowest point of each with velocities due to the highest point of *the other*. They will always remain in the same horizontal plane.

The other prop. that the line joining two particles whizzing in the same $\odot$ with the same energy touches a circle with directrix for radical axis, was original to me in 1853 or so.[4] It is involved in the in and circum scribed polygon business.[5] See Cayley[6] & Fox Talbot.[7] It was copied from the C & D.J. of P and A M. into a French book of mathematical varieties[8] which I have but cant find today.

I shoot you the ultramundane corpuscles[9] with the co^{m}p^s of the season.[10]

$$\frac{dp}{dt}$$

---

(1) ULC Add. MSS 7655, I, b/40.

(2) Edward Sang, 'On the motion of a heavy body along the circumference of a circle', *Trans. Roy. Soc. Edinb.*, **24** (1867): 59–71. See also Sang, 'Additional note on the motion of a body along the circumference of a circle', *ibid.*, **26** (1871): 449–57.

(3) See P. G. Tait, 'Note on pendulum motion', *Proc. Roy. Soc. Edinb.*, **7** (1872): 608–11, read 15 January 1872.

(4) 'Problems' set in the *Camb. & Dubl. Math. J.*, **8** (1853): 188; and see [J. C. Maxwell,] 'Solutions to problems', *ibid.*, **9** (1854): 7–11 (= *Scientific Papers*, **1**: 74–9). Drafts are reproduced in Volume I: 230–6, where see 230n on the radical axis of two circles.

(5) See the preliminary draft of Maxwell's solution to Problem II (Volume I: 235–6).

(6) Arthur Cayley, 'On the problem of the in-and-circumscribed triangle', *Phil. Trans.*, **161** (1871): 369–412.

(7) W. H. Fox Talbot, 'Researches on Malfatti's problem', *Trans. Roy. Soc. Edinb.*, **24** (1865): 127–38.

(8) Michel Jullien, *Problèmes de Mécanique Rationelle, disposés pour servir d'applications aux principes enseignés dans les cours*, 2 vols. (Paris, 1855), **1**: 349–52, where the source is given as *Camb. & Dublin Math. J.*, February 1854, p. 7. See Tait's reply (note (10)).

(9) See William Thomson, 'On the ultramundane corpuscles of Le Sage', *Proc. Roy. Soc. Edinb.*, **7** (1871): 577–89, read 18 December 1871; and see Number 377.

(10) In his reply of 2 January 1872 (ULC Add. MSS 7655, I, a/23) Tait writes: 'O dp/dt, It was *precisely* Trans. R.S.E. XXIV, 59, w^h caused me to look up old papers & Tait & Steele. *Jullien* is the book you mean & I have the same. I don't know whether I got y^r prop^n out of it, or out of U, or out of C. & D.M.J. but it has been given (as Ex. of Constr^d M^n) in all the Editions of T. & S. In the 4th it will have y^r name attached. I wrote a little Note for R.S.E. to point out how Sang's *three* long papers c^d be condensed into a few lines. Sh^d I publish? – Prob. Given three pts. on a ☉ find how to place it so that a particle (starting from rest at one) shall pass to the second in $\frac{1}{3}$rd of the time it takes to pass to the third. I am suffering from Vacation with *one*, and with *two*, Cs. ☊ / Has anyone shown that the Retina *wakes* (from sleep) sooner to the lowest of its three principal vibrations than to the others? If not, *I* have.' Tait refers to an example given in P. G. Tait and W. J. Steele, *A Treatise on the Dynamics of a Particle, with Numerous Examples* (London, 1856): 185–6.

399

POSTCARD TO PETER GUTHRIE TAIT
circa 4 JANUARY 1872
From the original in the University Library, Cambridge[1]

[Glenlair]

O T. Of course the readers of Alençon[2] in R.S.E. will be greatly obliged to you if you will give them an inspissated version and if they find it wondrous short it will not hold them long.[3] But above all publish your observation of the rosy dawn of vision.[4] For the red is the first sensation to evanesce with faintness of light, and the slowest in being awakened by the sudden appearance of light.[5] (The 1st observation I believe by seeing, the 2nd only as yet by reading.) Any physiological fact about colour vision is of great importance, and especially if not tacked to any theory.

Do you know of any one who has *worked out* the currents in a spinning plate in presence of a magnet? Kirchhoff is the only man beside T who knows how. I have been getting it out in a simple and applicable form much neater than I expected it wd come.[6] Has T got safe for Great Britain.[7] Is the Vaccation Personal or Filial?[8]

$$\frac{dp}{dt}$$

---

(1) ULC Add. MSS 7655, I, b/41.   (2) Makers of needlepoint lace.

(3) See Tait's discussion of his 'Note on pendulum motion' in his postcard of 2 January 1872 (see Number 398 notes (3) and (10)).

(4) See Tait's observation reported in his postcard of 2 January 1872.

(5) In his 'Note on a singular property of the retina', *Proc. Roy. Soc. Edinb.*, **7** (1872): 605–7, read 15 January 1872, Tait cites Maxwell's comment.

(6) By the principle of images: see Number 400 and the *Treatise*, **2**: 271–5 (§§ 668–9) on the 'Theory of Arago's rotating disk'.

(7) An allusion to a patent case in December 1871, in which Thomson successfully appealed for the prolongation of his 1858 patent on his mirror galvanometer; see S. P. Thompson, *The Life of William Thomson, Baron Kelvin of Largs*, 2 vols. (London, 1910), **2**: 619–21; and also Number 379 note (4). Maxwell wrote a poem 'A lecture on Thomson's mirror galvanometer', published in *Nature*, **6** (16 May 1872): 46 (= Thompson, *Life of Thomson*: 349n).

(8) In his reply of 6 January 1872 (ULC Add. MSS 7655, I, a/25) Tait writes: 'O *dp/dt* Whence get you your (seemingly) constant supply of Mr Lowe's more liberal sized cards? Ex fumo. As to the rotating disc I never tried it – still I think I could do so if necessary – but it is not so, as Jochmann (I think) has done it *very dodgily*, partly in Crelle, partly in Pogg. (the latter in Phil. Mag. about 4 years ago). I'll look them up for you if you like. The Retina goes in on Monday week. So does your Geometric Means. Can you come and read it yourself? The Vaccation is unfortunately Personal, and my left arm is so stiff that I trust to gravity & pressure to hold this card while I scribble thereon. What say you to $\phi(\nabla)$? ℘.'

Robert Lowe was Chancellor of the Exchequer in Gladstone's Liberal administration. In his budget of 1870 he had lowered postage; in 1871 he proposed a tax on matches. Tait's 'ex fumo' (from smoke) puns Lowe's 'Ex luce lucellum' (out of light a little gain) (*DNB*). On Jochmann's papers see Number 404 note (4). Tait alludes to his paper 'On the operator $\phi(\nabla)$', *Proc. Roy. Soc. Edinb.*, **7** (1872): 607–8, read 15 January 1872.

400
LETTER TO GEORGE GABRIEL STOKES
8 JANUARY 1872
From the original in the University Library, Cambridge[1]

Glenlair
Dalbeattie
8 Jan 1872

Dear Professor Stokes

I send you a paper for the Royal Society in which a peculiar kind of image of an electromagnetic system is shown to be formed by a plane sheet of conducting matter.[2]

If a man on board ship were to drop into the sea every second a piece of lead and a piece of cork attached to each other by a string of such a length that, in sinking, the cork is always one second in the rear of the lead, the series of plummets and corks would form a kind of trail in the rear of the vessel which is always sinking with uniform velocity while it retains its shape as a whole.

This gives a mental image of the trail of images of an electromagnet in a conducting sheet. The plummets are positive images and the corks negative images.

N.B. The paper is not offered for the Transactions, as it is to be put into a slightly different form in a separate book.[3]

Yours very truly
J. CLERK MAXWELL

---

(1) ULC Add. MSS 7655, M 429. First published in Larmor, *Correspondence*, 2: 31.

(2) J. Clerk Maxwell, 'On the induction of electric currents in an infinite plane sheet of uniform conductivity', *Proc. Roy. Soc.*, **20** (1872): 160–8 (= *Scientific Papers*, **2**: 286–96). See Number 404 on Maxwell's addition of the supplementary note to the paper.

(3) See the *Treatise*, **2**: 262–75 (§§654–69).

401

POSTCARD TO PETER GUTHRIE TAIT

19 JANUARY 1872
From the original in the University Library, Cambridge[1]

[Glenlair]

O T'. Tell me, ex cathedrâ, this, if α & β are vectors and $\gamma = V.\alpha\beta$ is not γ related to α and β in the same (right or left handed) way as z is related to x and y in the system of axes chosen? Or the reverse? Also is not the English of the above β multiplied by α?[2] I wish to be correct. You may if you please assume $S.\alpha\beta = 0$ and then $\alpha\,\beta\,\gamma$ may be made to fit $i\,j\,k$[3] or $x\,y\,z$ by a proper turning of the system as a whole.

Also are you satisfied with T' on thermoelectricity?[4] I see I have stated wrongly that k is sp h of η[5] whereas kt is the korrect $\theta\iota\nu\gamma$.[6] I wish to get you to press quam prox.[7] I am putting $\mathfrak{C}$ for velocity instead of $\dot{\rho}$[8] to please Bismarck?

$$\frac{dp}{dt}$$

---

(1) ULC Add. MSS 7655, I, b/42.

(2) See P. G. Tait, An *Elementary Treatise on Quaternions* (Oxford, 1867): 54–5, on the scalar and vector products of the multiplication of two vectors. Tait writes $S\alpha\beta = S\beta\alpha$ and $V\alpha\beta = -V\beta\alpha$, noting that 'the only difference is in the *sign* of the vector parts'.

(3) Hamilton's system of three mutually perpendicular unit vectors as lines of reference; see Tait, *Quaternions*: 9.

(4) P. G. Tait, 'On thermo-electricity', *Proc. Roy. Soc. Edinb.*, **7** (1871): 597–602. See Number 396.

(5) See Numbers 394 and 396.

(6) See the *Treatise*, **1**: 306 (§254) following Tait, 'On thermo-electricity': 599, where k is a constant for a metal and t the absolute temperature.

(7) In a card dated 25 January 1872 (ULC Add. MSS 7655, I, a/26) Tait wrote: 'O dp/dt I asked you to work out, for corroboration of my results the following case.

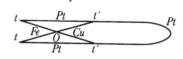

Pray do so soon – and add to the flavour by doing also this – *no* contact at O.

They are all devised with the view of bringing neutral points (otherwise inacceptible) within the range of mercury thermometers. If you can devise any better arrangement I shall be most grateful to you for communicating it. ℒ. / Lindsay out of all danger but useless to me for a month or 6 weeks to come.' James Lindsay was Tait's laboratory technician (see Knott, *Life of Tait*: 66, 73–4).

(8) See the *Treatise*, **2**: 236 (§617), where Maxwell uses the symbol $\mathfrak{C}$ for 'the (total) electric current'.

402

POSTCARD TO WILLIAM THOMSON

8 FEBRUARY 1872

From the original in the University Library, Cambridge[1]

[Cambridge]

[2]p433   *l*3 from bottom, 'infinitely mutual'[3] What are degrees of mutuality?

p448   *l*5 'irrational'[4] p462 *l*14 for 1867 put 1847[5]

p462   *l*17 ∂, 467 footnote en κ /p471 *l*14 sensibility? or susceptibility[6]

p471   *l*23 and 24 read, from the substance in that direction[7]

p478   *l*16 A B and C (see equations), bad arrangement of dashes[8]

$$\text{Should be}^{(a)} \quad \begin{matrix} A & B' & C'' \\ A'' & B & C' \\ A' & B'' & C \end{matrix} \quad \text{when} \quad \begin{matrix} B' = A'' \\ C' = B'' \\ A = B''^{(b)} \end{matrix}$$

line 28 made to turn round a fixed axis[9]

(a) {Thomson} I defined this   (b) {Thomson} $A\ B''\ C\,|\,A' = C$

(1) ULC Add. MSS 7655, II/55.

(2) Maxwell is here correcting proofs of Thomson's *Reprint of Papers on Electrostatics and Magnetism* (London, 1872).

(3) Compare Thomson, *Electrostatics and Magnetism*: 433; 'infinite smaller parts from infinite mutual distances'.

(4) Compare Thomson, *Electrostatics and Magnetism*: 448; 'irrotationally'.

(5) Possibly: Thomson, *Electrostatics and Magnetism*: 453; a reference to a letter to Liouville of 12 September 1847.

(6) Compare Thomson, *Electrostatics and Magnetism*: 472; 'inductive susceptibility'.

(7) See William Thomson, 'On the theory of magnetic induction in crystalline and non-crystalline substances', *Phil. Mag.*, ser. 4, **1** (1851): 177–86, esp. 181 (= *Electrostatics and Magnetism*: 472); 'If the sphere be of isotropic [read: 'non-crystalline' in the 1851 original] substance, the lines of its magnetization are in the same direction as the lines of force in the field into which it is introduced'.

(8) The equations for the magnetisation of a sphere of a homogeneous magnetisable substance in a field of force R, l, m, n being the direction cosines of the force and α, β, γ the components of induced magnetisation: $\alpha = (Al + B'm + C''n)R$, $\beta = (A''l + Bm + C'n)R$, $\gamma = (A'l + B''m + Cn)R$ (= *Electrostatics and Magnetism*: 479). These equations are modified and corrected from those in the original paper; see Thomson, 'On the theory of magnetic induction': 186. A, B, C are coefficients depending solely on the substance.

(9) Thomson had slightly modified the text of his 1851 paper 'On the theory of magnetic induction' to read: 'made to turn round an axis fixed perpendicular to the lines of force...' (*Electrostatics and Magnetism*: 480). For the original text see Number 278 note (10).

Observe how my invincible ignorance of certain modes of thought has caused Clausius to disagree with me (in a digestive sense) so that I failed in my attempts to boil him down and he does not occupy the place in my book on heat to which his other virtues entitle him.[10] If he can get himself assimilated now I shall appear in a state of disgregation.[11] Ergal lusting against Virial, and Virial against Ergal.[12] Any Prooves for $\frac{dp}{dt}$?

(10) See Rudolf Clausius, 'A contribution to the history of the mechanical theory of heat', *Phil. Mag.*, ser. 4, **43** (1872): 106–15 (trans. in the February 1872 number of the *Phil. Mag.* from Clausius's 'Zur Geschichte der mechanischen Wärmetheorie', *Ann. Phys.*, **145** (1872): 132–46), where he complained that Maxwell had intentionally suppressed his name from the *Theory of Heat* (London, 1871).

(11) On Clausius' concept of 'Disgregation', a measure of the arrangement of the molecules in a body, see his paper 'Ueber die Anwendung des Satzes von der Aequivalenz der Verwandlungen auf die innere Arbeit', *Ann. Phys.*, **116** (1862): 73–112, esp. 79. See M. J. Klein, 'Gibbs on Clausius', *Historical Studies in the Physical Sciences*, **1** (1969): 127–49, esp. 135–42.

(12) On 'virial' and 'ergal' see Number 356 note (3).

403

POSTCARD TO PETER GUTHRIE TAIT
12 FEBRUARY 1872
From the original in the University Library, Cambridge[1]

11 Scroope Terrace
Cambridge
12 Feb 1872

O T′ What makes you address to Glenlair? I have no time, strength or fury to smash. As for C. though I imbibed my $\Theta\Delta^{cs}$ from other sources, I know that he is a prime source and have in my work for Longman been unconsciously acted on by the motive not to speak about what I dont know.[2] In my spare moments, I mean to take such draughts of Clausiustical Ergon[3] as to place me in that state of disgregation in which one becomes conscious of the increase of the general sum of Entropy.[4] Meanwhile till

> Ergal & Virial[5] from their thrones be cast
> And end their strife with suicidal yell.

Electromagnetic Trails[6] are to be served up (on toast) by Stokes at R S on Thursday.[7] Note on Felici and Jochmann.[8]

I remain y^{rs} $\frac{dp}{dt}$

---

(1) ULC Add. MSS 7655, I, b/43. (2) See Number 402.
(3) On Clausius' term 'ergon (work)' see Number 356 note (3).
(4) Clausius had defended his concepts of 'disgregation' (see Number 402 note (11)) and 'entropy' (see Number 483 note (22)) in his paper 'A contribution to the history of the mechanical theory of heat'. *Phil. Mag.*, ser. 4, **43** (1872): 106–15, esp. 114.
(5) See Number 356 note (3).
(6) For Maxwell's explanation of the induction of electric currents in a conducting plane sheet, in terms of a moving 'train or trail of images', see Numbers 400 and 405.
(7) See Number 404.
(8) Tait had drawn Maxwell's attention to Jochmann in his card of 6 January 1872 (see Number 399 note (8)), and Maxwell may have been responding here to another card from Tait (undated and without a postmark, but very likely written in January 1872): 'O *dp/dt* I don't know how your prooves got here – since they were inserted in my letter box *without any* cover or address. No matter what Jochmann may have done *he did n't do* what you mention – so send us it in MSS. for the R.S.E. meeting on the 29th. So far as I see at present it is splendid. Also come yourself and expound it – especially as we should all like to smoke you at the Club &^{c} &^{c}. This is the first letter I have written (with the use of two hands) for a week ᘐ.' (ULC Add. MSS 7655, I, a/55). There was a meeting of the Royal Society of Edinburgh on 29 January 1872 (see *Proc. Roy. Soc. Edinb.*, **7** (1872): 615).

404

LETTER TO GEORGE GABRIEL STOKES

12 FEBRUARY 1872

From the original in the University Library, Cambridge[1]

> 11 Scroope Terrace
> Cambridge
> 12 February 1872

My dear Stokes

I send you a note on my paper on induction in a plate,[2] making mention of the researches of Felici[3] and Jochmann,[4] which I could not refer to in the country.

The mutual induction of the induced currents must not be neglected when the relative velocity of the magnet and plate is comparable with V,[5] which, for a copper plate 1 mm thick is about 25 metres per second and for a thicker plate is less, so that the secondary phenomena described in the paper ought to occur, as indeed they do with a thick plate and a high speed i.e.[6]

Primary phenomenon	Tangential Dragging
Secondary	Repulsion from disk
Tertiary	Attraction towards axis.

> Yours truly
> J. CLERK MAXWELL

---

(1) ULC Add. MSS 7656, M 430. First published in Larmor, *Correspondence*, **2**: 32.

(2) A supplementary note to his paper 'On the induction of electric currents in an infinite plane sheet of uniform conductivity', *Proc. Roy. Soc.*, **20** (1872): 160–8, esp. 167–8 (= *Scientific Papers*, **2**: 286–96, esp. 295–6). On his original submission of the paper to the Royal Society see his letter to Stokes of 8 January 1872 (Number 400).

(3) R. Felici, 'Saggio di una applicazione del calcolo alle correnti indotte'dal magnetismo in movimento', *Annali di Scienze, Matematiche, e Fisiche*, **4** (1853): 173–83; and Felici, 'Sulla teoria matematica dell'induzione elettro-dinamica', *ibid.*, **5** (1854): 35–58.

(4) E. Jochmann, 'Ueber die durch einen Magnet in einen rotirenden Stromleiter inducirten elektrischen Ströme', *Journal für die reine und angewandte Mathematik*, **63** (1864): 158–78, 329–31; (trans.) 'On the electric currents induced by a magnet in a rotating conductor', *Phil. Mag.*, ser. 4, **27** (1864): 506–28, and 'On induction in a rotating conductor', *ibid.*, **28** (1864): 347–9; Jochmann, 'Ueber die durch Magnetpole in rotirenden körperlichen Leitern inducirten elektrischen Ströme', *Ann. Phys.*, **122** (1864): 214–37.

(5) The velocity of the moving 'train or trail of images'; see Number 405.

(6) See Maxwell's discussion of the theory of Arago's rotating metallic disc in the *Treatise*, **2**: 275 (§669).

ABSTRACT OF PAPER ON ARAGO'S DISC[1]

circa 15 FEBRUARY 1872[2]

From *Nature* (29 February 1872)[3]

ON THE INDUCTION OF ELECTRIC CURRENTS IN AN INFINITE PLANE SHEET OF UNIFORMLY CONDUCTING MATTER

The currents are supposed to be induced in the sheet by the variation in position or intensity of any system of magnets or electromagnets.

When any system of currents is excited in the sheet, and then left to itself, it gradually decays, on account of the resistance of the sheet. At any point on the positive side of the sheet, the electromagnetic action is precisely the same as if the sheet, with its currents, retaining their original intensity, had been carried away in the negative direction with a constant velocity R, where R is the value, in electromagnetic measure, of the resistance of a rectangular portion of the sheet, of length l and breadth 2π. This velocity, for a sheet of copper of best quality of one millimetre thickness, is about twenty-five metres per second, and is, therefore, in general comparable with the velocities attainable in experiments with rotating apparatus.

When an electromagnet is suddenly excited on the positive side of the sheet, a system of currents is induced in the sheet, the effect of which on any point on the negative side is, *at the first instant*, such as exactly to neutralise the effect of the magnet itself. The effect of the decay of this system of currents is therefore equivalent to that of an image of the magnet, equal and opposite to the real magnet, from the position of the real magnet, in the direction of the normal drawn away from the sheet, with the constant velocity R.

When any change occurs in an electromagnetic system, whether by its motion or by the variation of its intensity, we may conceive the change to take place by the superposition of an imaginary system upon the original system; the imaginary system being equivalent to the difference between the original and the final state of the system.

The currents excited in the sheet by this change will gradually decay, and

---

(1) This abstract of Maxwell's Royal Society paper incorporates the supplementary note on the experiments of Felici and Jochmann; see Number 404.
(2) The date the paper was read to the Royal Society; see Number 404 note (2).
(3) *Nature*, **5** (1872): 354.

their effect will be equivalent to that of the imaginary system carried away from the sheet with the constant velocity R.

When a magnet or electro-magnet moves or varies in any continuous manner, a succession of imaginary magnetic systems like those already described is formed, and each, as it is formed, begins to move away from the sheet with the constant velocity R. In this way a train or trail of images, is formed, moves off, parallel to itself, away from the sheet, as the smoke of a steamer ascends in still air from the moving funnel.

When the sheet itself is in motion, the currents, relatively to the sheet, are the same as if the sheet had been at rest, and the magnets had moved with the same relative velocity. The only difference is, that whereas when the sheet is at rest no difference of electric potential is produced in different parts of the sheet, differences of potential, which may be detected by fixed electrodes are produced in the moving sheet.

The problem of Arago's whirling disc has been investigated by MM. Felici[4] and Jochmann.[5] Neither of these writers, however, has solved the problem so as to take into account the mutual induction of the currents in the disc. This is the principal step made in this paper, and it is expressed in terms of the theory of images, by which Sir W. Thomson solved so many problems in Statical Electricity.[6] In the case of the whirling disc, the trail of images has the form of a helix, moving away from the disc with velocity R, while it revolves about the axis along with the disc. Besides the dragging action which the disc exerts on the magnetic pole in the tangential direction, parallel to the motion of the disc, the theory also indicates a repulsive action directed away from the disc, and an attraction towards the axis of the disc, provided the pole is not placed very near the edge of the disc, a case not included in the investigation. These phenomena were observed experimentally by Arago, *Ann. de Chimie*, 1826.[7]

---

(4) See Number 404 note (3).   (5) See Number 404 note (4).

(6) See Number 301 note (10).

(7) François Arago, 'Note concernant les phénomènes magnétiques auxquels le mouvement donne naissance', *Ann. Chim. Phys.*, ser. 2, **32** (1826): 213–23.

406

LETTER TO WILLIAM HUGGINS

2 MAY 1872

From Campbell and Garnett, *Life of Maxwell* (2nd edn)[1]

11 Scroope Terrace
Cambridge
2 May 1872

My dear Sir

Toby and I enclose our photographs with our best regards to you and Kepler.[2] I had intended to be in London to-morrow,[3] but I am busy here. I hope the air-pump has recovered its cohesion. There seemed to be a solution of continuity between the mercury and the glass.

Yours very truly
J.C.M.

---

(1) *Life of Maxwell* (2nd edn): 293.

(2) Toby and Kepler were dogs. For Huggins' recollection of Kepler, who would bark an answer to numerical questions, see Larmor, *Correspondence*, **1**: 104.

(3) Probably to attend a meeting of the Royal Society. Huggins had submitted a paper 'On the spectrum of the great nebula in Orion, and on the motions of some stars towards or from the earth', but the paper was not read until 13 June, following receipt of a supplement; see *Proc. Roy. Soc.*, **20** (1872): 379–94.

FRAGMENT OF A LETTER TO PETER GUTHRIE TAIT

circa EARLY MAY 1872[1]

From the original in the University Library, Cambridge[2]

[Cambridge]

If the surfaces $\lambda_1\ \lambda_2\ \lambda_3$ divide space into cubes and if

$$\overline{\left|\frac{ds}{d\lambda_1}\right|}^2 = \overline{\left|\frac{dx}{d\lambda_1}\right|}^2 + \overline{\left|\frac{dy}{d\lambda_1}\right|}^2 + \overline{\left|\frac{dz}{d\lambda_1}\right|}^2 \&c$$

then $\dfrac{ds_1}{d\lambda_1} = \dfrac{ds_2}{d\lambda_2} = \dfrac{ds_3}{d\lambda_3} = p$ (a function of xyz or of $\lambda_1\ \lambda_2\ \lambda_3$).

But if R_{12} is the radius of curvature of s_1 in the plane of s_2 (for orthogonal surfaces)

$$\frac{1}{R_{12}} = \frac{\dfrac{d^2 s_1}{d\lambda_1 d\lambda_2}}{\dfrac{ds_1}{d\lambda_1}\dfrac{ds_2}{d\lambda_2}} = \frac{\dfrac{dp}{d\lambda_2}}{p^2} = \frac{1}{R_{32}}.$$

Figure 407,1

Hence the radii of curvature of the sections of the surface λ_2 made by the surfaces λ_1 and λ_3 are equal. But by Dupin's Theorem[3] these are principal curvatures. Hence the principal curvatures of the surface are equal at every point and the surface is a sphere. Now 3 sets of orthogonal spheres cannot be constructed except by making each set have a point of common contact. Prove this as you like. This is not published in any place as yet by $\dfrac{dp}{dt}$.[4]

It is neater and perhaps wiser to compose a nablody on this theme which is well suited for this species of composition.

Send any corrections of prooves to Cambridge, as a lot is going to press presently.

---

(1) See Numbers 408 and 409, to which this fragment is a preliminary.

(2) ULC Add. MSS 7655, I, b/104.

(3) The theorem that three families of orthogonal surfaces intersect in the lines of curvature. See Charles Dupin, *Développements de Géométrie* (Paris, 1813): 239–40.

(4) See his paper 'On the condition that, in the transformation of any figure by curvilinear co-ordinates in three dimensions, every angle in the new figure shall be equal to the corresponding angle in the original figure', *Proceedings of the London Mathematical Society*, **4** (1872): 117–19 (= *Scientific Papers*, **2**: 296–300), read 9 May 1872.

408

POSTCARD TO PETER GUTHRIE TAIT

9 MAY 1872

From the original in the University Library, Cambridge[1]

[Cambridge]

O T'. The collops of space[2] are served up to the Math Society this evening.[3] I am just going to look at your method of *drawing* a scientific brock before making him like the frightful porcupig. I have been studying in Bertrands edition of Lagrange the portentous equation

$$\frac{dT}{dq_1} = -\frac{dT}{dq_1}$$

not even with a magnifying glass can I distinguish between the two members, of which one is afflicted with $-$.[4] By a moderate use of suffixes it comes all right. T & T' use d and ∂[5] which I doubt but if you say $T_{\dot{q}} = T_{p\dot{q}} = T_p$[6] then $T_p = 2T_{p\dot{q}} - T_{\dot{q}}$ or diff.ing

$$\sum\left(\frac{dT_p}{dp}\delta p\right) + \sum\left(\frac{dT_p}{dq}\delta q\right) = \sum \dot{q}\delta p + \left[\sum(p\delta\dot{q}) - \sum\left(\frac{dT_{\dot{q}}}{d\dot{q}}\delta\dot{q}\right)\right] - \sum\left(\frac{dT_{\dot{q}}}{dq}\delta q\right)$$

the terms within [ ] cut out and then we get

$$\frac{dT_p}{dp} = \dot{q} \text{ and } \frac{dT_p}{dq} = -\frac{dT_{\dot{q}}}{dq} \text{ which is trew.}^{(7)}$$

$$\frac{dp}{dt}\left(= Q - \frac{dT}{dq}\right)^{(8)}$$

---

(1) ULC Add. MSS 7655, I, b/44.

(2) Collop: a slice of meat (*OED*); see Number 407.

(3) See Number 407 note (4).

(4) J. L. Lagrange, *Mécanique Analytique*, ed. Joseph Bertrand, 2 vols (Paris, $_3$1853–5), **1**: 413, in Bertrand's note 'Sur les équations différentielles des problèmes de mécanique' (**1**: 409–22). T is the kinetic energy, q the variable.

(5) Thomson and Tait, *Natural Philosophy*: 217–19.

(6) $T_{\dot{q}}$, $T_{p\dot{q}}$, T_p denote the kinetic energy expressed in terms of the velocities and the variables, the momenta and the velocities, and the variables and the momenta, respectively. See the *Treatise*, **2**: 188–91 (§§560–63).

(7) See the *Treatise*, **2**: 191–2 (§564) and Number 419.

(8) Bertrand's equation (A) in his note 'Sur les équations différentielles des problèmes de mécanique': 413.

409

POSTCARD TO PETER GUTHRIE TAIT

14 MAY 1872

From the original in the University Library, Cambridge[1]

[Cambridge]

O T′ Collops[2] occurred to me (in private) in April 1869. Presented to Math. Soc. & read 9th May 1872.[3] Spottiswoode[4] refers me to Methodes de Transformation en Géometrie &c par M. J. N. Haton de la Goupillière – Journal de l'Ecole Poly. XXV cahier 42 §VII.[5] I have no time this week to look him up. The *occasion* of my collops was Lamé Coordonnées Curvilignes[6] where collops are not xcept in posse. I see you are well entered with vermin when you can draw obrok. Why do you spell distortion with a t. We shall have Tortion next which would be torsure to look at and extorsion on the font of T.

$$\frac{dp}{dt}$$

---

(1) ULC Add. MSS 7655, I, b/45.   (2) See Number 408 note (2).

(3) See Number 407 note (4).

(4) William Spottiswoode, President of the London Mathematical Society, who chaired the meeting on 9 May 1872; see the *Proceedings*, **4** (1872): 111.

(5) J. N. Haton de la Goupillière, 'Méthodes de transformation en géométrie et en physique mathématique', *Journal de l'École Impériale Polytechnique*, **25**, cahier 42 (1867): 153–204, esp. 188–96.

(6) Gabriel Lamé, *Leçons sur les Coordonnées Curvilignes et leurs Divers Applications* (Paris, 1859).

410

REPORT ON A PAPER BY GEORGE BIDDELL AIRY ON THE MAGNETIC PROPERTIES OF IRON AND STEEL

17 MAY 1872

From the original in the Library of the Royal Society, London[1]

REPORT ON A PAPER ENTITLED 'EXPERIMENTS ON THE DIRECTIVE POWER OF LARGE STEEL MAGNETS, OF BARS OF MAGNETIZED SOFT IRON, AND OF GALVANIC COILS, IN THEIR ACTION ON EXTERNAL SMALL MAGNETS'. BY GEORGE BIDDELL AIRY, ASTRONOMER ROYAL C.B. P.R.S.[2]

The investigation of the magnetic properties of iron and steel is exceedingly important, both for the advancement of science and for purposes of utility.[3] The phenomena presented by pieces of iron and steel when magnetized, demagnetized and remagnetized in various ways are comparable in point of intricacy to the phenomena presented by the same piece of iron when twisted, untwisted and retwisted, while at the same time the magnetic experiments may be repeated as often as we please without mechanical injury to the iron itself, such as takes place after many twistings and untwistings. Hence a method of determining the distribution of magnetization in a piece of iron or steel is of great scientific importance, since it is by such means that we may hope to obtain some knowledge of the molecular structure of these substances.

---

(1) Royal Society, *Referees' Reports*, **7**: 152.

(2) George Biddell Airy, 'Experiments on the directive power of large steel magnets, of bars of magnetized soft iron, and of galvanic coils, in their action on external small magnets', *Phil. Trans.*, **162** (1872): 485–97. The paper was received by the Royal Society on 6 January 1872, and read on 8 February 1872; see the abstract in *Proc. Roy. Soc.*, **20** (1872): 158–9. The paper includes an 'Appendix containing an investigation of a galvanic coil on a small magnetic mass' by James Stuart (see Number 361). As a result of William Thomson's criticism in his referee report (see note (24)), Stuart revised and abbreviated his paper for publication: see the correspondence between Stokes, Airy and Stuart in June and July 1872 in Royal Greenwich Observatory Archive, ULC, Airy Papers 6/395, 145R–169R. Letters from Stokes to Airy of 10 and 13 December 1872 (Airy Papers 6/395, 180R–186R) explain how Stuart's revised appendix to Airy's paper had in error been read to the Royal Society as an independent paper on 5 December 1872 (and was to be published *in extenso* in *Proc. Roy. Soc.*, **21** (1872): 66–70), but that 'We have decided to reprint Mr Stuart's appendix that it may appear with your paper.'; see *Phil. Trans.*, **162** (1872): 493–6.   (3) See Numbers 466 and 467.

The method employed by our President appears to me to be remarkably well adapted to the particular case to which it was applied.(4) The direction and intensity of the magnetic force were ascertained at a number of points in two different surfaces completely surrounding the magnet. The graphical methods employed in dealing with the observations are also well worthy of study, as showing how results of amply sufficient accuracy may be obtained by means of easy processes with drawing instruments, and without the waste of calculating power, and risk of large errors, which often occurs in arithmetical processes.

I am therefore of the opinion that this paper should be printed in the Philosophical Transactions.

There are one or two points, however on which I should like to make a few remarks.

(1) The data given by the observations appear to me to furnish an excellent foundation for the application of what may be called the inverse method in the theory of attractions, that is the determination of the position and intensity of the attracting masses from the observation of the force at points in the surrounding space.

In the case before us two surfaces of revolution are described, surrounding the magnet at two different distances. In each of them, at intervals of $\frac{1}{10}$ of the length of the magnet, sections are taken, and the force determined at four points in each section. If we could devise or invent a mathematical function, the differential coefficients of which, with respect to the coordinates, would correspond to the forces at these points as found by experiment, then this would be the potential function of magnetic force for all space outside the magnet, and by *producing* the function inwards from the inner series of points towards the magnet, we might determine the force at the surface, and from this, since the distribution of imaginary magnetic matter is probably superficial, we could determine the density of this imaginary matter at every point of the surface.

But there is another method, which, like the method of this paper, is in the main graphical, and which would lead more directly to still more satisfactory results.

I shall first suppose that the magnetization is symmetrical about an axis as

---

(4) Compare William Thomson's judgment in his report on Airy's paper, dated 10 May 1872 (Royal Society, *Referees' Reports*, **7**: 151): 'The mode of measurement adopted, by a compass needle one inch long pivotted on a point, is not however capable of giving results of the accuracy desirable.... The results would, I believe, have been of much greater value if an exceedingly short needle hung by a silk fibre and carrying a light glass indicating arm, after the manner of Joule, had been employed.' On Joule's arrangement see Number 339 note (15).

in a cylindrical magnet and then consider the modification, for a rectangular bar. The results given in the paper are sufficient to determine the resultant force at any point of the surfaces surrounding the magnet, and the resolved part of the force perpendicular to the surface.

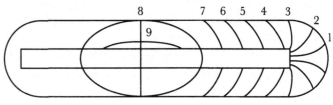

Figure 410,1

By means of Simpsons Rule,[5] or otherwise, let the value of $\int NdS$ be calculated, where S is the area of the surface of revolution measured from one apex, and N is the resolved part of the magnetic force normal to the surface.

A table may thus be formed containing the values of $\int NdS$ for each position of the compass-centre. From this we may determine the positions of the compass-centre corresponding to any required number of equidistant values of $\int NdS$. Let 1 2 3...8 be these points. Now take a *very short* magnetic needle, place its middle point at one of these points, and move it always in the direction of its own length, till it comes into contact with the magnet. It will thus trace out a *line of magnetic force*, the extremity of which should be marked on the magnet, or on the paper attached to it.

In this way a series of marks may be made on the magnet which will have the property, that the quantity of imaginary magnetic matter on a section of the magnet bounded by planes normal to its axis passing through two consecutive points of the series is the same for every such section.

Thus the distribution of magnetism may be determined for every part of the magnet except near its middle.

For this purpose it will be necessary to observe the longitudinal magnetic force at points on the line 89, perpendicular to the axis of the magnet, and to calculate $\int 2\pi r \, Xdr$. Thus a series of points 9 &c may be found and from these lines of force may be drawn whose intersections with the surface of the magnet will determine the distribution of magnetism near its middle point. If the magnet is of rectangular section, the process must be applied separately to the longer and the shorter sides of the section.

(2) With respect to the history of the enquiry I think it may be noticed that Biot (Traité de Physique T.3 Ch 6) showed that the quantity of free magnetism in any section [of] a long thin magnet as determined by Coulombs experiments may be represented by the formula

$$A'(\mu'^{-x} - \mu'^{x}) \, dx$$

---

(5) The method of determining the area under a curve by replacing the curve by a parabola, published by Thomas Simpson in his *Mathematical Dissertations* (London, 1743): 109–10.

where x is the distance of the section from the middle of the magnet and A' and μ' are constants.⁽⁶⁾ ⌊See also Dr Kaspar Rothlauf 'Ueber Vertheilung des Magnetismus in Cylindrischen Stahlstaben' München 1861 also confirms this formula by induction experiments.⌋⁽⁷⁾

Green, in section 17 of his Essay on Electricity &c has given a very ingenious though faulty method of determining the distribution of the permanent magnetization of a cylinder originally magnetized to saturation, on the ordinary hypothesis about magnetic induction combined with that of a coercive force of constant value.⁽⁸⁾

Green finds the density (λ) of free magnetism per unit of length at a distance x from the middle point to be

$$\lambda = Apa \frac{e^{\frac{px}{a}} - e^{-\frac{px}{a}}}{e^{\frac{pl}{a}} + e^{-\frac{pl}{a}}}$$

where a is the radius of the cylinder, $2l$ its length, A a constant and p a quantity to be found from (Neumanns) coefficient of induction⁽⁹⁾ from the equation

$$0.231863 - 2\log_e p + 2p = \frac{1}{\pi \kappa p^2}. \quad ^{(10)}$$

The whole quantity of free magnetism on the $+^{ve}$ side of the middle point is (when the cylinder is very long and thin) $\pi a A = M$.

Of this $\frac{1}{2}pM$ is on the flat end of the cylinder, and the distance of the centre of gravity of this free magnetism from the flat end is $\frac{a}{p}$.

When κ⁽¹¹⁾ is small (as in every substance except iron) p is large and the magnetism is almost all on the ends of the magnet. As κ increases, p diminishes and the magnetism extends further from the ends, as in iron. If κ is made infinite $p = 0$ and the magnetism at any section is simply proportional to the distance from the middle as in the hypothesis of p. 13* of the paper.⁽¹²⁾

---

(6) Jean Baptiste Biot, *Traité de Physique Expérimentale et Mathématique*, 4 vols. (Paris, 1816), **3**: 77. Maxwell states Biot's expression for free magnetism in the form as stated by George Green, *An Essay on the Application of Mathematical Analysis to the Theories of Electricity and Magnetism* (Nottingham, 1828): 69, who gives the reference to Biot's *Traité* as stated by Maxwell.

(7) See also Kaspar Rothlauf, 'Bestimmung der magnetischen Vertheilung in cylindrischen Stahlstäben mittelst Magneto-Induction', *Ann. Phys.*, **116** (1862): 592–606.

(8) Green, *Essay on the Application of Mathematical Analysis*: 69; see Number 466. On coercive force see Number 442 esp note (5).   (9) See Number 327 note (4).

(10) Maxwell here, and in the next paragraphs, draws on his account in the *Treatise*, **2**: 68–9 (§439).

(11) Neumann's coefficient of magnetic induction: see Number 327 note (4).

(12) Airy, 'Experiments on the directive power of large steel magnets': 491–2; 'the supposition that the intensity of magnetism is proportional to the distance from the centre of the magnet'. P. 13* was a supplementary page inserted in the MS of Airy's paper.

Greens method however is not perfect mathematically and indeed it leads to impossible results when κ is taken negative, as in diamagnetic substances. Thus[13]

κ	p	κ	p	
∞	0	11.8	0.07	
62.02	0.02	9.1	0.08	Value of κ for soft iron
48.42	0.03	7.5	0.09	from 30 to 33 by Thalèns
29.48	0.04	6.3	0.10	experiments.[14]
20.18	0.05	0.1	1.00	Hence p is from $\frac{1}{25}$ to $\frac{1}{27}$.
14.79	0.06	0.0	∞	
		negative imaginary		

Greens formula, however, represents very fairly the state of a long thin uniform cylinder magnetized to saturation by a powerful longitudinal force and then left to itself.

By comparing the observed values in the table at p. 13*[15] with those calculated on the supposition that the density of free magnetism is proportional to the distance from the middle point, and also with those for the galvanic coil it is easy to see that the magnetism of the real magnet is more confined to its extremities than that of the theoretical one but not so much as that of the galvanic coil.

1. Theoretical magnet of p13* density of magnetism x

2. Green's formula density of magnetism $e^{\frac{x}{a}} - e^{-\frac{x}{a}}$

3. Galvanic coil magnetism at the ends

The practical value of investigations such as those of Green is greatly diminished by two results of experiment. In the first place the intensity of the

---

(13) See the table printed in the *Treatise*, **2**: 68 (§439).

(14) Tobias Robert Thalèn, 'Recherches sur les propriétés magnétique du fer', *Nova Acta Regiae Societatis Scientiarum Upsaliensis*, ser. 3, **4** (1863): esp. 36; see Number 327 note (4), and the *Treatise*, **2**: 54–5 (§430).

(15) Airy, 'Experiments on the directive power of large steel magnets': 492.

temporary magnetization produced in soft iron by a magnetic force, though nearly proportional to that force when it is feeble, ceases to be so when the force is considerable (such for instance as that employed to magnetize steel bars). Even in the simplest case the law assumes a complicated form, but if the iron has been previously subjected to magnetic action the effect of a new force depends not only on this force but on the whole previous history of the piece of iron.

In the second place the permanent magnetism of a steel bar is probably different, according as it is the result of the first magnetization of the bar, or the final result of several magnetizations and reversals of polarity. See the experiments of Wiedemann, Pogg. Ann C. p. 235 (1857).[16]

(3) It appears to me that the investigation by Mr Stuart of the magnetic action of a cylindrical coil[17] would be rendered more general as well as more easily intelligible by deferring the expansion in spherical harmonics to a later part of the investigation.

The magnetic potential of a circular current is expanded in a series of spherical harmonics, which agrees with that given in Thomson and Taits Natural Philosophy Art 546 (III).[18] To obtain the magnetic potential due to an assemblage of circular currents constituting a solenoid, the terms of the series have to be subjected to a process of double integration between limits, which involves a good deal of calculation, and in the case of most mathematicians, a considerable risk of error.

Now the case of a solenoid of any form of section may be treated as Ampère has done at p94 of his Théorie des Phenomènes Electrodynamiques and at p188 of the same work.[19]

Break up each circuit into a great many elements, thus — round each element let the current circulate in the same direction. The circuit is thus transformed into a shell formed of elementary circuits. Now place such circuits one upon another so as to form a column. This column will be a column of solenoids of small section forming a solenoid of finite section, bounded by the two extreme sections and the coil of wire. The magnetic action at any point outside of the figure so bounded is, as Ampère has shown,

---

(16) Gustav Wiedemann, 'Ueber den Magnetismus der Stahlstäbe', *Ann. Phys.*, **100** (1857): 235–44.   (17) See note (2).
(18) Thomson and Tait, *Natural Philosophy*: 405–7, esp. 407; and see note (24).
(19) André Marie Ampère, *Théorie des Phénomènes Electro-dynamiques, uniquement déduite de l'expérience* (Paris, 1862): 94–108, 188–96 (esp. 95 for the term 'solénoide electro-dynamique'), and see Numbers 322 note (13) and 353 note (15).

identical with that of two uniform sheets of imaginary magnetic matter, forming the two extreme sections of the solenoid.[20] The numerical value of the surface-density of these sheets must be equal to the numerical value of the sum of the currents which flow across a line of unit length drawn on the surface of the coil parallel to its axis and if the column is vertical, and the current flows the way of the sun, the lower extremity must be coated with north-seeking magnetism.

The action of these two imaginary plane surfaces is identical with that of the coil for all points outside of the surface bounded by them and the coil.

For points within this closed surface, the resultant force due to the imaginary planes must be combined with a constant force parallel to the axis and equal to $4\pi\sigma$ where σ is the imaginary surface density on the sheet at the positive end of the axis.[21]

The magnetic force due to a solenoid of any form of section is thus identified with that due to two plane sheets.

If the solenoid consists of several layers of windings the corresponding plane sheets must be superposed, so as to make a sheet of variable density.

At this stage of the investigation we may introduce the expansion of the magnetic potential of the plane circular disk uniformly coated with imaginary magnetic matter. See Thomson & Tait §546.. II.[22]

$$V = \pi\sigma a \left\{ \frac{a}{r} - \frac{1}{4}\frac{a^3}{r^3} Q_2 + \frac{1.3}{4.6}\frac{a^5}{r^5} Q_4 - \&c \right\}$$

where a is the radius and r the distance from the centre and Q_2, Q_4 &c are zonal harmonics, the argument of which is the angle between r & the axis.[23] If V' is the value of this expression when σ is made negative and when r is the distance of the given point from the centre of the negative end of the coil and Q the corresponding harmonic then the complete value of the magnetic potential outside the coil is

$$V + V'.$$

It is evident that in the case of a very long solenoid the magnetic force at any point in the plane of either end is directed towards the centre of that end, as if all the magnetism had been concentrated at the ends of the coil.

It is only with the hope that some of the work of calculation may be dispensed with that I have suggested any alteration in the order of Mr Stuarts

---

(20) See also the discussion by William Thomson, 'A mathematical theory of magnetism', *Phil. Trans.*, **141** (1851): 243–85 (= *Electrostatics and Magnetism*: 340–404); and Number 332 note (12).

(21) On the magnetic action of plane current sheets see the *Treatise*, 2: 261–2 (§§652–3).

(22) Thomson and Tait, *Natural Philosophy*: 406.

(23) For Maxwell's similar discussion in the *Treatise* see *Treatise*, 2: 280–1 (§676).

investigation. His result is of the first importance and it is expressed in a form which we may call simple in a case of such complexity.[24]

The statement at the end of p 11 does not seem quite correct as it stands. 'It is evident, from the remarks of Articles 6 & 7 that a magnet cannot in any wise be represented as a system of revolving galvanic currents'.[25] What is proved by experiment is that the magnetic force in the neighbourhood of a large steel magnet is distributed according to a different manner from that in the neighbourhood of a uniformly coiled solenoid. Ampère however has shown that for each particle of the magnet we may substitute a small circuit carrying a current which will produce on external points precisely the same effect as the magnetic particle.[26]

The combination of such particles into a mass will be a finite magnet and the result of combining the molecular currents will be a distribution of currents such that

Interior equations[27]	Surface equations
$4\pi u = \dfrac{dC}{dy} - \dfrac{dB}{dz}$	$4\pi U = mC - nB$
$4\pi v = \dfrac{dA}{dz} - \dfrac{dC}{dx}$	$4\pi V = nA - lC$
$4\pi w = \dfrac{dB}{dx} - \dfrac{dA}{dy}$	$4\pi W = lB - mA$

(24) Compare Thomson's judgment in his report (note (4)): 'The Appendix containing the investigation by Mr Stewart deals with a subject which has already been exhaustively worked out, and which belongs to the generally taught and known elements of electro-magnetism. See, for instance, Thomson & Tait's "Natural Philosophy" §546, in which a method closely resembling that of Mr Stewart, but more simple, is given.' On the circumstances of the publication of Stuart's 'Appendix' see note (2).

(25) Thomson commented: 'The remark...is not justified by the premises, inasmuch as the comparison is made by means of a single finite solenoid. In fact Ampère has proved in a complete manner that any distribution of magnetism whatever can be represented, so far as its external effects are concerned, by a distribution of galvanic currents.' In response to these comments Airy informed Stokes, in a letter of 3 July 1872 (Airy Papers 6/395, 162R–V) that 'My expression about the impossibility of representing a magnet by currents is, inadvertently too strong, and I am glad to have had attention called to it. I meant currents of equal strength and in uniform coils, such as those in the experimental coil. I shall look to this in Proof.' See Airy, 'Experiments on the directive power of large steel magnets': 490.

(26) Ampère, *Théorie des Phénomènes Electro-dynamiques*: 188–96; see also Maxwell's discussion in the *Treatise*, **2**: 419 (§833).

(27) See Maxwell's equations (E) for electric currents in the *Treatise*, **2**: 231 (§607).

where A, B, C are the rectangular components of the magnetization and $u\,v\,w$ those of the internal currents, & $U\,V\,W$ those of the surface currents $l\,m\,n$ being the direction cosines of the normal to the surface of the magnet.

In this way the action of any magnet whatever may be represented by that of a system of currents. I do not think that the statement in p. 11 is intended to deny this, though it seems at first sight to do so.

J. Clerk Maxwell
17 May 1872

411

LETTER TO PETER GUTHRIE TAIT

24 MAY 1872

From the original in the University Library, Cambridge[1]

11 Scroope Terrace
24 May 1872

O. T',

Yours received as per opposite page. With regard to my position in space we go to Glenlair (Dalbeattie) on Monday evening. Address so till further notice. With respect to the medal.[2] Colin Mackenzie W.S.[3] 28 Castle Street has charge of my worldly goods and will, I have no doubt, take the medal off your hands, and keep it till I see him.

I suppose the R S.E is now in a state of æstivation in its vacant intersessional cave or I should return it my thanks for its unlooked for bounty.

It is strange, not indeed that W. Weber could not correctly integrate

$$\int_0^\pi \cos\theta \sin\phi \, d\phi$$

where
$$\tan\theta = \frac{A\sin\phi}{B + A\cos\phi}$$

but that every one should have copied such a wild result as

$$\frac{B}{\sqrt{A^2+B^2}} \frac{B^4 + \tfrac{7}{6}A^2B^2 + \tfrac{2}{3}A^2}{B^4 + A^2B^2 + A^4}.$$ [4]

---

(1) ULC Add. MSS 7655, I, b/46.

(2) The Keith prize medal, awarded by the Royal Society of Edinburgh for Maxwell's paper 'On reciprocal figures, frames, and diagrams of forces', *Trans. Roy. Soc. Edinb.*, **26** (1870): 1–40 (= *Scientific Papers*, **2**: 161–207); see *Trans. Roy. Soc. Edinb.*, **26** (1870–72): viii.

(3) Maxwell's cousin and solicitor (see *Life of Maxwell*: x; and Volume I: xviii).

(4) Wilhelm Weber, 'Ueber den Zusammenhang der Lehre vom Diamagnetismus mit der Lehre von dem Magnetismus und der Elektricität', *Ann. Phys.*, **87** (1852): 145–89, on 167 (= *Wilhelm Weber's Werke*, 6 vols. (Berlin, 1892–4), **3**: 555–90). For Maxwell's discussion of the issue see the *Treatise*, **2**: 78n (§443), on Weber's expression for the relation between the intensity of magnetisation produced in a magnetisable substance and the magnetising force. See also Number 350.

Of course there are two forms of the result according as *A* or *B* is greater.[a]

11 Scroope Terrace
Cambridge
24 May 1872

Received from Professor Peter Guthrie Tait the sum of Forty seven Pounds nine shillings and one penny.

£47..9'..1^d

24 May 1872
J.C.M.
JAMES CLERK MAXWELL

---

[a] {Tait}

$$\int_0^\pi \frac{\sin\phi\, d\phi}{\sqrt{1+\left(\frac{A\sin\phi}{B+A\cos\phi}\right)^2}} = \int_0^\pi \frac{\sin\phi\, d\phi(B+A\cos\phi)}{\sqrt{B^2+A^2+2AB\cos\phi}}$$

$$\cos\phi = x, \text{ limits } -1, +1$$

$$\int_{+1}^{-1} \frac{-dx(B+Ax)}{\sqrt{B^2+A^2+2ABx}} = \int_{B+A}^{B-A} \frac{-\frac{1}{A}dy\, y}{\sqrt{(A^2-B^2)+2By}}$$

$$= -\frac{1}{2AB}\left(\frac{(2By+A^2-B^2-\overline{A^2-B^2})dy}{\sqrt{}}\right.$$

$$= -\frac{1}{2AB}\left(\frac{1}{3B}(2By+A^2-B^2)^{\frac{3}{2}} - \frac{A^2-B^2}{2B}\sqrt{}\right).$$

412

LETTER TO ROBERT DUNDAS CAY

27 MAY 1872

From the original in the Library of Peterhouse, Cambridge[1]

> 11 Scroope Terrace
> Cambridge
> 27 May 1872

Dear Uncle Robert

I quite agree to your arrangement about the alterations and repairs to be paid by deducting £150 from the wayleave rents of this term and the same from the next, being £300 in all.

Your letter just arrived in time as we leave for Glenlair this evening. We shall be there, off and on, till we have to return to Cambridge in October.

I am to be 'Addle Examiner' on the new examination scheme next January[2] so I shall have plenty to do. This makes $3\frac{1}{2}$ Scotch examiners out of five, Ferrers being the $\frac{1}{2}$.[3]

The dissipations are now fiercely raging. Boat races being over balls begin, also flower shows processions, promenade concerts, peacocking on Kings Parade in splendour never seen in London out of doors, to say nothing of dinners and feasts ecclesiastical and secular, cleric and lay, wedded & celibate.

Katherine joins me in love to you all.

> Your afft nephew
> J. CLERK MAXWELL

(1) Peterhouse, Maxwell MSS (33).

(2) See *The Cambridge University Calendar for the Year 1873* (Cambridge, 1873): 26–8, for the regulations concerning the nomination by the Board of Mathematical Studies, and the subsequent appointment, of a third (Additional) examiner for the Mathematical Tripos.

(3) The other examiners were: William Davidson Niven (Trinity), George Pirie (Queens'), Norman Macleod Ferrers (Caius), and W. H. H. Hudson (St John's); see *Cambridge Calendar for 1873*: 521.

APPENDIX: THEOREM ON THE POTENTIAL FUNCTION FOR THE 1873 MATHEMATICAL TRIPOS[4]

circa SUMMER 1872

From the original in the Cavendish Laboratory, Cambridge[5]

[CONDITION OF MOTION IN THE INTERIOR OF A FLUID][6]

Shew that if within a certain region

$$\text{tr} \begin{cases} \dfrac{d^2V}{dx^2} + \dfrac{d^2V}{dy^2} + \dfrac{d^2V}{dz^2} = 0 \\ V \text{ is continuous and finite and satisfies the equation} \end{cases}$$

the quantity $R^2 = \overline{\dfrac{dV}{dx}}^2 + \overline{\dfrac{dV}{dy}}^2 + \overline{\dfrac{dV}{dz}}^2$ cannot be a maximum at any point within the region.[7]

---

(4) See *Cambridge Calendar for 1873*: 548. 'Prove that $/\dfrac{d^2\psi}{dx^2} + \dfrac{d^2\psi}{dy^2} + \dfrac{d^2\psi}{dz^2} + 4\pi\rho = 0, /$ where ψ is the potential of a gravitating system and ρ is the mean density of a sphere whose centre is at the point (x,y,z) when its radius becomes infinitely small. / Prove that if ψ is continuous and finite, and satisfies the equation $/\dfrac{d^2\psi}{dx^2} + \dfrac{d^2\psi}{dy^2} + \dfrac{d^2\psi}{dz^2} = 0, /$ throughout a given region, the quantity $\overline{\dfrac{d\psi}{dx}}^2 + \overline{\dfrac{d\psi}{dy}}^2 + \overline{\dfrac{d\psi}{dz}}^2$ cannot have a maximum value at any point within the region.'

(5) Maxwell Notebook, Cavendish Laboratory, Cambridge; copy in ULC Add. MSS 7655, V, n/l.

(6) Compare Maxwell's discussion of conditions under which the potential function has a maximum and minimum value in fluid motion in his letter to William Thomson of 15 May 1855 (Volume I: 312–13).

(7) The potential function V cannot therefore be a maximum at a point in the interior of a fluid; the velocity of the fluid cannot be a maximum at any point in the fluid. See Horace Lamb's discussion of Maxwell's theorem (as set in the Mathematical Tripos, 1873) in his *A Treatise on the Mathematical Theory of the Motion of Fluids* (Cambridge, 1879): 39–40.

413

NOTE TO PETER GUTHRIE TAIT
circa LATE JUNE 1872[1]

From Knott, *Life of Tait*[2]

If your straight lines, parabolas[3] &c have no resemblance at all to those things which men call by those names, I would as soon be J. Stuart Mill as call them so. But if they differ very slightly, then T′ is enrolled among the Boyle and Charles of ΘH who remain unhurt by Regnault &c.[4] But in Physics we must equally avoid confounding the properties and dividing the substance. In the one case we fall into the sin of rectification (Eccl. i. 15)[5] and in the other we see in every zig zag a proof of transubstantiation.

---

(1) Probably a reply to Tait's card of 11 June 1872 (see note (3)); and see his card of 28 June 1872 (see Number 414 note (2)).

(2) Knott, *Life of Tait*: 80.

(3) In his card of 11 June 1872 (ULC Add. MSS 7655, I, a/27) Tait wrote: 'O dp/dt, Certain T.E. circuits give as below

the bits of the broken line being straight, and therefore

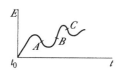 OA, AB, BC (in the expression for electromotive force) successive BITS of parabolas, all the axes being vertical. Does this not show that the wire giving the broken line is *one* substance from 0 to t_1, another from t_1 to t_2, yet another from t_2 to t_3 &c? Answer this as soon as you have pondered it.

Y^{rs} pv. / Have never yet got the length of C.M.'s office with the Medal. Am grinding away at these circuits all day in my Laboratory.' See P. G. Tait, 'On thermo-electricity: circuits with more than one neutral point', *Proc. Roy. Soc. Edinb.*, 7 (1872): 773–9, read 3 June 1872. E is the electromotive force, t the temperature, and Π the coefficient of the Peltier effect (see Number 322 esp. note (5)).

(4) For Tait's response see his card of 13 July 1872 (Number 417 note (2)). On Victor Regnault's work on the gas laws see Number 437 esp. note (8).

(5) Ecclesiastes chap. 1, verse 15; 'That which is crooked cannot be made straight: and that which is wanting cannot be numbered' (Authorised version).

414

POSTCARD TO PETER GUTHRIE TAIT

29 JUNE 1872

From the original in the University Library, Cambridge[1]

[Glenlair]

O T'.[2] That a metal should have any properties constant at various temperatures is an important discovery. That it should change these properties at certain temperatures is only to be expected. Exceptio probat regulam. But the investigation of these temperatures is important, especially if any other change of property takes place at them, e.g. resistance. I shall try and see Phil. Mag. for July.[3] Where are the Proofs! I shall send you shortly some remarks on T & T' for next edition.[4] I have been overhauling the Equations of motion and have got a way of deducing them (in Hamiltons form) from the variables their velocities and the forces acting *on them* alone,[5]

---

(1) ULC Add. MSS 7655, I, b/47.

(2) In reply to Tait's cards of 11 June 1872 (Number 413 note (3)), and of 28 June 1872 (ULC Add. MSS 7655, I, a/28): 'O dp/dt See next Phil. Mag., and say what I deserve for fighting *your* & T's battles. U don't answer about multiple neutral points. As you have reserved your oracular decision (only, I hope, till as now pressed to give it) add a few remarks on this theme. The curves give electromotive force in terms of diff^{ces} of temp.^{re} of junctions in circuits of iron with Platinum & diff^t. alloys of Plat. & Iridium. The latter can be plotted from the former by subtracting the ordinates of an oblique line drawn through the origin – i.e. the additions of Iridium seem to alter the neutral points without much altering the Kays (ks). ♄.' The 'battles' Tait alludes to were with Clausius, specifically with Clausius' critique of Maxwell's *Theory of Heat*: see Numbers 402 and 403.

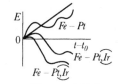

Figure 414,1

(3) In the Supplement to the *Philosophical Magazine* for July 1872 Tait published a paper 'On the history of the second law of thermodynamics, in reply to Professor Clausius', *Phil. Mag.*, ser. 4, **43** (1872): 516–18. Responding to Clausius' complaint about Maxwell's *Theory of Heat* (see Number 402, note (10)), Tait had published (in the May 1872 number of the *Phil. Mag.*) a 'Reply to Professor Clausius', *Phil. Mag.*, ser. 4, **43** (1872): 338. To contest Clausius' claims to priority over Thomson he introduced the problem of 'The behaviour of a thermoelectric circuit in which the hot junction is at a temperature higher than the neutral point, and where therefore heat *does of itself, pass from a colder to a hotter body*'. Clausius had discussed the problem of thermocouples in his paper 'Ueber die Anwendung der mechanischen Wärmetheorie auf die thermoelektrischen Erscheinungen', *Ann. Phys.*, **90** (1853): 513–44; and in his paper 'On the objection raised by Mr Tait against my treatment of the mechanical theory of heat', *Phil. Mag.*, ser. 4, **43** (1872): 443–6 (in the June 1872 number) he was able to meet Tait's argument. Tait's reply in the Supplement to the July number of the *Phil. Mag.* was to reiterate the claim that Thomson had first *correctly* formulated the second law of thermodynamics. See also Number 278 note (2).

(4) See Number 417 note (4).   (5) See the *Treatise*, **2**: 184–94 (§§ 553–67).

without considering the equations which give $\dot{x}$ in terms of $\dot{\phi}, \dot{\psi}$, or Φ in terms of X &c.[6] This is done by beginning with impulsive force.[7] It constitutes an improvement in my book and a preparation for Electrokinetics[8] and Magnetic action on Light.[9] Pray observe the dimensions of this card. Proove me my prooves and again I say reproove me my reprooves.

$$\frac{d}{dt}\frac{dT_p}{d\dot{q}} + \frac{dT_p}{dq} = \frac{dp}{dt}{}^{(10)}$$

(6) See Thomson and Tait, *Natural Philosophy*: 218–19; x, y, z are rectangular coordinates, $\dot{x}, \dot{y}, \dot{z}$ are component velocities; ψ, ϕ, θ are generalised coordinates of a material system, $\dot{\psi}, \dot{\phi}, \dot{\theta}$ are generalised velocity components; Ψ, Φ, Θ are generalised components of the force on the system, X, Y, Z are component forces of particles x, y, z.

(7) On the method of impulsive forces see Thomson and Tait, *Natural Philosophy*: 217–31.

(8) *Treatise*, **2**: 195–205 (§§ 568–77).

(9) *Treatise*, **2**: 399–417 (§§ 806–31).

(10) Compare Number 417.

415

REPORT ON A PAPER BY LATIMER CLARK[1] ON A STANDARD OF ELECTROMOTIVE FORCE

circa 2 JULY 1872[2]

From the original in the Library of the Royal Society, London[3]

REPORT ON M[r] LATIMER CLARK'S PAPER ON A VOLTAIC STANDARD OF ELECTROMOTIVE FORCE[4]

The Author describes his search for a Voltaic Element whose Electromotive Force shall be, under circumstances easily obtainable, as constant as possible. He has obtained such an element by placing a paste composed of mercurous sulphate and zincic sulphate between pure mercury and pure zinc. He has compared together a number of such elements by means of an arrangement which is apparently the best hitherto published for comparing electromotive forces. The merit of this arrangement seems to me to be due to the Author. He calls it a Potentiometer.[5]

This comparison having established the constancy of his standard element, the author has gone on to determine the value of its electromotive force in the electromagnetic system of measurement, introduced by W. Weber[6] and adopted, with slight modifications, by the British Association.[7] He has made this determination by means of the electrodynamometer constructed for the

---

(1) Josiah Latimer Clark, electrical engineer (Boase).

(2) According to the Royal Society's *Register of Papers Received* Clark's paper was referred to Maxwell on 28 June 1872, and to Wheatstone on 5 July 1872.

(3) Royal Society, *Referees' Reports*, **7**: 162.

(4) Latimer Clark, 'On a voltaic standard of electromotive force' (Royal Society, AP. 54.4). The paper was received by the Royal Society on 30 May 1872, and read on 20 June 1872; see the abstract in *Proc. Roy. Soc.*, **20** (1872): 444–8. The paper was communicated to the Royal Society by Sir William Thomson: see his letter to Stokes of 25 May [1872] (ULC Add. MSS 7656, K 184A; printed in Wilson, *Stokes–Kelvin Correspondence*, **2**: 371–2). An abridged version of Clark's paper, under the title 'On a standard voltaic battery', was subsequently published in *Phil. Trans.*, **164** (1874): 1–14; see note (12) and Number 462.

(5) See also Latimer Clark, *An Elementary Treatise on Electrical Measurement* (London, 1868): 106–8.

(6) W. Weber, 'Messungen galvanischer Leitungswiderstände nach einem absoluten Maasse', *Ann. Phys.*, **82** (1851): 337–69; (trans.) 'On the measurement of electric resistance according to an absolute standard', *Phil. Mag.*, ser. 4, **22** (1861): 226–40, 261–9.

(7) 'Report of the Committee... on standards of electrical resistance', *Report of the Thirty-third Meeting of the British Association for the Advancement of Science* (London, 1864): 111–76.

Committee of the British Association[8] and also by means of a Sine Galvanometer of his own construction.[9] Both of these determinations seem to have been conducted with every precaution, and the results agree in a very satisfactory manner. The electromotive force of the standard cell was found to be 1.457 Volts[10] each Volt being 10^5 in the metric-gramme-second electromagnetic system.

It remains, of course, to be seen whether other persons, by following the authors directions, can obtain a standard element agreeing within one tenth per cent. with that of the author, but the experiments cited are sufficient to show that he has invented a most valuable material standard, and that he has submitted it to proper tests.[11]

I am therefore of opinion that this paper should be printed in the Philosophical Transactions.[12]

Mr Clark was one of the earliest, and has remained one of the most persistent advocates of the adoption of electrical standards.[13] He has also been willing to adopt standards founded on considerations which, though

---

(8) See Number 416 note (3).

(9) See Latimer Clark, 'On a standard voltaic battery': 11–12. On sine galvanometers see Gustav Wiedemann, *Die Lehre vom Galvanismus und Elektromagnetismus*, 2 vols. (Braunschweig, 1861), **2**: 206–10.

(10) See also Clark, 'On a standard voltaic battery': 12.

(11) Clark acknowledged Maxwell's assistance in 'On a voltaic standard of electromotive force': ff. 30, 33, 40; and see Clark, 'On a standard voltaic battery': 9, 10, 12 for the same acknowledgments.

(12) In a report dated 3 September 1872 (Royal Society, *Referees' Reports*, **7**: 161) Sir Charles Wheatstone voiced a different opinion: 'I think it unnecessary to discuss the merits of Mr Latimer Clark's paper as it, in my opinion, belongs to a class not suited for publication in the Philosophical Transactions. It contains little, or nothing, that has not already been known to the scientific public, and the additional details now brought forward do not appear to me to be of sufficient importance to give it that claim.... This paper might properly find a place in a special technical publication'. In a letter to Stokes of 1 January 1873 (ULC Add. MSS 7656, K 189; printed in Wilson, *Stokes–Kelvin Correspondence*, **2**: 380) Thomson asked if the Royal Society's consequent rejection of Clark's paper for publication in the *Phil. Trans.* was 'an irreversible decree'. In a subsequent letter of 21 January [1873] (ULC Add. MSS 7656, K 182; in Wilson, *Stokes–Kelvin Correspondence*, **2**: 396–7) Thomson states that he had forwarded one of Stokes' letters to Latimer Clark, 'as I believe you intended that I might do so', also noting that 'in one or two parts Clark['s] paper may admit of abbreviation with advantage'. In a memorandum for Stokes of 23 January 1873 (ULC Add. MSS 7656, RS 900) Clark responded to the objections raised to his paper; and subsequently submitted an abridged version to the Royal Society (see note (4)).

(13) Latimer Clark and Sir Charles Bright, 'On the formation of standards of electrical quantity and resistance', *Report of the Thirty-first Meeting of the British Association for the Advancement of Science* (London, 1862), part 2: 37–8.

truly scientific, are by no means obvious to the practical electrician. He has advocated the use of distinct short names for certain multiples or submultiples of these standards chosen so as to be of a convenient magnitude for practical work. Of these the Ohm, or practical standard of electric resistance, is represented by a wire having this resistance. The Farad, or standard of capacity, is represented by a condenser of this capacity.

The Volt, or standard of electromotive force is represented roughly by a Daniell cell,[14] or more accurately by $\frac{1}{1.457}$ of Mr Clarks new cell.

These three standards, therefore, are represented by material objects which the electrician may have always beside him, ready for use in electric measurements. There is, however, a fourth term introduced by Mr Clark to denote the quantity of electricity with which a Volt would charge a Farad, or which a Volt would send through an Ohm in one second. This quantity he calls a Veber.

I am by no means prepared to say that it would not be desirable to have a short name for a standard quantity of electricity, for the other three terms have been found more acceptable than I expected they would become. This last standard, however, is invisible, and cannot well be kept in a laboratory. We have also to consider whether we do honour to the name of the founder of electromagnetic measurement by cutting off one half of the initial letter of his name. It would be far better to pronounce the W in the English way than to transpose the word to a wrong division of the Dictionary.[15]

The system to which all these standards belong is the Electromagnetic system. There is another mode of obtaining a standard of electromotive force by electrostatic methods, and this has been developed to a great extent by Sir W. Thomson in his various Electrometers.[16] The construction, however, of a standard electrometer, and the reduction of its readings to absolute measure, is an operation of great labour and difficulty.

The discovery, therefore of a *small* standard of electromotive force is important to electrostatics, as enabling us to test the value of the scale-readings of any electrometer.

---

(14) The electric battery which maintained a constant current invented by J. F. Daniell; see Number 235 note (11).

(15) In 'On a standard voltaic battery': 1 Clark omitted the 'Veber' from the list of units as given in 'On a voltaic standard of electromotive force': f. 2.

(16) William Thomson, 'Report on electrometers and electrostatic measurements', *Report of the Thirty-seventh Meeting of the British Association for the Advancement of Science* (London, 1868): 489–512 (= *Electrostatics and Magnetism*: 260–309).

Besides this, the determination of electromotive force of the new cell in electrostatic measure, compared with the value in electromagnetic measure, would lead to an independent value of the ratio of the electromagnetic to the electrostatic unit of electricity.

We must bear in mind, however, that the numerical value found by Mr Clark is affected by any error in the experiments by which the value of the Ohm was determined.[17]

J. CLERK MAXWELL

---

(17) See the 'Report of the Committee on standards of electrical resistance', *Report of the Thirty-fourth Meeting of the British Association for the Advancement of Science* (London, 1865): 345–67, esp. table facing 349.

416

LETTER TO GEORGE GABRIEL STOKES

8 JULY 1872

From the original in the University Library, Cambridge[1]

Glenlair
Dalbeattie
8 July 1872

My dear Stokes

The figures in Mr Latimer Clarks paper[2] are better than anything I could do. If therefore I can obtain the consent of the Society and of Mr Clark, I should like to obtain clichés of the engravings of the Electrodynamometer and its parts,[3] and in doing so I have supposed it best to begin with the Society for though I am acquainted with Mr Clark I have no direct relation with him in the capacity of referee of his paper.

I had already drawn figures, not so good as Mr Clarks, but they are not yet engraved, so that if there is any objection to my getting either the loan of the blocks or plates or impressions of them, my work will not be delayed.[4]

As some of the figures are already engraved I should think it likely that Mr Clark means to use them in some work of his own and that they have been engraved independently of the R.S. though they may first appear as illustrations in the Phil Trans.

With respect to the time at which I should have to send my last figures to the engraver I think the end of September is about the limit of safety.

Yours sincerely
J. CLERK MAXWELL

(1) ULC Add. MSS 7656, M 431. First published in Larmor, *Correspondence*, **2**: 33.

(2) 'On a voltaic standard of electromotive force'; see Number 415, esp. note (4).

(3) The engravings of the electrodynamometer and its torsion head, constructed for the British Association Committee on standards of electrical resistance, and referred to in the 'Report of the Committee on standards of electrical resistance', *Report of the Thirty-seventh Meeting of the British Association for the Advancement of Science; held at Dundee in September 1867* (London 1868): 474–522, on 478, were printed in Latimer Clark's paper 'On a standard voltaic battery', *Phil. Trans.*, **164** (1874): 1–14, on 7–8. See Maxwell's report on this paper (Number 462).

(4) See the *Treatise*, **2**: 330–1 (§725), where Clark's drawings are reproduced.

417

POSTCARD TO PETER GUTHRIE TAIT

15 JULY 1872

From the original in the National Library of Scotland, Edinburgh[1]

[Glenlair]

[2]Let xyz be the currents from A to Z in 3 conductors
PQR the electromotive forces in these conductors
abc their resistances – then

$$ax - P = by - Q = cz - R = E \text{ (say)}$$
$$x + y + z = 0$$
$$\therefore x = \frac{P-E}{a} \quad y = \frac{Q-E}{b} \quad z = \frac{R-E}{c}$$

Figure 417,1

$$e = \frac{\frac{P}{a} + \frac{Q}{b} + \frac{R}{c}}{\frac{1}{a} + \frac{1}{b} + \frac{1}{c}} \quad \text{and} \quad x = \frac{1}{a} \frac{P\left(\frac{1}{b} + \frac{1}{c}\right) - Q\frac{1}{b} - R\frac{1}{c}}{\frac{1}{a} + \frac{1}{b} + \frac{1}{c}}. \tag{1}$$

Let x_c be the value of x when $b = \infty$ and x_b that when $c = \infty$ or when the second or third conductor is cut then by (1)

$$x_c = \frac{P-R}{a+c} \quad x_b = \frac{P-Q}{a+b} \quad \text{whence}$$

$$x = \frac{x_b\left(\frac{1}{a} + \frac{1}{b}\right) + x_c\left(\frac{1}{a} + \frac{1}{c}\right)}{\frac{1}{a} + \frac{1}{b} + \frac{1}{c}}$$

or

$$x = c\frac{x_b(a+b) + x_c(a+c)}{bc + ca + ab}.$$

---

(1) National Library of Scotland, MS 1004 f. 41.

(2) For the context see Numbers 413 and 414. The card was written in reply to Tait's card of 13 July 1872 (ULC Add. MSS 7655, I, a/29): 'Pray *dp/dt* give me *again, at once,* and *in complete form,* your solution of this thermo-electric case. Either I have made an exceedingly stupid blunder, or I have made an exceedingly great discovery: & I wish to know *which*. This can only be done by my *not* telling you the result I have arrived at. The experiments are all made, & graphically delineated, so that there can be no mistake about *them*. Given, separately, the resistances of the Zn, the Cu, & the Fe (the latter including that of the galvanometer) calculate the current when the arrangement is complete from the observed currents when the zinc, & the copper, wires are (separately) cut. ♄.'

Figure 417,2

I can do no more to this.[3]

The binder of T & T' has observed the maxim One stitch in nine saves time. See what a broad P.C. I have written to you with a new pen. I must go now to a swarm of bees in a yew tree. What of the $=^{ns}$ of motion?[4]

$$F + \frac{dT_{\dot{q}}}{dq} = \frac{dp}{dt}{}^{(5)}$$

---

(3) In his card of 16 July 1872 (ULC Add. MSS 7655, I, a/31) Tait replied: 'dp/dt thou that shirkest the question behold it *again*. 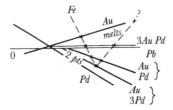 I don't require to be taught how to work resistances, and simple equations. My purpose was more awful. *What are* the electromotive forces in the three wires respectively, in terms of what they w^d be were each of the three wires separately cut? ♄.' In his card of 17 July 1872 (ULC Add. MSS 7655, I, a/32) Tait responded: 'O dp/dt I fear your Algebra, as well as your Reasoning, is in fault. You give me $x = c\dfrac{x_b(a+b) + x_c(a+c)}{bc + ca + ab}$.

I had found (putting it into your notation) $x = \dfrac{x_b c(a+b) + x_c b(a+c)}{bc + ca + ab}$. But what I wanted to know from you was *why* there sh^d be any Fe–Zn electromotive force in the Cu branch of the triple arc. Goose that. — Y^{rs} ♄.' In a card of 19 July 1872 (ULC Add. MSS 7655, I, a/33) Tait added: 'O dp/dt I have proven today by experiment what I had lately been led to suspect was the true cause of double neutral points. It is the villain Fe, who is thermo-electrically $(-)$ as regards his σ up to a pretty high temperature & then suddenly gets his σ made $(+)$. I shot at him from the neutral point of Au–Pd, with double arc sometimes leaning to one side, then to the other: & here is the result.

Figure 417,3

So you see my shots have taken effect. What say you to this on the firm ground of theory and of hypothesis? Also answer my other?. pv.'

(4) See Number 414. In a card of 15 July 1872 (ULC Add MSS 7655, I, a/30) Tait wrote: 'O dp/dt I return to you χηding ϑanξ for the νῶτς on T & T'. But don't claim originality till you can prove your case – vide *Phil. Mag.* for July (*Suppl.*) & see how Clausius fares after his many years boasting. Have you seen the German ed^n of T & T' where Hamiltonianism & Lagrangism are remodelled on the advice of Strutt & Boltzmann – the former given almost immediately after the appearance of the Book, the latter two years ago? *I also* proposed to T. two years ago a method which is like as two peas to yours, but he would none of it – and sent his own to the Germans; or, rather, compelled me to do so – of course under violent protest, w^h may perhaps break out in the second (English) edition now preparing. To my χτρημ delight I caught

APPENDIX: POSTCARD TO PETER GUTHRIE TAIT

7 AUGUST 1872

From the original in the University Library, Cambridge[6]

[Glenlair]

O T'. Are you in the secular capital or in the metropolis? I address[7] to the latter.

Yours $\dfrac{dp}{dt}$

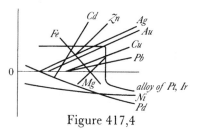

Figure 417,4

(by pure chance) on Saturday last a French nobleman who has shown me how to deposit (electrolytically) tenacious *feuilles* of Nickel, Cobalt, &c &c. I had made out for myself that morning the position of Nickel. It is as below. The question I asked you on Saturday really means 'Can we by 3 metals (in treble arc) sweep the field in abridged notation style? i.e. from $\alpha = 0$, $\beta = 0$, $\gamma = 0$, get by combination $A\alpha = B\beta = C\gamma = 0$?' If I am right I can take A, B, & C so as to *aim* at any point I like, and thus thoroughly investigate the mysterious course of the queer alloy. ♑.' See Tait's paper 'On thermo-electricity: circuits with more than one neutral point', *Proc. Roy. Soc. Edinb.*, **7** (1872): 773–9.

(5) The Lagrangian form of the equations of motion. See Number 419 and the *Treatise*, **2**: 192 (§564).

(6) ULC Add. MSS 7655, I, b/48.

(7) Proofs; to the 'Union Club, St Andrews'.

418

LETTER TO LATIMER CLARK
16 JULY 1872
From the original in the University Library, Cambridge[1]

Glenlair
Dalbeattie
16 July 1872

My dear Sir

I had lately the pleasure of reading your paper on a Standard Voltaic Element.[2] I shall certainly not be satisfied with merely reading about it, for I must make a nearer acquaintance with it.

I observed that you had engraved a figure of the Electrodynamometer[3] and my present object in writing to you is to ask if it would be convenient to you to allow me to have the block or a copy of it as an illustration to my book on Electricity.[4]

I had already made a diagram of it from memory, but a figure of this kind is unsatisfactory compared with a figure of an actual instrument.[5]

The experimental researches in your paper are of course known to me only by your report of them, but I think they are as good a piece of work as I have seen for some time.

The best test of the uniformity of your voltaic element would be to get it set up by people in different places, where they would get zinc from different sources and would differ slightly in their mode of preparing the mercurous sulphate. The use of mercury as the negative metal is a great merit, not only because the negative surface remains fluid and of uniform properties but because its effects when it gets in contact with the zinc are so different from what happens in the case of copper.

I have looked over all the formulae for the dynamometer and find them correct. I have not attacked the arithmetic.

I have taken the opportunity of this vacation to boil down a good deal of matter relating to electrical instruments which was in my book before, but it is now far more digestible.

I think I am right in saying that you use the word Farad to signify a certain capacity and that a Farad is a condenser having this capacity.[6]

---

(1) ULC Add. MSS 7655, II/59.
(2) See Number 415.
(3) See Number 416 note (3).
(4) See the *Treatise*, **2**: 330–1 (§725).
(5) See Number 416.
(6) See Number 415.

Prof. Jenkin speaks of a Farad as a quantity of electricity.[7]

I think it is better to define it as a capacity as I think you do and then the Ohm is a piece of wire, the Volt a voltaic element (or a multiple thereof) and a Farad is a condenser.

These are all visible things.

Yours very truly
J. CLERK MAXWELL

(7) Fleeming Jenkin, *Electricity and Magnetism* (London, 1873): 160. On Maxwell's prior knowledge of Jenkin's book see his annotation to its proof (Number 385: Appendix).

DRAFT ON THE INTERPRETATION OF LAGRANGE'S AND HAMILTON'S EQUATIONS OF MOTION

circa JULY 1872[1]

From the original in the University Library, Cambridge[2]

ON THE INTERPRETATION OF LAGRANGE'S AND HAMILTON'S EQUATIONS OF MOTION

by J. Clerk Maxwell, Prof^r of Experimental Physics, Cambridge[3]

The following statement has nothing original in it,[4] but I think that our attention cannot be too often directed to the most important theorem in physical science – that which deduces, from the given motion of a connected system, the forces which act on it.

Our popular dynamical ideas are far too exclusively drawn from the dynamics of a particle. It is true that the most important ideas in dynamics may be illustrated by the motion of a single particle, but it is unfortunate that in expressing the relations between these ideas we have sometimes adopted a form of expression, which, though true for a particle, is not easily applicable to a connected system.

For instance, if, after defining velocity and momentum, we have to define the kinetic energy of a particle, we may do it in three different ways, thus,

$$\text{Twice the kinetic energy is} = \text{mass} \times \text{square of velocity}$$
$$= \frac{\text{square of momentum}}{\text{mass}}$$
$$= \text{velocity} \times \text{momentum}.$$

Of these three definitions, the first, which is the common form, involves the unimaginable concept of the square of a velocity, the second involves the equally unimaginable square of the momentum, whereas the factors in the third definition are both of them quantities of which we can form a distinct

---

(1) See Numbers 414 and 417; and see note (4).

(2) ULC Add. MSS 7655, V, e/9.

(3) Compare Maxwell's paper 'On the proof of the equations of motion of a connected system', *Proc. Camb. Phil. Soc.*, **2** (1873): 292–4, read 3 February 1873 (= *Scientific Papers*, **2**: 308–9). See also the *Treatise*, **2**: 184–94 (§§563–67).

(4) Compare Tait's comment in his card of 15 July 1872 (Number 417 note (4)).

idea. They are both vectors. In particle-dynamics they are coincident in direction. In the dynamics of a system their directions are, in general, different, and the multiplication must be performed on Hamiltonian principles, and the scalar part taken. In every case the result is a scalar quantity, the kinetic energy of the system.

In the case of a system having n degrees of freedom let

$q_1 \, q_2 \ldots q_n$ be those variables on which the position of the system depends.

$\dot{q}_1 \, \dot{q}_2 \ldots \dot{q}_n$ the velocities of those variables, that is to say the rate at which they increase

$p_1 \, p_2 \ldots p_n$ the momenta of these variables, that is to say the impulses necessary to produce the actual motion.

Then T, the kinetic energy, may be *defined* as

$$T = \frac{1}{2}(p_1 \dot{q}_1 + p_2 \dot{q}_2 + \ldots + p_n \dot{q}_n). \tag{1}$$

But the quantities $p_1 \ldots p_n$ are homogeneous linear functions of $\dot{q}_1 \ldots \dot{q}_n$ so that T may be expressed in two other forms

$$T_{\dot{q}} = \frac{1}{2} P_{11} \dot{q}_1^2 + \frac{1}{2} P_{22} \dot{q}_2^2 + \&c + P_{12} \dot{q}_1 \dot{q}_2 + \&c \tag{2}$$

$$T_p = \frac{1}{2} Q_{11} p_1^2 + \frac{1}{2} Q_{22} p_2^2 + \&c + Q_{12} p_1 p_2 + \&c. \tag{3}$$

Of these two expressions for the kinetic energy, the first, $T_{\dot{q}}$ is that employed by Lagrange, the second, T_p was introduced by Hamilton.

The coefficients P_{11} &c in which the two suffixes are the same may be called moments of inertia and the coefficients P_{12} &c in which the suffixes are different may be called products of inertia.[5]

When the product of inertia corresponding to a given pair of variables is zero, these variables are said to be *conjugate* to each other.

In like manner we may call the coefficients Q_{11} &c the moments of mobility, and Q_{12} &c the products of mobility.

The system of coefficients P is inverse to the system Q.

We can also deduce p_r from $T_{\dot{q}}$ and $\dot{q}_r$ from T_p.[6]

---

(5) See the *Treatise*, **2**: 193 (§565).

(6) The two main sources for Maxwell's discussion are (see *Treatise*, **2**: 184n (§553)): Arthur Cayley, 'Report on the recent progress of theoretical dynamics', in the *Report of the Twenty-seventh Meeting of the British Association for the Advancement of Science* (London, 1858): 1–42, esp. 2, 12, 14–15 (on the dynamical equations of Lagrange and Hamilton); and Thomson and Tait, *Natural Philosophy*: 217–31. See also Joseph Bertrand's note 'Sur les équations différentielles des problèmes de mécanique' in his edition of Lagrange's *Mécanique Analytique*, 2 vols. (Paris,

$$\text{(4)} \qquad p_r = \frac{dT_{\dot{q}}}{d\dot{q}_r} \qquad\qquad \dot{q}_r = \frac{dT_p}{dp_r} \qquad\qquad \text{(5)}$$

$$\text{(6)} \qquad P_{rs} = \frac{d^2 T_{\dot{q}}}{d\dot{q}_r\, d\dot{q}_s} \qquad\qquad Q_{rs} = \frac{d^2 T_p}{dp_r\, dp_s} \qquad\qquad \text{(7)}$$

$$\frac{dT_{\dot{q}}}{dq_r} + \frac{dT_p}{dq_r} = 0. \qquad\qquad \text{(8)}$$

The final equation as given by Lagrange, is

$$F_r = \frac{dp_r}{dt} - \frac{dT_{\dot{q}}}{dq_r}.^{(7)} \qquad\qquad \text{(9)}$$

As given by Hamilton it is

$$F_r = \frac{dp_r}{dt} + \frac{dT_p}{dq_r}.^{(8)} \qquad\qquad \text{(10)}$$

It is of great advantage to the student to be able to connect the equations as they thus stand with easily remembered dynamical ideas. The first term on the right hand of each equation expresses the fact that part of the force is expended in increasing the momentum p. The second term indicates that if the increase of the variable q has a direct effect in increasing the kinetic energy, a force will arise from this circumstance. According to Lagranges expression it would appear as if the kinetic energy had a tendency to increase, and to do work as it increases. This arises from the fact that the kinetic energy is expressed in terms of the velocities. Now it is not the velocities which obey Newton's law of persevering in their actual state, but the momenta or 'quantities of motion'. Hence if we wish to apply Newtons law we must express the kinetic energy in terms of the momenta and use Hamiltons form of the equations of motion.[9] We then see at once that the second term indicates that if a given displacement has a direct tendency to increase the kinetic energy, the momenta remaining the same, a quantity of work, equal to this increase of kinetic energy is performed by the external force F during the displacement.

We may give a still simpler form to Hamiltons equation by taking as the

---

₃1853–5), **1**: 409–22 (see Number 408); Part II, Section IV of the *Mécanique Analytique*: 282–98; W. R. Hamilton, 'On a general method in dynamics', *Phil. Trans.*, **124** (1834): 247–308, esp. 260–2; and Hamilton, 'Second Essay on a general method in dynamics', *Phil. Trans.*, **125** (1835): 95–144, esp. 96–8.

(7) As in the *Treatise*, **2**: 192 (§564).

(8) As in the *Treatise*, **2**: 190 (§561).

(9) See P. M. Harman, 'Newton to Maxwell: the *Principia* and British physics', *Notes and Records of the Royal Society*, **42** (1988): 75–96, esp. 87–8.

displacement the actual displacement $\partial q = \dot{q}\partial t$ which takes place in the time ∂t. The equation then becomes an expression for the work done by the force F during this time.

$$\partial W_r = F_r \partial q = \dot{q}_r \partial t \frac{dp_r}{dt} + \frac{dT_p}{dq_r}\partial q_r \qquad (11)$$

but since $\dot{q}_r = \dfrac{dT_p}{dp_r}$ we may write this

$$F_r \partial q_r = \frac{dT_p}{dp_r}\partial p_r + \frac{dT_p}{dq_r}\partial q_r. \qquad (12)$$

Now the total work done by the external forces in the time ∂t is $F_1 \partial q_1 + F_2 \partial q_2 +$ &c and the total increment of kinetic energy is

$$\left(\frac{dT_p}{dp_1}\partial p_1 + \frac{dT_p}{dq_1}\partial q_1\right) + \left(\frac{dT_p}{dp_2}\partial p_2 + \frac{dT_p}{dq_2}\partial q_2\right) + \text{&c}.$$

The equality of these two quantities is expressed by the principle of the conservation of energy.

But the Hamiltonian equations enable us to assert that the terms composing the first quantity are equal to the corresponding terms of the second quantity, each to each, or

$$F_1 \partial q_1 = \frac{dT_p}{dp_1}\partial p_1 + \frac{dT_p}{dq_1}\partial q_1 \qquad (13)$$

or in words

The work done by the force F_1 during the actual motion of the system in the time ∂t, is equal to the part of the actual increment of T_p which is due to the increment of the momentum p_1 and to the increment of the variable q_1.

Thus the increment of the kinetic energy is, by means of Hamilton's equations, divided into a number of parts, each of which is traced to the action of a particular force.

420

LETTER TO WILLIAM THOMSON

10 AUGUST 1872

From the original in the University Library, Cambridge[1]

Glenlair
Dalbeattie
10 Aug 1872

O T

I enclose an interesting account of M^r & Mrs Brown of Charles Street, Windsor particularly the latter, whose patient observations of the fire ball deserve all praise.[2]

Tell the committee of Electric Standards to abandon the attempt to explain the numerical value of the Ohm Volt & Farad in metres or centimetres grammes &c. The true interpretation of the Latimer Clark jargon*[3] is that electricians and telegraphists being accustomed to large distances and small weights, have adopted as unit of length a quadrant of the earths meridian or 10^7 metres and as unit of mass 10^{-11} grammes leaving the second of mean time in its accustomed place as unit of time.[4]

Latimer Clark tells me that you dissuaded him from defining a Farad as a dose of electricity and persuaded him to define it as the capacity of a (very large) condenser.[5]

Jenkin in his little book sticks to the dose.[6]

---

* Jargon – A rare and valuable stone from Ceylon probably useful to the electrician as well as to the spectroscopist.[3]

---

(1) ULC Add. MSS 7655, II/61A.

(2) The enclosure is not extant. On 8 August 1872 *The Times* carried a report on 'The weather and the storm': 'A house occupied by Mr Brown, Charles Street Windsor, was struck by what its inmates described as a thunderbolt, and considerable damage done to the interior. Mr and Mrs Brown were at a window attending to some flowers when the latter saw a large ball of fire, about a foot in diameter, rushing through the air from the north-east; it was red and glowing, and revolved with great velocity as it approached. Mrs Brown drew back from the window as it neared the house. The ball of fire struck the chimney stack over the roof of the next room, shattered the chimney-pot and brickwork, and drove them into the room. Mrs Brown rushed into the apartment, but found it filled with blue flame and apparently on fire, while a strong sulphureous smell pervaded the place.'

(3) On the supposed discovery of an element 'jargonium' (by absorption spectroscopy) see H. C. Sorby, 'On jargonium, a new elementary substance associated with zirconium', *Proc. Roy. Soc.*, **17** (1869): 511–15. See also Number 468 notes (17) and (18).

(4) See the *Treatise*, **2**: 244–5 (§629) on electrical units.

(5) See Numbers 415 and 418; and see note (8).

(6) See Number 418 esp. note (7).

On the one hand the ohm and the Farad are both visible representations of secondary units, if the farad is a condenser and the ohm a wire while the volt is a Daniell cell of a certain degree of badness.[7]

On the other hand if the farad is a dose of electricity a farad condenser is one which holds a farad per volt and a farad current is one which transmits a farad per second, and in speaking of an electric dose we require a short word to give effect.

Thus – 'Mrs Brown, on a rough estimate, is of opinion, that the fire ball must have contained at least a farad of the electric fluid.

Its potential, at the instant of striking the chimney stack, must have been several megavolts. Mrs Brown, who, with more than the lightning's speed, pursued the fiery globe, had probably a resistance of not more than 1000 Ohms at her command. Her courage, therefore in making herself mistress of all the details of the phenomenon deserves a public recognition by the British Association'.[8]

I am now very near the point at which the definition of a Farad must be printed so I should like to hear from you about it.

---

(7) See the *Treatise*, **2**: 244 (§629).

(8) Thomson's reply (ULC Add. MSS 7655, II/62) is dated 24 August 1872: 'Dear Maxwell / A pint is a pint whether there is liquor in it or not and it is *not* in the abstract a quantity of liquid. So of the microfarad. You may buy a microfarad (of tinfoil & paraffined paper, or of mica &^{c}) and you may buy a pint or a quart measure, of pewter or silver. You might of course buy a pint of beer or of water; and when electrotyping, electric light, &^{c} become commercial we may perhaps buy a microfarad or a megafarad of electricity (perhaps even of hody⟨*l*⟩* [* betraying the citizenship of the inventors of *V* dealers in such commodities] or meric, or omer† [† not to be confounded with the Home or Be.tray unit], as no doubt when we recognise the reality of these fluids we shall be able to measure them in microfarads). I am glad you agree with me that if there is to be a name given it had better be given to a real purchaseable tangible, object than to a quantity of electricity. I daresay Jenkin may be right enough however still in using the expression a microfarad of electricity, meaning as much electricity as a micro-farad holds when filled up till its gauge marks 1 volt. (A glass pint's measure would be filled not to over flowing, but up to a certain mark. Still the piece of glass so marked would be called a pint.) / Everett proposes to call forces metrims or centrims or decims or millims according to the fundamental mass! / I shall never have any thing to do with Veber, till Omer and Hody are generally accepted. / Ohms and Volts I suppose are *in* and they are undoubtedly convenient. So also is the microfarad, as the name of a condenser. But we don't want more names. Those are enough for all purposes, and it would be not any convenience, but rather the reverse, to bring in a separate name for the dose. On this account & from the analogy of a pint of beer we may (with F.J.) talk of a microfarad of elec^y. Yours T. / I am taking two sisters in law &^{c} for a cruise to West Highlands beginning Monday next & likely to last about a fortnight. Where are you to be after that? Address if posting on or before Wed^y care of the Right Rev the Bishop of Argyll   Bishopton   Loch Gilphead. / I did not get your letter of the 10th till my arrival at the Be.tray last week & every day was prevented from answering it.' See Maxwell's discussion in the *Treatise*, **2**: 244–5 (§629); and on Jenkin see Number 450 esp. note (13).

As for poor Veber[9] it is too bad to cut off half his head during his life time. Ohm has been spared any such indignity and Volta and Faraday have only lost vowels and retain their places in the dictionary. I suppose the next thing out will be Walter for Volta to make all square.

I have received your proofs[10] in which we read Hydrokenetic passim. What new light is this?

$$\text{Yours } \frac{dp}{dt}$$

More corrections[11]

    p517   5 from bottom   plane for place
    523   twice   Plücker for Plücher
            'Ieames de la Pluche'
    534   last paragraph unsymbolic for non-analytic

---

(9) See Number 415.
(10) Of Thomson's *Reprint of Papers on Electrostatics and Magnetism* (London, 1872).
(11) Only 'Plücker' (*Electrostatics and Magnetism*: 523) was corrected in the printed text.

421

LETTER TO JAMES THOMSON

2 SEPTEMBER 1872

From the original in the Library of The Queen's University, Belfast[1]

Glenlair
Dalbeattie
2 Sept 1872

My dear Thomson

With respect to the history of my knowledge of the path of rays in a medium of continuously variable index of refraction[2] I had it in my mind when I came to visit your brother Sir[a] William in December 1852 (I think).[3] I then thought it *easiest* to calculate the path of the ray by translating the problem into the emission theory and treating the ray as a moving body acted on by forces depending on the variation of the index of refraction.[4] This was done by making the potential $= 2\mu^2 +$ constant. Of course I knew that this was only an artifice, justifiable only because the emission and undulation theories are mutually equivalent[b] when the proper alterations of the hypothesis are made.

I would therefore give Wollaston some credit for his paper[5] provided it is right on the emission theory. But your brother showed me how easy it is to begin with the right hypothesis, that is, by making the velocity *inversely* proportional to μ and calculating the change of wave-front.

In 1853 I sent the Cambridge & Dublin M.J. a problem[6] about the path

---

(a) {William Thomson} ⟨Sir⟩   (b) {William Thomson} in respect to the path of rays

(1) James Thomson Papers, MS 13/22d, The Queen's University of Belfast Library.

(2) Prompted by a draft of James Thomson's paper, 'On atmospheric refraction of inclined rays, and on the path of a level ray', *Report of the Forty-second Meeting of the British Association for the Advancement of Science; held at Brighton in August 1872* (London, 1873), part 2: 41–5.

(3) In a letter to Maxwell of 11 January 1873 (copy in James Thomson Papers MS 13/22e), writing with reference to the draft 'postscript' to his paper 'On atmospheric refraction of inclined rays' (see note (12)), Thomson noted: 'You may observe that I refer to your visit to my brother as in Dec. 1851 or 1852 I was not sure which as in your letter to me you thought it was in 1852 & in your writing to Dr Everett lately I observe you mention it as having been about Xmas 1851 or so.' On Maxwell's proposed visit to William Thomson in December 1851, see a letter from J. P. Joule to W. Thomson, 3 December 1851 (ULC Add. MSS 7342, J 96).

(4) See P. S. Laplace, *Traité de Mécanique Céleste*, 5 vols. (Paris, An VII [1799]–1825), **4**: 231–76.

(5) W. H. Wollaston, 'Observations on the quantity of horizontal refraction; with a method of measuring the dip at sea', *Phil. Trans.*, **93** (1803): 1–11. See note (11).

(6) See the third of the 'Problems' in the *Camb. & Dubl. Math. J.*, **8** (1853): 188.

of a ray in a medium in which

$$\mu = \frac{\mu_0 a^2}{a^2 + r^2}$$

where μ_0 and a are constant and r is the distance from a fixed point.[7]

Such rays move in circles.

This problem was intended to illustrate the fact that the principal focal length of the crystalline lens is very much shorter than anatomists calculate it from the curvature of its surfaces and the index of refraction of its substance.[8]

If you measure the focal distance and curvatures of a sheep's lens the index of refraction as calculated comes out above 2 whereas no animal substance has an index above 1.45 or so.

The reason is, the increase of density towards the centre of the lens, so that the rays pass nearly tangentially through a place where the density is varying. I also set a question about the conditions of a horizontal ray of light having a greater curvature than that of the earth, in the Cambridge Examination for 1870.[9]

But I should prefer that you said nothing about me in your paper. I did not invent your very clear statement and proof about the radius of curvature, and your remarks about the advantage of using first principles instead of derived maxims is entirely original.

An immense heap of matter has been written about atmospheric refraction by Bessel Clairaut &c &c[10] and a question has been set on it on the first Tuesday afternoon after Jan 12th of each year at Cambridge for many years

---

(7) See [J. C. Maxwell,] 'Solutions to problems', *Camb. & Dubl. Math. J.*, **9** (1854): 7–11, esp. 9–11 (= *Scientific Papers*, **1**: 76–9); and for a draft see Volume I: 232–5. See Number 249.

(8) See Volume I: 235n.

(9) See *The Cambridge University Calendar for the Year 1870* (Cambridge, 1870): 502–3, question (3): 'A ray of light passes through a medium whose index of refraction varies continuously; prove that $\frac{d}{ds}\left(\mu \frac{dx}{ds}\right) = \frac{d\mu}{dx}$, s being the length of the path of the ray to a point whose coordinates are (x, y, z). / If in air $\mu - 1$ varies as the square of the density and if μ at a certain place is $\frac{3400}{3399}$ and if the height of the homogeneous atmosphere be five miles, prove that when the temperature is constant, the effect of refraction on distant horizontal objects is to increase the Earth's apparent radius as found from the dip from 4000 to 5230 miles: and that if the temperature over a frozen sea increase about 6 °F for every hundred feet of ascent, objects may be seen reflected in the sky.'

(10) For a comprehensive review (including an account of Bessel's work) see C. Bruhns, *Die Astronomische Strahlenbrechung in ihrer historischen Entwickelung* (Leipzig, 1861).

back, so the subject has been well twisted this way and that. I am surprised at Lloyd falling into the mistake you point out.[11]

What I have done in this matter belongs to the category of the confused calculations and Cambridge Questions not at all to that of your statement of first principles and your proof that the centre of curvature lies in that stratum which if μ increased uniformly would have the index 2μ.[c]

I do not see that I have any other connexion with your paper than as taking an interest in your enquiry when I heard you were thinking of horizontal rays in air, and much more now that I have read your very clear statement which puts not only atmospherical refraction but also the method of explaining physical phenomena by physical theories, quite in a new light, showing that it is better to go back to the very beginning than to rest in secondary principles.

I have marked for deletion what relates to me and I do not see that its omission will injure the paper in any way.[12]

Yours very truly
J. CLERK MAXWELL

(c) {William Thomson}?

(11) See Humphrey Lloyd, *Elements of Optics* (Dublin, 1849): 108–9, on atmospheric refraction. The point to which Maxwell is alluding is Thomson's discussion of the theory that a ray of light suffers refraction at each successive lamina of air: that 'its whole foundation, in oblique transition of the light across laminae with gradual change of density in those successively traversed, vanishes in the case of a horizontal ray' (Thomson, 'On atmospheric refraction of inclined rays': 41).

(12) With his letter of 11 January 1873 Thomson enclosed a 'postscript' (ULC Add. MSS 7655, II/224) which he proposed to append to the printed text of his paper 'On atmospheric refraction of inclined rays'. This 'postscript' repeats, in paraphrased and slightly re-ordered form, apposite passages from Maxwell's letter of 2 September 1872. In his letter of 11 January 1873 Thomson wrote in explanation of his decision to include reference to Maxwell in his paper: 'When I recv^d your letter of 2 September last from Glenlair relat[ing] to a reference I had made to your investigations or views as to the tending of rays of light in the atmos. or in other mediums of continuously varying index of refraction, in which you mentioned to me some particulars of what you had done & in which you said you would prefer I should say nothing about you in my paper, I altered the passage which had referred to you & quite omitted mention of you in it & then I sent the paper to Mr Griffiths to be printed. / However I afterwards showed a copy of the paper to my brother when I was over in Scotland with him & I showed him your letter & he said he would advise me notwithstanding what you said to annex to my paper an abstract of your letter and I have accordingly written a note proposed to be annexed at the end of my paper and this note I think is just such as he proposed that I should prepare. He thought the things you had done in the matter would be very desirable to be referred to; and I have myself always felt much interest in the conditions of the crystalline lens of the eye since you told me about it. So I hope I have done no harm and shall not have displeased you in making the mention of you and of your

communications with my brother on this subject in the note of which I send you a press copy on thin paper. /...I did not find time to prepare the proposed note till after the proof sheet of the paper came to me about a week ago and now it has been necessary for me to send to Mr G. (Ass^t Gen Sec^y Brit Assoc) the proof sheet corrected without waiting first to consult you about the foot note referring to you. / I send the copy however in the wish that if you do not like the foot note to be inserted you might favour me by writing *direct* to Mr Griffith...asking him to cancel that concluding note or asking him to make any alteration on it that you may think suitable. / ...You may understand that its omission would not in any way spoil or injure my paper.' In the event, Maxwell left Thomson's 'postscript' unaltered; see Thomson, 'On atmospheric refraction of inclined rays': 44–5.

422

POSTCARD TO PETER GUTHRIE TAIT

4 OCTOBER 1872

From the original in the University Library, Cambridge[1]

O T′ How about electromagnetic 4^{nions} as in proof slip 106, 107? which please annotate and return. I suspect that I am not sufficiently free with the use of the Tensor symbol[2] in devectorizing such things as r (distance between two points). The great want of the day is a Grammar of 4^{nions} in the form of dry rules as to notation & interpretation not only of S, T, U, V but of . ( ) and the proper position of $d\sigma$ &c.[3] Contents, Notation, Syntax, Prosody, Nablody.

Yours $\frac{dp}{dt}$

Glenlair 4 Oct 1872

(1) ULC Add. MSS 7655, I, b/49. Previously published in Knott, *Life of Tait*: 151.
(2) See Number 353 note (9).
(3) See Number 353 note (9).

423

LETTER TO PETER GUTHRIE TAIT

9 OCTOBER 1872

From the original in the University Library, Cambridge[1]

Glenlair
9 October 1872

O T'

I am very sorry to hear the reason why I heard nothing of you for a while. I hope that home will be more conducive to health than even the metropolitan city.

I think I had better consecrate ρ to its prescriptive office of denoting indicating or reaching forth unto the point of attention $(x\,y\,z)$. I shall therefore say at 590[2]

If this vector be denoted by $\mathfrak{A}$[3] and if ρ denote the vector from the origin to a given point of the circuit, and $d\rho$ an element of the circuit

$$J = -S\mathfrak{A}\,d\rho\ ^{(4)}$$

and we way write equation (2)[5]

$$p = \int\left(F\frac{dx}{ds} + G\frac{dy}{ds} + H\frac{dz}{ds}\right)ds$$

or
$$p = -\int S\mathfrak{A}\,d\rho.\ ^{(6)}$$

Has ρ a *name*?

It is no ordinary vector carrying a point from one thing to another. It is rather the tentacle or feeler which reaches from the subject to the object.

Is he the Scrutator?[7]

---

(1) ULC Add. MSS 7655, I, b/50. Previously published (in part) in Knott, *Life of Tait*: 151.

(2) See the *Treatise*, **2**: 214 (§590), on electromagnetic action between two circuits.

(3) $\mathfrak{A}$ is the vector potential of a circuit at a point x, y, z, its components being F, G, H, and depends on the position of an element of the circuit ds in the electromagnetic field.

(4) Substituting for the element ds three components dx, dy, dz resolved in the directions of the axes x, y, z, Maxwell defines a quantity $J = F\frac{dx}{ds} + G\frac{dy}{ds} + H\frac{dz}{ds}$.

(5) *Treatise*, **2**: 212 (§586). Considering the electromagnetic action between primary and secondary circuits Maxwell defines a quantity p which measures the part of the electrokinetic momentum of the secondary circuit depending on the primary current, and writes $p = \int J\,ds$.

(6) See note (4). He concludes: 'The vector $\mathfrak{A}$ represents in direction and magnitude the time-integral of the electromotive force which a particle placed at the point (x, y, z) would experience if the primary circuit were suddenly stopped. We shall therefore call it the Electrokinetic Momentum *at the point* (x, y, z).' (*Treatise* §590).

(7) Examiner of votes, at Cambridge (*OED*).

I am glad to hear of the 2nd edition of 4^{nion}. I am going to try, as I have already tried, to sow 4^{nion} seed at Cambridge. I hope and trust that nothing I have yet done may produce tares.[8]

But the interaction of many is necessary for the full development of a new notation for every new absurdity discovered by a beginner is a lesson. Algebra is very far from O.K. after now some centuries, and diff calc is in a mess and $\iiint$ is equivocal at Cambridge with respect to sign.

We put down everything, payments, debts, receipts, cash, credit, in a row or column and trust to good sense in totting up.

I send back slips 101–8 which please return soon as they are in the throes of revision and I have no more copies on hand.

Yours truly
J. CLERK MAXWELL

Just received a Separat Abdruck from Klausius.[9]

---

(8) Injurious weed among corn (biblical and figurative usage, *OED*).

(9) Very likely Clausius' paper 'Ueber den Zusammenhang des zweiten Hauptsatzes der mechanischen Wärmetheorie mit dem Hamilton'schen Princip', *Ann. Phys.*, **146** (1872): 585–91, of which there is a reprint in Maxwell's library (Cavendish Laboratory, Cambridge). For Maxwell's comments on the controversy among 'learned Germans' about the reduction of the second law of thermodynamics to Hamilton's principle see Number 483, esp. note (28).

424

LETTER TO GEORGE BIDDELL AIRY
16 OCTOBER 1872
From the original in the Royal Greenwich Observatory Archive[1]

Glenlair
Dalbeattie
16 Oct 1872

Dear Sir[2]

I have instructed Messrs Macmillan[3] to forward a copy of my essay on Saturn's Rings to M. Faye.[4]

About the year 1864 I made an investigation (unpublished) of the condition of a ring consisting of imperfectly elastic bodies, in great numbers and colliding with one another.[5]

I found that such a ring, if composed of bodies having a coefficient of restitution above a certain value (which I forget) would be continually knocked about, so that the bodies would be describing paths of their own, and the ring would remain a ring of detached bodies, and therefore transparent.[6]

It would obtain the supply of energy required for the collisions by getting flatter and thinner.

But if the bodies were only as elastic as common stones, this great disturbance would not be kept up, and the stones would subside into contact with each other, forming a great flat cake of loose rubbish, kept together by

---

(1) Royal Greenwich Observatory Archive, ULC, Airy Papers 6/259, 204R–V.

(2) In reply to a letter from Airy of 14 October 1872 (Airy Papers 6/259, 203R–V): 'Dear Sir / Having remarked in the French Comptes Rendus a notice of a paper by M. Hirn on the theory of Saturn's Rings considered as collections of discrete molecules, I called the attention of M. Faye to the circumstances that you had very completely investigated the state of the rings on that supposition:– but I could only refer him to an abstract of your paper which I had made in the Monthly Notices of the R. Astronomical Society. / M. Faye has alluded to my communication in an address to the Academy. / Could you send M. Faye a copy of your quarto paper? to the address (A Monsieur/M. Faye / President de l'Académie des Sciences / au Palais de l'Institut / à Paris. / Or, if you prefer it, send it to me that I may forward it to him. / The publication as a separate paper is very unfortunate:– such volatile tracts are very soon lost. / I am, dear sir, / Yours faithfully / G. B. Airy.'

On 16 September 1872 H. A. Faye had read to the Académie des Sciences a 'Note relative à un mémoire de M. Hirn sur les conditions d'équilibre et sur la nature probable des anneaux de Saturne', *Comptes Rendus*, **75** (1872): 645–6. Airy had written to him on 26 September 1872 (Airy Papers 6/259, 201R–V), commending Maxwell's 'very able paper' on Saturn's rings.

(3) On the circumstances of publication of Maxwell's *On the Stability of the Motion of Saturn's Rings* (Cambridge, 1859) (= *Scientific Papers*, **1**: 288–376) see Volume I: 599, 612.

(4) See note (2).   (5) Number 224.

(6) See Number 224 §3.

its mutual gravitation, but always grinding one part against another in a sluggish manner instead of working itself up, as a ring of glass balls would do, till they were all flying about like a swarm of bees.

Yours faithfully
J. CLERK MAXWELL

425

FROM A LETTER TO LEWIS CAMPBELL

19 OCTOBER 1872

From Campbell and Garnett, *Life of Maxwell*[1]

Glenlair
Dalbeattie
19 October 1872

…Lectures begin 24th. Laboratory rising, I hear, but I have no place to erect my chair, but move about like the cuckoo, depositing my notions in the chemical lecture-room 1st term; in the Botanical in Lent, and in Comparative Anatomy in Easter.

I am continually engaged in stirring up the Clarendon Press, but they have been tolerably regular for two months. I find nine sheets in thirteen weeks is their average. Tait gives me great help in detecting absurdities. I am getting converted to Quaternions, and have put some in my book, in a heretical form, however, for as the Greek alphabet was used up, I have used German capitals from $\mathfrak{A}$ to $\mathfrak{Z}$ to stand for Vectors, and, of course, ∇ occurs continually. This letter is called 'Nabla', and the investigation a Nablody.[2] You will be glad to hear that the theory of gases is being experimented on by Profs. Loschmidt[3] and Stefan[4] of Vienna, and that the conductivity of air and hydrogen are within 2 per cent of the value calculated from my experiments on friction of gases,[5] though the diffusion of one gas into another is '*in erglanzender ubereinstimmung mit $\frac{dp}{ds}$ schen Theorie.*'[6]

---

(1) *Life of Maxwell*: 383–4.   (2) See Number 348 note (3).

(3) Joseph Loschmidt, 'Experimental-Untersuchungen über die Diffusion von Gasen ohne poröse Scheidewände', *Wiener Berichte*, **61**, Abtheilung II (1870): 367–80; *ibid.*, **62**, Abtheilung II (1870): 468–78. See Number 470.

(4) Josef Stefan, 'Über die Gleichgewicht und die Bewegung, insbesondere die Diffusion von Gasmengen', *Wiener Berichte*, **63**, Abtheilung II (1871): 63–124; Stefan, 'Untersuchungen über die Wärmeleitung in Gasen', *ibid.*, **65**, Abtheilung II (1872): 45–69; Stefan, 'Über die dynamische Theorie der Diffusion der Gase', *ibid.*, **65**, Abtheilung II (1872): 323–63.

(5) Stefan, 'Untersuchungen über die Wärmeleitung in Gasen': 47–8. Following Boltzmann's discovery of an arithmetical error in Maxwell's expression for the thermal conductivity of a gas (see Number 263 note (24)), Stefan discussed modifying Maxwell's theory: see his paper 'Untersuchungen über die Wärmeleitung in Gasen', *Wiener Berichte*, **72**, Abtheilung II (1876): 69–101.

(6) Garbled from Stefan, 'Über die dynamische Theorie der Diffusion der Gase': 324.

426

LETTER TO GEORGE BIDDELL AIRY

28 OCTOBER 1872

From the original in the Royal Greenwich Observatory Archive[1]

> 11 Scroope Terrace
> Cambridge
> 28 Oct 1872

Dear Sir[2]

I should like very much to see the memoir of M. Hirn,[3] which I will return to you as soon as I can.

I see in Les Mondes of the 24th Oct that M. Hirn has become acquainted with your letter to M. Faye containing an account of my essay.[4]

Macmillan tells me the essay was sent at once to M. Faye[5] so M. Hirn may have seen it, though he might have acquired all that appears from his statement by reading your notice in the Astronomical Societies notices.[6]

The interest of the speculations on the constitution of Saturns rings is not likely to be soon exhausted for the solution of the various mathematical problems which it suggests takes a long time, and when these are solved we are liable to make mistakes in applying them to the physical problems and so we have to examine the whole speculation afresh, searching not for bad mathematics, but for bad reasoning.

> Yours faithfully
> J. CLERK MAXWELL

The Astronomer Royal[7]

---

(1) Royal Greenwich Observatory Archive, ULC, Airy Papers 6/259, 208R–V.

(2) In reply to a letter from Airy of 26 October 1872 (Airy Papers 6/259, 205R): 'Dear Sir / I have heard nothing from M. Faye about your paper concerning Saturn's rings. / M. Hirn has sent me a copy of his paper. Would you like to peruse it? I can place it in your hands only on loan, as I must retain it for the Observatory. / I am, dear Sir, / Faithfully yours / G. B. Airy.'

(3) See note (2); and G. A. Hirn, *Mémoire sur les Conditions d'Équilibre et sur la Nature Probable des Anneaux de Saturne* (Paris, 1872).

(4) See *Les Mondes*, **29** (24 October 1872): 288–9, a report of Faye's 'Note relative à un mémoire de M. Clerk-Maxwell, sur la stabilité des anneaux de Saturne', *Comptes Rendus*, **75** (1872): 793–4, giving an account of Airy's letter to him of 26 September 1872 (see Number 424 note (2)).

(5) See Number 424.

(6) See Airy's review 'On the stability of the motion of Saturn's rings', *Monthly Notices of the Royal Astronomical Society*, **19** (1859): 297–304.

(7) Airy's reply is dated 29 October 1872 (Airy Papers 6/259, 210R–V): 'Dear Sir / I send by Book Post my copy of M. Hirn's Essay on Saturn's Rings / I have just learned the address of

M. Hirn... Perhaps you could send *him* a copy of your Essay. / The mode of publication of the Adams Prize Essays was very unfortunate. Practically they are totally lost to the world. I suggested some years ago that arrangement should be made for their regular appearance in the Cambridge Phil. Soc. Transactions: but I know not whether any thing was done.' (See Volume I: 612n). Maxwell sent Hirn a copy of his Essay; acknowledged in a letter from Hirn to Maxwell of 25 November 1872 (ULC Add. MSS 7655, II/68).

427

NOTE[1] TO PETER GUTHRIE TAIT
12 NOVEMBER 1872
From the original in the University Library, Cambridge[2]

[Cambridge]

Address 11 Scroope Terrace, Cambridge.

I hope the surgical operation is to be carried out on prooves only, not on mémoires. As for Trägheit,[3] none but himself can be his explanation. I defy you to explain him by central forces not involving velocities.

---

(1) On proofs (of *Treatise* §§ 692–725), date as postmark.

(2) ULC Add. MSS 7655, IV/2.

(3) 'Laziness', Tait's nickname (see Knott, *Life of Tait*: 182–3) for the generalisation of the theorem in Thomson and Tait, *Natural Philosophy*: 217 (§ 312): 'The energy of the motion generated suddenly in a mass of incompressible liquid given at rest completely filling a vessel of any shape, when the vessel is suddenly set in motion, or when it is suddenly bent out of shape in any way whatever, subject to the condition of not changing its volume, *is less than the energy of any other motion it can have with the same motion of its bounding surface.*' Thomson's theorem on extremal conditions which determine the bounding surface of an incompressible fluid enclosed within a flexible and extensible envelope was first formulated in his 'Notes on hydrodynamics. V. On the vis-viva of a liquid in motion', *Camb. & Dubl. Math. J.*, **4** (1849): 90–4 (= *Math. & Phys. Papers*, **1**: 107–12). Thomson published a statement of the generalised minimum theorem, which Tait nicknamed 'Laziness', in his paper 'On some kinematical and dynamical theorems', *Proc. Roy. Soc. Edinb.*, **5** (1863): 113–15 (= *Math. & Phys. Papers*, **4**: 458–9): 'Given any material system at rest. Let any parts of it be set in motion suddenly with given velocities, the other parts being influenced only by their connections with those which are set in motion, the whole system will move so as to have less kinetic energy than belongs to any other motion fulfilling the given velocity conditions'. See *Natural Philosophy*: 217–25 for discussion and proof of the theorem.

428

LETTER TO PETER GUTHRIE TAIT
LATE 1872 – EARLY 1873[1]

From the original in the University Library, Cambridge[2]

I hereby declare C. Neumann Not Guilty of *reading* T on the hydrokinetic illustration of Θ.H. currents.[3] He may have heard of it or *tried* to read it but if he had read it he would not have written such original bosch.[4]

Neumann's is not an illustration but a physical theory. He adopts the Unitarian view asserting, without a pang, that vitreous electricity is a fluidum, while resinous is inseparably joined with ponderable matter.[5]

This fluidum obeys two Princips the Potential ditto and that des isotropen Druckes[6] which last, be it observed, is nothing more than the Boyle & Charles gaseous laws, which being admitted introduce absolute charge to any extent and the squeezing of electricity under Druck.[7] In this abhandlung C. N. steers clear of this by considering only *steady* currents. Woe to him when he goes further. He will fare even worse!

The density of this fluidum varies with temperature, and namely in the same ratio as that of the ponderable body. But the absolute density of the fluidum at 0 °C is different for different metals.

Hence if we know the relative thermoelectric position of two metals at 0 °C, and also their dilatations per 1 °C their neutral point can be found. (Here the theory lies open to experiment.)

Be it carefully observed that this theory professes to account for nothing but

---

(1) The letter relates to Tait's interest in thermo-electricity at this time, and to a recent paper by Carl Neumann (see notes (4) and (13)).

(2) ULC Add. MSS 7655, I, b/105.

(3) On Thomson's analogy see Number 393 note (7).

(4) Carl Neumann, 'Vorläufige Conjectur über die Ursachen der thermoelektrischen Ströme', *Berichte über die Verhandlungen der Königlich Sächsischen Gesellschaft der Wissenschaften zu Leipzig, Math.-Phys. Klasse*, **24** (1872): 49–64.

(5) That is: positive and negative electricity; see the *Treatise*, **1**: 31 (§27). On the concept of electricity as a fluid see note (10).

(6) Neumann bases his theory on 'das Princip der Potentiellen Kräfte und das Princip des isotropen Druckes'; see his 'Vorläufige Conjectur': 52. On his concept of pressure see note (7).

(7) Neumann states: 'dass das Princip des isotropen Druckes nicht nur in Hydrodynamik und Aërodynamik, sondern auch in andern Gebieten der theoretischen Physik eine Rolle zu spielen'; Neumann, 'Vorläufige Conjectur: 63.

Seebeck's effect,⁽⁸⁾ Peltiers⁽⁹⁾ and Thomson's⁽¹⁰⁾ are alike unreferred to. The word Thomson occurs in reference to his experimental researches⁽¹¹⁾ which are here said to confirm the doctrine of the slope of the line of a metal depending on its rate of dilatation.⁽¹²⁾

All things considered, this lucubration, if ever demonstrated to be true by the language of facts, will furnish me with arguments sufficient for the deglutition of my own hat, if not head, before I go on to swallow so crude a morsel.⁽¹³⁾

$$\frac{\partial p}{\partial t}$$

---

(8) The discovery 'of thermoelectric currents in circuits of different metals with their junctions at different temperature' (*Treatise*, **1**: 302 (§250)); see Thomas Seebeck, 'Magnetische Polarisation der Metalle und Erze durch Temperatur-Differenz', *Abhandlungen der Königlichen Akademie der Wissenschaften zu Berlin* (Aus dem Jahren 1822–23): 265–373.

(9) The discovery 'that, when a current of electricity crosses the junction of two metals, the junction is heated when the current is in one direction, and cooled when it is in the other direction' (*Treatise*, **1**: 300 (§249)); see J. A. C. Peltier, 'Nouvelles expériences sur la caloricité des courans électriques', *Ann. Chim. Phys.*, ser. 2, **56** (1834): 371–86. On Thomson's use of the symbol Π for the coefficient of the Peltier effect see Number 322 note (5).

(10) Thomson's discovery 'of the reversible effect of an electric current upon an unequally heated conductor of one metal' (*Treatise*, **1**: 305 (§253)); see William Thomson, 'On the electro-dynamic qualities of metals', *Phil. Trans.*, **146** (1856): 649–751, esp. 649–709 (= *Math. & Phys. Papers*, **2**: 189–327, esp. 189–266). Maxwell argues that Thomson's experiments, which established 'that the current produced opposite effects in copper and in iron', and 'shew that positive electricity in copper and negative electricity in iron carry heat with them from hot to cold', contradict the theory that either positive or negative electricity were a 'fluid, capable of being heated and cooled, and of communicating heat to other bodies, [for] we should find the supposition contradicted by iron for positive electricity, and by copper for negative electricity'; see the *Treatise*, **1**: 305 (§253).

(11) Thomson, 'On the electro-dynamic qualities of metals': 649–709.

(12) Neumann, 'Vorläufige Conjectur': 60.

(13) In his Rede Lecture on 'Thermo-electricity', *Nature*, **8** (1873): 86–8, 122–4, esp. 87–8, Tait echoes Maxwell's remarks on Neumann.

NOTES TO PETER GUTHRIE TAIT

circa DECEMBER 1872

From the microfilm of the originals in Edinburgh University Library[1]

[1]   *For Science in 1872 in 'Belgravia' Dec 1872, p. 188.*

'Is Electricity Life?' by Henry Lake.[2] Here is a bit. The ocean, for instance, is compounded of water and salt; one is an electric, the other is not. The friction of these causes the phosphorescent appearances so often observed at sea. &c &c in same style.

Electricity of kissing – danger of mutual destruction obviated by the existence of electric atmospheres. A person who has the small pox cannot be electrified, while sparks of electricity may be drawn from a patient dying of cholera. The hand draws from the sensitive plant the electricity which it contains more than other plants; and its leaves at once fall flaccidly, until a new supply of electric force renders them once more turgid.

[2]   *Astronomy at Cambridge in 1872*[3]

The Earth is now ascertained to have the form of an ellipse.

It revolves about its axes. In Winter it revolves about its longer axis AB, but in Summer about its shorter axis CD, thus producing the changing of the seasons.

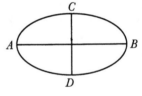

Figure 429,1

---

(1) Edinburgh University Library, Mic. M.134. Tait's Scrapbook (where these notes are preserved) is in private possession.

(2) Henry Lake, 'Is electricity life?', *Belgravia*, **9** (December 1872): 188–96.

(3) Possibly from a Natural Sciences Tripos examination paper. (Maxwell was not an examiner in 1872.)

430

ARTICLE ON ELECTROMAGNETISM[1]

LATE 1872 – EARLY 1873

From the originals in the University Library, Cambridge[2]

ELECTROMAGNETISM[3]

The attraction of light particles by amber and that of iron by the loadstone were known to the ancients. Other phenomena were afterwards discovered to be related to those exhibited by amber and were classed together as Electric phenomena. A different set of phenomena were found to be related to those of the loadstone, and were called Magnetic phenomena. Many conjectures were formed as to the relation between these two sets of phenomena, but at last in 1822 Oersted discovered the mutual action between an electric current and a magnet,[4] and this discovery forms the starting point of the science of Electromagnetism which treats of electric and magnetic phenomena in their relation to each other. Ampère in 1823 discovered the mathematical form of the law of the mechanical force acting between two electric currents.[5] His investigation is in its way a model of scientific method,[6] and his formula is the foundation of that form of our science which admits that bodies may act on one another at a distance.

In the present article we shall follow the path pointed out by Faraday which leads to results mathematically identical with those of Ampère but never loses sight of the phenomena which take place in the ⟨media⟩ ⌞space⌟ between the bodies which are observed to act on each other.

Faraday had made considerable progress in illustrating the mutual action between electric currents and magnets, when in 1831 he made his great discovery of the fact that an electric current is produced in a closed circuit when a magnet, or a conductor carrying an electric current, is moved

---

(1) Published in the *English Cyclopaedia*, supplementary volume on 'Arts and Sciences' (London, 1873), columns 854–7.

(2) From the manuscript and corrected proofs in ULC Add. MSS 7655, V, c/18. The changes from the manuscript and Maxwell's corrections to the proofs are recorded.

(3) Compare 'Part IV. Electromagnetism' of the *Treatise*.

(4) See Number 238 note (17), and the *Treatise*, **2**: 128–9 (§§475–6).

(5) A. M. Ampère, 'Mémoire sur la théorie mathématique des phénomènes électrodynamiques uniquement déduite de l'expérience', *Mémoires de l'Académie Royale des Sciences*, **6** (1827): 175–388, esp. 252–3; and see the *Treatise*, **2**: 146–50 (§§502–8), and Volume I: 305–6n.

(6) 'The whole, theory and experiment, seems as if it had leaped, full grown and full armed, from the brain of the "Newton of electricity".' (*Treatise*, **2**: 162 (§§528)).

relatively to the closed circuit, or when the strength of the inducing current is varied. The first two series of Faradays *Experimental Researches* in which he describes his experiments, and deduces from them the laws of the phenomena, may be read as an example of a form of scientific method different from that of Ampère.[7]

Faraday soon afterwards found that an electric current acts on itself as well as on other currents. When it is increasing in strength this self inductive action tends to check the current. When it is diminishing it tends to maintain the current. Faraday was at once struck with the analogy between these phenomena of an electric current and those of a current of water in a pipe, which requires a force to start it and which continues in motion till it is stopped by some other force.[8]

In the case of the pipe these phenomena are attributed to the inertia of the water, which like all other material substances perseveres in its state of rest or motion, except in so far as that state is changed by the application of force.

In the case of the electric current in ⟨the state of⟩ which we find a persistence of exactly the same kind we naturally look for a similar explanation. But as Faraday shews, there are important differences between the two cases. The inertia of the water in the pipe depends only on the length and the section of the pipe and not on the form into which the pipe may be coiled or bent.

The apparent inertia of the electric current on the other hand depends on the shape of the wire which carries it. If the wire is made into a coil with its windings all in one direction the current has great persistence. If the wire is doubled on itself so that in adjacent portions the currents are opposite, the persistence is exceedingly small.

Besides this, we have the fact that a current in one circuit induces a current in a neighbouring circuit, a phenomenon which has no counterpart in the case of water in separate pipes.

Hence if Faradays phenomenon is due to the inertia of matter in motion this matter is not to be sought for in the wire itself but in the space surrounding the wire. It is to Sir William Thomson that the idea is due, that everywhere in the neighbourhood of an electric current, and wherever magnetic action can be traced there is matter of some kind the motion of which is determined by the currents and magnets, and that the phenomena

---

(7) Compare the *Treatise*, **2**: 164–8 (§§ 530–5).

(8) Compare Maxwell's discussion of the Ninth Series of Faraday's 'Experimental researches in electricity' (*Electricity*, **1**: 322–43; and see Number 238 note (15)) in the *Treatise*, **2**: 180–3 (§§ 546–52).

of induction are due to the persistence of this motion while those of attraction are due to its centrifugal force.[9] This idea has been developed by the writer of this article in a series of papers on the theory of Molecular Vortices in the Philosophical Magazine for 1861–2.[10]

But the connexion of all electromagnetic phenomena may be traced in a manner independent of this theory, by assuming only that a system of electric currents in given positions forms, with the surrounding medium, a connected system similar to those of which the equations of motion have been fully investigated by Lagrange.[11]

Lagrange supposes the position of every part of the system to be expressed in terms of a set of variables or coordinates x_1 x_2 &c, the number of which is equal to the number of degrees of freedom of the system. These coordinates vary with the time, and we shall for brevity write $\dot{x}_1$ for $\dfrac{dx_1}{dt}$, and call $\dot{x}_1$ the velocity of the coordinate x_1.

The whole dynamical theory of such a connected system depends on the value of the kinetic energy or vis viva of the system which is a homogeneous quadratic function of the velocities, the coefficients being in general functions of the coordinates. Hence

$$T = \tfrac{1}{2} L_1 \dot{x}_1^2 + \tfrac{1}{2} L_2 \dot{x}_2^2 + \&c + M_{12} x_1 x_2 + \&c \tag{1}$$

where T is the kinetic energy of the system, L_1 L_2 &c functions of the coordinates which we may call moments of inertia and M_{12} &c other functions which we may call products of inertia.

If we differentiate the expression for T with respect to $\dot{x}_1$ we obtain

$$\xi_1 = \frac{dT}{d\dot{x}_1} = L_1 \dot{x}_1 + M_{12} \dot{x}_2 + \&c. \tag{2}$$

This quantity ξ_1 is the momentum of the system with respect to the coordinate x_1. In the theory of the motion of unconnected particles the momentum of each particle depends only on its own motion, but when the motion is that of a connected system the momentum of each coordinate will depend on the velocity of other coordinates unless these coordinates are conjugate to each other.

---

(9) In his paper 'Dynamical illustrations of the magnetic and the heliocoidal rotatory effects of transparent bodies on polarized light', *Proc. Roy. Soc.*, **8** (1856): 150–8.

(10) J. C. Maxwell, 'On physical lines of force', *Phil. Mag.*, ser. 4, **21** (1861): 161–75, 281–91, 338–48; *ibid.*, **23** (1862): 12–24, 85–95 (= *Scientific Papers*, **1**: 451–513).

(11) See the *Treatise*, **2**: 184–94 (§§553–67); and compare Number 419.

If X_1 denotes the external force applied to the system tending to increase x_1 then by Lagranges equation[12]

$$X_1 = \frac{d\xi_1}{dt} - \frac{dT}{dx_1}. \tag{3}$$

Hitherto we have introduced no distinction between different kinds of coordinates. We shall now suppose that the positions of the various circuits in the field are expressed by the coordinates x_1 &c their velocities by $\dot{x}_1$ &c, their momenta by ξ_1 &c the forces which are impressed on them by X_1 &c. We might also express by y_1 the position of a particle of electricity in one of these circuits, and by $\dot{y}_1$ its velocity but since one particle of electricity in the circuit is like another the value of y_1 can not enter into the dynamical equations and the state of things will be completely determined by $\dot{y}_1$ $\dot{y}_2$ &c the strengths of the electric currents in the circuits 1 2 &c.

Hence in the expression for T, the kinetic energy of the system the coefficients L, M &c will be functions of the mechanical coordinates x_1 x_2 &c and not of the electrical coordinates y_1 y_2 &c.

The expression will consist of three parts. The first part involves squares and products of the mechanical velocities and the second squares and products of the electric currents while the third involves products of mechanical velocities and electric currents.

The first part belongs to the ordinary dynamics of the system and it may be shown by experiment (Maxwell's Electricity Part IV Chap VI)[13] that the third part, if it exists, is of insensible value. Hence we have only to consider the second part of the kinetic energy, which involves squares and products of the electric currents.[14]

Let us take the case of two currents only, in which case

$$T = \tfrac{1}{2}L_1\dot{y}_1^2 + M\dot{y}_1\dot{y}_2 + \tfrac{1}{2}L_2\dot{y}_2^2. \tag{4}$$

Here T is the kinetic energy of the electric system, $\dot{y}_1$ and $\dot{y}_2$ are the currents, L_1 and L_2 are the moments of inertia (in an electrical sense) of the circuits and M is the product of inertia. The quantities L_1 M L_2 depend only on the form and ⌊relative⌋ position of the circuits, and may be calculated when these are given.

Writing η_1 and η_2 for the electromagnetic momenta of the circuits we find

$$\begin{aligned}\eta_1 &= L_1\dot{y}_1 + M\dot{y}_2 \\ \eta_2 &= M\dot{y}_1 + L_2\dot{y}_2.\end{aligned} \tag{5}$$

---

(12) See the *Treatise*, **2**: 198–200 (§573).
(13) See the *Treatise*, **2**: 200–5 (§§574–77); and see Number 340 esp. note (9).
(14) See the *Treatise*, **2**: 206–10 (§§578–84); and Number 333.

If Y_1 Y_2 are the external electromotive forces in the two circuits

$$Y_1 = \frac{d\eta_1}{dt} \quad Y_2 = \frac{d\eta_2}{dt} \tag{6}$$

and if X_1 X_2 are the external mechanical forces on the conducting circuits required to overcome the forces arising from the action of the currents

$$X_1 = -\frac{dT}{dx_1} \quad X_2 = -\frac{dT}{dx_2}. \tag{7}$$

In the general expression for the force in equation (3) there are two terms. The second of these disappears in (6) because the expression for T does not involve y_1. The first disappears in (7) because the electric part of T does not involve $\dot{x}_1$ or ξ_1.

Equations (6) express the whole theory of the induction of electric currents, and equations (7) the whole theory of the mechanical action between circuits carrying electric currents.

For simplicity let us suppose the form of each circuit invariable so that L_1 and L_2 are constants but let their relative positions depend on the coordinate x, which we may call their distance. M will be a function of x which when the circuits are parallel and in the same direction will generally diminish as x increases.

Let us suppose that there is a current $\dot{y}_1$ in the first circuit and that there is no external electromotive force acting in the second except the resistance of the circuit to the current, which may be written $Y_2 = -R_2\dot{y}_2$. Equation (6) becomes

$$-R_2\dot{y}_2 = \frac{d\eta_2}{dt} \tag{8}$$

or integrating with respect to t

$$Ry_2 = (\eta_2) - [\eta_2] \tag{9}$$

where R denotes the resistance of the second circuit, y_2 the whole quantity of electricity which flows through it during a certain time, (η_2) the value of the momentum at the beginning and $[\eta_2]$ that at the end of the time.

If the second current $\dot{y}_2$ is zero both at the beginning and at the end of the time ⌞then by equation (5)⌟

$$Ry_2 = (M\dot{y}_1) - [M\dot{y}_1]. \tag{10}$$

Hence there is a positive induced current when the value of $M\dot{y}_1$ is diminished and a negative current when it is increased whether by the variation of the primary current $\dot{y}_1$ or by the variation of M due to relative motion of the circuits. All the phenomena of the induction of currents are included in this result.

Again X is the mechanical force which is required to balance the electric force acting between the circuits. Hence the force of the electric action is

$$-X = \frac{dT}{dx} = \frac{dM}{dx}\dot{y}_1\dot{y}_2. \tag{11}$$

Hence the force between the circuits is proportional to the product of the currents in them, and tends to increase M, that is, in the case of two parallel circuits in the same direction, to draw them together, or to attract them. All the phenomena of the mechanical action between currents are included in this result.

The problem of the mutual action of two circuits is thus reduced to the calculation of the coefficient M.[15] In the case of two linear closed curves of which the elements are ds_1 and ds_2

$$M = \iint \frac{ds_1 \, ds_2 \cos \epsilon}{r} \tag{12}$$

where r is the distance between the elements ds_1 ds_2 and ϵ the angle between their directions and the integration is to be extended first round one circuit and then round the other.[16] The deduction of this formula from known facts and the calculation of the value of M in different cases will be found in the work on electricity already referred to.

According to the theory of this article, what we call an electric current is accompanied by a real motion of matter, which takes place not merely in the conducting wire but in the apparently empty space round it.

Admitting the existence of this invisible moving medium, we may find by mathematical methods the vis viva of any portion of it and the distribution of pressure in different directions. The action of these pressures is found to account for the observed attractions and repulsions of electric currents so that we have no need to assume that bodies can act on each other at a distance.

The velocity with which electric disturbances are propagated through this medium can be calculated from known experimental data, and it is found to agree very closely with the velocity of light. Besides this it can be shown that the only kind of electric disturbance which can be propagated through the medium is a transverse displacement and this is the kind of disturbance to which optical inquirers have traced the phenomena of light. Hence we have great reason to believe that light is an electromagnetic phenomenon, and that the radiation of light and heat as well as the forces of electricity and

---

(15) The 'coefficient of mutual induction' between two circuits (*Treatise*, **2**: 210 (§584)); and see Number 350.

(16) See the *Treatise*, **2**: 159 (§524).

magnetism depend on one and the same medium, a medium truly material and capable of comparison with the kinds of matter with which we are more familiar though hitherto it has escaped the direct observation of our senses.

For the literature of this view of electromagnetism the reader is referred to Faradays Experimental Researches;[17] to Sir William Thomsons Electrical Papers[18] now being reprinted; to the Reports of the British Association 'On Electrical Standards' particularly those of 1863, 1867 and 1869,[19] and to Maxwell's paper on the Electromagnetic Field, Phil Trans. 1865.[20] For that of the ⟨opposite⟩ other way of treating the subject he is referred to Ampère, Mém de l'Institut 1823,[21] J. Neumann Berlin Trans 1845;[22] W. Weber Elektrodynamische Maasbestimmungen in the Leipzic Transactions from 1846 onwards,[23] a most important contribution to science. See also a masterly paper by Helmholtz on the equations of the motion of electricity in Crelle's Journal for 1870.[24] The whole subject is well treated in Wiedemann's *Galvanismus*.[25]

---

(17) Faraday, *Electricity*.

(18) Thomson, *Electrostatics and Magnetism*.

(19) 'Report of the Committee on standards of electrical resistance', in the *Report of the Thirty-third Meeting of the British Association for the Advancement of Science* (London, 1864): 111–76; *Report of the Thirty-seventh Meeting*...(London, 1868): 474–522; and the *Report of the Thirty-ninth Meeting*...(London, 1870): 434–8.

(20) See Number 238 esp. note (1).   (21) See note (5).

(22) F. E. Neumann, 'Die mathematischen Gesetze der inducirten elektrischen Ströme', *Physikalische Abhandlungen der Königlichen Akademie der Wissenschaften zu Berlin. Aus dem Jahre 1845* (Berlin, 1847): 1–87.

(23) Wilhelm Weber, 'Elektrodynamische Maassbestimmungen', in *Abhandlung bei Begründung der Königlichen Sächsischen Akademie der Wissenschaften* (1846): 211–378; in *Abhandlungen der Königlichen Sächsischen Gesellschaft der Wissenschaften*, **1** (1852): 199–381; and (with R. Kohlrausch) ibid., **3** (1857): 219–92 (= *Wilhelm Weber's Werke*, 6 vols. (Berlin, 1892–4), **3**: 25–214, 301–471, 609–76).

(24) Hermann Helmholtz, 'Ueber die Bewegungsgleichungen der Elektricität für ruhende leitende Körper', *Journal für die reine und angewandte Mathematik*, **72** (1870): 57–128.

(25) Gustav Wiedemann, *Die Lehre vom Galvanismus und Elektromagnetismus*, 2 vols. (Braunschweig, $_2$1872–3).

431

NOTE ON FORBES' WORK ON COLOURS FOR THE *LIFE OF FORBES*[1]

circa 1872

From the original in the University Library, Cambridge[2]

[FORBES ON COLOURS]

In a paper entitled Hints towards a Classification of Colours read before the Royal Society of Edinburgh Dec 4, 1848 & Jan 15 1849[3] Forbes called attention to the importance of a method of defining colours with precision both for scientific and for artistic purposes. In this paper he adopted from Lambert and Mayer[4] not only their arrangement of colours in a pyramid or a triangle but their choice of the colours which are to be regarded as primary, namely red, yellow and blue. He afterwards attempted to form a permanent diagram of colours selected from the collection of artificial enamels employed in the Vatican fabric of mosaic pictures[5] by comparing these enamels with the tints formed by the mixture of the primaries on a rapidly revolving disk. He found, however on attempting to form a neutral gray by the combination of red blue and yellow, that the resulting tint could not be rendered neutral by any combination of these colours; and the reason was found to be that blue and yellow do not make green but a pinkish tint, when neither prevails in the combination. It was plain that no addition of red to this could produce a neutral tint.[6] The fact that green cannot be formed by a mixture of blue and

---

(1) J. C. Shairp, P. G. Tait and A. Adams-Reilly, *The Life and Letters of James David Forbes, F.R.S., D.C.L., LL.D., late Principal of the United College in the University of St Andrews, &c* (London, 1873): 464–5.

(2) ULC Add. MSS 7655, V, b/17.

(3) J. D. Forbes, 'Hints towards a classification of colours', *Phil. Mag.*, ser. 3, **34** (1849): 161–78; and see *Proc. Roy. Soc. Edinb.*, **2** (1848–9): 190, 214–16.

(4) Forbes, 'Hints towards a classification of colours': 161, 168–70; and see Tobias Mayer, 'De affinitate colorum commentatio', in *Opera Inedita*, ed. G. C. Lichtenberg (Göttingen, 1775): 33–42; and J. H. Lambert, *Beschreibung einer mit Calauischem Wachse ausgemalten Farbenpyramide* (Berlin, 1772).

(5) See Forbes, 'Hints towards a classification of colours': 177–8.

(6) This statement is drawn from a supplementary note on Forbes' experiments in Maxwell's paper 'Experiments on colour, as perceived by the eye, with remarks on colour-blindness', *Trans. Roy. Soc. Edinb.*, **21** (1855): 275–98, esp. 291–2 (= *Scientific Papers*, **1**: 145–6). On the circumstances under which this note was added to the proofs of Maxwell's paper, see Volume I: 302–3.

yellow was pointed out by E. C. Wünch* and by Young†⁽⁷⁾ but the contrary was still believed by the highest optical authorities. The reason why mixtures of blue and yellow pigments are often green was soon after explained by Helmholtz;⁽⁸⁾ and⁽ᵃ⁾ one of Forbes pupils who⁽ᵇ⁾ witnessed his experiments was led by them to make experiments on the mixtures of the colours of the solar spectrum which showed that a yellow equal to that of the spectrum can be produced by the mixture of green and red light.⁽⁹⁾

* Versuche und Beobachtungen über die Farben des Lichts, Leipzig 1792⁽⁷⁾

† Lecture XXXVII⁽⁷⁾

(a) {Tait} Clerk Maxwell who was

(b) {Tait} ⟨who⟩ and

(7) Young states: 'we may consider white light as composed of a mixture of red, green, and violet only'; see Thomas Young, *A Course of Lectures on Natural Philosophy and the Mechanical Arts*, ed. P. Kelland, 2 vols. (London, 1845), **1**: 344. See also Chrétien-Ernst Wünsch, *Versuche und Beobachtungen über die Farben des Lichts* (Leipzig, 1792), where Young's selection of red, green and violet as the three primary colours is anticipated. (This work is cited in Young, *Course of Lectures*, **1**: 344n.)

(8) Hermann Helmholtz, 'Ueber die Theorie der zusammengesetzten Farben', *Ann. Phys.*, **87** (1852): 45–66. Helmholtz demonstrated that while the mixture of coloured lights is an additive process, pigment mixing is subtractive: see Volume **I**: 300n.

(9) J. Clerk Maxwell, 'On the theory of compound colours, and the relations of the colours of the spectrum', *Phil. Trans.*, **150** (1860): 57–84, esp. 77–8 (= *Scientific Papers*, **1**: 436).

432

MANUSCRIPT ON THE CLASSIFICATION OF THE PHYSICAL SCIENCES[1]

LATE 1872 – EARLY 1873[2]

From the original in the University Library, Cambridge[3]

REMARKS ON THE CLASSIFICATION OF THE PHYSICAL SCIENCES

According to the original meaning of the word Physical Science would be that knowledge which is conversant with the order of nature, that is, with the regular succession of events whether mechanical or vital in so far as it has been reduced to a scientific form. The Greek word Physical would thus be the exact equivalent of the Latin word Natural.[4]

In the actual development, however, of modern science and its terminology, these two words have come to be restricted each to one of the two great branches into which the knowledge of nature is divided according to its subject-matter. Natural Science is now understood to refer to the study of organized bodies and their development while Physical Science investigates those phenomena primarily which are observed in things without life, though it does not give up its claim to pursue this investigation when the same phenomena take place in the body of a living being.

In forming a classification of sciences our aim must be to determine the best arrangement of these sciences in the state in which they now exist. We therefore make no attempt to map out a scheme for the science of future ages. We can no more lay down before hand the plan according to which science will be developed by our successors than we can anticipate the particular discoveries which they will make.

Still less would we found our classification on the order in time according to which different sciences have been developed. This would be no more scientific than the classification of the properties of matter according to the senses by which we have become acquainted with their existence.

It is manifest that there are some sciences, of which we may take arithmetic as the type, in which the subject matter is abstract, capable of exact

---

(1) Maxwell served as 'Physical Sciences' editor of the *Britannica*; this manuscript formed the substance of the article on 'Physical Sciences', in *Encyclopaedia Britannica* (9th edn) **19** (Edinburgh, 1885): 1–3. See note (14).

(2) See Maxwell's reference to the publication of the *Treatise, infra*; and note (13).

(3) ULC Add. MSS 7655, V, h/9.

(4) Compare Volume I: 419–31, 662–74.

definition, and incapable of any variation arising from causes unknown to us, which would in the slightest degree alter its properties.

Thus in arithmetic the properties of numbers depend entirely on the definitions of these numbers and these definitions may be perfectly understood by any person who will attend to them.

The same is true of theoretical geometry though, as this science is associated in our minds with practical geometry, it is difficult to avoid thinking of the probability of error arising from unknown causes affecting the actual measurement of the quantities.

There are other sciences again of which we may take biology as the type, in which the subject matter is concrete, not capable of exact definition and subject to the influence of many causes quite unknown to us.

Thus in biology many abstract words such as species, generation &c may be employed but the only thing which we can define is the concrete individual and the ideas which the most accomplished biologist attaches to such words as species or generation have a very different degree of exactness from those which mathematicians associate, say, with the class or order of a surface, or with the umbilical generation of conicoids.

Sciences of this kind are rich in facts, and will be well occupied for ages to come in the coordination of these facts, though their cultivators may be cheered in the mean time by the hope of the discovery of laws like those of the more abstract sciences, and may indulge their fancy in the contemplation of a state of scientific knowledge when maxims cast in the same mould as those which apply to our present ideas of dead matter will regulate all our thoughts about living things.

What is commonly called Physical Science occupies a position intermediate between the abstract sciences of arithmetic algebra and geometry and the morphological and biological sciences.

The principal Physical Sciences are as follows.

A The Fundamental Science of Dynamics or the doctrine of the Motion of Bodies as affected by Force.

The divisions of Dynamics are[5]

α Kinematics, or the investigation of the kinds of motion of which a body or system of bodies is capable without reference to the cause of these motions.[6] This science differs from ordinary geometry only in introducing the idea of motion, that is change of position going on continuously in space and time.

---

(5) See Number 266 and Volume I: 665–6.
(6) On the term 'kinematics' see Volume I: 665n.

Kinematics includes, of course, geometry, but in every existing system of geometry, the idea of motion is freely introduced, to explain the tracing of lines the sweeping out of surfaces and the generation of solids.

β Statics, or the investigation of the equilibrium of forces, that is to say, the conditions under which a system of forces may exist without producing motion of the body to which they are applied. Statics includes the discussion of systems of forces which are equivalent to each other.

γ Kinetics or the relations between the motions of material bodies and the forces which act on them.[7] Here the idea of matter as something capable of being set in motion by force, and requiring a certain force to generate a given motion is first introduced into physical science.

δ Energetics or the investigation of the force which acts between two bodies or parts of a body as dependant on the conditions under which action takes place between one body or part of a body and another so as to transfer energy from one to the other.[8]

The science of Dynamics may be divided in a different manner with respect to the nature of the body whose motion is studied. This forms a cross division.

1 Dynamics of a particle, including its kinematics or the theory of the tracing of curves, its statics, or the doctrine of forces acting at a point, its kinetics or the elementary equations of motion of a particle, and its energetics including, as examples, the theory of collision and that of central forces.

2 Dynamics of a connected system, including the same subdivisions. This is the most important section in the whole of Physical Science as every dynamical theory of natural phenomena must be founded on it. I shall be happy to make a short statement of this if desirable.

The subdivisions of this again are

2a Dynamics of a Rigid System, or a body of invariable form.
2b Dynamics of a Fluid, including the discussion
    I   of its possible motion
    II   of the conditions of its equilibrium (Hydrostatics)
    III of the action of force in producing motion (Hydrodynamics) (Not so unsatisfactory since Helmholtz[9] Stokes & Thomsons[10] investigations.)

---

(7) See Number 377 note (4).

(8) See W. J. M. Rankine, 'Outlines of the science of energetics', *Edinburgh New Philosophical Journal*, **2** (1855): 120–41.

(9) See especially: Hermann Helmholtz, 'Über Integrale der hydrodynamischen Gleichungen, welche den Wirbelbewegungen entsprechen', *Journal für die reine und angewandte Mathematik*, **55** (1858): 25–55.

(10) See especially: G. G. Stokes, 'On the steady motion of incompressible fluids', *Trans.*

    IV   of the forces called into play by change of volume.
2c Dynamics of an Elastic Body.
2d Dynamics of a Viscous Body.

B The secondary Physical Sciences.

Each of these sciences consists of two divisions or stages. In the elementary stage it is occupied in deducing from the observed phenomena certain general laws, and then employing these laws in the calculation of all varieties of the phenomena.

In the dynamical stage the dynamical laws already discovered are analysed and shown to be equivalent to certain forms of the dynamical relations of a connected system (A.2) and the attempt is made to discover the nature of the dynamical system of which the observed phenomena are the motions.

This dynamical stage includes of course several other stages rising one above the other. For we may successfully account for a certain phenomenon, say the turning of a weather cock towards the direction of the wind, by assuming the existence of a force having a particular direction and tending to turn the tail of the cock in that direction. In this way we may account not only for the setting of the weathercock but for its oscillations about its final position. This therefore is entitled to rank as a dynamical theory.

But we may go on and discover a new fact that the air exerts a pressure and that there is a greater pressure on that side of the cock on which the wind blows. This is a further development of the theory as it tends to account for the force already discovered.

We may go on and explain the dynamical connexion between this inequality of pressure and the motion of the air regarded as a fluid.

Finally we may explain the pressure of air on the hypothesis that the air consists of molecules in motion, which strike against each other and against the surface of any body exposed to the air.

The dynamical theories of the different physical sciences are in very different stages of development, and in almost all of them a sound knowledge of the subject is best acquired by adopting, at least at first the method which we have called elementary, that is to say the study of the connexion of the phenomena peculiar to the science without reference to any dynamical explanations or hypotheses.

Thus we have

Camb. Phil. Soc., **7** (1842): 439–53; and their series of 'Notes on hydrodynamics', *Camb. & Dubl. Math. J.*, **2** (1847): 282–6; *ibid.*, **3** (1848): 89–93, 121–7, 209–19; *ibid.*, **4** (1849): 90–4.

I Theory of Gravitation

with discussion of the weight and motion of bodies near the earth the whole of physical astronomy and figure of the earth. There is a great deal of dynamics here but we can hardly say that there is even a beginning of a dynamical theory of the method by which bodies gravitate towards each other.

II Theory of the action of Pressure and Heat in changing the dimensions and state of Bodies.

This is a very large subject and might be divided into two parts one treating of the action of Pressure and the other of Heat. But it is much more instructive to study the action of both causes together, because they produce effects of the same kind, and therefore mutually influence each other. Hence the term Thermodynamics might be extended to the whole subject were it not that it is already restricted to a very important department relating to the transformation of energy from the thermal to the mechanical form and the reverse.

The divisions of the subject are

a Physical states of a substance, Gaseous, liquid, and solid.
   Elasticity of volume in all three states.
   Elasticity of figure in the solid state.
   Viscosity in all three states Plasticity in the solid state.
   Surface-tension or Capillarity.
   Tenacity of solids, Cohesion of liquids, Adhesion of gases to liquids & solids.
b Effects of heat in
   raising temperature
   altering size and form
   changing physical state
c Thermometry   d Calorimetry
e Thermodynamics or the mutual convertibility of heat and work.
f Dissipation of energy by
   Diffusion of matter by mixture
   Diffusion of motion by internal friction of fluids
   Diffusion of heat by conduction.
g Theory of propagation of Sound, vibrations of strings rods and other bodies.

See my book on Heat (Longmans)[11] for a sketch of this subject.

---

(11) J. Clerk Maxwell, *Theory of Heat* (London, 1871, $_2$1872).

III Theory of Radiance

a Geometrical Optics – Theory of conjugate Foci and of Instruments.
b Velocity of Light in different media.
c Prismatic analysis of Light – Spectroscopy.
    Radiant Heat   Visible Radiance   Ultraviolet rays
    Calorescence &c   Fluorescence &c
d Colours of thin plates, diffraction &c.
d′ Proof of the existence of wave-lengths and wave periods (preparation for dynamical theory).
e Polarized Light   radiant heat &c.
e′ The disturbance is transverse to the ray.
f Quantity of energy in the total radiation from a hot body. Prévosts Theory of Exchanges[12] &c.
g Theory of Three Primary Colours.

IV Electricity and Magnetism

a Electrostatics or distribution and effects of electricity in equilibrium.
b Electrokinematics or distribution of currents in conductors.
c Magnetism and Magnetic Induction (Diamagnetism &c).
d Electromagnetism or the effects of an electric current at a distance.

Under b we may discuss Electrochemistry or the theory of Electrolysis.

Under c Terrestrial Magnetism and Ships Magnetism and after d comes Electrokinetics or electromagnetic phenomena considered with reference to the fundamental science of dynamics.

There is also Faradays discovery of the effect of magnetism on light and the electromagnetic theory of light.

See my book on Electricity and Magnetism Clarendon press series Vol I is printed off & will be published when Vol II is printed.[13]

J. CLERK MAXWELL

I quite approve of an article on Measurement,[14] including
a Systems of measures and National standards
b Methods of measurement.

---

(12) Pierre Prevost, 'Mémoire sur l'équilibre du feu', *Journal de Physique*, **38** (1791): 314–22; Prevost, *Du Calorique Rayonnante* (Paris/Geneva, 1809).

(13) See Number 448, esp. note (5).

(14) An article on 'Measures and Measurement' is proposed in a draft 'Outline of Scheme of Physical Sciences' (ULC Add. MSS 7655, V, h/8) to which Maxwell's MS may be a response. See note (1).

There ought also to be some indication of the branches of mathematics which have hitherto been found most useful in Physical Science.

I have not included Chemistry in my list, because, though ⟨Physical⟩ Dynamical Science is continually reclaiming large tracts of good ground from the one side of Chemistry, Chemistry is extending with still greater rapidity on the other side, into regions where the dynamics of the present day must put her hand upon her mouth.

But Chemistry is a Physical Science, and that of very high rank. I do not, however, pretend to be able to go over its possessions and to show strangers the boundaries.

433

LETTER OF REFERENCE FOR JAMES THOMSON[1]

7 JANUARY 1873

From a holograph copy in the University Library, Glasgow[2]

COPY OF CERTIFICATE BY PROFESSOR CLERK MAXWELL

Professor James Thomson of Belfast is a man of sound scientific attainments and is thoroughly acquainted with the principles of Engineering. He has proved this by the works he has executed, by the inventions he has patented and by the discoveries in science which he has published. Of all men I know I consider him the best qualified to succeed Professor Rankine in the University of Glasgow and to maintain the high character of the education of that University.

(signed)   J. CLERK MAXWELL
Professor of Experimental Physics
in the University of Cambridge

Cambridge, January 7th 1873

---

(1) On the circumstances of James Thomson's candidature for the Professorship of Engineering in the University of Glasgow see S. P. Thompson, *The Life of William Thomson Baron Kelvin of Largs*, 2 vols. (London, 1910), **2**: 632–3.

(2) Glasgow University Library, Kelvin Papers, T 128. Previously published in A. T. Fuller, 'James Clerk Maxwell's Glasgow manuscripts: extracts relating to control and stability', *International Journal of Control*, **43** (1986): 1593–612, on 1611–12.

434

POSTCARD TO WILLIAM THOMSON

22 JANUARY 1873[1]

From the original in the King's College London Archives[2]

[Glenlair]

The Tomlinson Correspondence is found.[3]

Our knowledge of magnetization is probably statistical. The doctrine that magnetic energy is potential ditto while electromagnetic energy is kinetic leads to hopeless confusion especially when currents act on magnets.[4] Now a current is certainly a kinetic thing Q.E.D. It is very remarkable that in spite of the *curl* in the electromagnetic equations of all kinds[5] Faradays twist of polarized light[6] will not come out without what the schoolmen call local motion.[7]

$$\frac{dp}{dt}$$
(a)

(a) {Thomson} Clerk Maxwell $\left(\dfrac{dp}{dt}\right)$ Keep K Seen Sep 22/99

(1) January 1873 seems a likely date for Maxwell's card to Thomson: see notes (3) and (7). No year is visible in the postmark. A note in the King's College archive records that the British Museum suggests 1872 as the likely date for its printing.

(2) Maxwell Papers, King's College London Archives. First published in Larmor, 'Origins': 748.

(3) Maxwell may well be alluding to his correspondence with Charles Tomlinson (in 1869) about the publication of the manuscripts of Henry Cavendish: see Numbers 435 and 459, and also Maxwell's letter to Thomson of 25 March 1873 (Number 448) on his intention to edit the Cavendish papers. (4) See the *Treatise*, **2**: 246–51 (§§630–38).

(5) See the *Treatise*, **2**: 237–8 (§619) where Maxwell writes the general equations of the electromagnetic field in quaternion form, writing $V\nabla\sigma$ for the curl of the vector σ. On 'curl' see the *Treatise*, **1**: 28 (§25), and Number 347.

(6) On Faraday's discovery of the rotation of the plane of polarization of linearly polarised light in a magnetic field see the *Treatise*, **2**: 400 (§807); and Michael Faraday, 'On the magnetization of light and the illumination of magnetic lines of force', *Phil. Trans.*, **136** (1846): 1–20 (= *Electricity*, **3**: 1–26). In his paper 'Dynamical illustrations of the magnetic and the heliocoidal rotatory effects of transparent bodies on polarized light', *Proc. Roy. Soc.*, **8** (1856): 150–8, Thomson had argued that the phenomenon could be explained by a vortical theory of magnetism. See Maxwell's letter to Thomson of 10 December 1861 (Volume I: 692–8).

(7) Compare the *Treatise*, **2**: 416 (§831); 'I think we have good evidence for the opinion that some phenomenon of rotation is going on in the magnetic field, [and] that this rotation is performed by a great number of very small portions of matter, each rotating on its axis'. Proofs of *Treatise* §§801–30 (on the magnetic action on light and the theory of molecular vortices) are dated January 1873 (ULC Add. MSS 7655, IV/2).

435
DRAFT LETTER TO THE DUKE OF DEVONSHIRE[1]
LATE JANUARY – EARLY FEBRUARY 1873[2]
From the original in the University Library, Cambridge[3]

My Lord Duke

In the interest of science and at the suggestion of several scientific men I write to ask your help in securing the preservation of those manuscripts of Henry Cavendish which relate to electricity.

Mr Tomlinson informs me[4] that these papers are in the possession of Thomas Harris Esqre only son of the late Sir William Snow Harris.[5] They were put into the hands of Sir William by the Earl of Burlington.[6] Sir W. Snow Harris quoted them in his books on Electricity[7] and used to speak of their importance and of the use he intended to make of them.[8] At his death, however they passed into the hands of his son, ‖ and Mr Tomlinson then made some efforts to get the papers deposited in the library of the Royal Society. There seems to have been some difficulty about giving up the papers but I should think this difficulty would be removed if the papers were asked for by your Grace who I understand to be the representative of the Earl of Burlington and of Henry Cavendish.

If the papers were in your own possession ‖ or in that of a responsible public body men of science would be relieved from the anxiety which they must feel when such papers are liable to [....]

Many men of science are naturally anxious that the preservation of papers so important should not depend on the accidents attendant on the transmission of such manuscripts from hand to hand and all such anxiety would be removed if your Grace whom I understand to be the representative both of the Hon Henry Cavendish and of the Earl of Burlington were to take steps to obtain the papers from Mr Harris.

The permanent security of these papers depends at present on the mode in which they may be handed down from o[ne....]

---

(1) William Cavendish, Seventh Duke of Devonshire, Chancellor of the University of Cambridge.

(2) See Numbers 434, 448 and 459.   (3) ULC Add. MSS 7655, II/90.

(4) In 1869; see Number 459.   (5) Sir William Snow Harris had died in 1867.

(6) The Duke himself, who had succeeded his grandfather as second Earl of Burlington in 1834, succeeding his cousin as Seventh Duke of Devonshire in 1858 (*DNB*); see Number 459.

(7) William Snow Harris, *A Treatise on Frictional Electricity*, ed. C. Tomlinson (London, 1867): 23, 45, 58, 121, 208, 223.

(8) See Maxwell's account in *The Electrical Researches of the Honourable Henry Cavendish, F.R.S.* (Cambridge, 1879): xl–xli.

Men of science are anxious that papers so important should be both safe and accessible. This would be the case if they were in the possession of your Grace whom I understand to be the representative of the author and of the Earl of Burlington who deposited them with Sir W. S. Harris.

Mr Harris is naturally unwilling to place them in the hands of persons who have no right to them, but if he were requested by your Grace to restore them to the family of the author I have no doubt he would do so.[9]

The following extract from a note in Sir W. Thomson's recent work on Electrostatics and Magnetism will indicate the importance of these papers not only to the ⟨history⟩ of science and to the biography of Cavendish but to the science of electricity in its present state.

Extract[10]

For the knowledge of the present ownership of I am entirely indebted to Charles Tomlinson Esqre FRS 3 Ridgmount Terrace, Highgate, N, whose letter I enclose. He gives the address of Thomas Harris Esqre Barrington House, Southsea.

---

(9) But see Number 459.

(10) Compare *The Electrical Researches of ... Cavendish*: xxxix, where Maxwell quotes Thomson's note of 2 July 1849, reproduced in his *Electrostatics and Magnetism*: 180n, on the accuracy of Cavendish's value for the ratio of the capacity of a disc to that of a sphere of the same radius; 'Cavendish's unpublished MSS...[are] a most valuable mine of results....It is much to be desired that...[they] should be published complete'.

436

ON A PROBLEM IN THE CALCULUS OF VARIATIONS IN WHICH THE SOLUTION IS DISCONTINUOUS[1]

FEBRUARY 1873[2]

From the original in the University Library, Cambridge[3]

[ON THE RIDER ON THE THIRD QUESTION IN THE MATHEMATICAL TRIPOS PAPER OF WEDNESDAY AFTERNOON, 15 JANUARY 1873][4]

The question itself was suggested by some of the road making problems of Dupin[5] and was as follows.

If the velocity of a carriage along a road is proportional to the cube of the cosine of the inclination of the road to the horizon, determine the path of quickest ascent from the bottom to the top of a hemispherical hill, and shew that it consists of the spherical curve described by a point of a great circle which rolls on a small circle described about the pole with a radius $\frac{\pi}{6}$, together with an arc of a great circle. How is the discontinuity introduced into the problem?[6]

Taking a as the radius of the sphere and referring the curve to θ and ϕ the polar distance and azimuth and writing as usual p for $\frac{d\phi}{d\theta}$ we find for the element of length

$$ds = \sqrt{1 + p^2 \sin^2 \theta}\, d\theta$$

and for the element of ascent

$$dz = -\sin\theta\, d\theta$$

---

(1) A problem mentioned by Maxwell in his letter to William Thomson of 21 March 1871 (Number 362; see esp. note (7) for a preliminary draft of the problem).

(2) This manuscript draft is a preliminary to Maxwell's paper 'On a problem in the calculus of variations in which the solution is discontinuous', *Proc. Camb. Phil. Soc.*, **2** (1873): 294–5 (= *Scientific Papers*, **2**: 310); read 3 February 1873.

(3) ULC Add. MSS 7655, V, d/13.

(4) As stated in 'On a problem in the calculus of variations': 294.

(5) Charles Dupin, *Applications de Géométrie et de Mécanique* (Paris, 1822): 75–186.

(6) As stated in *The Cambridge University Calendar for the Year 1873* (Cambridge, 1873): 544.

whence we find putting α for the inclination of the curve to the horizon

$$\cos^2 \alpha = \frac{\cos^2 \theta + p^2 \sin^2 \theta}{1 + p^2 \sin^2 \theta}$$

and the quantity to be made a minimum is $V = \int \frac{ds}{\cos^3 \alpha}$ taken from the equator to the pole or in terms of θ only $V = \int_0^{\frac{\pi}{2}} \frac{(1 + p^2 \sin^2 \theta)^2}{(\cos^2 \theta + p^2 \sin^2 \theta)^{\frac{3}{2}}} d\theta$.

The solution by the calculus of variations is easy. The variable ϕ does not appear and therefore the sole condition is to be found by differentiating the expression under the integral sign with respect to p and equating the result to zero. This gives the equation

$$p \sin^2 \theta (p^2 \sin^2 \theta + 4 \cos^2 \theta - 3) = 0$$

whence we find either

$$p = 0 \quad \text{or} \quad p = \pm \sqrt{3 - \cot^2 \theta}$$

whence it follows that

$$\cos \alpha = \cos \theta \quad \text{or} \quad \cos \alpha = \pm \tfrac{1}{2} \sqrt{3}.$$

When θ is less than $\frac{\pi}{6}$ the first solution corresponds to a minimum and the other two are impossible. When θ is greater than $\frac{\pi}{6}$ the first solution corresponds to a maximum and the other two to minima.

Hence the path must [be] a curve of constant inclination of 30° to the horizon from the bottom of the hill to that point at which the surface of the hill itself has this inclination. From this point to the top the path must be the great circle for which $p = 0$.

This solution would apply to the case of any solid of revolution with its axis vertical but in the case of a sphere the determination of the path of constant slope is easy. For the plane normal to the path passes through the centre of the sphere and is always inclined 30° to the vertical. It therefore always touches the small circle described about the pole with that radius and if a point fixed in the plane coincides with the centre of the sphere, while the sphere rolls on this circle, any point which coincides with the surface of the sphere will trace on that surface the path of constant slope required.

By suppressing [from] the rolling plane all but that circle of it which is always a great circle of the sphere the statement is reduced from solid to spherical geometry as in the statement of the question.

Note. It is manifest that if the inclination of the road is so small that it winds several times round the hill, the distance between consecutive windings is everywhere equal to the circumference of the small circle. In the case before us this circumference is equal to half a great circle.

If the time along a horizontal radius is taken for unity the time from the base of the hemisphere to the cusp is $\frac{8}{3}$ and the time up the arc of the great circle to the pole is

$$\frac{1}{3}+\frac{1}{4}\log_e 3$$

making the whole time of ascent

$$3+\frac{1}{4}\log_e 3.$$

The equation of the curve is

$$x = \cos\phi(1-4\sin^2\phi)$$
$$y = \sin\phi\left(\frac{5}{2}-3\sin^2\phi\right)$$
$$z = \frac{\sqrt{3}}{2}\sin\phi.$$

=437=

LECTURE[1] ON FARADAY'S LINES OF FORCE[2]

EARLY 1873[3]

From the originals in the University Library, Cambridge[4]

[1][5]   ON FARADAYS LINES OF FORCE

The statement has been made so often that I almost need your pardon for repeating it, that modern times have been distinguished from all that preceded them by the greater development of industry and by the greater progress of physical science. The men who, in recent times, have devoted themselves either to searching out the forces of nature, or to rendering these forces available for the supply of human wants, have made a deeper and more enduring mark on the face of the world than its rulers and conquerors, its philosophers and statesmen, its preachers and poets. Our meeting tonight is in commemoration of James Watt, the results of whose labours I have no intention to enumerate. It is true that tonight we have met in his native place, and that we have been reminded of his features by the statue at the door and of his name by the title of this building but in any other part of the habitable globe if we wish for something to remind us of James Watt we have only to look about us. Conquerors may have carried a people captive from their own land and planted them in another, but the steam engine has drawn away to its encampment on the coal measures all the craftsmen and smiths and every cunning workman, till the ancient rules and maxims of simple life, such as sufficed for the guidance of James Watt and his contemporaries, have broken down under the pressure of the multitude of the workers and the exigencies of their work. The legislator of the older type was counted famous when he had instituted laws and customs by which violence was checked, and every man was encouraged to abide in the condition and station wherein he was born. The development of industry has introduced new modes of gaining a livelihood and abolished others so that both employers and employed in their endeavour to walk in the paths of honour and virtue, have new problems set before them of a more complicated order than our fathers had to solve.

---

(1) This draft apparently forms the text of a lecture to the Greenock Philosophical Society in honour of the anniversary of the birth of James Watt on 19 January 1736. See notes (9) and (10).

(2) The main text is a draft of Maxwell's lecture to the Royal Institution on Friday, 21 February 1873; see 'On action at a distance', *Proceedings of the Royal Institution of Great Britain*, **7** (1873–5): 44–54 (= *Scientific Papers*, **2**: 311–23); and see Number 438.

(3) See notes (1) and (2).   (4) ULC Add. MSS 7655, V, c/19, 20.

(5) ULC Add. MSS 7655, V, c/19.

There is no doubt that the invention of James Watt has like all other divine gifts greatly increased our responsibility. Every one of us requires more than ever, especially in those short intervals which labour allows us, to call to mind the nobler ends of human life. The beauty and dignity of a well ordered life are not the exclusive property of a primitive people but to preserve them amid the rattle of machinery and the press of business demands a more constant vigilance and involves a higher mental cultivation than was required by the contemporaries of James Watt.

James Watt is also connected both directly and indirectly with the other characteristic of our time, the growth of physical science. His own researches on Heat and on its action on water can hardly be separated from the use that he made of them – the economising of the forces at our disposal by turning them as much as possible into the channel of work useful to us.[6] The same principle, considered still with reference to the steam engine, is the foundation of the next great step in our scientific knowledge of heat – Carnots 'Reflexions on the motive power of fire'.[7] The most important contribution to our accurate knowledge of heat on various bodies is also by a Frenchman and is also connected with the steam engine, that of M. Regnault.[8]

But I understand that the progress of the science of heat since the time of Watt has been described to you already by Dr Joule,[9] who has himself made the most important measurements on which the theory of heat depends, and who has with a rare sagacity contributed to the future progress of almost every branch of physical science by his numerous measurements of energy in all its various forms.

Sir William Thomson also has laid before you some of the results of modern speculation as to the precise nature of the motion to which the phenomena of heat and electricity are due, and has shown that the explanation of these phenomena by the intestine motion of agitation of the particles of bodies has reached a stage in which it not only submits to the test of exact calculation,

---

(6) J. P. Muirhead, *The Origin and Progress of the Mechanical Inventions of James Watt*, 3 vols. (London, 1854); Muirhead, *The Life of James Watt, with Selections from his Correspondence* (London, 1858).

(7) Sadi Carnot, *Réflexions sur la Puissance Motrice du Feu et sur les Machines propres à développer cette puissance* (Paris, 1824).

(8) H. V. Regnault, *Relation des Expériences entreprises ... pour déterminer les principales lois et données numériques qui entrent dans le calcul des machines à vapeur*, 3 vols. (Paris, 1847–70); reprinted from *Mémoires de l'Académie des Sciences de l'Institut de France*, **21** (1847): 1–767; *ibid.*, **26** (1862): iii–x, 3–928; *ibid.*, **37**, part 1 (1868): 3–575; and **37**, part 2 (1870): 599–968.

(9) Joule had delivered a lecture, 'On some facts in the science of heat developed since the time of Watt', to the Greenock Philosophical Society on 19 January 1865; see D. S. L. Cardwell, *James Joule, A Biography* (Manchester, 1989): 183, 313.

but leads of itself to the knowledge of new phenomena, the existence of which has been afterwards verified by experiment.[10]

I propose tonight to lead you into a different field of speculation, and to ask you to turn your minds to the familiar though mysterious phenomenon of the transmission of force. The mode in which Faraday was led by his peculiar genius and unremitting investigations to look on this phenomenon is different from that generally adopted by other modern inquirers, and my special aim will be to enable you to place yourselves at Faradays point of view, and to enable you to understand what he meant by the phrase 'Lines of Force' which we meet with so frequently in his writings.[11]

In order to do so I must have the indispensable help of your own best powers of thought. If I had merely to describe to you some new discovery in science, I should be able to avail myself of your previous knowledge as a foundation, and to erect thereon a representation of the new fact which you were to place beside those old ones which you knew before. The greater your previous knowledge, the easier would be my task. But what I have to do is something quite different. I have to shew you facts with which you are already acquainted in a light of a different character from that which the most illustrious philosophers have shed upon them – a light which the wisest among them would probably have avoided as deceptive and misleading had it been presented to him in his own time, because the slow yet steady progress of science has only in more recent times prepared us for its reception.

I have therefore to begin at the very beginning and any previous training you may have had in scientific ideas must be for the present as if it had never been.

We have to consider the mode in which one body acts on another, or rather the mode in which two bodies act on each other, for such action is always mutual. And here I would have you notice how very important right opinions on matters of this kind are. Wrong opinions in dynamics are the cause of errors which run through every department of life. The ordinary forms of speech which we cannot avoid using are the product of a time when men were satisfied with a few rough notions on matters of this kind, deduced from casual observation but sufficient for the purposes of ordinary life. I do not here allude to the phrases of the sun rising and such like, which are perfectly scientific methods of indicating an actual fact. I refer rather to the inveterate association between motion and effort which causes us when we see a body

---

(10) Possibly his lecture at Greenock in January 1869 on 'Elasticity viewed as a mode of motion'; see S. P. Thompson, *The Life of William Thomson Baron Kelvin of Largs*, 2 vols. (London, 1910), **2**: 1243.

(11) Compare Maxwell, 'On action at a distance': 44 (= *Scientific Papers*, **2**: 311).

moving in any direction to consider it as exerting a continued effort to travel in that direction, just as we ourselves would have to labour continuously if we had to make a long journey over a rough country.

Another association derived from the same source is that, because the traveller cannot help knowing in which direction he is toiling onwards, so we must always know the direction of our own motion, or at least whether we are in motion or at rest. It is impossible to overestimate the influence which the experience of smooth sailing has had on the minds of men in enabling them to get rid of these habits of thought. It is only by reading the works of the great founders of mechanical science and those of the philosophers of the old school that we can see how great was the labour of establishing right opinions on these points, and how tenaciously the wrong opinions were held by men, who, if they had lived now, would have certainly been eminent in science themselves. By these labours, however, the whole atmosphere of scientific thought appears to have been changed, and many statements, then thought paradoxical, are now accepted by the beginner without the slightest feeling of strangeness.

But the process is by no means complete, and a great deal has yet to be done before even the whole of what is called the scientific world is thoroughly free of dynamical errors.

And this will never be done merely by teaching everybody mathematics. What is necessary and sufficient is that the facts should be presented to the mind, and that the mind should be forced into contact with the facts.

There are certain facts then to which I wish you to apply your minds.

We see that bodies move, and that the direction and velocity of the motion of a particular body do not always remain the same. We find, however that when any change occurs in the motion of the body we can account for it by supposing that another body in the neighbourhood has in some way produced this change and we are confirmed in this supposition by observing that a change of motion of a kind exactly opposite has occurred in the other body.

The most familiar illustrations of these facts are those presented by the collisions of bodies projected through the air or of balls rolling on a smooth billiard table. In these cases both the bodies which act on each other are solid and visible bodies and their masses are comparable to each other. In those cases in which one of the bodies is the earth or a body connected with the earth the alteration of motion of the larger body is so exceedingly small that it is not perceived, and the reciprocal nature of the action is lost sight of. In other cases, as when a bullet flies through the air, the nature of the action is in some degree hidden, on account of the air, one of the bodies which act, being invisible.

Here again we may observe how important the observation of special phenomena has been in calling up in the minds of men those true ideas of things by which they may rightly understand not only these special phenomena but every ordinary occurrence.

The first true ideas about relative motion were derived from the experience of men who travelled by water, and the first true ideas about the reciprocity of force were probably derived from observations on games with balls. In ordinary circumstances, the motions of bodies are affected by so many different causes, that until some exceptionally simple phenomenon presents itself, we do not know what is the right thing to attend to first. As soon however as we become acquainted with this more simple phenomenon and we have been put in the right way of looking at it, either by our own efforts or by the teaching of others, then we know in ourselves that we have obtained a key to one department of the mystery of nature, and that however different any other phenomenon of motion may be from that which gave us the key, the key must nevertheless be equally appropriate to it.

Such exceptionally simple phenomena, when purposely produced, are called illustrative experiments. They are so called because they throw light on the subject, and enable the mind to see clearly those truths which it is unable to distinguish when they are exemplified in the more complicated form of ordinary occurrences.

This is the chief, and indeed the only value of an illustrative experiment. When once the mind has grasped the truth which it illustrates, the experiment has fulfilled its purpose. When we have seen the action and reaction of two balls striking each other we make no special measurements to prove that this action and reaction are equal and opposite. I am not aware that anyone ever even proposed to make such a measurement, or suggested a method of doing it. All that is necessary is to direct the mind to the experiment till it perceives that in this case the action between the two balls is reciprocal, and it immediately concludes that in all cases the action of bodies on each other may be reduced to reciprocal actions between pairs of the bodies.

These reciprocal actions are called forces, and the doctrine may be stated thus – that every force is *between* two bodies, that is to say, that whatever the force is which acts on one body, it is something which at the same time acts in the opposite direction on some other body.

We now come to the special subject of our consideration in this lecture. Admitting that the action between two bodies is always reciprocal, what is the condition that there shall be such action between two given bodies. Must the two bodies be in actual contact, or can they act on each other when at a distance? On the one hand it has been argued that matter has no power of acting where it is not, and it has been shown that in many cases in which force appears to be transmitted to a distance the action really takes place by means of a series of bodies, or parts of bodies, occupying the intervening space or moving across it.

Thus when we ring a bell by means of a bellrope and wire the successive parts of the rope and the wire are first tightened, and then moved, till at last the bell is rung at a distance by a process in which all the intermediate particles of the rope and the wire have taken part one after the other. We may also ring a bell by forcing a little air into a long tube at the other end of which is a piston which is made to fly out and strike the bell. Here the different portions of air in the tube are moved one after another and the action of the piston at the one end is communicated to the piston at the other end by a process of interaction between a series of portions of air every pair of which may be considered in actual contact.

It is clear therefore that, in certain cases, the action between bodies at a distance may be accounted for by a series of actions between a system of bodies which fill up the intervening space, and it is asked whether in cases in which we cannot perceive the intermediate agents it is not more philosophical to admit the existence of a medium which we cannot yet perceive than to admit that a body can act in a place where it is not. Experiments Tuning Fork Corks in water

To a person ignorant of the existence and properties of air the transmission of force by means of that invisible medium must appear as unaccountable as any other example of action at a distance and yet we know that the action in this case is transmitted with a known velocity by the successive action of contiguous portions so that a sensible time elapses before the force is transmitted from the one end of the tube to the other. Why should we not conclude that the familiar mode of communication of motion by pushing and pulling with our hands is the type and exemplification of all action between bodies, even in cases in which we can observe nothing between the bodies which appears to take part in the action. Experiments on magnets

The advocates of the doctrine of action at a distance on the other hand have not been silenced by these arguments. What right say they have we to assert that a body cannot act where it is not? Do we not see instances of action at a distance in the case of a magnet, which acts on another magnet, not only at a distance, but with the utmost indifference to any object which may be placed in the intervening space. If this action depends on something between the two magnets it cannot surely be indifferent whether the space between them is filled with air or not or whether wood or glass be placed between the magnets. And do not the heavenly bodies act on one another across immense intervals which are certainly not filled with anything which can sensibly resist the motion of the filmiest tail of a comet. Magnets

Besides this, the law of Newton, which every astronomical observation only tends to establish more firmly, asserts that when we know the masses of two bodies and the distance between them we can determine their mutual action from these facts alone, and that we require no additional information about the distribution of other bodies, around or between them. The one portion of matter may be a thousand miles deep in the interior of the earth and the other 100,000 miles deep in the interior of the sun and still the matter surrounding each portion will have no influence on their mutual action. Surely if a medium takes part in transmitting the action, it must make some difference whether the space between the bodies contains nothing but this medium, or whether it is full of dense matter?

But the advocates of action at a distance are not content with instances of this kind, in which the phenomenon even at first sight appears to favour their doctrine. They push their operations into the enemys camp, and assert that even in those cases in which the action is apparently that of contiguous portions of matter, the contiguity is only apparent – that a space always intervenes between the bodies which act on each other, and that so far from action at a distance being impossible it is the only kind of action which ever occurs. Even when one body supports another, they show that they are not in contact by actually measuring the distance between them. If I lay one lens of glass on another, I perceive a set of coloured rings near the place where the one rests on the other.[12] These rings were first explained by Newton who showed that the colour depends on the distance between the surfaces of the two glasses and that as this distance increases as we move further from the point where the one lens rests on the other the colours are arranged in rings about this point the colour of the ring thus forming a measure of the distance between the surfaces.[13] If the lenses are in actual contact, the central point of Newtons Rings is black. But when I simply lay the one lens on the other the central point is not black and it follows that the one lens supports the weight of the other although no part of the surfaces are in contact. To make sure of this I press the lenses together. The colour of the central spot changes, and as the pressure is increased a series of colours appears till at last the central spot becomes black and we then know that the surfaces are in optical contact. It follows that the surfaces were not in optical contact but at a measurable distance even when pressed together by a force considerably greater than the weight of the upper lens and that therefore one piece of glass can act on another piece of glass while a measurable distance intervenes between the nearest parts of their surfaces. This experiment succeeds equally well under the exhausted receiver of an air pump so that the air is certainly not the medium by means of which this action at a distance is effected.

Newton's Rings

---

(12) See Number 438.
(13) Isaac Newton, *Opticks* (London, $_3$1721): 168–98 (Book II, Part I).

Why then should we continue to maintain a doctrine founded only on the rough experience of a prescientific age that matter cannot act at a distance instead of admitting that all the facts from which our ancestors concluded that contact was essential to action were really cases of action at a distance in which the distance was too small to be discovered by their means of observation. If we are ever to discover the laws of nature we must deduce them by a careful reasoning from the facts of nature, according to our very best information, and not by dressing up in philosophical language the loose opinions of men who had no knowledge of the facts which throw most light on these laws.

And as for those who imagine etherial or other media to account for these actions, without any evidence of the existence of these media, and without first making sure that the media will do their work, and who fill all space three and four times over with ethers of different sorts, why, the less these men talk about their philosophical scruples in admitting action at a distance the better.

When the cumbrous celestial machinery of the Ptolemaic System was got rid of, when the comets had shattered to pieces those crystal spheres by which the planets were supposed to be carried round, and when the cycles and epicycles, orb in orb, by which astronomers had so long contrived to 'save appearances' were blown aside into the Paradise of Fools various attempts were made to supply their place in the heavens. Of these one of the most notable in its time was that of Descartes, who supposed the heavenly bodies to swim along in a medium which fills all space or rather, since he regarded space as essentially material, in that substance which we call space the fluidity of which, where it is fluid, arises from its moving in certain whirls or vortices, and the solidity of which, where it appears solid, arises simply from its quiescence, quiet being, as he remarks, infinitely superior to the best glue for holding things together.

The physical speculations of Descartes are as remarkable for their utter disregard of the first principles of dynamics as his mathematical writings are for the fertility of the genius they display.[14] He seems never to have understood what is meant by the mass of a body as distinguished from its size or its weight and in this ignorance he has been followed by Spinoza, and by most of the professed metaphysicians down to the present day. But the vigour of mind and the boldness of his methods have given a vitality to some of his erroneous opinions which is not even yet extinct, so that we find them springing up in the minds of men who certainly never came in contact with his writings.

---

(14) Compare Maxwell's comments on Descartes' *Principia Philosophiæ* in Number 350: Appendix, and Number 377.

When Newton demonstrated that the force which acts on each of the heavenly bodies depends on the distance and position of the other bodies, and is directed towards these bodies, and therefore may be described as an attraction, the new theory met with violent opposition from the advanced philosophers of the day. They described the doctrine of gravitation as a return to the exploded method of explaining everything by occult causes, attractive virtues, and the like.[15]

Newton himself, with that wise moderation which was characteristic of all his speculations, answered that he made no pretence of explaining the *mechanism* by which the heavenly bodies act on each other. What he had done was to determine the direction and magnitude of the force acting on each body, and to show how it may be deduced from a knowledge of their relative positions. This was the step in science which Newton asserted he had made. To explain the *cause* of this action was a quite distinct step, and this step Newton in his Principia does not attempt to make.

But so far was Newton from asserting that bodies really act on one another at a distance, independently of anything between, that in a letter to Bentley, which has often been quoted, he says

Newton — It is inconceivable that inanimate brute matter should, without the mediation of something else, which is not material, operate upon and affect other matter without mutual contact; as it must do, if gravitation, in the sense of Epicurus be essential and inherent in it.... That gravity should be innate, inherent, and essential to matter, so that one body can act upon another at distance though a vacuum, without the mediation of anything else, by and through which their action and force may be conveyed from one to another, is to me so great an absurdity, that I believe no man who has in philosophical matters a competent faculty of thinking can ever fall into it.[16]

But the true history of Newtons speculations on this subject may be guessed at from one of his Optical queries relative to a medium or ether.

Is not this medium much rarer within the dense bodies of the sun, stars and planets than in the empty celestial spaces between them. And in passing from them to great distances does it not grow denser and denser perpetually and thereby cause the gravity of those great bodies to one another, each body endeavouring to go from the denser parts of the medium to the rarer.[17]

And Colin Maclaurin one of his most illustrious disciples tells us

---

(15) Leibniz's correspondence with Samuel Clarke is the classic source for the controversy.

(16) *Four Letters from Sir Isaac Newton to Doctor Bentley containing some Arguments in Proof of a Deity* (London, 1756): 25–6. In his lecture 'On action at a distance': 48 (= *Scientific Papers*, **2**: 316) Maxwell noted that Faraday had cited this passage, also in an attempt to provide a Newtonian pedigree for his denial of action at a distance. See Faraday, *Electricity*, **3**: 532n, 571.

(17) Newton, *Opticks*: 325 (Query 21).

It appears from his letters to Mr Boyle that this was his opinion early, and if he did not publish it sooner it proceeded from hence only, that he found he was not able, from experiment and observation to give a satisfactory account of its operation in producing the chief phenomena of nature.

MacLaurin

Maclaurin goes on to say

Possibly some unskillful men may have fancied that bodies might attract each other by some charm or unknown virtue without being impelled or acted on by other bodies, or by any other powers of whatever kind and some may have imagined that a mutual tendency may be essential to matter, tho' this is directly contrary to the *inertia* of matter described above, but surely Sir Isaac Newton has given no grounds for charging him with either of these opinions.[18]

It appears therefore that both Newton and Maclaurin, so far from considering the law of gravitation a final explanation of the phenomena to which it refers, felt that if that law could be explained as the result of any action of something in the space intervening between the bodies this explanation would form a new and distinct step in science, and they would be ready to welcome it as filling up an acknowledged gap in our knowledge of things.

Newton, we have seen, attempted this step but found it was beyond his power with the means at his disposal, and I need scarcely tell you, that even with our vastly greater stock of scientific methods, the task has seldom been attempted, and never accomplished.

But another of Newtons most brilliant disciples Roger Cotes who edited the second edition of the Principia for Newton adopts quite a different tone of thought. He says that just as we infer, from experiments made in Europe, how bodies will behave in America, so when we find that all the bodies we know gravitate towards each other, we have as good a right to say that gravitation is an essential property of matter as to infer that any other property of matter such as extension mobility or impenetrability is essential to it in America because we find them in all bodies that we know in Europe.[19]

And when the Newtonian philosophy gained ground in Europe it was the opinion of Cotes, rather than that of Newton that became most prevalent, till at last Boscovich propounded a theory in which bodies were supposed to consist of a great number of mathematical points, each endowed with the power of attracting or repelling the other points according to fixed laws

---

(18) Colin MacLaurin, *An Account of Sir Isaac Newton's Philosophical Discoveries* (London, 1748): 110–11.

(19) See Cotes' 'Editoris praefatio in editionem secundam' to Issac Newton, *Philosophiæ Naturalis Principia Mathematica* (Cambridge, $_2$1713). On Cotes' preface to *Principia*, compare Maxwell's comment in Number 439.

depending on the distance.[20] How it happens that a congeries of mathematical points, when once set in motion, is able to persevere in its motion, and to do a fixed amount of work before it can be stopped, is not explained by the supporters of this theory, and I venture to say that the explanation will never be effected by endowing mere mathematical points with powers of attraction or repulsion however complicated.

But if we consider the history of science with respect to the extension of its boundaries, and leave out of account for the present the development of its ideas, it was most important that the great step made by Newton should be extended to every branch of science to which it is applicable, and this could only be done by studying the effects of forces between bodies at a distance, without attempting to explain how the force is transmitted. No men therefore were better fitted to apply themselves exclusively to the first part of the problem, than those who considered the second part quite unnecessary.

Hence those who during the last century and the early part of the present studied so successfully the laws of electricity and magnetism such as Cavendish, Coulomb, and Poisson,[21] paid no regard to those old notions of 'magnetic effluvia' and 'electrical atmospheres' which had been put forth in the previous century,[22] but turned their undivided attention to the determination of the law according to which the parts of electrified or magnetized bodies attract or repel each other. In this way the true laws of these actions were discovered, and this was done by men who never doubted that the action took place at a distance, without the intervention of any medium and who would have regarded the discovery of such a medium as complicating rather than as explaining the undoubted phenomena of attraction.

We have now arrived at the great discovery of the connexion between electricity and magnetism, by which the theory of action at a distance was to be far more severely tried. Professor Oersted of Copenhagen while lecturing to a private class on the electric current, made a wire red hot by transmitting the current through it, and brought it near a magnetic needle.[23] He had done so several times with the needle perpendicular to the current without noticing any effect, but this time he placed the current parallel to the needle, when, to his surprise, the needle moved so as to set itself perpendicular to the current. He found that the action of the current on the pole of a magnet was

(20) See the Appendix *infra* and note (47); and see also Number 294 note (32).
(21) See also Number 450 notes (6), (7) and (8).
(22) See J. L. Heilbron, *Electricity in the 17th and 18th Centuries* (Berkeley/Los Angeles/London, 1979); and R. W. Home's introduction to *Aepinus's Essay on the Theory of Electricity and Magnetism* (Princeton, 1979): 65–188.   (23) See Number 238 note (17).

neither an attraction nor a repulsion but a force tending to make a magnetic pole move at right angles to the plane passing through it and the wire. He expressed this by saying that 'the electric conflict acts in a revolving manner'.

The most obvious deduction from this new fact was that the action of the current on the magnet is not a push-and pull force, but a rotatory force, and the minds of many were set a speculating on vortices and streams of ether whirling round the current.

But Ampère, by a combination of mathematical skill with experimental ingenuity, first proved that two electric currents act on one another, and then analyzed this action into the resultant of a system of push and pull forces between the elementary parts of these currents.(24)

By a further hypothesis, that a reentering current exists in every molecule of a magnet,(25) he also fully explained the actions between currents and magnets and those of magnets on each other, illustrating every part of his theory by well devised experiments.

But the action at a distance, as defined by Ampère, though a push and pull force, depends for its magnitude, not only on the distance between the acting portions of the currents and on their strengths, but on their relative directions, that is, on the angles which they make with each other and with the line joining them, so that, considered as an ultimate fact, it is one of extreme complexity, as compared with the ordinary law of attraction; and it is not to be wondered at that many attempts have been made to resolve it into something of greater apparent simplicity. But before mentioning any of those attempts directly founded on the formula of Ampère, I shall direct your attention to the independent labours of Faraday to elucidate and illustrate the discovery of Oersted.

No man more conscienscously and systematically laboured to improve all his powers of mind than did Faraday from the very earliest period of his scientific career. But whereas the general course of development of science had begun with mathematics and astronomy, so that the ideas and methods of these sciences had been applied to every new investigation in turn, Faraday seems to have had no opportunity of prosecuting mathematics into its higher branches, and his knowledge of astronomy was derived merely from books. Hence though he knew enough of the history of astronomy to have a profound respect for the great discovery of Newton, he regarded the attraction of gravitation as a sort of sacred mystery, which, as he was not an astronomer, he had no right to gainsay or doubt, his duty being to believe it in the exact form in which it was delivered to him. In short though he believed in the

(24) See Number 430 note (5).
(25) See the *Treatise*, 2: 419 (§833); and Number 410 note (19).

attraction of the heavenly bodies, his faith was dead, and he was not imbued with the doctrine of attraction, like the eighteenth century school and their followers.[26]

Besides this, the mathematical treatises of Poisson & Ampère in which the doctrine of attractions was applied with the greatest success to those electrical and magnetic phenomena into which Faraday threw the whole vigour of his powers, are of so technical a form, that, to derive any assistance from them, a man must have been thoroughly trained to mathematical study, and it is very doubtful if such a training can be begun with advantage in mature years.

Thus Faraday, with his original and penetrating intellect, his devotion to science, and his opportunities for experiment, was debarred from following the course of thought which had led to the great achievements of the French philosophers and was obliged to explain the phenomena to himself by a symbolism which he could understand, instead of adopting what had hitherto been the tongue of the learned.

The symbolism which, in the mind of Faraday, became so significant, and which, in his speech and writings, gave trouble to so many men of science, is that which I have spoken of as Faradays Lines of Force.

Filings The idea of lines of force as shown for instance by iron filings is nothing new they had been observed repeatedly and investigated mathematically as an interesting curiosity of science. But let us hear Faraday himself as he introduces the method which became so powerful in his hands. Exp Res 3234.

It would be a voluntary and unnecessary abandonment of most valuable aid, if an experimentalist, who chooses to consider magnetic power as represented by lines of magnetic force, were to deny himself the use of iron filings. By their employment, he may make many conditions of the power, even in complicated cases, visible to the eye at once, may trace the varying direction of the lines of force and determine the relative polarity, may observe in which direction the power is increasing or diminishing; and in complex systems may determine the neutral point, or places where there is neither polarity nor power even when they occur in the midst of powerful magnets. By their use probable results may be seen at once, and many a valuable suggestion gained for future leading experiments.[27]

When a small piece of iron, such as a single filing, is placed in the magnetic field, that is to say in the space in the neighbourhood of magnets or currents, it becomes magnetized in a certain direction, depending on the distribution of magnetic force. Another filing placed in the magnetic field will also become a little magnet. Now if one of these filings is brought near the other, they will

---

(26) See Maxwell's letter to Faraday of 9 November 1857 and Faraday's reply of 13 November; Volume I: 548–52. (27) Faraday, *Electricity*, **3**: 397.

act on each other the poles of opposite names which be nearest each other will approach and rush together and remain in contact and the other poles will turn themselves so as to be in the direction of the magnetic force. If any other filings are in the neighbourhood they will stick themselves on to the exposed poles so as to form a long fibre, the direction of which is that of the magnetic force. A new filing can only stick to the end of the fibre and not to any other part of its length for all the poles except the extreme ones are neutralised by opposite poles in contact with them.

If filings are scattered over a sheet of paper in the magnetic field then when the paper is gently tapped, the filings draw together, filing to filing, till the paper is covered not with mere dots of iron, but with little lines or fibres, and the direction of these fibres is plainly seen in every part of the field.

This is what we may call the physiological explanation of the lines of magnetic force, as delineated by iron filings.

To investigate them more closely, let us take a small magnet and carry it about the field. You observe that wherever the magnet is placed, its direction coincides with that of the fibres of iron filings. But the magnet tells us more than the filings did, for it has two ends, one marked N and the other marked S and by observing the direction of these ends we can distinguish the northern and the southern direction of the line of filings.

We can now define the lines of force somewhat more exactly. Take a very small compass needle and, starting from any point of the paper, go due north (as shown by the compass) and you will trace out part of a line of magnetic force ending usually in a north pole, a point where the north end of the compass will be drawn straight down and the compass will be indifferent in all horizontal directions.

If you steer due south you will trace out the other part of the line of force ending usually in a south pole.

The lines of force due to an electric current do not terminate in north and south poles but are closed or endless curves surrounding the current.

I have supposed the lines of force to be drawn on a flat piece of paper but it is evident that by using a needle free to turn in every direction vertically as well as horizontally we might draw lines of force through the air filling all the space round a magnet or current.

Let us now consider the ordinary scientific explanation of the lines of force. Let us take the case of a simple bar magnet having a north pole and a south pole. The north pole of the compass needle is repelled from the north pole of the bar magnet with a certain force depending on the distance and it is attracted towards the south pole of the bar with a force also depending on the distance. The actual force acting on the north pole of the compass needle is the mechanical resultant of these two forces. If the compass needle is very small compared with the distance of the bar, the forces acting on the south pole will be nearly equal and opposite to those acting on the north pole and their resultant also will be equal and opposite.

Hence the direction of a line of force at any point represents the direction of the resultant of two forces each directed towards or from a fixed point called a pole and each varying inversely as the square of the distance. It is an easy matter for a trained mathematician to calculate the forms of the lines of magnetic force from these conditions but to his mind the magnetic action is represented much more distinctly by the two forces directed to the two poles of the bar magnet than by the complicated system of curves, the investigation of which he regards only as a mathematical recreation.

But let us see what use Faraday made of these lines and to what results he was led and let us compare his method both as respects power accuracy and distinctness with that of the professed mathematicians.

The first thing to observe in Faradays use of the lines of force is that he uses them to represent not only the direction but the magnitude of the magnetic lines of force at every part of the field. It is evident even to the eye that when the lines converge the force is increasing in the direction of the convergence but the statements of Faraday relative to this subject show a constantly increasing clearness of definition which attains complete development in 3073 Series XXVIII.

A point equally important to the definition of these lines is, that they represent a determinate and unchanging amount of force. Though, therefore their forms, as they exist between two or more centres or sources of magnetic power may vary greatly, and also the space through which they may be traced, yet the sum of power contained in any one section of a given portion of the lines is exactly equal to the sum of power in any other section of the same lines however altered in form or however convergent or divergent they may be at the second place.[28]

That is to say that if we draw a number of these lines forming a little bundle[29] and if we measure the section of this bundle at different points of its length, the area of the section multiplied by the strength of the magnetic force will be the same at all these points.[30]

This conclusion which is mathematically true on the old theory of magnetism is one at which I am not aware that the professed mathematicians had arrived at the time when Faraday, without the help of technical mathematics, both saw its importance and proved its truth.

---

(28) Faraday, *Electricity*, **3**: 329.
(29) Compare Faraday, *Electricity*, **3**: 435; 'magnets may be looked upon as the habitations of bundles of lines of force'.
(30) On Maxwell's mathematical theory of lines of force see Volume I: 367–9, 371–5.

Lecture on Faraday's lines of force, early 1873 805

This remarkable property of the lines of force by which we may estimate the variation of the force as we pass along any bundle of lines by the degree of concentration of the lines leads to another conception of high mathematical significance and also due to Faraday.

By drawing the lines in a systematic manner it is evident that we might indicate the intensity of the magnetic force not only along a particular line but in every part of the field by the degree of concentration of the lines, that is by the *number* of the lines which pass through a square inch of a section taken perpendicular to their direction. The definite statement of this conception is given in one of his later memoirs Series XXVIII par 3122[31] but the frequent use of the expressions amount of the lines of force and number of lines of force in his earlier papers shows that he was guided by this conception from the first.[32]

Thus then we see that Faraday converted the lines of force from a mere scientific curiosity into a complete definition of the magnetic state of every part of the field.

The strength of the north pole of a magnet is measured at once by the number of lines which diverge from it. If the magnet is the only magnet in existence all these lines, whatever be their intermediate course converge again to the south pole of the magnet and return through the substance of the magnet to the north pole. If there are other magnets in the field some of the lines from the north pole of one magnet may go to the south pole of a different magnet but in all cases the number which meet at any pole measures the strength of that pole.

In the case of an electric current the lines of force form rings round the current.

If the strength of a magnet is increased Faraday conceives new lines of force as being developed within the magnet and causing the whole system to expand. If the strength of the magnet is diminished the lines of force contract towards the magnet and some of them disappear within it. In the same way when an electric current in a wire increases or diminishes, the system of lines of force round it expands or contracts.

By this remarkable mathematical conception, which is described in the

---

(31) Faraday, *Electricity*, **3**: 349; 'the direction of the *lines of force*... and the relative amount of force, or of lines of force in a given space, [is] indicated by their concentration or separation, *i.e.* by their number in that space'.

(32) These expressions do not occur in Faraday's early papers, collected in his *Electricity*. Compare Maxwell's comments in the *Treatise*, **2**: 174–5 (§541) which qualify this assertion; and his claim that '[Faraday's] method of conceiving the phenomena was also a mathematical one', in the Preface to the *Treatise*, **1**: x, dated 1 February 1873.

second series of his researches (238, 239)[33] each line of force is regarded as having a continuous existence, so that it preserves its identity during all the changes of form which may arise from alterations in the position or strength of magnets or currents.

The diagrams which you see[34] are intended to illustrate the lines of force as definite in number as well as direction. The first represents a single magnetic pole whose strength is 36 placed among the lines of the earths magnetic force. The 36 lines of force belonging to the pole instead of proceeding from it in straight lines are all deflected towards the opposite pole of the earth and the lines of the earths force from the other pole are deflected from their originally straight directions.

Let us now briefly mention some of the uses which Faraday made of this conception of lines of force.

Let a conducting wire carrying a current be placed in the magnetic field, how will it move. The answer is simple. It will endeavour to embrace as many of the lines of force as possible so that they may pass through the electric circuit in the positive direction. To do this every portion of the wire will be urged across these lines of force with a mechanical force which is perpendicular both to the wire and to the lines of force.

Every question relating to the mechanical force acting on a current may be solved with mathematical accuracy by this simple rule that the work done during any motion of the current is equal to the number of new lines embraced by it multiplied by the strength of the current.

Again if a conducting circuit be placed in the magnetic field and any change occurs either in the position of this circuit or in the positions or the strengths of magnets or currents so that the number of lines of force embraced by the circuit is altered then an induced current will take place in the circuit, the total amount of which multiplied by the resistance of the circuit is equal to the diminution of the number of lines of force embraced by the circuit.

Another very remarkable proof of Faradays insight is given by his statement of the true form of the law of the force acting on diamagnetic bodies. In the second of his papers on diamagnetism he thus sums up the whole results of his experiments in language which in a mathematical point of view could hardly be improved.

All the phænomena resolve themselves into this, that a portion of such matter when under magnetic action, tends to move from stronger to weaker places or points of force.[35]

---

(33) Faraday, *Electricity*, **1**: 68–9.　　　(34) Not extant.
(35) Faraday, *Electricity*, **3**: 69 (par. 2418).

Here then we have the lines of magnetic force used as a powerful instrument by which Faraday was enabled to define with mathematical precision the whole laws of electromagnetism in language free from mathematical technicalities. His method then considered simply as a piece of mathematical apparatus for treating certain questions, has great merit. But he did not stop here. He went on from the conception of geometrical lines of force to that of physical lines of force and found wherever these lines of force existed that certain effects were there taking place intimately related to these lines of force. One of his most remarkable statements with respect to the physical character of the lines of magnetic force is that in every motion due to magnetic force the lines of force are shortened so that wherever there are lines of magnetic force there is a tendency to longitudinal contraction and lateral separation of the lines.[36]

Here then is a distinct physical state which Faraday thinks he perceives in the medium in which these lines exist. It consists of a tension like that of a rope in the direction of the lines of force combined with a pressure in all directions at right angles to these lines.

This is quite a new view of action at a distance reducing it to a phenomenon of the same kind as that action at a distance which we exert by means of our tools and ropes and connecting rods.

If we examine the lines of force in the diagrams or by means of iron filings we see that whenever the lines of force pass directly from one point to another, there is attraction between the poles and when the lines from the two poles avoid each other and are dispersed into space the poles repel each other, so that in both cases the poles are drawn in the direction of the resultant of the lines of force.

To test this theory of a physical tension along the lines of force we must examine whether such tension would produce the actually observed forces. To do this involves the study of the equilibrium of stresses in a body a subject which has been treated only within the present century and for the development of which we are indebted in the first place to engineers who studied it in order to know what forces are called into play in their machines and structures and in the second place to optical inquirers who have endeavoured to understand the forces involved in the propagation of light in an elastic medium.

Taking advantage therefore of the theory of stress as laid down for instance in Professor Rankines excellent work on Applied Mechanics[37] and supposing

---

(36) Faraday, *Electricity*, **3**: 437.
(37) W. J. M. Rankine, *A Manual of Applied Mechanics* (London/Glasgow, 1858): 92–3, 113–16.

that wherever there is magnetic force, there is a state of stress,[38] consisting of a tension in the direction of the lines of force combined with a pressure in all directions at right angles to these lines, the numerical value of the tension and the pressure being equal and both proportional to the *square* of the intensity of the magnetic force at the place then we find by a simple calculation

First that every part of the medium will be in equilibrium under the action of these stresses, provided it does not contain a magnetic pole or an electric current. Hence this hypothesis is quite consistent with the perfect mobility of the medium.

Second if a magnetic pole exists it will not be in equilibrium under the forces which act on it, but will be moved in the direction of the lines of force with a mechanical force the value of which is the product of the strength of the pole and the intensity of the magnetic force.

Third if an electric current crosses the lines of force, it will not be in equilibrium but will experience a mechanical force urging it across the lines of magnetic force and the value of this force agrees with what we know about it.

When the muscles of our bodies are excited by that stimulus which we are able in some unknown way to apply to them their fibres tend to shorten themselves and at the same time to expand laterally. If we knew the mechanical stress at every point of the muscle we could determine the force which it exerts in moving the limb though we might be quite unable to find out the cause of the tension of the muscle as produced at the will of its owner.

According to the theory of magnetic lines of force which I have been describing the magnetic field is in some way put into a state of stress like that of the muscle, the lines of force tending to shorten themselves and expand laterally and it appears that if this stress has a certain definite relation to the degree of concentration of the lines of force it will produce a mechanical effect exactly corresponding with what actually takes place.

Of course it does not follow that this is the actual mode in which magnetic attraction occurs. All we have done is to show that if a medium is in this state of stress it will produce the effects which are known to occur. If therefore we feel any desire to account for magnetic action at a distance by means of an action taking place in the intervening medium, this hypothesis deserves our consideration even though it furnishes no explanation of how the state of stress is produced or maintained.

In our bodily actions we are conscious of an act of will and we presently

---

(38) Maxwell had referred to Rankine's text in his paper 'On physical lines of force. Part I. The theory of molecular vortices applied to magnetic phenomena', *Phil. Mag.*, ser. 4, **21** (1861): 161–75, esp. 163 (= *Scientific Papers*, **1**: 453), in expounding a theory of magnetism as a result of '*stress* in the medium'.

become aware that a corresponding outward act has been done by us involving motions of our bodies and of other bodies extending to a considerable distance. We investigate the mechanism of our bodies and find that our muscles have been put into a certain state of stress and that motion has ensued the motion being communicated from one part to another till the required act was done.

This explanation is by no means complete for it furnishes no account of the method by which the will acts on the muscles nor does it even investigate the forces of cohesion which enable the muscles to support the state of tension. Nevertheless the simple fact that it substitutes an action which is propagated continuously along a material substance for one of which we know only a cause and an effect at a distance from each other induces us to accept it as a real addition to our knowledge.

For similar reasons we may be justified in bestowing much thought on this physical hypothesis about lines of force in the hope that it may substitute an action between consecutive parts of a medium for an action supposed to take place immediately at a distance.

[2][39] I wish in the last place to point out some results of the theory that electrical and magnetic forces act between bodies not directly but by the intervention of a medium. It follows from this that if by any means one of the bodies could be instantaneously annihilated or at least deprived of its electrical or magnetic properties, the ether would continue to be acted on by the medium for a certain time just as if the first body had still been there just as you continue to hear my voice for a certain time after I am here speaking, while the sound is still travelling through the air.

In fact it follows from our theory that electrical and magnetic forces require time for their transmission and that each body puts the medium round it into a certain state which is communicated from part to part of the medium at a certain rate.

The question therefore naturally arises – Have we any means of determining this rate? or velocity of transmission of magnetic force from one place to another? – The science of electrical measurements is indebted for its present degree of accuracy mainly to Prof W Weber, the fellow labourer of Gauss. From his results we can obtain data to calculate the speed of the transmission of magnetic force. The value calculated from his experiments is 314000000 metres or 19   miles in a second.[40] Now the velocity of light

---

(39) ULC Add. MSS 7655, V, c/20. Endorsed: 'Faraday's Lines of Force'.
(40) Weber's value for the ratio between the electrostatic and electromagnetic units is 310,740 mm/sec; see Number 238 note (22), and *Treatise*, 2: 387 (§787). See also Volume I: 685.

according to Foucaults direct measurements is [298 millions of metres per second].[41] Both the measurement of the velocity of light and that of the quantities on which the rate of transmission of magnetic force depends are operations of great delicacy. The electromagnetic experiment has been repeated in two forms distinct from each other and from that of Weber by Sir W Thomson[42] and by myself.[43] We both obtained a value considerably less than that of Weber. The conclusion to which we are led is that whatever light is and whatever magnetism and electricity may be, they depend on the same thing – that light in fact is an electromagnetic phenomenon and that the waves of light consist of small alternating magnetic disturbances.

This theory of light leads us at once to the explanation of the polarization of light. It agrees in all points with the theory of undulations except that where the ordinary theory sees a displacement of ether our theory sees a displacement of electricity and where the ordinary theory sees a rotation of particles of ether our theory sees a magnetic force in the direction of the axis of rotation.

We are not therefore attempting to fill up all space three and four times over with new ethers to do this that and the other but are trying to understand how the one ether which the phenomena of light have compelled us to admit is capable also of other modes of action and that [light and electromagnetic] phenomena are manifestations of these.

And we must not consider this ether as something [like] vapour the wreaths of which have no power to bend. Even when it is employed only in transmitting the dazzling rays of the sun it is supporting very considerable forces. The ordinary magnetic force of the earth in this country is equivalent to a tension of about an eighth of a grain weight on a square foot and some of Mr Joules magnets can produce a magnetic force equivalent to a tension of about 200 lbs weight on the square inch.[44] These are very considerable forces to be exerted and supported by the ether.

I have already said that hardly any progress has been made in accounting for the attraction of gravitation. If however we propose to account for it in the

---

(41) As stated in the published lecture 'On action at a distance': 53 (= *Scientific Papers*, 2: 322); and see Number 238 note (25).

(42) As described in the 'Report of the Committee on standards of electrical resistance', *Report of the Thirty-ninth Meeting of the British Association* (London, 1870): 434–8, on 434–6. See also *Treatise*, 2: 372–3, 387 (§§772, 787).   (43) See Number 289.

(44) Compare *Treatise*, 2: 258 (§646) where he gives a figure of 'about 140 pounds weight on the square inch'. Joule had described his magnets in his 'Description of a new electro-magnet', *Annals of Electricity*, 6 (1841): 431–3, and his 'Account of experiments with a powerful electro-magnet', *Phil. Mag.*, ser. 4, 3 (1852): 32–6.

same way as we have done for magnetism we must admit that there is pressure instead of tension along the lines of force and tension instead of pressure at right angles to them and that here where we sit the ether is supporting a vertical pressure of more than 37000 tons on the square inch. The strength of steel is nothing to this. I by no means assert this as a fact but as a specimen of the results to which we may be led by a theory which must be verified before we can believe it.

APPENDIX: MANUSCRIPT FRAGMENT ON DYNAMICAL PRINCIPLES
circa 1873[45]
From the original in the University Library, Cambridge[46]

[MATTER AND DYNAMICS]

In studying electrical and other phenomena for the purpose of explaining them on dynamical principles, there are certain axioms so well established in the better known parts of dynamics that we are entitled to expect them to prove universally true.

For instance, we obtain from ordinary dynamical considerations the idea of matter as a thing capable of motion but not changing its state of motion except in so far as it is acted on by external forces, that is, forces between the body in question and other bodies.

We must of course learn what is meant by a state of motion and how changes of that state are to be measured. We must also learn by experience that these changes, in the case of a material body depend on what we call the mass of the body itself as well as on those external relations to other bodies which we call forces. As soon as we clearly understand how the 'laws of motion' by which this dependence is expressed lead to results consistent with facts, we have formed an idea of mass as the quantitative aspect of matter which is as necessary a part of our thoughts as the triple extension of space or the continual flux of time.

I do not think it necessary to enquire whether this is the metaphysical idea of matter, or whether any metaphysician has come to the conclusion that the

---

(45) This MS fragment seems to have relation to the 1873 lecture 'On action at a distance': see note (47). The fragment is therefore reproduced here, though a date of early 1873 is conjectural. (46) ULC Add. MSS 7655, V, c/10.

property commonly called inertia is the fundamental and inseparable part of matter. We may be satisfied with our dynamical reasons for asserting that the mass of a body is a measurable and constant quantity and that for all dynamical purposes a body must be measured by its mass and not by any other property such as its volume, its weight, or its chemical activity.

I have made these remarks because an opinion seems to be in circulation that all phenomena can be explained by the hypothesis that there are certain moveable points whose motions are determined by their relative positions and which are therefore called centres of force.[47] As long as it was supposed that the ultimate parts of bodies were themselves small bodies of finite size, these ultimate parts were called atoms, but as we have no evidence as to the size and shape of these atoms some have thought it more philosophical to speak of them as centres of force, without attributing to them any finite extension. This would be quite legitimate, provided each centre of force is admitted to have mass, so that the mass of all the centres taken together shall be equal to that of the body which they form. It seems, however, that the idea of mass is so bound up with that of extension in many minds that in giving up the size and shape of the atoms they have apparently lost sight of their mass.

Torricelli, in his fourth lecture to the Accademia della Crusca has expressed the relation between the idea of matter on the one hand and those of force and momentum on the other neither of which can exist without the other.[48]

---

(47) In 'On action at a distance': 49 (= *Scientific Papers*, **2**: 317) Maxwell cites a review of Mary Somerville, *On Molecular and Microscopic Science*, 2 vols. (London, 1869), 'Mrs Somerville on molecular and microscopic science', *Saturday Review*, **27** (Feb. 13, 1869): 219–20, where the reviewer maintained that Boscovich 'had not quite got so far as the strict modern view of "matter" as being but an expression for modes or manifestations of "force"'. By contrast, Maxwell noted that Boscovich 'did not forget, however, to endow his mathematical points with inertia'. Compare Maxwell's discussion of Faraday's theory of 'all space as a field of force' in the *Treatise*, **2**: 164 (§529) where, alluding to Faraday's 'A speculation touching electric conduction and the nature of matter', *Phil. Mag.*, ser. 3, **24** (1844): 136–44, and 'Thoughts on ray-vibrations', *ibid.*, **28** (1846): 345–50 (= *Electricity*, **2**: 284–93; **3**: 447–52), he noted that '[Faraday] even speaks of the lines of force belonging to a body as in some sense part of itself', but maintained: 'This, however, is not a dominant idea with Faraday.'. See also Number 287.

(48) See Number 287 note (12); and Number 294: Appendix and note (29). Maxwell cites this passage in the concluding article of the *Treatise*, **2**: 438 (§866), in support of his claim that 'there must be a medium or substance in which the energy exists after it leaves one body and before it reaches the other'.

438

LETTER TO HENRY BENCE JONES[1]

4 FEBRUARY 1873

From the original in the Library of the Royal Institution[2]

11 Scroope Terrace
Cambridge
4 Feb 1873

Dear Sir

I send you by book post my lecture.[3] When you have done with it pray let me have it again. Some numbers &c must be inserted to agree with the experiments actually made at the lecture.

I enclose for Mr Wills[4] a list of the things which will be wanted. If any of them are not to hand I will devise something else if I know a day or two before.

I also enclose a diagram to explain Newtons Rings[5] which I think will make the subject plainer.

If, from your experience of lectures, you think mine will take more than the hour, pray let me know.

Yours faithfully
J. CLERK MAXWELL

---

(1) Secretary of the Royal Institution.

(2) W. H. Bragg Box 28, Miscellaneous Papers, the Royal Institution, London.

(3) 'On action at a distance'; see *Proceedings of the Royal Institution of Great Britain*, **7** (1873–5): 44–54 (= *Scientific Papers*, **2**: 311–23). The lecture was read on 21 February 1873.

(4) Thomas Wills, assistant in the chemical laboratory; see *Proceedings of the Royal Institution*, **6** (1870–2): iii.

(5) See Maxwell, 'On action at a distance': 46–7 (= *Scientific Papers*, **2**: 313–14); and Number 437 note (13).

ESSAY FOR THE ERANUS CLUB[1] ON SCIENCE AND FREE WILL

11 FEBRUARY 1873

From Campbell and Garnett, *Life of Maxwell*[2]

DOES THE PROGRESS OF PHYSICAL SCIENCE TEND TO GIVE ANY ADVANTAGE TO THE OPINION OF NECESSITY (OR DETERMINISM) OVER THAT OF THE CONTINGENCY OF EVENTS AND THE FREEDOM OF THE WILL?

11 FEBRUARY 1873

The general character and tendency of human thought is a topic the interest of which is not confined to professional philosophers. Though every one of us must, each for himself, accept some sort of a philosophy, good or bad, and though the whole virtue of this philosophy depends on it being our own, yet none of us thinks it out entirely for himself. It is essential to our comfort that we should know whether we are going with the general stream of human thought or against it, and if it should turn out that the general stream flows in a direction different from the current of our private thought, though we may endeavour to explain it as the result of a wide-spread aberration of intellect, we would be more satisfied if we could obtain some evidence that it is not ourselves who are going astray.

In such an enquiry we need some fiducial point or standard of reference, by which we may ascertain the direction in which we are drifting. The books written by men of former ages who thought about the same questions would be of great use, if it were not that we are apt to derive a wrong impression from them if we approach them by a course of reading unknown to those for whom they were written.

There are certain questions, however, which form the *pièces de résistance* of philosophy, on which men of all ages have exhausted their arguments, and

---

(1) 'Under the name of Erănus (or pic-nic) a club of older men... who had been "Apostles" together in 1853–7, revived the habit of meeting together for the discussion of speculative questions' (*Life of Maxwell*: 366, 434). The club included Fenton John Anthony Hort and Joseph Barber Lightfoot (see Volume I: 314, 384, 506, 585; and *Life of Maxwell*: 434).

(2) *Life of Maxwell*: 434–44; reprinted and corrected (see note (17)) in *Life of Maxwell* (2nd edn): 357–66.

which are perfectly certain to furnish matter of debate to generations to come, and which may therefore serve to show how we are drifting. At a certain epoch of our adolescence those of us who are good for anything begin to get anxious about these questions, and unless the cares of this world utterly choke our metaphysical anxieties, we become developed into advocates of necessity or of free-will. What it is which determines for us which side we shall take must for the purpose of this essay be regarded as contingent. According to Mr F. Galton, it is derived from structureless elements in our parents, which were probably never developed in their earthly existence, and which may have been handed down to them, still in the latent state, through untold generations.[3] Much might be said in favour of such a congenital bias towards a particular scheme of philosophy; at the same time we must acknowledge that much of a man's mental history depends upon events occurring after his birth in time, and that he is on the whole more likely to espouse doctrines which harmonise with the particular set of ideas to which he is induced, by the process of education, to confine his attention. What will be the probable effect if these ideas happen mainly to be those of modern physical science?

The intimate connexion between physical and metaphysical science is indicated even by their names. What are the chief requisites of a physical laboratory? Facilities for measuring space, time, and mass. What is the occupation of a metaphysician? Speculating on the modes of difference of co-existent things, on invariable sequences, and on the existence of matter.

He is nothing but a physicist disarmed of all his weapons – a disembodied spirit trying to measure distances in terms of his own cubit, to form a chronology in which intervals of time are measured by the number of thoughts which they include, and to evolve a standard pound out of his own self-consciousness. Taking metaphysicians singly, we find again that as is their physics, so is their metaphysics. Descartes, with his perfect insight into geometrical truth, and his wonderful ingenuity in the imagination of

---

(3) Francis Galton, 'On blood-relationship', *Proc. Roy. Soc.*, **20** (1872): 394–402. For Maxwell's further discussion of Galton's concept of 'structureless elements', and his critique of Darwin's theory of 'pangenesis' (a theory of heredity in which cells of the body were supposed to give off 'gemmules') which Galton's paper investigates, see his article on 'Atom' in *Encyclopaedia Britannica* (9th edn), **3** (Edinburgh, 1875): 36–49, on 42 (= *Scientific Papers*, **2**: 461). At a meeting of the Cambridge Philosophical Society on 25 November 1872 Maxwell's comment on Darwin's theory of 'pangenesis' was recorded in the *Proceedings*: 'Professor Maxwell spoke of the difficulty of conceiving chemical molecules in sufficient quantity being packed in these small gemmules' (*Proc. Camb. Phil. Soc.*, **2** (1872): 289). Maxwell makes a similar point in his 'Atom' article.

mechanical contrivances, was far behind the other great men of his time with respect to the conception of matter as a receptacle of momentum and energy. His doctrine of the collision of bodies is ludicrously absurd. He admits, indeed, that the facts are against him, but explains them as the result either of the want of perfect hardness in the bodies, or of the action of the surrounding air. His inability to form that notion which we now call force is exemplified in his explanation of the hardness of bodies as the result of the quiescence of their parts.

Neque profecto ullum glutinum possumus excogitare, quod particulas durorum corporum firmius inter se conjungat, quàm ipsarum quies. *Princip., Pars* II. LV.[4]

Descartes, in fact, was a firm believer that matter has but one essential property, namely extension, and his influence in preserving this pernicious heresy in existence extends even to very recent times. Spinoza's idea of matter, as he receives it from the authorities, is exactly that of Descartes; and if he has added to it another essential function, namely thought, the new ingredient does not interfere with the old, and certainly does not bring the matter of Descartes into closer resemblance with that of Newton.

The influence of the physical ideas of Newton on philosophical thought deserves a careful study. It may be traced in a very direct way through Maclaurin[5] and the Stewarts[6] to the Scotch School, the members of which had all listened to the popular expositions of the Newtonian Philosophy in their respective colleges. In England, Boyle and Locke reflect Newtonian ideas with tolerable distinctness, though both have ideas of their own.[7] Berkeley, on the other hand, though he is a master of the language of his time,

---

(4) R. Descartes, *Principia Philosophiæ* (Amsterdam, 1644): 62 (Pars Secunda, Prop. LV) (nor assuredly are we able to devise any glue which could join together the particles of hard bodies more strongly than does their own rest).

(5) Colin MacLaurin, *An Account of Sir Isaac Newton's Philosophical Discoveries* (London, 1748), see also Number 437; idem, *A Treatise of Fluxions*, 2 vols. (Edinburgh, 1742).

(6) The Aberdeen (Marischal College) mathematics professor John Stewart published a translation and commentary on *Sir Isaac Newton's Two Treatises of the Quadratures of Curves and Analysis by Equations of an infinite Number of Terms, explained* (London, 1745); and 'Some remarks on the laws of motion, and the inertia of matter', in *Essays and Observations, Physical and Literary, read before a Society in Edinburgh and published by them*, 3 vols. (Edinburgh, 1754–71), **1**: 70–140. The Edinburgh mathematics professor Matthew Stewart was in the geometrical tradition (following Robert Simson), publishing 'A solution of Kepler's problem', in *Essays and Observations, Physical and Literary*, **2**: 105–44, and *The Distance of the Sun from the Earth determined by the Theory of Gravity* (Edinburgh, 1763). He was the father of Dugald Stewart, author of *Elements of the Philosophy of the Human Mind*, 3 vols. (Edinburgh, 1792–1827), which contains substantive discussion of mathematics, metaphysics and natural philosophy.

(7) On Locke see also Number 287.

is quite impervious to its ideas.⁽⁸⁾ Samuel Clarke is perhaps one of the best examples of the influence of Newton;⁽⁹⁾ while Roger Cotes, in spite of his clever exposition of Newton's doctrines, must be condemned as one of the earliest heretics bred in the bosom of Newtonianism.[10]

It is absolutely manifest from these and other instances that any development of physical science is likely to produce some modification of the methods and ideas of philosophers, provided that the physical ideas are expounded in such a way that the philosophers can understand them.

The principal developments of physical ideas in modern times have been –

1st. The idea of matter as the receptacle of momentum and energy. This we may attribute to Galileo and some of his contemporaries. This idea is fully expressed by Newton, under the form of Laws of Motion.

2nd. The discussion of the relation between the fact of gravitation and the maxim that matter cannot act where it is not.

3rd. The discoveries in Physical Optics, at the beginning of this century. These have produced much less effect outside the scientific world than might be expected. There are two reasons for this. In the first place it is difficult, especially in these days of the separation of technical from popular knowledge, to expound physical optics to persons not professedly mathematicians. The second reason is, that it is extremely easy to show such persons the phenomena, which are very beautiful in themselves, and this is often accepted as instruction in physical optics.

4th. The development of the doctrine of the Conservation of Energy. This has produced a far greater effect on the thinking world outside that of technical thermodynamics.

As the doctrine of the conservation of matter gave a definiteness to statements regarding the immateriality of the soul, so the doctrine of the conservation of energy, when applied to living beings, leads to the conclusion that the soul of an animal is not, like the mainspring of a watch, the motive power of the body, but that its function is rather that of a steersman of a vessel – not to produce, but to regulate and direct the animal powers.[11]

5th. The discoveries in Electricity and Magnetism labour under the same disadvantages as those in Light. It is difficult to present the ideas in an adequate manner to laymen, and it is easy to show them wonderful experiments.

6th. On the other hand, recent developments of Molecular Science seem

---

(8) Compare Volume I: 247.   (9) See Number 437 note (15).
(10) See Number 437 esp. note (19).
(11) Compare Maxwell's letter to Lewis Campbell of 21 April 1862 (Volume I: 712).

likely to have a powerful effect on the world of thought. The doctrine that visible bodies apparently at rest are made up of parts, each of which is moving with the velocity of a cannon ball, and yet never departing to a visible extent from its mean place, is sufficiently startling to attract the attention of an unprofessional man.

But I think the most important effect of molecular science on our way of thinking will be that it forces on our attention the distinction between two kinds of knowledge, which we may call for convenience the Dynamical and Statistical.

The statistical method of investigating social questions has Laplace for its most scientific[12] and Buckle for its most popular expounder.[13] Persons are grouped according to some characteristic, and the number of persons forming the group is set down under that characteristic. This is the raw material from which the statist endeavours to deduce general theorems in sociology. Other students of human nature proceed on a different plan. They observe individual men, ascertain their history, analyse their motives, and compare their expectation of what they will do with their actual conduct. This may be called the dynamical method of study as applied to man. However imperfect the dynamical study of man may be in practice, it evidently is the only perfect method in principle, and its shortcomings arise from the limitation of our powers rather than from a faulty method of procedure. If we betake ourselves to the statistical method, we do so confessing that we are unable to follow the details of each individual case, and expecting that the effects of widespread causes, though very different in each individual, will produce an average result on the whole nation, from a study of which we may estimate the character and propensities of an imaginary being called the Mean Man.

Now, if the molecular theory of the constitution of bodies is true, all our knowledge of matter is of the statistical kind. A constituent molecule of a body has properties very different from those of the body to which it belongs. Besides its immutability and other recondite properties, it has a velocity which is different from that which we attribute to the body as a whole.

The smallest portion of a body which we can discern consists of a vast number of such molecules, and all that we can learn about this group of molecules is statistical information. We can determine the motion of the centre of gravity of the group, but not that of any one of its members for the

---

(12) P. S. de Laplace, *Théorie Analytique des Probabilités* (Paris, 1812).
(13) Thomas Henry Buckle, *History of Civilization in England*, 2 vols. (London, 1857–61), esp. 1: 19–22. Maxwell had read the first volume of Buckle's *History* on its publication (see Volume I: 576).

time being, and these members themselves are continually passing from one group to another in a manner confessedly beyond our power of tracing them.

Hence those uniformities which we observe in our experiments with quantities of matter containing millions of millions of molecules are uniformities of the same kind as those explained by Laplace and wondered at by Buckle, arising from the slumping together of multitudes of cases, each of which is by no means uniform with the others.

The discussion of statistical matter is within the province of human reason, and valid consequences may be deduced from it by legitimate methods; but there are certain peculiarities in the very form of the results which indicate that they belong to a different department of knowledge from the domain of exact science. They are not symmetrical functions of the time. It makes all the difference in the world whether we suppose the inquiry to be historical or prophetical – whether our object is to deduce the past state or the future state of things from the known present state. In astronomy, the two problems differ only in the sign of t, the time; in the theory of the diffusion of matter, heat, or motion, the prophetical problem is always capable of solution; but the historical one, except in singular cases, is insoluble. There may be other cases in which the past, but not the future, may be deducible from the present. Perhaps the process by which we remember past events, by submitting our memory to analysis, may be a case of this kind.

Much light may be thrown on some of these questions by the consideration of stability and instability.[14] When the state of things is such that an infinitely small variation of the present state will alter only by an infinitely small quantity the state at some future time, the condition of the system, whether at rest or in motion, is said to be stable; but when an infinitely small variation in the present state may bring about a finite difference in the state of the system in a finite time, the condition of the system is said to be unstable.[15]

It is manifest that the existence of unstable conditions renders impossible the prediction of future events, if our knowledge of the present state is only approximate, and not accurate.

(14) See Maxwell's letter to Francis Galton of 26 February 1879 (to be reproduced in Volume III).

(15) Compare Balfour Stewart, *The Conservation of Energy. Being an Elementary Treatise on Energy and its Laws* (London, 1874): 155–6; considering an egg balanced in unstable equilibrium he observed: 'Not... that its movements are without a cause, but... its movements are decided by some external impulse so exceedingly small as to be utterly beyond our powers of observation.' Maxwell referred to Stewart's text in his similar discussion of singularities in a dynamical system in his review in *Nature*, **19** (1879): 141–3, esp. 142 (= *Scientific Papers*, **2**: 760) of Balfour Stewart and P. G. Tait, *Paradoxical Philosophy. A sequel to the Unseen Universe* (London, 1878).

It has been well pointed out by Professor Balfour Stewart[16] that physical stability is the characteristic of those systems from the contemplation of which determinists draw their arguments, and physical instability[17] that of those living bodies,[18] and moral instability that of those developable souls, which furnish to consciousness the conviction of free will.

Having thus pointed out some of the relations of physical science to the question, we are the better prepared to inquire what is meant by determination and what by free will.

No one, I suppose, would assign to free will a more than infinitesimal range. No leopard can change his spots, nor can any one by merely wishing it, or, as some say, *willing* it, introduce discontinuity into his course of existence. Our free will at the best is like that of Lucretius's atoms – which at quite uncertain times and places deviate in an uncertain manner from their course.[19] In the course of this our mortal life we more or less frequently find ourselves on a physical or moral watershed, where an imperceptible deviation is sufficient to determine into which of two valleys we shall descend. The doctrine of free will asserts that in some such cases the Ego alone is the determining cause. The doctrine of Determinism asserts that in every case, without exception, the result is determined by the previous conditions of the subject, whether bodily or mental, and that Ego is mistaken in supposing himself in any way the cause of the actual result, as both what he is pleased to call decisions and the resultant action are corresponding events due to the same fixed laws. Now, when we speak of causes and effects, we always imply some person who knows the causes and deduces the effects. Who is this person? Is he a man, or is he the Deity?

If he is man – that is to say, a person who can make observations with a certain finite degree of accuracy – we have seen that it is only in certain cases that he can predict results with even approximate correctness.

---

(16) B. Stewart and J. N. Lockyer, 'The sun as a type of the material universe. Part II: The place of life in a universe of energy', *Macmillan's Magazine*, **18** (1868): 319–27; Stewart, *Conservation of Energy*: 154–67.

(17) Reading: 'instability', following *Life of Maxwell* (2nd edn): 362–3.

(18) Stewart and Lockyer, 'The sun as a type of the material universe': 325–6; Stewart, *Conservation of Energy*: 161, noting that a human being or animal is 'a machine of a delicacy that is practically infinite, the conditions or motions of which we are utterly unable to predict'.

(19) Lucretius, *De Rerum Natura*, Book II, 289–93. Maxwell quotes the passage on the 'swerve' of Lucretian atoms in his MS on the 'Kinetic Theory of Gases' written for William Thomson in Summer 1871 (Number 377, see esp. note (5)); and see 'Molecules', *Nature*, **8** (25 September 1873): 437–41, on 440 (= *Scientific Papers*, 2: 373).

If he is the Deity, I object to any argument founded on a supposed acquaintance with the conditions of Divine foreknowledge.

The subject of the essay is the relation to determinism, not of theology, metaphysics, or mathematics, but of physical science – the science which depends for its material on the observation and measurement of visible things, but which aims at the development of doctrines whose consistency with each other shall be apparent to our reason.

It is a metaphysical doctrine that from the same antecedents follow the same consequents. No one can gainsay this. But it is not of much use in a world like this, in which the same antecedents never again concur, and nothing ever happens twice. Indeed, for aught we know, one of the antecedents might be the precise date and place of the event, in which case experience would go for nothing. The metaphysical axiom would be of use only to a being possessed of the knowledge of contingent events, *scientia simplicis intelligentiæ* – a degree of knowledge to which mere omniscience of all facts, *scientia visionis*, is but ignorance.

The physical axiom which has a somewhat similar aspect is 'That from like antecedents follow like consequents.' But here we have passed from sameness to likeness, from absolute accuracy to a more or less rough approximation. There are certain classes of phenomena, as I have said, in which a small error in the data only introduces a small error in the result. Such are, among others, the larger phenomena of the Solar System, and those in which the more elementary laws in Dynamics contribute the greater part of the result. The course of events in these cases is stable.

There are other classes of phenomena which are more complicated, and in which cases of instability may occur, the number of such cases increasing, in an exceedingly rapid manner, as the number of variables increases. Thus, to take a case from a branch of science which comes next to astronomy itself as a manifestation of order: in the refraction of light, the direction of the refracted ray depends on that of the incident ray, so that in general, if the one direction be slightly altered, the other also will be slightly altered. In doubly refracting media there are two refracting rays, but it is true of each of them that like causes produce like effects. But if the direction of the ray within a biaxal crystal is nearly but not exactly coincident with that of the ray-axis of the crystal, a small change in direction will produce a great change in the direction of the emergent ray. Of course, this arises from a singularity in the properties of the ray-axis, and there are only two ray-axes among the infinite number of possible directions of lines in the crystal; but it is to be expected that in phenomena of higher complexity there will be a far greater number of singularities, near which the axiom about like causes producing like effects ceases to be true. Thus the conditions under which gun-cotton explodes are far from being well known; but the aim of chemists is not so much to predict the time at which gun-cotton will go off of itself, as to find a kind of gun-cotton which, when placed in certain circumstances, has never yet exploded, and this even when slight irregularities both in the manufacture and in the storage are taken account of by trying numerous and long continued experiments.

In all such cases there is one common circumstance – the system has a quantity of potential energy, which is capable of being transformed into motion, but which cannot begin to be so transformed till the system has reached a certain configuration, to attain which requires an expenditure of work, which in certain cases may be infinitesimally small, and in general bears no definite proportion to the energy developed in consequence thereof. For example, the rock loosed by frost and balanced on a singular point of the mountain-side, the little spark which kindles the great forest, the little word which sets the world a fighting, the little scruple which prevents a man from doing his will, the little spore which blights all the potatoes, the little gemmule which makes us philosophers or idiots. Every existence above a certain rank has its singular points: the higher the rank, the more of them. At these points, influences whose physical magnitude is too small to be taken account of by a finite being, may produce results of the greatest importance. All great results produced by human endeavour depend on taking advantage of these singular states when they occur.

> There is a tide in the affairs of men
> Which, taken at the flood, leads on to fortune.[20]

The man of tact says 'the right word at the right time', and, 'a word spoken in due season how good is it!' The man of no tact is like vinegar upon nitre when he sings his songs to a heavy heart. The ill-timed admonition hardens the heart, and the good resolution, taken when it is sure to be broken, becomes macadamised into pavement for the abyss.

It appears then that in our own nature there are more singular points – where prediction, except from absolutely perfect data, and guided by the omniscience of contingency, becomes impossible – than there are in any lower organisation. But singular points are by their very nature isolated, and form no appreciable fraction of the continuous course of our existence. Hence predictions of human conduct may be made in many cases. First, with respect to those who have no character at all, especially when considered in crowds, after the statistical method. Second, with respect to individuals of confirmed

---

(20) Shakespeare, *Julius Caesar*, Act IV, Scene iii, 217–18.

character, with respect to actions of the kind for which their character is confirmed.

If, therefore, those cultivators of physical science from whom the intelligent public deduce their conception of the physicist, and whose style is recognised as marking with a scientific stamp the doctrines they promulgate, are led in pursuit of the arcana of science to the study of the singularities and instabilities, rather than the continuities and stabilities of things, the promotion of natural knowledge may tend to remove that prejudice in favour of determinism which seems to arise from assuming that the physical science of the future is a mere magnified image of that of the past.

440

POSTCARD TO PETER GUTHRIE TAIT

12 FEBRUARY 1873

From the original in the University Library, Cambridge[1]

[Cambridge]

If there is any better way than by a long helix I should like to know it. It may be somewhat improved by connecting the ends by an iron bar, or by a tube as T does.

Begin with a thin tube (not of iron) put iron disks at both ends with holes in them. Wind the bobbin thus formed with wire, the diameter of the wire of different layers being proportional to the square root of the diameter of the layer and the resistances of the whole about equal to that of the battery & connexions. Then connect the iron disks by means of an iron bar outside the coil. This will make the external magnetic effect very small and throw the force on the space within the bobbin. Is it for rotation of plane of polarization?[2] I have not got to the Phil Mag[3] but will today. If you put 'immediate' or any other word beyond the direction on the obverse of a card you infringe H.M.'s gracious statutes.[4]

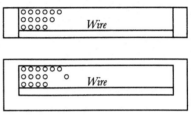

Figure 440,1

$$\frac{\partial p}{\partial t}$$

---

(1) ULC Add. MSS 7655, I, b/51.

(2) See Tait's experiments as reported in his paper 'On a possible influence of magnetism on the absorption of light, and some correlated subjects', *Proc. Roy. Soc. Edinb.*, **9** (1876): 118. On the Faraday magneto-optic effect see Number 434.

(3) In the February 1873 number of the *Philosophical Magazine* there was published a paper by Oliver Heaviside, 'On the best arrangement of Wheatstone's bridge for measuring a given resistance with a given galvanometer and battery', *Phil. Mag.*, ser. 4, **45** (1873): 114–20. There are notes by Maxwell on Heaviside's paper (ULC Add. MSS 7655, V, c/44) which outline his brief reference in the *Treatise* (2nd edn) §350. Of this paper Heaviside later recollected: 'Sent Maxwell a copy, and he noted it in his 2nd Edn'; from a Heaviside notebook cited by Bruce Hunt, *The Maxwellians* (Ithaca, NY/London, 1991): 58.

(4) See Number 356 esp. note (6).

441

LETTER TO PETER GUTHRIE TAIT
circa early 1873[1]

From the original in the University Library, Cambridge[2]

O T.! If a man will not read Lamé[3] how should he know whether a given thing is ν? Again, if a man throws in several triads of symbols & jumbles them up, pretending all the while that he has never heard of geometry, will not the broth be thick and slab?[4] If the problem is to be solved in this way by mere heckling of equations through ither[5] I doubt if you are the man for it as I observe that you always get on best when you let yourself and the public know what you are about.

I return your speculations on the $\phi(U\nu)\,ds$.[6] Observe, that in a magnet placed in a magnetic field the stress function is not in general self conjugate, for the elements are acted on by couples. But the $=^n$ of $=^m$ is very properly got as you get it.

Search for a physical basis for

$$S\,.\,\nabla^2\sigma\,\nabla\sigma\,^{(7)}$$

as a term of the energy developed in a medium by a variable displacement σ. When found make a note of, and apply to oil of turpentine, eau sucrée &c for it brings out the right sort of action on light of all colours.[8] But the mischief is $V\nabla\sigma$ which it is manifest can be produced without working any physical change inside a body. The very rotation of $\oplus$ produces it. Now $\nabla^2\sigma$ is a

---

(1) See notes (4) and (6).

(2) ULC Add. MSS 7655, I, b/103. Previously published in Knott, *Life of Tait*: 117, 147–8.

(3) Gabriel Lamé, *Leçons sur les Fonctions Inverses des Transcendantes et les Surfaces Isothermes* (Paris, 1857).

(4) Compare Maxwell's comments in his letter to Tait of 22 July 1873 (Number 468) on Tait's paper 'On orthogonal isothermal surfaces. Part I', *Trans. Roy. Soc. Edinb.*, **27** (1873): 105–23.

(5) ither: Scottish 'other' (*OED*). Knott (*Life of Tait*: 117n) comments: 'expressive Scottish phrase, meaning lack of method'.

(6) See P. G. Tait, 'Additional note on the strain function, &c', *Proc. Roy. Soc. Edinb.*, **8** (1873): 84–6, read 17 March 1873; ν is the normal vector of the surface element ds, U the versor (see Number 353 note (9)).

(7) See note (9).

(8) Maxwell is discussing the property of media 'to cause the plane of polarization to travel to the right or left, as the ray travels through the substance...[where] the property is independent of the direction of the ray within the medium, as in turpentine, solution of sugar, &c' (*Treatise*, **2**: 401 (§810)), in the context of his discussion of the Faraday magneto-optic effect.

vector.[9] Turn it alternately in the direction of $V\nabla\sigma$ & oppositely and you have increase & diminution of energy, & therefore a tendency to set like a magnet. The comfort is that $\nabla^2\sigma$ cannot subsist of itself.

Of course the resultant force on an element is of the form $V.\nabla^3\sigma$ and if σ is a function of z only, and $Sk\sigma = 0$

$$X = -\frac{d^3\eta}{dz^3}$$

$$Y = \frac{d^3\xi}{dz^3}.\quad{}^{(10)}$$

This is the only explanation of terms of this form in an isotropic or fluid medium and since the rotation of plane of polarization is roughly proportional to the inverse square of the wave-length,[11] terms of this form must exist.

$$\frac{dp}{dt}$$

---

(9) See Number 468, where Maxwell writes $\nabla^2\sigma.V\nabla\sigma = S\nabla^2\sigma\nabla\sigma$, where $V\nabla\sigma$ is the 'curl' of the vector function σ (see Number 434 note (5)).

(10) See Number 468 for Maxwell's discussion of these relations; and the *Treatise*, **2**: 413–14 (§830), in the context of his treatment of the Faraday magneto-optic effect.

(11) Émile Verdet, 'Recherches sur les propriétés optiques développées dans les corps transparents par l'action du magnétisme', *Ann. Chim. Phys.*, ser. 3, **69** (1863): 415–91.

REPORT ON A PAPER BY FREDERICK GUTHRIE[1] ON THE ELECTRICAL PROPERTIES OF HOT BODIES

circa 25 FEBRUARY 1873[2]

From the original in the Library of the Royal Society, London[3]

REPORT ON PROF. GUTHRIE'S PAPER 'ON A NEW RELATION BETWEEN HEAT AND ELECTRICITY'[4]

In this paper are described a number of interesting experiments on the electrical properties of hot bodies as compared with those of cold ones, and on differences in these properties depending on the sign of the electrification of the hot solid body.

It is to be hoped that the author intends more fully to work out the subject, as he has now acquired sufficient data to direct him in choosing the proper points for investigation.

The theoretical position from which the author starts, and that to which he thinks his results lead him, are nowhere very clearly stated, and the reader is apt to attribute to the author opinions, which are, very likely, not held by him. I am by no means certain, therefore, whether all the following remarks really apply to the paper or not.

(1) In the experiments, a hot body, a ball or a wire, is electrified either by conduction or induction. When the body is white hot, this electrification is rapidly discharged, and the electrification of the inducing or 'inductric' body is also discharged.

When the body is only red hot, its electrification is discharged when positive but retained when negative, and at a dull red heat it discharges a negatively charged body but only when itself uninsulated.

In the account of these experiments the readers attention is directed to the

---

(1) Professor at the School of Science, South Kensington 1869, FRS 1871 (Boase).

(2) According to the Royal Society's *Register of Papers Received* Guthrie's paper was referred to Maxwell on 22 February 1873, and to Jenkin on 27 February 1873.

(3) Royal Society, *Referees' Reports*, **7**: 245.

(4) Frederick Guthrie, 'On a new relation between Heat and Electricity' (Royal Society, AP. 55.7); the paper is endorsed 'Archives June 19/73'. The paper was received by the Royal Society on 10 January 1873, and read on 13 February 1873; see the abstract in *Proc. Roy. Soc.*, **21** (1873): 168–9. Guthrie published a revise of his paper, 'On a relation between heat and static electricity', *Phil. Mag.*, ser. 4, **46** (1873): 257–66.

hot body and to the other electrified body, but the dielectric body, in this case the air, between the solid bodies is not explicitly referred to; and even in the concluding section (§63) where the conception of a 'coercitive' force (analogous to the so called 'coercitive' or 'coercive' force of hard steel for magnetism)[5] is introduced, it is not clearly stated in what body this force is to be looked for. The reader is led to look for it rather in the hot ball (which is a good conductor, and therefore destitute of such a power) than in the surrounding air.[6]

The authors own opinion is, I suppose, that this coercitive force is a power possessed by air and other dielectrics of resisting electromotive force up to a certain point, at which the power gives way, and discharge occurs; and that when the dielectric is heated the electromotive force required to produce discharge is much less than when the dielectric is cold.

In this opinion I, for one, agree, and I should think it would find general acceptance among all those who have studied the effect of heat on dielectrics. Thus the discharging power of the heated air in the voltaic arc, of flames, of hot glass (see Buff's experiments)[7] of warm gutta-percha &c are well known.[8] The discharging of power of a glowing slow-match is employed in Sir W. Thomson's portable electrometer[9] for ascertaining the potential of the air at the place of the burning match.

For the more complete investigation of the phenomena I would suggest that the attention should be confined to observation of what takes place in the air near a hot electrified surface, and in particular

1   by observations in the dark, to ascertain if there is any luminous discharge or glow
2   by observing what currents of air are formed and whether an artificial wind increases or diminishes the effect

---

(5) A force which prevents the loss of magnetism once induced; see the *Treatise*, **2**: 44–5 (§424).

(6) Guthrie, 'On a new relation between Heat and Electricity', f. 30; 'There is, with frictional electricity, a force comparable to what is called "coercitive" force with magnetism. This force is no more electric tension than magnetic coercitivism is magnetic strength. Like magnetic coercitive force it is overcome by heat.... The hot body furnishes a field of open gates into which, out of which and in which the electricities move untrammelled.'

(7) Heinrich Buff, 'Ueber die electrische Leitfähigkeit des erhitzten Glases', *Annalen der Chemie und Pharmacie*, **90** (1854): 257–83.

(8) See the *Treatise*, **1**: 423–4 (§§367–8).

(9) See Thomson's 'Report on electrometers and electrostatic measurements', *Report of the Thirty-seventh Meeting of the British Association for the Advancement of Science* (London, 1868): 489–512, esp. 501–7 (= *Electrostatics and Magnetism*: 292–302 and Plate II, Figs. 8, 9 and 10).

3   by observing the effect of the introduction of dust smoke and flame into the surrounding air.

As a useful guide in such researches the XII & XIII series of Faraday's researches[10] may be studied.

According to Faradays experiments which are in many points confirmed by those of Wiedemann & Rühlmann[11] the electric discharge in air and other gases begins where the electromotive force is most able to break down the resistance. In homogeneous gases this will be at the surface of the smaller electrode, and in unequally heated gases at the hot electrode.

If the electromotive force diminishes rapidly as we recede from the electrode, the discharge goes only a short distance, and charges the air. The charged air is carried off by currents, and new air arrives to be charged again.

To trace the course of the charged air, and to detect it clinging to oppositely electrified surfaces is an interesting research which has been only partially carried out by Thomson.[12]

The next point is the different results according to the positive or negative electrification of the hot electrode. Faraday found (1501)[13] that a negative surface can discharge air at a tension a *little* lower than a positive surface, but that when discharge takes place *much more* passes each time from the positive than from the negative surface.

This refers to air at the ordinary temperature, and was found by Wiedemann & Rühlmann to be the case also at low pressure, and with other gases.

Professor Guthries experiments agree together in showing that a hot surface has the greatest discharging power when positively electrified.

The interpretation of these results must, I think, be sought for in some difference in the nature of the dielectric at the opposite electrodes, produced by the action of the electromotive force. We know that in ordinary electrolytes the matter in contact with the + electrode differs from that in contact with

---

(10) Michael Faraday, 'Experimental researches in electricity. – Twelfth series. On induction', *Phil. Trans.*, **128** (1838): 83–123 (= *Electricity*, **1**: 417–72); Faraday, 'Experimental researches in electricity. – Thirteenth series. On induction', *Phil. Trans.*, **128** (1838): 125–68 (= *Electricity*, **1**: 473–532).

(11) G. Wiedemann and R. Rühlmann, 'Über den Durchgang der Electricität durch Gase', *Berichte über die Verhandlungen der Königlich Sächsischen Gesellschaft der Wissenschaften zu Leipzig, math.-phys. Klasse*, **23** (1871): 333–85. See the *Treatise*, **1**: 424–5 (§370).

(12) William Thomson, 'Measurement of the electromotive force required to produce a spark in air between parallel metal plates at different distances', *Proc. Roy. Soc.*, **10** (1860): 326–38 (= *Electrostatics and Magnetism*: 247–59).

(13) Faraday, *Electricity*, **1**: 479; and see the *Treatise*, **1**: 425 (§370).

the − electrode, and in this way one electrode may be more favourable to discharge than the other. We also know from Sir B. C. Brodie's experiments[14] that an action, apparently electrolytic, occurs in several gases.

I make these remarks because in §22 the author uses language about different kinds of electricity which, at least at first sight, seems intelligible only on the hypothesis that the crudest form of the 'Two Fluid' theory is a physical fact; and that the operation of charging a body with a unit of + electricity can be physically distinguished from the act of removing a unit of − electricity from the same body.[15]

From what I have said, it is manifest that I do not agree with the title of the paper as a description of its contents. The experiments relate to the effects of heat on air as altering its electrical properties, particularly its insulating power. I cannot therefore recommend the present paper to be printed in the Transactions, though I think that the research, if successfully carried out, might furnish matter for a very valuable communication.[16]

J. CLERK MAXWELL

---

(14) B. C. Brodie, 'An experimental inquiry on the action of electricity on gases. I. On the action of electricity on oxygen', *Phil. Trans.*, **162** (1872): 435–84.

(15) Guthrie, 'On a new relation between Heat and Electricity', f. 8; 'The whole aspect of the phenomena with hot iron balls which we have hitherto been considering, is of a nature to convince the actual experimenter that in all the above cases the collapse of the leaves [of an electroscope] is due to the release of their prevalent electricity rather than to the accession of electricity of the opposite kind.' Guthrie retained this paragraph (with only trivial verbal changes) in his 'On a relation between heat and static electricity': 260.

(16) In a letter to Stokes of 27 May 1873 (Royal Society, *Referees' Reports*, **7**: 244) Fleeming Jenkin was severely condemnatory of Guthrie's paper: 'I consider it unsuitable for publication. It contains numerous experiments all of which are clearly explicable on well established principles.... Prof^r Guthrie's reasoning and explanations are quite without value and I think a judicious friend should give him a hint to withdraw the paper or only retain so much of it as is purely experimental – a short abstract of this is all that should ever be published.'

443

POSTCARD TO PETER GUTHRIE TAIT

3 MARCH 1873
From the original in the National Library of Scotland, Edinburgh[1]

[Cambridge]

O T'. If, in your surface-integrals,[2] ds is an element of surface is not ds a vector? and does not multiplication by $U\nu$[3] scalarize it? In your next edition tell us if you consider an element of surface otherwise than as $V\,d\alpha\,d\beta$ where α and β are vectors from the origin to a point in the surface defined by the parameters a, b.

Here the element of surface is a vector whose tensor is the area and whose versor is $U\nu$.[4] These things I have written that our geometrical notions may in Quaternions run perpetual circle, multiform and mix and nourish all things. Such ideas are slowly percolating through the strata of Cartesianism trilinearity and determinism that overlie what we are pleased to call our minds. I hope you will read us a good rede in May.[5] Give it us hot and strong for our brains are soft and our hearts are hard and we need packing needles and saltpetre.

What day of May and what title?[6]

$$\frac{dp}{dt}$$

---

(1) National Library of Scotland, MS 1004 f. 42. Previously published (in part) in Knott, *Life of Tait*: 151.

(2) P. G. Tait, 'Additional note on the strain function, &c', *Proc. Roy. Soc. Edinb.*, **8** (1873): 84–6, read 17 March 1873.

(3) See Number 441 esp. note (6).   (4) See Number 353 note (9).

(5) Tait's Rede Lecture at Cambridge.

(6) Tait's Rede Lecture on 'Thermo-electricity' was read on 23 May 1873, and published in *Nature*, **8** (1873): 86–8, 122–4.

444

POSTCARD TO PETER GUTHRIE TAIT

5 MARCH 1873

From the original in the University Library, Cambridge[1]

[Text written in mirror-reversed script:]

Why have *you* forgotten to send
Alice.[2] We remain in Wonderland
till she appears.
Till then no more from
yours truly
$$\frac{dp}{dt}$$

The text reads:
'Why have *you* forgotten to send Alice. We remain in Wonderland till she appears.
Till then no more from

yours truly

$$\frac{dp}{dt}'.$$

(1) ULC Add. MSS 7655, I, b/52.
(2) Lewis Carroll, *Through the Looking-glass, and what Alice found there* (London, 1872).

445

LETTER TO PETER GUTHRIE TAIT

10 MARCH 1873

From the original in the University Library, Cambridge[1]

11 Scroope Terrace
10 March 1873

O T′[2]

Θαγξ φορ Αλλες.

(1) I have no Assistant. If I can do you any service well & good, if not, why not?

(2) Prof Liveing[3] will lend you his bags, give you his gases and furnish you with lime light. If you are particular about your lantern bring it yourself like Guy Fawkes or the man in the Moon.

The gases will go for half an hour if you want them for longer say so.

Bring your own galvanometer.

3 Thermopylæ exist but Peltier[4] only in the form of a repulsive electrometer and the effet Thomson[5] is an 'effect defective'.

The Senate House is a place to write in, to graduate in and to vote in. The Public Orator I believe can speak in it provided he employs the Latin Tongue.

What those venerable walls would say if the vernacular were sounded within them I dare not even think. If you have a good audience there will not be much echo from Geo II or Pitt[6] and if you erect a lofty platform the light spot on the screen, and the under side of your table may be seen by all.

5 If you do your $\Theta.H.$[7] as you did your Quaternions to the British Asses[8] you will do very well always remembering that to speak familiarly of a 2nd Law as of a thing known for some years, to men of culture who have never even heard of a 1st Law, may arouse sentiments unfavourable to patient attention.

---

(1) ULC Add. MSS 7655, I, b/52A. Previously published (in part) in Knott, *Life of Tait*: 251–2.

(2) On Tait's Rede Lecture on 'Thermo-electricity'; see Number 443 esp. note (6).

(3) G. D. Liveing, Professor of Chemistry at Cambridge (Venn).

(4) See Number 428 note (9).

(5) See Number 428 note (10).

(6) Cambridge University buildings near the Senate House.

(7) See note (2).

(8) Tait's 1871 address to Section A of the British Association; see the *Report of the Forty-first Meeting of the British Association for the Advancement of Science; held at Edinburgh in August 1871* (London, 1872), part 2: 1–8.

Your prop. about a distribution on a sphere is right. It is equivalent in the 1st instance to the distribution due a uniform shell of radius a which latter produces an attraction towards the centre of the shell or towards its image according as the point is outside or inside the sphere.

Both Moral & Intellectual Entropy are noble subjects though the dictum of Pecksniff concerning the idea of Todgers be unknown to me and not easily verified.$^{(9)}$

I do not know much about reversible operations in morals. The science or practice depends chiefly on the existence of singular points in the curve of existence at which influences, physically insensible produce great results. The man of tact says the right word at the right time, and a word spoken in due season how good is it? The man of no tact is like vinegar upon natron when he sings his songs to a heavy heart. The ill timed admonition only hardens the conscience, and the good resolution, made just when it is sure to be broken, becomes macadamized into pavement for the abyss.*

'καλὸν δὲ τὸ ζηλοῦσθαι εν καλῶ πάντοτε'.$^{(10)}$

Yrs $\frac{\partial p}{\partial t}$

---

* Sermons Vol III$^{(11)}$

---

(9) Mr Pecksniff and Mrs Todgers are characters in Dickens' *Martin Chuzzlewit*. Tait may have been alluding to Pecksniff's exclamation (in Chap. 10): 'O my friend, Mrs Todgers! To barter away that precious jewel, self-esteem, and cringe to any mortal creature – for eighteen shillings a week!'

(10) The sentence ('The emulation of a good man is always a good thing') appears twice in the writings of John Chrysostom, in his commentaries on 'Galatians' and 'Hebrews'. (Source: 'Ibycus' and with the assistance of the Department of Classics, Harvard University.)

(11) Possibly: Joseph Butler's sermon 'Upon human nature'; see *The Works of... Joseph Butler*, 2 vols. (Oxford, 1849–50), 2: 29–37. See also Number 439.

446

POSTCARD TO PETER GUTHRIE TAIT

12 MARCH 1873

From the original in the University Library, Cambridge[1]

[Cambridge]

I hope you have my letter on ways and means.[2] I shall do the best I can to make it work. Only tell me the time of your appearing that we may prepare our arches and send round to them that are bidden.

$$\frac{\partial p}{\partial t}$$

---

(1) ULC Add. MSS 7655, I, b/53.
(2) Number 445.

447

REPORT ON A PAPER BY JAMES JAGO[1] ON EXPERIMENTS ON VISION

circa 24 MARCH 1873[2]

From the original in the Library of the Royal Society, London[3]

REPORT ON Dr JAGO'S PAPER ON 'VISIBLE DIRECTION'[4]

This paper contains a description of a number of interesting experiments on vision when one or both eyes are subjected to pressure. I have found that my own sensations agree with the description given in the paper in those cases which I have tried. I have not, however, in any case, obtained a displacement of 30° by means of pressure, as I was unwilling to employ the requisite degree of force. Nevertheless I have no doubt of the correctness of the description of most of the phenomena.[5]

It is when the author draws his conclusions that I fail to follow him. I have been unable to find the slightest connexion between the experiments and the doctrine finally laid down – that visible direction is determined by the direction of the optic nerve where it enters the eye.[6] On the contrary, all the

---

(1) St John's 1835, MD Oxford 1859, FRS 1870 (Venn).

(2) According to the Royal Society's *Register of Papers Received* Jago's paper was referred to Maxwell on 21 March 1873, and to Burdon-Sanderson on 26 March 1873.

(3) Royal Society, *Referees' Reports*, **7**: 247.

(4) James Jago, 'Visible direction. Being an elementary contribution to the study of monocular and binocular vision' (Royal Society, AP. 55.8). The paper was received by the Royal Society on 12 February 1873, and read on 13 March 1873; see the abstract in *Proc. Roy. Soc.*, **21** (1873): 213–17. In the archives of the Royal Society there is a letter from Jago to T. H. Huxley (Secretary of the Royal Society) of 11 March 1873 (Royal Society, AP. 55.9) excusing his absence when the paper was read, and enclosing some supplementary material (AP. 55.10). The paper is endorsed 'Archives May 15/73'.

(5) In a report dated 12 May 1873 (Royal Society, *Referees' Reports*, **7**: 246) John Scott Burdon-Sanderson (Professor of Practical Physiology and Histology at University College, London 1870, FRS 1867 (*DNB*)) disagreed. He reported that: '[Jago] considers it possible by means of the "wedge" to press on the posterior half of the eyeball so as to cause it to move forwards. I have endeavoured to perform the manipulation as directed by the Author, and have thus satisfied myself (1) that it is not possible by these means to press upon the posterior half of the eye unless an amount of violence is used which I cannot suppose that the Author contemplated; and (2) that the principal and only important effect of the manipulation is to *deform* the eyeball, the amount of *displacement* produced being very inconsiderable.'

(6) Jago, 'Visible direction', f. 15; 'Visible direction is a function of the terminal direction of the Optic nerve.'

phenomena described seem to agree with the doctrine that in forming our opinion of the position of bodies in space we are guided chiefly by the muscular sensations arising from our efforts to look directly at these bodies with one or with both eyes.[7]

D[r] Jago, indeed, contributes additional evidence of the fact that the object we look at has its image on a definite point of the retina so that we 'bisect' the object looked at in the same sense that the astronomer 'bisects' a star. He has also shown that the power of keeping the axis of collimation (that is the line joining the optic centre of the eye with the centre of the 'foramen centrale')[8] fixed on an object is not much interfered with by lateral pressure, and that in fact we may continue to look steadily at the same object while the pressure is being applied.[9] But he does not seem to have noticed what happens to the free eye during the effort of the pressed eye to maintain its parallelism. I find that the free eye moves in the same direction in which the muscles of the pressed eye must act to maintain the pressed eye in its position, or in other words in the opposite direction to that in which the applied pressure tends to turn the pressed eye.

This arises, I suppose, from the habit we have of working the muscles of both eyes at the same time, so as to keep the eyes parallel.

The subject of visible direction, or the conclusions we draw as to the position of objects in space, is rather psychological than physiological and does not appear to be a strong point with our author.[10] He is accurate with respect to the theory of corresponding points of the two retinæ, which is a purely optical question, but seems to have a half-expressed opinion concerning the relation of the position of certain fibres of the optic nerve to the position we attribute to objects seen by means of these fibres.

With respect to the final doctrine – of visible direction as determined by the direction of the extremity of the optic nerve, D[r] Jago tells us that the optic nerve itself cannot be excited by acting on points in its course and it has yet

---

(7) Hermann Helmholtz, 'On the normal motions of the human eye in relation to binocular vision', *Proc. Roy. Soc.*, **13** (1864): 186–99; Helmholtz, *Handbuch der physiologischen Optik* (Leipzig, 1867): 457–86. See Number 279.

(8) A depression of the retina of the eye. For Maxwell's discussion (with reference to colour vision and Haidinger's brushes) see Volume I: 201, 318, 636, 652.

(9) Jago, 'Visible direction', ff. 4–5, where he declares this 'fact' to be 'fundamental to the inquiry'.

(10) Compare Burdon-Sanderson's comment (see note (5)): 'the Author regards the apparent direction of an object as dependent on the "flexure" of the terminal portion of the optic nerve. I object to this hypothesis... if there were any such flexure as the Author supposes it would be entirely contrary to physiological experience to suppose that it would have any effect on the character of the impressions conveyed by the nerve to the centre'.

to be shown that it has any other function than that of transmitting impressions received on the retina, and in particular that it shares the power which the muscles undoubtedly possess, of acquainting us with their state of contraction or relaxation. The muscles of the eyes, being used for no other purpose than to regulate the position of the eyes, have all their associations connected with visual impressions; and the mode, (well described by the author of the paper) in which we *feel* our way to the stereoscopic union of two pictures, shows the importance of the muscular sense in the act of vision.

I think, therefore, that before transferring to the optic nerve a function hitherto supposed to be confined to the nerves of muscles, we require more evidence than is here presented; and I do not think the paper as it stands should be printed in the Philosophical Transactions.

JAMES CLERK MAXWELL

448

LETTERS TO WILLIAM THOMSON
25 MARCH 1873[1]
From the originals in the University Library, Glasgow[2]

[1]   Observe the address $\begin{cases} \text{Glenlair} \\ \text{Dalbeattie} \end{cases}$

25 March 1873

Dear Sir William

I am requested by the Board of Mathematical Studies to ascertain from you, whether, in the event of your being nominated by the Board as Additional Examiner for Mathematical Honours in 1874, and the nomination confirmed by the Senate, you would undertake the duties of the office. (See Cambridge Calendar p26).[3]

                                                      Yours truly
                                                  J. CLERK MAXWELL
                                                           President

[2]   The Chancellor is now fairly engaged to collect the Cavendish papers.[4] I think he will give them to the University Library. I am just going to walk the plank with them in the interest of physical science.

I am going to Glenlair tomorrow which accounts for the false date of my formal epistle.

I expect my book will reach you this week.[5] There has been some costiveness about the binding, as it was bound to be out some time ago.

                                                                    $\dfrac{dp}{dt}$

---

(1) See Maxwell's appended note *infra*.

(2) Glasgow University Library, Kelvin Papers, M 33, 34.

(3) Thomson accepted the appointment; see *The Cambridge University Calendar for the Year 1874* (Cambridge, 1874): 26, 163.

(4) See Number 435.

(5) According to the Clarendon Press advertisement in *Nature*, **7** (27 March 1873): cv, the *Treatise* was published that week.

449

FROM A LETTER TO LEWIS CAMPBELL

3 APRIL 1873

From Campbell and Garnett, *Life of Maxwell*[1]

Glenlair
Dalbeattie
3 April 1873

The roof of the Devonshire Laboratory is being put on, and we hope to have some floors in by May, and the contractors cleared out by October.[2] We are busy electing School Boards here.[3] The religious difficulty is unknown here. The chief party is that which insists on keeping down the rates; no other platform will do. All candidates must show the retrenchment ticket.

The Cambridge Philosophical Society have been entertained by Mr Paley on Solar Myths, Odusseus as the Setting Sun, etc.[4] Your Trachiniæ[5] is rather in that style, but I think Middlemarch[6] is not a mere unconscious myth, as the Odyssey was to its author, but an elaborately conscious one, in which all the characters are intended to be astronomical or meteorological.

Rosamond is evidently the Dawn. By her fascinations she draws up into her embrace the rising sun, represented as the Healer from one point of view, and the Opener of Mysteries from another; his name, Lyd Gate, being compounded of two nouns, both of which signify something which opens, as the eye-lids of the morn, and the gates of day. But as the sun-god ascends, the

---

(1) *Life of Maxwell*: 385–7.   (2) See Numbers 463 and 464.
(3) Following the Elementary Education Act of 1870.
(4) F. A. Paley, 'On the name "Odusseus" signifying "setting sun" and the Odyssey as a solar myth', *Proc. Camb. Phil. Soc.*, **2** (1873): 295–7; read 17 February 1873. Paley deployed F. Max Müller's theory of myths as narratives deriving from words originally descriptive of the sun; see note (8) and F. M. Turner, *The Greek Heritage in Victorian Britain* (New Haven/London, 1981): 104–12. See also Number 359 note (4).
(5) See *Sophocles. The Text of the Seven Plays*, ed. Lewis Campbell (Oxford, 1873). In his subsequent edition of Sophocles's 'Trachiniae' in his *Sophocles. The Plays and Fragments*, 2 vols. (Oxford, 1871–81), **2**: 240, Campbell remarked: 'Whatever truth may underlie this theory [that the tale of Hercules is a solar myth], it can have no bearing, as Mr Paley would be the first to admit, on the interpretation of the Trachiniae.'
(6) George Eliot's novel *Middlemarch, A Study of Provincial Life*, 4 vols. (London/Edinburgh, 1871–2). For comment on Maxwell's 'usual brilliant immediacy' in his analysis of *Middlemarch* in relation to solar mythology, see Gillian Beer, '"The death of the sun": Victorian solar physics and solar myth', in J. B. Bullen, ed., *The Sun is God: Painting, Literature and Mythology in the Nineteenth Century* (Oxford, 1989): 159–80, on 174.

same clouds which emblazoned his rising, absorb all his beams, and put a stop to the early promise of enlightenment, so that he, the ascending sun, disappears from the heavens. But the Rosa Munda of the dawn (see Vision of Sin) reappears as the Rosa Mundi in the evening, along with her daughters ♀ and ☿,⁽⁷⁾ in the chariot of the setting sun, who is also a healer, but not an enlightener.⁽⁸⁾

Dorothea, on the other hand, the goddess of gifts, represents the other half of the revolution. She is at first attracted by and united to the fading glories of the days that are no more, but after passing, as the title of the last book expressly tells us, 'from sunset to sunrise',⁽⁹⁾ we find her in union with the pioneer of the coming age, the editor.

Her sister Celia, the Hollow One, represents the vault of the midnight sky, and the nothingness of things.

There is no need to refer to Nicolas Bulstrode, who evidently represents the Mithraic mystery, or to the kindly family of Garth, representing the work of nature under the rays of the sun, or to the various clergymen and doctors, who are all planets. The whole thing is, and is intended to be, a solar myth from beginning to end.

---

(7) Venus and Mercury.

(8) In his essay on 'Comparative mythology' Friedrich Max Müller argued that 'Mythology is only a dialect, an ancient form of language'; see his *Chips from a German Workshop*, **2** (London, 1867): 143. The theory of mythology as deriving from words descriptive of the sun is central to his argument: 'The simple story of nature which inspired the early poet.... When he was the Sun kissing the Dawn, he dreamt of days and joys gone for ever. And when the Dawn trembled, and grew pale, and departed, and when the Sun seemed to look for her... the Sun seemed to die away in the far West... the tragedy of nature... is the lifespring of all the tragedies of the ancient world.... The Sun freshens the Dawn, and dies at the end of the day, according to an inexorable fate, and bewailed by the whole of nature.... There was but one name by which they could express love... it was the blush of the day, the rising of the sun.... And this... is fully confirmed by an analysis of ancient speech.'; see *Chips from a German Workshop*, **2**: 106–8, 129–30.

(9) *Middlemarch*, Book Eight: 'Sunset and Sunrise'.

REVIEW OF FLEEMING JENKIN, *ELECTRICITY AND MAGNETISM*[1]

circa APRIL 1873

From *Nature* (15 May 1873)[2]

ELECTRICITY AND MAGNETISM. BY FLEEMING JENKIN, F.R.S.S.L. AND E., M.I.C.E., PROFESSOR OF ENGINEERING IN THE UNIVERSITY OF EDINBURGH. (LONDON: LONGMANS AND CO., 1873)[3]

The author of this text-book tells us with great truth that at the present time there are two sciences of electricity – one that of the lecture-room and the popular treatise; the other that of the testing-office and the engineer's specification. The first deals with sparks and shocks which are seen and felt, the other with currents and resistances to be measured and calculated. The popularity of the one science depends on human curiosity; the diffusion of the other is a result of the demand for electricians as telegraph engineers.

The text-book before us, which is the work of an engineer eminent in telegraphy, is designed to teach the practical science of electricity and magnetism, by setting before the student as early as possible the measurable quantities of the science, and giving him complete instructions for actually measuring them.

The difference between the electricity of the schools and of the testing office has been mainly brought about by the absolute necessity in practice for definite measurement. The lecturer is content to say, under such and such circumstances, a current flows or a resistance is increased. The practical electrician must know how much resistance, or he knows nothing; the difference is analogous to that between quantitative and qualitative analysis.[4]

It is not without great effort that a science can pass out of one stage of its existence into another. To abandon one hypothesis in order to embrace another is comparatively easy, but to surrender our belief in a mysterious agent, making itself visible in brilliant experiments, and probably capable of accounting for whatever cannot be otherwise explained; and to accept the notion of electricity as a measurable commodity, which may be supplied at a

---

(1) The review is anonymous, but the style and content point strongly to Maxwell as the reviewer: but the *Nature* archives cannot confirm this attribution.
(2) *Nature*, **8** (1873): 42–3.
(3) See Number 385.
(4) Fleeming Jenkin, *Electricity and Magnetism* (London, 1873): vii.

potential of so many Volts at so much a Farad,⁽⁵⁾ is a transformation not to be effected without a pang.

It is true that in the last century Henry Cavendish led the way in the science of electrical measurement,⁽⁶⁾ and Coulomb invented experimental methods of great precision.⁽⁷⁾ But these were men whose scientific ardour far surpassed that of ordinary mortals, and for a long time their results remained dormant on the shelves of libraries. Then came Poisson⁽⁸⁾ and the mathematicians,⁽⁹⁾ who raised the science of electricity to a height of analytical splendour, where it was even more inaccessible than before to the uninitiated.

And now that electrical knowledge has acquired a commercial value, and must be supplied to the telegraphic world in whatever form it can be obtained, we are perhaps in some danger of forgetting the debt we owe to those mathematicians who, from the mass of their uninterpretable symbolical expressions, picked out such terms as 'potential',[10] 'electromotive force'[11] and 'capacity',[12] representing qualities which we now know to be capable of direct measurement, and which we are beginning to be able to explain to persons not trained in high mathematics.

Prof. Jenkin has, we think, made great progress in the important work of reducing the cardinal conceptions of electromagnetism to their most intelligible form, and presenting them to the student in their true connection.

The distinction between free electricity and latent, bound, combined, or dissimulated electricity, which occurs so frequently, especially in continental works on electricity, is not, so far as we can see, even alluded to in these pages; so that the student who takes Prof. Jenkin as his sole guide will not have his mind infected with a set of notions which did much harm in their day. On the other hand, terms which are really scientific – the use of which has led to a clearer understanding of the subject – are carefully defined and rendered familiar by well-chosen illustrations.

---

(5) On these terms see Numbers 415, 418, 420.

(6) Compare the reference to Cavendish in Maxwell's lecture 'On Faraday's Lines of Force' (Number 437); and his draft letter to the Duke of Devonshire on Cavendish's electrical manuscripts (Number 435).

(7) See Volume I: 354.   (8) See Volume I: 354.

(9) A. M. Ampère, F. E. Neumann and W. E. Weber: see Volume I: 255, 262, 305.

(10) George Green, *An Essay on the Application of Mathematical Analysis to the Theories of Electricity and Magnetism* (Nottingham, 1828); and C. F. Gauss, 'Allgemeine Lehrsätze...', in *Resultate aus den Beobachtungen des magnetischen Vereins in Jahre 1839* (Leipzig, 1840): 1–51. See Volume I: 258n, 261–2n.

(11) Franz Neumann, 'Die mathematischen Gesetze der inducirten elektrischen Ströme', *Physikalische Abhandlungen der Königlichen Akademie der Wissenschaften zu Berlin*, Aus dem Jahre 1845 (Berlin, 1847): 1–87.   (12) On Cavendish see Number 435 note (10).

Thus we find that men of the most profound scientific acquirements were labouring forty years ago to discover the relation between the nature of a wire and the strength of the current induced in it. By the introduction of the term 'electromotive force' to denote that which produces or tends to produce a current, the phenomena can now be explained to the mere beginner by saying that the electromotive force is determined by the alterations of the state of the circuit in the field, and is independent of the nature of the wire, while the current produced is measured by the electromotive force divided by the resistance of the circuit. To impress on the mind of the student terms which lead him in the right track, and to keep out of his sight those which have only led our predecessors, if not ourselves, astray, is an aim which Prof. Jenkin seems to have kept always in view.

To the critical student of text-books in general, there may appear to be a certain want of order and method in the first part of this treatise, the different facts being all thrown into the student's mind at once, to be defined and arranged in the chapters which follow. But when we consider the multiplicity of the connexions among the parts of electrical science, and the supreme importance of never losing sight of electrical science as a whole, while engaged in the study of each of its branches, we shall see that this little book, though it may appear at first a mighty maze, is not without a plan, and though it may be difficult to determine in which chapter we are to look for any particular statement, we have an excellent index at the end to which we may refer.

The descriptions of scientific and telegraphic instruments have all the completeness and more than the conciseness which we should look for from a practical engineer, and in a small compass contain a great deal not to be found in other books. The preface contains an outline of the whole subject, traced in a style so vigorous, that we feel convinced that the author could, with a little pains bestowed here and there, increase the force of his reasoning by several 'Volts', and at the same time diminish by an 'Ohm' or two the apparent stiffness of some of the paragraphs, so as to render the book more suitable to the capacities of the 'Microfarads'[13] of the present day.

---

(13) See Number 420 esp. note (8); on a 'microfarad' see Jenkin, *Electricity and Magnetism*: 159.

451

LETTER TO PETER GUTHRIE TAIT

2 MAY 1873

From the original in the University Library, Cambridge[1]

> 11 Scroope Terrace
> Cambridge
> 2 May 1873

Dear Tait

Will you dine with us on Friday 23rd May at 7 oClock?[2] or on Saturday 24th (Victoria Reg. et Vid).[3]

What stay do you make in Cambridge? Can I do anything for you in the way of preparation percunctation[4] or operation?

> Yours truly
> J. CLERK MAXWELL

---

(1) ULC Add. MSS 7655, I, b/54.
(2) The day of Tait's Rede Lecture: see Number 443 note (6).
(3) Queen Victoria's birthday.
(4) *viz*, delay; see Number 465 note (8) and *OED* 'percunctorily'.

452

LETTER TO PETER GUTHRIE TAIT

7 MAY 1873
From the original in the University Library, Cambridge[1]

11 Scroope Terrace
Cambridge
May 7 1873

Dear Tait

It will give Mrs Maxwell and myself much pleasure if you and Mrs Tait will favour us with your company at dinner on Friday 23rd May at 7 o'Clock p.m.[2]

You can have bags of O and H (separate) about 2 cubic feet or more of each. You would have to get a Grace of the Senate if you wished Knallgas[3] and the Coroner would be in attendance outside with the Curator of the Anatomical Museum.

I am going to ascertain the facilities for the introduction of gas for your Bunsen. You can always get up a good heat with H & O.

There are a couple of concave mirrors for radiant heat which will be scoured up.

The size of diagrams is determined by that of their minimum visible which should not be less than 1.5 inch for a symbol 0.5 for the breadth of a line.

A thermoelectric diagram of $4^{ft} \times 6^{ft}$ would I think be visible.

The V.C. is no judge of such matters as the relative value of written forms committal and extempore. You should rather ask a Presbytery or the congregation of Kilmalcolm. You may, if you please, print it off first and then give us something quite different vivâ voce.

Do you bring a divided scale for the light spot to wag on?

What do you mean by referring to Dr Redtail[4] as an 'effusion'? I am indeed but slightly acquainted with him nevertheless I never doubted that he came into existence by ordinary generation. How then was he 'effunded'? And how have I, still in life I hope, passed into his Form?

Mrs Maxwell desires me to say that if Mrs Tait comes with you she would be happy if you would stay with us and so escape the rigour of those statutes which forbid ladies staying in College.

Yours truly
J. CLERK MAXWELL

---

(1) ULC Add. MSS 7655, I, b/55.   (2) See Number 451 note (2).
(3) A detonating mixture of oxygen and hydrogen.
(4) Sir William Thomson's parrot; see S. P. Thompson, *The Life of William Thomson Baron Kelvin of Largs*, 2 vols. (London, 1910), **2**: 630–1, 634.

453
LETTER TO GEORGE GABRIEL STOKES
13 MAY 1873
From the original in the Library of the Royal Society, London[1]

11 Scroope Terrace
Cambridge
13 May 1873

My dear Stokes

I have read Sir George Airy's 'Magnetical Observations on the Britannia and Conway Tubular Iron Bridges'.[2]

I consider that these observations supply valuable data with respect to the distribution of magnetism in any iron structure of great size and tolerably regular form and that besides their present value these observations may be found valuable hereafter in determining the question of the permanence or the gradual alteration of the properties of iron structures exposed to great strain.[3]

I therefore recommend this paper to be printed in the Philosophical Transactions of the Royal Society.

Yours very truly
J. CLERK MAXWELL

---

(1) Royal Society, *Referees' Reports*, **7**: 221.

(2) George Biddell Airy, 'Magnetical observations in the Britannia and Conway tubular iron bridges', *Phil. Trans.*, **163** (1873): 331–9. The paper was received by the Royal Society on 12 October 1872 (with a 'Postscript' received on 22 October), and read on 19 December 1872; see the abstract in *Proc. Roy. Soc.*, **21** (1872): 85–6.

(3) Airy recorded an anomalous reading for the tube of the Britannia Bridge on the Anglesey side of the Menai Strait. As he recorded in the 'Postscript' to his paper, subsequent inquiry led him to attribute the anomaly to an accident which had occurred during the construction of the bridge; see Airy, 'Magnetical observations': 337–9. In a letter to Stokes of 21 April 1873 (Royal Society, *Referees' Reports*, **7**: 220) William Thomson commented: 'The point referred to in the Postscript seems to me particularly interesting and valuable. I think there can be little if any doubt but that the cause of the peculiarity of magnetic action found in the Anglesea Water tube is there truly explained. This very remarkable discovery is a lesson of faith and practice to all investigators:– never carelessly or unconscientiously to slur over any "anomaly".'

454

LETTER TO PETER GUTHRIE TAIT

15 MAY 1873

From the original in the University Library, Cambridge[1]

> 11 Scroope Terrace
> Cambridge
> 15 May 1873

My dear Tait

If you wish a lime light and a thermoelectric pile on which you can rely you had better fetch them with you. You can get gas bags here.[2]

You can have a tripod erected steady enough for your galvanometer but you have given no specification as to height.

Also if you wish the upper windows of the Senate House pasted up with brown paper it shall be done, on demand.

> Yours truly
> J. CLERK MAXWELL

---

(1) ULC Add. MSS 7655, I, b/56.

(2) See Numbers 445 and 452.

455

REPORT ON A PAPER BY DUGALD M'KICHAN[1] ON THE DETERMINATION OF THE NUMBER OF ELECTROSTATIC UNITS IN THE ELECTROMAGNETIC UNIT OF ELECTRICITY

circa 20 MAY 1873[2]

From the original in the Library of the Royal Society, London[3]

REPORT ON M^r M'KICHAN'S PAPER
DETERMINATION OF THE NUMBER OF ELECTROSTATIC UNITS IN THE ELECTROMAGNETIC UNIT[4]

The aim of the experiments described in this paper is the determination of a physical constant of the nature of a velocity, the absolute magnitude of which is independent of the particular system of units of time and space used in the experiments. The scientific importance of the determination is of the highest order. Not only does it enable us to pass from any measurement made on the electrostatic system to the corresponding one on the electromagnetic system but it enables us to compare our standard measures with what we have great reason to believe is one of the most permanent magnitudes in nature.

The difficulty of the investigation arises from the largeness of the ratio to be measured. To do this by few steps requires batteries of great electromotive force, condensers of great capacity, wires sometimes of great resistance, and sometimes of great conductivity, and in all cases electrometers and galvanometers of great delicacy. To divide the measurements into convenient stages requires the construction of a number of new instruments, none of which can be perfected without much time and trouble.

The determination made by M^r M'Kichan depends on three kinds of data,

---

(1) A Glasgow student of William Thomson's (who communicated the paper to the Royal Society); see S. P. Thompson, *The Life of William Thomson, Baron Kelvin of Largs*, 2 vols. (London, 1910), **1**: 525, **2**: 1026–7.

(2) According to the Royal Society's *Register of Papers Received* M'Kichan's paper was referred to Maxwell on 16 May 1873, and to Jenkin on 22 May 1873.

(3) Royal Society, *Referees' Reports*, **7**: 249.

(4) Dugald M'Kichan, 'Determination of the number of electrostatic units in the electromagnetic unit made in the Physical Laboratory of Glasgow University', *Phil. Trans.*, **163** (1873): 409–27. The paper was received by the Royal Society on 15 April 1873, and read on 15 May 1873; see the abstract in *Proc. Roy. Soc.*, **21** (1873): 290–2.

derived from the Electrometer, the Electrodynamometer, and the British Association's Unit of Resistance respectively.

It differs from the method described by myself in 1868[5] in using separate methods to determine the electrostatic and the electromagnetic effects of the same current, instead of balancing the one force against the other, as in my experiment.

This involves the use of Sir W. Thomsons Absolute Electrometer[6] and of his admirable heterostatic method, in which the electromotive force to be measured is deduced from the difference of two distances between the attracted surfaces and does not require an exact measurement of either.[7] This gives a very great advantage over the method used by me, which required the determination, always very precarious, of the absolute distance between two nearly parallel surfaces, one of which was freely suspended.

The electromagnetic measurement was also performed by means of an instrument capable of far more precise measurement than that which I employed.[8]

The other datum used in the calculation was the B.A. Unit as determined in 1864.[9] Any correction hereafter discovered to be necessary in the received value of this unit must be also applied to the number arrived at in this paper.

All things considered I regard this investigation as probably far more accurate than any yet made, and that both the matter and the method render the paper worthy of a place in the Philosophical Transactions.[10]

J. CLERK MAXWELL

---

(5) Number 289.

(6) See Number 289 note (11). M'Kichan employed Thomson's 'new absolute electrometer'; see Thomson's supplementary note ('added May 1870') to his 'Report on electrometers and electrostatic measurements' (1867) in his *Reprint of Papers on Electrostatics and Magnetism* (London, 1872): 287–92, and Plate III facing 287.

(7) Thomson classified electrometers as either 'idiostatic', where 'the whole electric force depends on the electrification which is itself the subject of the test', or 'heterostatic', where 'besides the electrification to be tested, another electrification maintained independently of it is taken advantage of' (*Electrostatics and Magnetism*: 308). The 'new absolute electrometer' was described as being 'heterostatic', for 'the potential of the auxiliary charge is tested and maintained...by an idiostatic arrangement forming part of the instrument itself' (*ibid.*: 287).

(8) M'Kichan acknowledged Maxwell's suggestion of a method of comparison of the two large coils and the third suspended coil of the electrodynamometer, so as to determine the magnetic moment of the suspended coil. See M'Kichan, 'Determination of the number of electrostatic units in the electromagnetic unit': 425–6.

(9) 'Report of the Committee on standards of electrical resistance', *Report of the Thirty-fourth Meeting of the British Association for the Advancement of Science* (London, 1865): 345–67, esp. table facing 349.

(10) In a brief letter to Stokes of 30 May 1873 (Royal Society, *Referees' Reports*, 7: 248) Fleeming Jenkin also recommended publication.

Electromagnetic constant v centimetres per second		Velocity of Light centimetres per second	
Weber & Kohlrausch 1856[11]	310.74×10^8	Fizeau[12]	314×10^8
Maxwell 1868[13]	288×10^8	Foucault[14]	298.36×10^8
M'Kichan 1872	293×10^8	Cornu (by Fizeaus method) 1872[15]	298.5×10^8

Note

The only part of the paper which I think might be made more clear with a little pains is that which describes the method used to eliminate the effects of terrestrial magnetism from the observations of the Electrodynamometer.[16] The axis of the suspended coil, when in equilibrium, appears to have been nearly in the magnetic meridian, for the + and − readings are not very different. But in the one case the constant multiplier requires to be increased, and in the other diminished, on account of the terrestrial magnetism either conspiring with, or acting against, the elastic moment of torsion of the wire of suspension.

The heating of the wire by the current does not seem to have sensibly affected its elasticity.

---

(11) See Number 238 note (22). (12) See Number 238 note (24).
(13) See Number 289 note (14). (14) See Number 238 note (25).
(15) Alfred Cornu, 'Détermination nouvelle de la vitesse de la lumière', *Comptes Rendus*, **76** (1873): 338–42; (trans.) 'A new determination of the velocity of light', *Phil. Mag.*, ser. 4, **45** (1873): 394–7.
(16) By observing the deflections of the suspended coil when a given current passed first in one direction and then in the other; magnets were fixed near the coils to neutralise the action of terrestrial magnetism. See M'Kichan, 'Determination of the number of electrostatic units in the electromagnetic unit': 412–13.

456

LETTER TO ROBERT DUNDAS CAY

22 MAY 1873

From the original in the Library of Peterhouse, Cambridge[1]

11 Scroope Terrace
Cambridge
May 22 1873

Dear Uncle

I enclose receipt.[2] We are very glad to hear that Aunt Jane is so much better. This is the first mild day we have had. I hope it will do Aunt Jane good, though 'Assembly weather'[3] has a very bad name.

This seat of learning is at present in a wild turmoil of boat races, concerts, flower shows, Divine Services pic-nics processions feasts, organ recitals, Rede Lectures, balls, syndicates Cam pollution boards Swedenborgian lectures to young men, young mens lectures to young women, military bands in the College gardens, London organists in the College chapels, pianos and red cloth in the College halls, nothing at all in the College lecture-rooms. Senate house full of youths whom we know, as in manners so in doctrine, to be fit to be admitted to the title of Inceptor in Arts and so on, with love to Aunt Jane and all the family from Katherine & myself.

Your affectionate nephew
J. CLERK MAXWELL

---

(1) Peterhouse, Maxwell MSS (36).   (2) See Volume I: 682.
(3) The annual meeting of the General Assembly of the Church of Scotland.

ON THE EFFECT OF GRAVITY ON THE TEMPERATURE OF A COLUMN OF GAS: REPLY TO FRANCIS GUTHRIE[1]

circa 25 MAY 1873[2]

From *Nature* (29 May 1873)[3]

CLERK-MAXWELL'S KINETIC THEORY OF GASES[4]

Your correspondent, Mr. Guthrie, has pointed out an, at first sight, very obvious and very serious objection to my kinetic theory of a vertical column

---

(1) A letter from Francis Guthrie (Boase), addressed from Graaf Reinet College, Cape Colony (South Africa), was headed 'Kinetic theory of gases' in *Nature*, **8** (22 May 1873): 67. 'On page 300 of the second edition of Maxwell's excellent little text-book on the "Theory of Heat", it is stated, as a result of the kinetic theory of gases therein set forth, that "gravity produces no effect in making the bottom of the column" (of gas) "hotter or colder than the top." / I cannot see how this result follows from the kinetic theory of gases. On the contrary, it seems obvious that thermal equilibrium can only subsist according to the kinetic theory, where the molecules encounter each other with equal average amounts of *work* or *vis viva*, and in order that this may be the case, the velocity of the molecules (and consequent temperature) of any upper layer must be less than that of the molecules in the layer next below; since, in order to encounter each other, the former must descend, and acquire velocity, while the latter must ascend and lose it. This would establish a diminution of temperature from the bottom to the top of a column of air at the rate (in the absence of any counteracting cause) of 1 °F. for 113 ft. of height, as can easily be verified from the fact that on account of the specific heat of air 1 lb. requires 183 foot-pounds to raise its temperature 1 °F. Radiation may diminish this and tend to produce equilibrium, but nevertheless it seems obvious from these two opposing tendencies a residual inequality of thermal condition would result, and that the top of a column would be cooler than the bottom. That this would be the case if the air were in general motion in the form of upward and downward currents, will not, I presume, be disputed; and surely molecular [?] is on the same footing. If the particles of air are moving in every direction with great absolute velocity, in what respect does this differ from air currents? In fact, all the particles which at any epoch of time are moving in any given direction constitute an air-current in that direction, mingled, it is true, with currents in other directions, but moving with accelerated velocity if descending, and with retarded velocity if ascending, and thus always tending to produce a diminution of temperature with height as a condition of gaseous thermal equilibrium.' In his *Theory of Heat* (London, $_2$1872): 300 Maxwell had concluded that: 'We find that if a vertical column of gas were left to itself, till by the conduction of heat it had attained a condition of thermal equilibrium, the temperature would be the same throughout, or, in other words, gravity produces no effect in making the bottom of the column hotter or colder than the top.... This result... proves that gravity has no influence in altering the conditions of thermal equilibrium in any substance, whether gaseous or not.'   (2) See notes (1) and (3).   (3) *Nature*, **8** (29 May 1873): 85.

(4) The title under which Maxwell's letter to *Nature* was published.

of gas. According to that theory, a vertical column of gas acted on by gravity would be in thermal equilibrium if it were at a uniform temperature throughout, that is to say, if the mean energy of the molecules were the same at all heights. But if this were the case the molecules in their free paths would be gaining energy if descending, and losing energy if ascending. Hence, Mr. Guthrie argues, at any horizontal section of the column a descending molecule would carry more energy down with it than an ascending molecule would bring up, and since as many molecules descend as ascend through the section, there would on the whole be a transfer of energy, that is, of heat, downwards; and this would be the case unless the energy were so distributed that a molecule in any part of its course finds itself, on an average, among molecules of the same energy as its own. An argument of the same kind, which occurred to me in 1866,[5] nearly upset my belief in calculation, and it was some time before I discovered the weak point in it.[6]

The argument assumes that, of the molecules which have encounters in a given stratum, those projected upwards have the same mean energy as those projected downwards. This, however, is not the case, for since the density is greater below than above, a greater *number* of molecules come from below than from above to strike those in the stratum, and therefore a greater number are projected from the stratum downwards than upwards. Hence since the total momentum of the molecules temporarily occupying the stratum remains zero (because, as a whole, it is at rest), the smaller number of molecules projected upwards must have a greater initial velocity than the larger number projected downwards. This much we may gather from general reasoning. It is not quite so easy, without calculation, to show that this difference between the molecules projected upwards and downwards from the same stratum exactly counteracts the tendency to a downward transmission of energy pointed out by Mr. Guthrie. The difficulty lies chiefly in forming exact expressions for the state of the molecules which instantaneously occupy a given stratum in terms of their state when projected from the various strata in which they had their last encounters. In my paper in the *Philosophical Transactions*, for 1867, on the 'Dynamical Theory of Gases',[7] I have entirely avoided these difficulties by expressing everything in terms of what passes through the boundary of an element, and what exists or takes place inside it.[8] By this method, which I have lately carefully verified

---

(5) See Numbers 259 §9 and 260.

(6) See Numbers 259 note (33), 263 and 266 note (8).

(7) J. Clerk Maxwell, 'On the dynamical theory of gases', *Phil. Trans.*, **157** (1867): 49–88 (= *Scientific Papers*, **2**: 26–78).

(8) Maxwell, 'On the dynamical theory of gases': 86–7 (= *Scientific Papers*, **2**: 75–6). See note (6).

and considerably simplified, Mr. Guthrie's argument is passed by without ever becoming visible. It is well, however, that he has directed attention to it, and challenged the defenders of the kinetic theory to clear up their ideas of the result of those encounters which take place in a given stratum.[9]

J. CLERK MAXWELL

(9) See Numbers 472, 473 and 481.

458

LETTER TO JOHN WILLIAM STRUTT

26 MAY 1873

From the original in private possession[1]

11 Scroope Terrace
Cambridge
26 May 1873

My dear Strutt

I am glad to hear you are writing a book on Acoustics. (Why not call it Theory of Sound?)[2] The Clarendon Press published Donkins book.[3] They appear to act very nearly in the same way as other printers. They print, I think, very well but very slow. I had great difficulty at first in getting them to use tall capitals instead of those small capitals which are no bigger than small letters. In such cases I did not make much impression unless I wrote both to the Secretary of the Delegates[4] and to the printer. When these things were settled I had no more difficulties with the printers, and they were very intelligent & careful. Thomson & Tait seem to think the Oxford press no better than other presses.[5]

You speak modestly of a want of Sound books in English. In what language are there such, except Helmholtz,[6] who is sound, not because he is German but because he is Helmholtz. ⌞The next best book is Herschel[7] whom you may regard as of German & organic descent.⌟ Observe Deschanels theory that the sound of an organ pipe is excited by the vibrations of the thick wooden lip of the mouthpiece. 'This lip is itself capable of vibrating in unison with any note lying within a wide range, and the note which is actually

---

(1) Rayleigh Papers, Terling Place, Terling, Essex. Published in part in R. J. Strutt, *John William Strutt, Third Baron Rayleigh* (London, 1924): 80–1.

(2) J. W. Strutt, Baron Rayleigh, *The Theory of Sound*, 2 vols. (London, 1877–8).

(3) W. F. Donkin, *Acoustics. Theoretical. Part I* (Oxford, 1870).

(4) Bartholomew Price: see Number 367 note (3).

(5) Thomson and Tait were in serious dispute with the Clarendon Press arising from the publication of their *Treatise on Natural Philosophy* in 1867; the second edition was published by Cambridge University Press in 1879. In a letter to Thomson of 6 January 1870 Tait declared – with reference to the demands from the Press for payment for corrections in proof – that 'as we cannot spare time for constant disputes about money matters the sooner our connection is terminated the better'; and on 25 April 1875 he exulted: 'Hurrah! We are at last our own masters!' (Edinburgh University Library, Gen. 2169: 199, 208).

(6) Hermann Helmholtz, *Die Lehre von den Tonempfindungen, als physiologische Grundlage für die Theorie der Musik* (Braunschweig, 1863).

(7) J. F. W. Herschel, 'Sound', in *Encyclopædia Metropolitana; or Universal Dictionary of Knowledge...Second Division. Mixed Sciences*, **2** (London, 1830): 747–824.

emitted is determined by the resonance of the column of air in the pipe.'[8] This is what organists desirous of scientific knowledge have to receive and believe.

Another doctrine delivered to such persons is that any one with a mere smattering of science ought to understand completely the motion of the air at the mouth hole, say, of a flute.

Many thanks for your paper on Bessels functions.[9]

I do not expect to be in London on 12th June as I shall be in Scotland then. We go about the 3rd or 4th.

Yours very truly
J. CLERK MAXWELL

---

(8) A. Privat Deschanel, *Elementary Treatise on Natural Philosophy*, translated and edited, with extensive additions, by J. D. Everett, 4 parts (London, 1870–2), Part IV: 838. Everett subsequently rewrote and corrected the passage; see Deschanel, *Natural Philosophy* (London, $_4$1877): 838.

(9) J. W. Strutt, 'Notes on Bessel functions', *Phil. Mag.*, ser. 4, **44** (1872): 328–44.

459
LETTER TO CHARLES TOMLINSON[1]
29 MAY 1873
From the original in the Library of the Institution of Electrical Engineers[2]

11 Scroope Terrace
Cambridge
29 May 1873

My dear Sir

I think we shall need your kind assistance again in the matter of the Cavendish Papers. The Duke of Devonshire to whom I communicated the information I received from you in 1869 wrote to Mr Harris, explaining the circumstances under which the papers had been placed in his father's hands and requesting him to return them to him.[3] This was six weeks ago and the Duke has received no answer and is afraid that it looks as if Mr Harris does not mean to part with the papers if he can help it. The Duke has therefore asked me to consult you on the subject as the person most likely to be able to render assistance.

In the first place would the address 'Thomas Harris Esqre Barrington House Southsea', be safe to carry the letter to him. If not, we must improve the direction of the next letter.

I have no clear idea of the objections which Mr Harris may have to return the M.SS to the person who lent them to his father, and who is also the lawful owner of them.

With regard to the question how far the experiments of Cavendish may be supposed to have anticipated those of Sir W. S. Harris, I should myself expect, judging from the published writings of the two persons that the unpublished writings of Cavendish would be found to have nothing in common with the publications of Harris.

Harris' experimental methods have all the aspect of being his own. He gradually improved them till he could get consistent results, just as Sir W. Thomson has improved methods somewhat similar[4] by the help of his

---

(1) Scientific author and lecturer, FRS 1867 (Boase).
(2) Institution of Electrical Engineers, London, Special Collection MSS 3.
(3) See Number 435.
(4) The reference is to Thomson's addition of a guard-ring (see his *Electrostatics and Magnetism*: 281–6, and Number 289 note (11)) to the attracted disc electrometer first constructed by Snow Harris; see W. Snow Harris, 'On some elementary laws of electricity', *Phil. Trans.*, **124** (1834): 213–45. Compare Maxwell's discussion in the *Treatise*, **1**: 266–9 (§§216–17).

mathematical powers till they have attained still greater accuracy, and can estimate the quantities in absolute measure.⁽⁵⁾

I hope you will be able to suggest some method of making his Grace's application effectual.

Yours very truly
J. CLERK MAXWELL

(5) In his 'Report on electrometers and electrostatic measurements' (1867) Thomson commented: 'it occurred to me to take advantage of the fact noticed by Harris, but easily seen as a consequence of Green's mathematical theory, that the mutual attraction between two conductors used as in his experiments is but little influenced by the form of the unopposed parts' (*Electrostatics and Magnetism*: 282). In his paper 'On the mathematical theory of electricity in equilibrium. I. On the elementary laws of statical electricity', *Camb. & Dubl. Math. J.*, **1** (1846): 75–95 (=*Electrostatics and Magnetism*: 15–37), Thomson commented on Harris' style of experimentation. Referring to Harris' paper 'Inquiries concerning the elementary laws of electricity', *Phil. Trans.*, **126** (1836): 417–52, Thomson noted the absence of 'precautions...in the experiments described in Mr Harris's memoir...[thus] the results are accordingly unavailable for the accurate *quantitative* verification of any law, on account of the numerous unknown disturbing circumstances by which they are affected' (*Electrostatics and Magnetism*: 24–5).

460

REPORT ON A PAPER BY JOHN WILLIAM STRUTT ON THEOREMS RELATING TO VIBRATIONS

26 JUNE 1873

From the original in private possession[1]

REPORT ON 'SOME GENERAL THEOREMS RELATING TO VIBRATIONS' – BY THE HON J. W. STRUTT[2]

I have long thought that the deduction of general theorems on vibrations from the general equations of motion of a connected system and the enunciation of these theorems in intelligible language would be one of the greatest services that a mathematician could do to Natural Philosophy. I am not well read in the literature of the subject but I have never met with dynamical discussions either of vibrations or undulations which take the full advantage of Lagranges method of dynamical reasonings by keeping clear of all hypotheses as to the mechanism by which the connexions of the system are maintained.

The theorems before us are just of the kind required to guide the speculative enquirer in his meditations on the vibrations of compound molecules, the radiation & absorption of light &c. A comparison with Sir J. F. W. Herschels justly celebrated theorem on forced vibrations[3] will show that since that time a real improvement in method has taken place.

If the mathematician can put the natural philosopher in possession of a method by which he may reason directly from the phenomena to the forces which produce them (as is done in the *differential* equations of Dynamics) this will answer his ends much better than if by integrating the equations the result of any particular hypothesis could be calculated.

I hope that the theorems of this paper when they appear in the work on

---

(1) Rayleigh Papers, Terling Place, Terling, Essex.

(2) J. W. Strutt, 'Some general theorems relating to vibrations', *Proceedings of the London Mathematical Society*, **4** (1873): 357–68; read 12 June 1873.

(3) J. F. W. Herschel, 'Sound', in *Encyclopædia Metropolitana...Second Division. Mixed Sciences*, **2** (London, 1830): 747–824, esp. 811–13 (§§323–31); 'provided the time elapsed since the commencement of the vibrations be long enough to allow of our regarding the number of previous vibrations as infinite, or which comes to the same, long enough to have allowed all traces of the initial vibrations to have been destroyed by resistance, friction, &c, these last will either exactly destroy each other, or, if they leave a residue, that residue will consist in a vibratory motion, having the same period with the primary impulse.' See J. W. Strutt, Baron Rayleigh, *The Theory of Sound*, 2 vols. (London, 1877–8), **1**: 108–9.

Acoustics⁽⁴⁾ may be stated a little more explicitly for the general public than they are here for the Mathematical Society (to suppose whom ignorant of any 'known' theorem would be an impertinence).

For instance, there would be no harm in showing that the general equation of vibration of a conservative system is linear with respect to $\left|\dfrac{d}{dt}\right|^2$ so that when expressed as a product of factors, each factor is of the form $\left(\left|\dfrac{d}{dt}\right|^2 + p^2\right)$.⁽⁵⁾

Thus the determination of the normal types is equivalent to the solution of this equation.

When dissipation exists the equation contains odd powers of $\dfrac{d}{dt}$ but the roots are of course still in pairs each of which pairs corresponds to a normal type of decaying vibration.

At p. 5 'the corresponding theorem relating to alteration of the potential energy'⁽⁶⁾ should be actually enunciated for the benefit of natural philosophers not members of L.M.S. It is proved that the addition of a mass to any part of the system either increases or leaves unaffected every moment of inertia belonging to the system considered as having its type determined by a set of fixed multipliers of the variables. If we suppose this mass added continuously the types of the normal vibrations will change continuously, but since the moment of inertia is stationary at these normal vibrations as regards the variation of the multipliers the moment of inertia of the normal vibrations must increase as the mass increases.

Constraint of any kind is shown at p ⁽⁷⁾ to shorten the period of the fundamental vibration.⁽⁸⁾ If it be objected that the fixation of the Sun would lengthen the year, it may be replied that if this fixation is effected by the application of a force binding the Sun to a fixed point and if this force rises from 0 to ∞ then there are at first two periods in the system, of which one is at first ∞.

The subject of harmonic types has great light thrown on it in this paper. The solution of physical problems on vibration conduction of heat, distribution of electricity &c depends on the discovery of the series of harmonic

---

(4) Strutt stated that his paper was preliminary to the 'preparation of a work on Acoustics'; see 'Some general theorems relating to vibrations': 357; and also Number 458, esp. note (2).

(5) p is the period of vibration.

(6) See Strutt, 'Some general theorems relating to vibrations': 359, where the text was apparently unchanged for publication.

(7) Space in MS.

(8) Strutt, 'Some general theorems relating to vibrations': 359.

types proper to the problem. We know the form of these types for a uniform closed curve, a sphere, certain sectors of a sphere, a cylinder and a few other cases, but the student can find but little information as to the general theory of harmonic types and their use when found. The fact that their use depends upon each harmonic type being *conjugate* to every other is given in this paper[9] and should be stated as clearly as it deserves.

The existence and properties of the Dissipation Function are clearly made out.[10] This is a matter of great importance. Many excellent investigations are rendered worthless from a neglect of dissipation,[11] amplitudes of forced vibrations come out zero or infinite in an absurd way. For equations containing dissipation terms see my paper on Governors Proc R.S. 1868.[12]

In Acoustics and Radiation there is a peculiar kind of dissipation which does not involve viscosity namely dissipation of undulations into an infinite medium, as when sound from an organ pipe escapes into the Atmosphere, or along an infinite tube as in Question 7, Jan 18, 1867, $1\frac{1}{2}$ to 4 Cambridge Math Tripos paper.[13] See also Qu ix Jan 21 1869 $1\frac{1}{2}$ to 4 for undulations in a dissipative medium,[14] showing that the refrangibility is irregular near an absorption band[15] ⟨where the dispersion is shown to be above the average so that the light is weakened not only by absorption but by dispersion at the band⟩. The ⟨refrangibility⟩ dispersion may become negative near an absorption

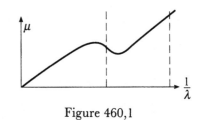

Figure 460,1

---

(9) Strutt, 'Some general theorems relating to vibrations': 361–3.

(10) Strutt, 'Some general theorems relating to vibrations': 363–6.

(11) See Strutt, 'Some general theorems relating to vibrations': 364, where he states that the 'existence of the [dissipation] function F does not seem to have been recognised hitherto, and indeed is expressly denied in the excellent "Acoustics" of the late Prof. Donkin (p. 101)'; compare W. F. Donkin, *Acoustics* (Oxford, 1870): 101.

(12) J. Clerk Maxwell, 'On governors'; *Proc. Roy. Soc.*, **16** (1868): 270–83, esp. 275, equation (6) and 278, equations (13) (= *Scientific Papers*, **2**: 111, 115).

(13) *The Cambridge University Calendar for the Year 1867* (Cambridge, 1867): 492; see Number 299 note (14).

(14) *The Cambridge University Calendar for the Year 1869* (Cambridge, 1869): 502. See Number 300: Appendix.

(15) Maxwell's examination question was later reprinted by Strutt; see Lord Rayleigh, 'The theory of anomalous dispersion', *Phil. Mag.*, ser. 6, **48** (1899): 151–2, who stated that: 'I have lately discovered that Maxwell, earlier than Sellmeier or any other writer, had considered this question. His results are given in the Mathematical Tripos Examination for 1869 (see 'Cambridge Calendar' for that year).' On the discovery of anomalous dispersion, see C. Christiansen, 'Ueber die Brechungsverhältnisse einer weingeistigen Lösung des Fuchsins; brieflicher Mittheilung', *Ann. Phys.*, **141** (1870): 479–80; and on its interpretation in terms of the

band so that a spot of light if refracted in a horizontal plane by the absorptive medium, and in a vertical plane by a glass prism might have the form shown in the margin.⁽¹⁶⁾

A collection of reciprocal properties such as that of section 3 and other physical cases of reciprocity would be useful if the mathematical foundation of the reciprocity were expressed in its simplest terms.⁽¹⁷⁾

E.g. If a series of imperfect elastic balls be placed not in contact with their centres in a straight line and if the first ball be projected against the second with velocity V and if after any number of impacts among the balls the last goes off with momentum M then if this last ball were projected in the reverse direction against the original system with velocity V the first will go off with momentum M.

Note 1. Sir W. Thomson is gone cable-laying for 3 months⁽¹⁸⁾ and has not had time to peruse the paper, which he regrets as he is busy with vibrations.
Note 2. I regard this paper as proper to be printed by the Society.
Note 3. Address till October Glenlair, Dalbeattie.

J. CLERK MAXWELL
26 June 1873

interaction of ether vibrations with the oscillatory frequencies of molecules, see W. Sellmeier, 'Ueber die durch Aetherschwingungen erregten Mitschwingungen Körpertheilchen und deren Rückwirkung auf die ersteren, besonders zur Erklärung der Dispersion und ihrer Anomalien', *Ann. Phys.*, **145** (1872): 399–421, 520–49; *ibid.*, **147** (1872): 386–403, 525–54. See Number 461. Strutt had himself referred to the phenomenon of anomalous dispersion in a paper 'On the reflection and refraction of light by intensely opaque matter', *Phil. Mag.*, ser. 4, **43** (1872): 321–38, on 322; 'Below the absorption-band the material vibration is naturally the higher, and hence the effect of the associated matter is to increase (abnormally) the virtual inertia of the aether, and therefore the refrangibility. On the other side the effect is the reverse.', citing a paper by Sellmeier, 'Zur Erklärung der abnormen Farbenfolge im Spectrum einiger Substanzen', *Ann. Phys.*, **143** (1871): 272–82. For discussion see Lord Kelvin, *Baltimore Lectures on Molecular Dynamics and the Wave Theory of Light* (Cambridge, 1904): 76–9.

(16) μ is the refractive index, λ the wavelength.

(17) Strutt, 'Some general theorems relating to vibrations': 366–8. See Numbers 480 and 482.

(18) See S. P. Thompson, *The Life of William Thomson Baron Kelvin of Largs*, 2 vols. (London, 1910), **2**: 636–9.

MANUSCRIPT ON THE THEORY OF ANOMALOUS DISPERSION

circa 1873[1]

From the original in the University Library, Cambridge[2]

[CONNEXION OF ABSORPTION AND DISPERSION][3]

[1] Let ξ denote the displacement of the æther, x_1 x_2 &c the displacements of different constituents of a molecule.

If we suppose the action between the æther and a body in it to be like that of a liquid on an immersed body, the force acting between them will depend not on their relative displacement $\xi - x$ but on their relative acceleration $\ddot{\xi} - \ddot{x}$.

The vibrations of molecules which have definite periods, and which produce emission and absorption of particular kinds of light are due to forces between the parts of the molecule and not to forces between the molecule and the æther. For they are in great measure independent of the physical state of the molecule.

We may therefore assume as a probable form of the equations

$$0 = \ddot{\xi} + \alpha \frac{d^2 \xi}{dy^2} + \beta_1(\ddot{\xi} - \ddot{x}_1) + \beta_2(\ddot{\xi} - \ddot{x}_2) + \&c$$

$$0 = m_1 \ddot{x}_1 + \gamma_{12}(\dot{x}_1 - \dot{x}_2) + \delta_{12}(x_1 - x_2)$$

$$0 = m_2 \ddot{x}_2 + \gamma_{12}(\dot{x}_2 - \dot{x}_1) + \delta_{12}(x_2 - x_1).$$

We may consider only x_1 and x_2 at present as two variables are enough to give a special time of vibration. But we may deduce the equations for molecules of any degree of complexity by considering their kinetic energy per unit of volume T their potential energy V[4] and their function of dissipation F[5] each of which is a homogeneous quadratic function, the first of the xs the second and third of the $\dot{x}$s.

Assuming that the solution is of the form

$$\xi = A e^{ly} \cos n(t + \mu y)$$

---

(1) The document may well have been written consequent on Number 460: see notes (4) and (5).

(2) ULC Add. MSS 7655, V, f/9.   (3) Endorsed thus.

(4) Symbols employed by J. W. Strutt, 'Some general theorems relating to vibrations', *Proceedings of the London Mathematical Society*, **4** (1873): 357–68, esp. 357; see Number 460.

(5) See Number 460, esp. note (11).

where n is the frequency of vibration and μ is the index of refraction we find

$$\begin{vmatrix} -n^2(1+\beta_1+\beta_2)+(n^2\mu^2-l^2+2iln\mu), & n^2\beta_1, & n\beta_2 \\ n\beta_1^2, & -(m_1+\beta_1)n^2+\delta+i\gamma n, & -(i\gamma n+\delta) \\ n\beta_2^2, & -(i\gamma n+\delta), & -(m_2+\beta_2)n^2+\delta+i\gamma n \end{vmatrix} = 0$$

to determine μ the index of refraction and l the coefficient of absorption in terms of n the frequency $= \dfrac{2\pi}{\lambda}$.

Putting $m = 1+\beta_1+\beta_2 \quad m_1' = m_1+\beta_1 \quad m_2' = m_2+\beta_2$ and remembering that if the ray is not altogether absorbed in the first millimetre of the medium l must be very small and also γ we find

$$\mu^2 = m + \frac{\delta(\beta_1+\beta_2)^2 - (m_1'\beta_2^2 + m_2'\beta_1^2)n^2}{m_1' m_2' n^2 - (m_1'+m_2')\delta}.$$

[2] In the Senate house examination Thursday afternoon Jan 21, 1869 I set a question of this kind modified to make the result as simple as possible.[6]

One kind of atoms was introduced each connected to a particle of the æther by a force varying as the distance. No force between the atoms. The æther elastic.

If $\rho =$ density and E elasticity of æther displacement ξ
$\quad \sigma =$ density of atoms
force between atoms of æther in unit of volume $\sigma p^2(x-\xi) + \sigma R \dot{x} - \dot{\xi}$.

$$\rho \ddot{\xi} - E \frac{d^2\xi}{dy^2} + \sigma R(\dot{\xi}-\dot{x}) + \sigma p^2(\xi-x) = 0 \quad \text{for æther}$$

$$\sigma \ddot{x} + \sigma R(\dot{x}-\dot{\xi}) + \sigma p^2(x-\xi) = 0 \quad \text{for atoms.}$$

Assuming that the solution is of the form $Ce^{ly} \cos n(t-\mu y)$

$$\frac{d}{dt} = -in \qquad \frac{d^2}{dt^2} = -n^2$$

$$\frac{d}{dy} = l-in\mu \qquad \frac{d^2}{dy^2} = l^2 - n^2\mu^2 - 2il\mu n$$

$$+\rho n^2 + E(l^2 - n^2\mu^2 - 2il\mu n) \quad n^2\sigma$$

---

(6) See Number 460; and Number 300: Appendix.

REPORT ON A PAPER BY LATIMER CLARK ON A STANDARD VOLTAIC BATTERY[1]

26 JUNE 1873

From the original in the University Library, Cambridge[2]

REPORT ON M[r] LATIMER CLARKS PAPER 'ON A STANDARD VOLTAIC BATTERY'[3]

I consider that the invention of a voltaic cell whose electromotive force is so constant that it may be employed as a standard for the comparison of other electromotive forces is one of the greatest services which can be done to electrical science.

In the absence of such a standard, the value of each electromotive force must be deduced from the results of a set of experiments which require delicate and costly instruments, and a laboratory free from vibration and from magnetic disturbances, not to speak of an amount of skill and of leisure of which few are possessed.

By the use of M[r] Clark's cell, any practical electrician, with his ordinary instruments and methods, may determine the value of an electromotive force at once.

For the verification of the constancy of this cell M[r] Clark has employed a method founded on that of Poggendorff[4] but capable I think of greater accuracy.

The chief merit, however, of the paper, is the determination, in electromagnetic measure, of the value of the electromotive force of the standard cell. I am not acquainted with any instance in which such great care

---

(1) See Number 415, Maxwell's report on the first version of Clark's paper.

(2) ULC Add. MSS 7655, V, c/54. The manuscript is endorsed: '1873. Latimer Clark by Clerk Maxwell' (and is a stray from the Royal Society's *Referees' Reports*).

(3) Latimer Clark, 'On a standard voltaic battery', *Phil. Trans.*, **164** (1874): 1–14. The paper was received by the Royal Society and read on 19 June 1873; see the abstract in *Proc. Roy. Soc.*, **21** (1873): 422. For the circumstances of the publication of the paper see Number 415 notes (4) and (12).

(4) J. C. Poggendorff, 'Methode zur quantitativen Bestimmung der elektromotorischen Kraft inconstanter galvanischer Ketten', *Ann. Phys.*, **54** (1841): 161–91. Poggendorff's method is described by Gustav Wiedemann, *Die Lehre vom Galvanismus und Elektromagnetismus*, 2 vols. (Braunschweig, $_2$1872–3), **1**: 351–60.

has been bestowed upon the management of the Electrodynamometer⁽⁵⁾ and the Sine Galvanometer,⁽⁶⁾ or in which such consistent results have been obtained.

I think therefore that this paper deserves a place in the Philosophical Transactions, as one which shews a marked advance in the science of electrical measurement.⁽⁷⁾

J. CLERK MAXWELL
Glenlair 26 June 1873

(5) See Number 416 note (3).   (6) See Number 415 note (9).

(7) In a report dated 1 July 1873 (Royal Society, *Referees' Reports*, **7**: 232) Sir Charles Wheatstone voiced a contrary opinion: 'I have already reported on Mr Latimer Clark's paper which is now presented with some abridgements.... I can only repeat the objections I formerly made to it'. For Wheatstone's comments on the first version of Clark's paper see Number 415 note (12). For confirmation of the accuracy of Clark's standard cell see a letter from W. Bottomley to Stokes of 26 March 1873 (Royal Society, *Referees' Reports*, **7**: 231).

463

FIXTURES AND INSTRUMENTS IN THE CAVENDISH LABORATORY

JUNE 1873[1]

From the original in the University Library, Cambridge[2]

CAVENDISH LABORATORY[3]
FIXTURES & PRINCIPAL INSTRUMENTS IN THE DIFFERENT ROOMS[4]

Ground floor. (1) Under Lecture Room
Furnace, oven & boiler
iron retort for oxygen, &c

2 large gas holders
copper cylinders 2 feet diameter 6 feet deep in wooden vats. Pullies & weights for d°

Blowpipe & table for glass blowing

Battery of 80 trays Thomson's arrangement zincs 20 inches square: connexions for same

Working Table 6′ × 3′, 3 feet high.
Large Drawers for Copper-sulphate, &c with place above for carboys & acids

2 Small room next the last
Turning lathe
Bench & tools
Screw tap &c

---

(1) See note (2) and Number 464.

(2) ULC, CUR, 55.2 (187). A holograph copy (ULC Add. MSS 7655, V, j/2) is endorsed: 'List of Instruments for Cavendish Laboratory by Prof^r Maxwell June 1873'.

(3) The laboratory had been previously referred to as the 'Devonshire Laboratory': see Number 449.

(4) This list constitutes a statement of Maxwell's aims (see Number 464), rather than an account of the instruments actually acquired at the commencement of the Laboratory. Compare Maxwell's list of 'Instruments in the Cavendish Laboratory' (ULC Add. MSS 7655, V, j/4; to be published in Volume III) dated 29 April 1874. See Number 365 for a preliminary outline of the design of the Laboratory; and the account of 'The new physical laboratory of the University of Cambridge', *Nature*, **10** (1874): 139–42.

3   Heat Room
      Stone table
      Barometer by Casella (I have this)
      Aneroid Barometer
      Thermometers (All Centrigrade) Standard to 100 °C.
            — delicate for atmospheric temperatures
            — for boiling points
            — Wet & dry bulb
      Dew point instrument by Casella
      Column of mercury (in the tower) for great pressures, connected to Heat room.
      Bunsen's air pump[5] by falling water (in the tower, connected to Heat room and to lecture room).
      Sprengel's air pump[6]
      Joule's air pump by mercury[7]
      Deloeils air pump[8] for exhaustion or compression (glass cylinders and long pistons working loosely in them)
      Bramah's press[9] (in gun metal)
      Water engine, Schmid's Patent N°. III (Makers in Gloucester, I cannot yet ascertain the name of the firm.)
      Water tank, 4 feet diameter, 3 feet deep
      Calorimeter (after Regnault)[10]
      Bunsens Ice Calorimeter[11]
      Apparatus for viscosity of gases (belongs to me at present).[12]

(5) Robert Bunsen, *Gasometry: Comprising the leading Physical and Chemical Properties of Gases*, (trans.) H. E. Roscoe (London, 1857): 14.

(6) Hermann Sprengel, 'Researches on the vacuum', *Journal of the Chemical Society*, 3 (1865): 9–21; Sprengel, 'The invention of the water air-pump', *Phil. Mag.*, ser. 4, 45 (1873): 153–4. See S. P. Thompson, *The Development of the Mercurial Air-Pump* (London, 1888): 14–15.

(7) J. P. Joule, ['On a mercurial air-pump',] *Proceedings of the Literary and Philosophical Society of Manchester*, 12 (1873): 43, 55–6, 57–8. See Thompson, *Mercurial Air-Pump*: 9.

(8) J. A. Deleuil, 'Machine pneumatique construite sur un nouveau principe', *Comptes Rendus*, 60 (1865): 571–2; (trans.) 'Air pump constructed on a new principle', *Phil. Mag.*, ser. 4, 29 (1865): 487.

(9) A hydraulic press invented in 1795 by Joseph Bramah; see *Encyclopaedia Britannica* (11th edn), 4 (Cambridge, 1910): 417–18.

(10) H. V. Regnault, 'Sur les chaleurs latentes de la vapeur aqueuse à saturation sous diverses pressions', *Mémoires de l'Académie Royale des Sciences de l'Institut de France*, 21 (1847): 635–728, esp. 665–7 and Plate VII Fig. 10.

(11) Robert Bunsen, 'Calorimetrische Untersuchungen', *Ann. Phys.*, 141 (1870): 1–31 and Plate I; (trans.) 'Calorimetric researches', *Phil. Mag.*, ser. 4, 41 (1871): 161–82 and Plate V. See J. Clerk Maxwell, *Theory of Heat* (London, 1871): 61–2.

(12) See Number 252 and Plate IV.

4 Balance Room
    Balance to 5 Kilo.   Secretan 1372
       —   4 Kilo   —   1378
    Set of British weights
    Set of French weights
    Several rough balances (Mordan's patent)
    Standard yard and pound
    Standard mètre and kilogramme
    Ten foot rod
    4 mètre sliding 'wire parlant'
    Gauge up to 1 foot
    Micrometer screw gauge (Becker)
    Rolling disk   (Becker)
    Dividing engine
    Spherometer
    Kathetometer (Stäudinger, Giessen)

5 Pendulum Room
    Standard clock with electric connexion to all the clocks in the Museum
    Stone pillar for the same
    8 common clocks in connexion
    2 or more journeyman clocks in connexion for experiments
    Vacuum case for pendulum experiments
    Stone foundation & pillar
    Steinheil's 'Passage Prisma'[13] in window
    Jenkins governor & driving gear & chronograph barrel[14]
    Suspension wire, mirror & scale for determining moments of inertia

6 Magnetic Room
    Kew magnetometer,[15] by Becker
    Dip needle, Joule's suspension, with circle[16]
    Joules pair of magnets for horizontal intensity[17]
    Theodolite by Eichens of Paris called 'Aba' 360 fr.

---

(13) C. A. von Steinheil, 'Ueber das Passage prisma', *Astronomische Nachrichten*, **24** (1846): cols. 269–74.

(14) See Numbers 210 notes (2) and (3) and 219 note (8).

(15) Maxwell's letters (dated 20 March and 4 May 1874) concerning the magnetometer, written to G. M. Whipple of the Kew Observatory, will be published in Volume III. See also E. Sabine, 'Results of the magnetic observations at the Kew Observatory from 1857-8 to 1862 inclusive', *Phil. Trans.*, **153** (1863): 273–84.

(16) See Number 339 notes (15) and (16).   (17) See Number 327 note (7).

Stone foundation for theodolite
4 mirrors 2 inches square fixed in walls
Revolving Coil, driving gear ⎫
Governor, telescope, scale ⎬ From Brit. Ass.
Wheatstones bridge and galvanometer ⎭
the property of British Association.[18]
Base for the coil of brick with stone top, 2 feet high 3 feet square
Electrodynamometer (Belongs to Brit. Ass.)[19]
Large standard coil 50 cm diameter
Helmholtz tangent galvanometer[20]
Thomson's suspended coil for magnetic intensity[21]

7 Lecture Room
3 Black boards hung like sash windows
2 scales 8′ × 1 with hinged screens to
fold over them, painted white
without but black within.
Thomson's Quadrant Electrometer[22]
— Reflecting Galvanometer[23]

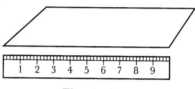
Figure 463,1

2 lime lights
In the table are 5 taps for gas 3 for water 2 for oxygen 1 for steam and 1 connected with Bunsens air pump in the Tower.
3 sinks for water 2 flues for noxious flumes
2 pairs of electrodes of great battery below.
Above on the wall are a pair of electrodes connected with electric machine in the dry electric room, and one connected with the atmospheric collector on the Tower.
Fly wheel driven by a winch with pulley and band.
In the loft above lecture room
Suspension of Foucaults Pendulum[24]

---

(18) See Numbers 210 note (2) and 219 note (9).

(19) See Number 416 note (3).

(20) Described by Gustav Wiedemann, *Die Lehre vom Galvanismus und Elektromagnetismus*, 2 vols. (Braunschweig, 1861), **2**: 197; and see the *Treatise*, **2**: 318–19, 330 (§§713, 725).

(21) See the *Treatise*, **2**: 328 (§724).

(22) Described by William Thomson in his 'Report on electrometers and electrostatic measurements', *Report of the Thirty-seventh Meeting of the British Association* (London, 1868): 489–512, esp. 490–7 and Plate 5 (= *Electrostatics and Magnetism*: 262–81). See the *Treatise*, **1**: 272–4 (§219); and G. Green and J. T. Lloyd, *Kelvin's Instruments and the Kelvin Museum* (Glasgow, 1970): 22–4 and Plate 5.

(23) See Numbers 379 note (4) and 399 note (7).

(24) See Number 364 note (7).

— Blackburns Pendulum[25]
Pulley & shaft on friction wheels for Thomson's endless chain[26]
Clock on East Side of Lecture room
White screen for projection
Electric Lamp
Large 'aquarium' tank of glass 4′ × 1′..6″ × 1′..6″

8 Professor's Laboratory
Drawers & cases for glass apparatus
Tap & sink for washing the same
Set of chemicals for ordinary testing

9 Apparatus Room
Cabinets with drawers below to the height of 3 feet and glass doors above to the height of 8 feet.
Large electromagnet with glass case and suspensions for diamagnetic experiments.
Large induction coil
Magneto electric machine (Gramme?[27] Wild?)[28]

10 Private Room
Book case for special library of the Laboratory
Desk   Working-table

11 Large Laboratory
10 Working tables
1 Frame for measurements electric & other
Reflecting galvanometer & curtains
Cases for instruments in constant use
Tap & sink

12 Electric Room
Endless web of flannel to dry the air worked by clockwork, weights or water.[29]

---

(25) The pendulum arrangement due to Hugh Blackburn (see Volume I: 238n), consisting of a spherical pendulum suspended by strings; see P. G. Tait and W. J. Steele, *A Treatise on the Dynamics of a Particle* (London, $_3$1871): 224–5.   (26) See Number 328.

(27) Z. T. Gramme, 'Sur une machine magnéto-électrique produisant des courants continus', *Comptes Rendus*, **73** (1871): 175–8.

(28) H. Wilde, 'On some improvements in electromagnetic induction machines', *Phil. Mag.*, ser. 4, **45** (1873): 439–50 and Plate VIII.

(29) See 'The new physical laboratory of the University of Cambridge': 141; 'Mr. Latimer Clark's contrivance... [to absorb] moisture from the air... so that the electrical instruments in the room are preserved in a highly insulating condition'.

Winters electrical machine[30] ⎫
Holtz[31] — ⎬ connexion to Lecture Room
Varleys[32] — ⎭
Thomson's Reciprocal Electrophorus by water[33]
    — Mouse mill[34]
    — Portable Electrometer[35]
    — Absolute Electrometer[36]
    — Electroplatymeter[37]
Connexion to Collector of Atmospheric Electricity on the Tower
Large Tin Condenser
Microfarad (Worden & Co.)
Ohm
Latimer Clarks Standard Cell[38]
Spherical condenser
Electrophorus[39]
Maxwell's electric balance (made)[40]

13 Photographic Room
    Window of yellow glass
    Shelves for chemicals
    Tap & sink

14 (15) 2 Optical Rooms
    Foucaults Heliostat[41]

---

(30) Karl Winter, ['Ein neuer Electrophor-Apparat',] *Berichte über die Mittheilungen von Fremde der Naturwissenschaften in Wien*, **2** (1847): 449–50.

(31) See Number 260 note (16).   (32) See Number 260 note (17).

(33) See Number 302 note (2).

(34) See S. P. Thompson, *The Life of William Thomson Baron Kelvin of Largs*, 2 vols. (London, 1910), **1**: 573; and Green and Lloyd, *Kelvin's Instruments*: 24 and Plate 7.

(35) See William Thomson, 'Report on electrometers and electrostatic measurements': 501–7 and Plate 6 Figs 8–10; and Green and Lloyd, *Kelvin's Instruments*: 22 and Plate 4.

(36) See William Thomson, 'Report on electrometers and electrostatic measurements': 497–501; and Number 289 note (11).

(37) See William Thomson, 'On new instruments for measuring electrical potentials and capacities', *Report of the Twenty-fifth Meeting of the British Association for the Advancement of Science; held at Glasgow in September 1855* (London, 1856), part 2: 22; and Thomson, 'On the measurement of electrostatic capacity', *Journal of the Society of Telegraph Engineers*, **1** (1873): 394–9, esp. 396–7.

(38) See Number 415.   (39) See the *Treatise*, **1**: 255–6 (§208).

(40) See Number 243 and Plates III and XI.

(41) Léon Foucault, 'Sur un moyen d'affaiblir les rayons du soleil au foyer des lunettes', *Comptes Rendus*, **63** (1866): 413–15; (trans.) 'On a means of weakening the solar rays in the focus of telescopes', *Phil. Mag.*, ser. 4, **32** (1866): 396–7.

Spectroscope (made)
Compound colour apparatus (made)
Scale for measuring focal lengths
Steinheils fluid prism
— reading telescope
Fizeau's 'conjugate telescopes'[42]
Microscope with graduated vertical movement
Noberts grating[43]
Prisms for bisulphide of carbon (made)[44]

16 Radiant Heat Room
Thermopile and galvanometer of small resistance
Metallic mirrors &c.

17 Calculating Room
Drawing board parallel ruler & scales
Beam compass   Protractor
Amsler's Planimeter[45]

18 Acoustics
Organ bellows & wind chest
Organ pipe one side glass
Monometric gas jets (Koenig)
Tuning forks and resonators
Monochord
Helmholtz' Siren[46]

19 Tower
Mast at top with water dropping } connected to Electricity &
Collector for atmospheric electricity } Lecture room
Lightning conductor
In the stair
Bunsen's airpump by falling water connected to Heat and Lecture Room
Column of mercury for high pressures connected to Heat room

---

(42) See Number 227 note (4).
(43) F. A. Nobert, 'Die Interferenz-Spectrumplatte', *Ann. Phys.*, **85** (1852): 80–2.
(44) See Number 355 esp. note (10).
(45) Jakob Amsler, 'Ueber das Polar-Planimeter', *Polytechnisches Journal*, **140** (1856): 321–7.
(46) To demonstrate the interference of sound and beats; see Hermann Helmholtz, *Die Lehre von den Tonempfindungen als physiologische Grundlage für die Theorie der Musik* (Braunschweig, 1863): 241–3.

20 Store Room
    Apparatus for strength of materials   effect of strains on iron & magnets
    Shaft for winding coils
    Wire drawing and straightening
    Glass tubes
    Copper wire
    Gutta percha covered wire
    Steel piano wire
    Caouchouc tubes

464

FROM A DRAFT LETTER TO HENRY WILKINSON COOKSON[1]

5 JULY 1873

From Campbell and Garnett, *Life of Maxwell*[2]

Glenlair
5 July 1873

I enclose a provisional list of fixtures and apparatus required for the Laboratory.[3]

At present I am not able to estimate the prices of many of the articles.

Some of them are in the market, and have simply to be ordered; others require to be constructed specially for the Laboratory.

I have begun with a list arranged according to the places and rooms in the Laboratory, but, of course, all small things must be kept in cases, either in the apparatus room, or in the special rooms.

The special duty of the professor of experimental physics is to teach the sciences of heat and electricity, and also to encourage physical research. The Laboratory must therefore contain apparatus for the illustration of heat and electricity, and also for whatever physical research seems most important or most promising.

The special researches connected with heat which I think most deserving of our efforts at the present time are those relating to the elasticity of bodies, and in general those which throw light on their molecular constitution; and the most important electrical research is the determination of the magnitude of certain electric quantities, and their relations to each other.

These are the principles on which I have been planning the arrangement of the Laboratory. But if in the course of years the course of scientific research should be deflected, the plans of work must vary too, and the rooms must be allotted differently.

I agree with you that the income of the Museums must be largely increased in order to meet the demands of this and other new buildings, and I am glad that the University is able to increase it.

It is impossible to procure many of the instruments, as they are not kept in stock, and have to be made to order. Some of the most important will require a considerable amount of supervision during their construction, for their whole value depends on their fulfilling conditions which can as yet be determined only by trial, so that it may be some time before everything is in working order.

---

(1) Peterhouse 1827, Fellow 1836, Master 1847–76, Vice-Chancellor 1848, 1863–4, 1872–3 (Venn). (2) *Life of Maxwell*: 352–3. (3) Number 463.

POSTCARD TO PETER GUTHRIE TAIT

circa 8 july 1873

From the original in the University Library, Cambridge[1]

[Glenlair]

O T'.[2] T is selfconsistent.[3] For take XVI and find α by XIV.[4]

$$\alpha = \frac{dH}{dy} - \frac{dG}{dz} = \frac{1}{3}\alpha - \frac{1}{3}\int \frac{d\beta}{dy}dx - \frac{1}{3}\int \frac{d\gamma}{dz}dx + \frac{1}{3}\alpha \left(+ \frac{1}{3}\alpha - \frac{1}{3}\int \frac{d\alpha}{dx}dx \right)$$
$$= \alpha + 0 \quad \text{(by (a) p. 401)}.[5]$$

(1) ULC Add. MSS 7655, I, b/57.

(2) Maxwell was replying to Tait's card of 7 July 1873 (ULC Add. MSS 7655, I, a/35): 'O dp/dt See T, *Reprint of Electrostatics*, p. 402. The integrals in the values of F, G, H have a factor ($\frac{1}{3}$) w^h was not in the original paper. 4^{ions} say the factor should be $\frac{1}{2}$. What do you say? It is curious that T sh^d be *twice* wrong. Thus $V.\nabla\sigma = \tau$ gives $\sigma = \frac{1}{2}\int V\tau d\rho + \nabla u$; for $\nabla\int V\tau d\rho = \Sigma(\iota\nabla\tau\iota) = 3\tau - \tau = 2\tau$. You have said nothing of Ångström. Shall I send you my proofs on the subject? ☞ / Thermal Cond^y of Argentan varies by temp^{re} about $\frac{1}{5}$th as much as that of Fe.' For Maxwell's comments on Ångström's work on thermal conductivity, and on Tait's paper, see his card of 24 July 1873 (Number 469, esp. notes (7), (8) and (9)). Tait had first requested Maxwell's comments in a card of 30 June 1873 (ULC Add. MSS 7655, I, a/34): '38 George Sq. Edin^h 30/6/73. O dp/dt, See'st thou what a splendid lark you have missed at Cambridge? On pondering farther on the question I should prefer to write $-(S.\nabla\nabla_1)\phi\rho$ in place of $\nabla S.\nabla_1\phi\rho$. But neither of them is good, as the ρ & ∇ *together* amount to mere artificial introduction of i, j, k: and therefore really do not introduce variables at all. It raises, however, a novelty as regards $\iiint d_f(\ )$, & $\iint ds(\ )$. / Did I ever ask you about the extraordinary error in Ångström's Conductivity (Thermal) paper? He takes an integral for the diff. =^{n} w^h is true only if rad^n & convection are 0. ☞. / If χ be the strain-function the work done is expressible as $\Sigma[S\chi\alpha\chi\beta - S\alpha\beta][S\chi\gamma\chi\delta - S\gamma\delta]$. This has 21 terms.' Tait is alluding to his paper 'Additional note on the strain function, &c', *Proc. Roy. Soc. Edinb.*, **8** (1873): 84–6.

(3) Tait's reference (see note (2)) is to Thomson's 'A mathematical theory of magnetism', *Phil. Trans.*, **141** (1851): 243–85, esp. 283–4 (= *Electrostatics and Magnetism*: 341–404, esp. 402, where Thomson introduced the correction to his equations (XV) and (XVI) as mentioned by Tait in his card of 7 July 1873).

(4) For a solenoidal distribution of magnetism $\frac{d\alpha}{dx} + \frac{d\beta}{dy} + \frac{d\gamma}{dz} = 0$ (Thomson's equation (a)), where α, β, γ are the components of the intensity of magnetisation at any internal point in a magnet, Thomson states equations (XIV), $\alpha = \frac{dH}{dy} - \frac{dG}{dz}, \beta = \frac{dF}{dz} - \frac{dH}{dx}, \gamma = \frac{dG}{dx} - \frac{dF}{dy}$, 'where F, G, H are three functions to a certain extent arbitrary', and he obtains (XV), $F = \frac{1}{3}\iint dy\, dz \left(\frac{d\beta}{dy} - \frac{d\gamma}{dz} \right) + \frac{d\psi}{dx}$, and similar equations for G and H, where ψ denotes an arbitrary function, and obtains (XVI), $F = \frac{1}{3}\int (\beta dz - \gamma dy) + \frac{d\psi}{dx}$, and similar equations for G and H (the factor $\frac{1}{3}$ in (XV) and (XVI) being appended to the 1872 reprint of the paper).

(5) See note (4).

But how un4^{ionic} is all this and indeed it is only expressible in base Cartesians.

$$F = \frac{1}{3}\int_0^z \beta dz - \frac{1}{3}\int_0^y \gamma dy + \frac{d\psi}{dx}. \quad (6)$$

I cannot interpret $\frac{1}{2}\int V\tau d\rho$ as having a definite value at a point in space independent of how you get to it. T's integrations are all conducted in rectangular trammels. Express, (if you can,) (XV)$^{(7)}$ in 4^{ions}!

I admit that $\Sigma(\iota V\tau\iota) = 2\tau$ but deny that $\int V\tau d\rho$ is a quantity capable of V-tion, if ρ (the cunctator)$^{(8)}$ is free to poke about as him pleases. But here is wisdom. Let $\alpha\,\beta\,\gamma$ be components of τ and let $S\nabla\tau = 0^{(9)}$ not only within the magnet but everywhere. Then $V.\nabla\sigma = \tau^{(10)}$ gives $\sigma = -\frac{1}{4\pi}\iiint \frac{V\nabla\tau}{\tau(\rho-\rho')}$.

What are the coordinates of T?

$$\frac{dp}{dt}$$

---

(6) Thomson's equation (XVI); see note (4).   (7) See note (4).
(8) One who hesitates (cognomen for Quintus Fabius Maximus).
(9) The solenoidal condition; see Number 396 note (8).
(10) The curl of σ; see Number 396 note (8).

466

LETTER TO HENRY AUGUSTUS ROWLAND[1]

9 JULY 1873

From the original in the Library of The Johns Hopkins University[2]

Glenlair
Dalbeattie
9 July 1873

Dear Sir

Your letter and M.S. have been forwarded to me this morning. I have read your paper with great interest and I think the whole of it is of great value and should be published as soon as possible because the subject is one of great importance, and the value of results such as yours is just beginning to be appreciated.[3]

I am sorry that your paper has arrived too late to be communicated to the Royal Society of London, and there will be no more meetings till November otherwise it would have given me great pleasure if you would allow me to communicate your paper to the Society. I hope however that if you have any other papers of the same sort you will give us an opportunity of making them known in this country.

I gather however from your letter that you would consider the Philosophical Magazine a suitable place for your paper to appear in.[4] It is certainly the best medium of publication for any researches in exact science. The are several other scientific periodicals but most of them circulate among a class of readers such that their Editors are apt to be suspicious of any article involving exact methods.

Your M.S. is so clear both in style and penmanship that I think the correction of the proofs will be a very easy matter. If I send it to the Phil. Mag., and if it is likely to appear at once, would you rather have the proofs sent to you or will it be sufficient if I look them over?

I may be mistaken in glancing over the paper, but I have not seen clearly

---

(1) Of the Rensselaer Polytechnic Institute in Troy, New York.

(2) Henry Augustus Rowland Papers MS. 6, Milton S. Eisenhower Library, The Johns Hopkins University, Baltimore.

(3) Rowland's study of the properties of magnetic metals, and his postulation of a magnetic analogue to Ohm's law for electric circuits, were not understood by the editors of the *American Journal of Science*; see J. D. Miller, 'Rowland's magnetic analogue to Ohm's law', *Isis*, **66** (1975): 230–41. See also D. W. Jordan, 'The magnetic circuit model, 1850–1890: the resisted flow image in magnetostatistics', *British Journal for the History of Science*, **23** (1990): 131–73, esp. 150–2.

(4) Henry A. Rowland, 'On magnetic permeability, and the maximum of magnetism of iron, steel, and nickel', *Phil. Mag.*, ser. 4, **46** (1873): 140–59.

whether your magnetization formula rests on a purely empirical foundation, or whether you can give any physical reason for adopting it.[5] You have also an investigation about a cylindric magnet.[6] If as I suppose the work is similar to Green's[7] I should like to see it in full, for if you have satisfactorily got over a piece of Greens work which is very precarious mathematics[8] you deserve great credit.[9]

Yours very truly
J. CLERK MAXWELL

Address till October as above   afterwards 11 Scroope Terrace, Cambridge

---

(5) Rowland, 'On magnetic permeability': 144. Rowland explained the reasoning behind his derivation of his expression for magnetisation in his paper 'Studies on magnetic distribution', *Phil. Mag.*, ser. 4, **50** (1875): 257–77, 451–9, esp. 258–63.

(6) Rowland, 'On magnetic permeability': 144–6.

(7) George Green, *An Essay on the Application of Mathematical Analysis to the Theories of Electricity and Magnetism* (Nottingham, 1828): 69 (= *Mathematical Papers of the Late George Green*, ed. N. M. Ferrers (Cambridge, 1871): 111).

(8) See Number 410; and the *Treatise*, **2**: 68 (§439).

(9) In his 'Studies on magnetic distribution': 258, Rowland noted that 'Green, in his "Essay", has obtained a formula which gives the same distribution; but he obtains it by a series of mathematical approximations which it is almost impossible to interpret physically'.

467
LETTER TO HENRY AUGUSTUS ROWLAND
12 JULY 1873
From the original in the Library of The Johns Hopkins University[1]

Glenlair
Dalbeattie
12 July 1873

Dear Sir

Mr Francis, the Editor of the Phil. Mag, will be very glad to have your paper, for the Magazine.[2]

From the largeness of some of your values of λ & μ[3] I suspected some difference between your units and the received ones, but on more careful examination I find that these quantities are really much larger for certain values of M[4] than has been supposed. Thalèn[5] used the magnetic force of the Earth, which although it is most important for ships and is most easily obtained is too small to bring out the largest value of μ.

If $\kappa = 32$[6] $\mu = 403$ nearly,[7] which lies between your values for different pieces of iron for small values of M.[8]

---

(1) Henry Augustus Rowland Papers MS. 6, Milton S. Eisenhower Library, The Johns Hopkins University, Baltimore.

(2) Maxwell enclosed a letter of 11 July 1873 which he had received from William Francis (Rowland Papers): 'I shall be much pleased to receive Mr Rowland's paper for insertion in the Phil. Mag. The subject is undoubtedly one of the highest importance and from your description of it must be an exceedingly valuable one. Directly I receive the MS I will have it put into type, and shall feel much indebted to you for the perusal of the proofs.'

(3) Henry A. Rowland, 'On magnetic permeability, and the maximum of magnetism of iron, steel, and nickel', *Phil. Mag.*, ser. 4, **46** (1873): 140–59, esp. 141, 152–3. Rowland adopts Thomson's term 'magnetic permeability' (*Electrostatics and Magnetism*: 482–6). He follows Maxwell in the *Treatise*, **2**: 54 (§430), where μ is termed 'Coefficient of Magnetic Induction'; and from Maxwell's relation $\mu = 4\pi\kappa + 1$ (where κ is 'Neumann's Coefficient of Magnetization by Induction'), Rowland writes $\mu = \lambda/4\pi$. See Number 327 esp. note (3).

(4) Rowland, 'On magnetic permeability': 144, 152–3. Rowland defines M as the 'magnetizing-force of helix'. In his subsequent paper 'On the magnetic permeability and maximum of magnetism of nickel and cobalt', *Phil. Mag.*, ser. 4, **48** (1874): 321–40, esp. 322n, Rowland defined his notation in relation to that employed by Maxwell in the *Treatise*, stating that Maxwell's quantity $\mathfrak{H}$ (the 'magnetic force') corresponded to $4\pi M$ in his former paper.

(5) T. R. Thalén, 'Recherches sur les propriétés magnétiques du fer', *Nova Acta Regiae Societatis Scientiarum Upsaliensis*, ser. 3, **4** (1863). See Number 327 note (4).

(6) See note (3) and Number 327.

(7) From Maxwell's relation $\mu = 4\pi\kappa + 1$ (see note (3)).

(8) Rowland, 'On magnetic permeability': 152 (Table II).

There seems to be a mistake or rather perhaps miscopying at p 13 in the calculation of $Q'^{(9)}$ for a ring.

It should be
$$Q' = 2n'i\mu \int_{-R}^{+R} \frac{\sqrt{R^2-x^2}}{a-x} dx$$
$$= 4\pi n'i\mu \left(a - \sqrt{a^2-R^2}\right). \quad (10)$$

The expression developed in a series is correct as you have given it.

At p. 21 the reason why some take the direct action of the helix into account is that they are seeking for κ, not for μ.[11]

Now μ represents the permeability of what is inside the helix, that of air being unity.

κ represents the *increase* of permeability due to the substitution of iron for air, this increase being divided by 4π.[12]

The only disadvantage of using a ring of metal is the difficulty of determining its actual magnetic state. You can only determine *differences*.[13] In the case of a bar you can determine the number of lines of force at the middle of the bar by placing your coil there, and sliding it off the bar quickly. I should think this might be done with a bar long enough to get rid of the direct action of the ends at the middle point and not too long to perform the sliding off of the coil in a short enough time.

There are two other advantages of straight bars.

(1) The magnetizing helix may be made once for all and with great care.
(2) The magnetism of the bar may be disturbed by passing longitudinal electric currents through it, by tension pressure or torsion &c.

I understand from your paper the peculiarity of *magnetic* and *burnt* iron.[14]

---

(9) In 'On magnetic permeability': 144, Rowland defines Q' as the 'lines of force *in* bar at any point'; and in his subsequent paper 'On the magnetic permeability and maximum of magnetism of nickel and cobalt': 322n, he explained that Maxwell's 'magnetic induction' $\mathfrak{B}$ corresponded to Q in his former paper.

(10) Compare Rowland, 'On magnetic permeability': 145, where the first expression has the coefficient 4. i is the strength of current, n' and R the number of coils and resistance per metre, a the area of the ring.

(11) Compare Rowland, 'On magnetic permeability': 148–9.

(12) See the *Treatise*, 2: 54 (§430), where Maxwell states the relation $\kappa = \dfrac{\mu-1}{4\pi}$.

(13) See Rowland, 'On magnetic permeability': 147. In his paper 'On the magnetic permeability and maximum of magnetism of nickel and cobalt': 336 Rowland acknowledged Maxwell's point.

(14) Iron 'burnt' by welding; see Rowland, 'On magnetic permeability': 149.

But I think that if a characteristic curve (say Table II & III)⁽¹⁵⁾ of each were plotted it would be more easily understood.⁽¹⁶⁾

The behaviour of hard steel should also be compared with soft iron both when normal and when longitudinally magnetized.

There are important differences between the effects of a new magnetizing force according as it acts in the same or in the opposite direction to the residual magnetism.

It would be interesting also to trace the effects of previously magnetizing the iron transversely as Dr Joule did with a gun barrel by passing a current down the tube and up outside so making it a ring-magnet.⁽¹⁷⁾

The molecules are then placed with their axes mostly transverse to the length and should therefore be easily acted on by a longitudinal magnetizing force. Hence I suppose by magnetizing first transversely and then measuring λ for longitudinal magnetization you will obtain a very large value of λ.

You have seen, no doubt, in the journals that M. Jamin has succeeded in making a very powerful magnet.⁽¹⁸⁾ A knowledge of the best kind of steel for magnets and how to temper and magnetize them is of great importance to science and very few scientific men or instrument makers know anything about it.

Would you like to have separate copies of your paper? & how many?

Yours truly
J. CLERK MAXWELL

(15) Rowland, 'On magnetic permeability': 152. Table II gives values for 'iron, magnetic', Table III for 'iron, burnt'.

(16) Compare Rowland's comments in 'On magnetic permeability': 149, 153–4.

(17) Joule had described various experiments on magnetisation (though not the arrangement mentioned by Maxwell), in his 'Account of experiments demonstrating a limit to the magnetizability of iron', *Phil. Mag.*, ser. 4, **2** (1851): 306–15, 447–56.

(18) Jules Jamin, 'Sur la théorie de l'aimant normal et sur le moyen d'augmenter indéfiniment la force des aimants', *Comptes Rendus*, **76** (1873): 789–94; (trans.) 'On the theory of the normal magnet, and the means of augmenting indefinitely the power of magnets', *Phil. Mag.*, ser. 4, **45** (1873): 432–7.

LETTER TO PETER GUTHRIE TAIT

22 JULY 1873

From the original in the University Library, Cambridge[1]

Glenlair 22 July 1873

O. T.

I beg leave to report that I consider the first two pages of Prof. Taits Paper on Orthogonal Isothermal Surfaces[2] as deserving and requiring to be printed in the Transactions of the R.S.E. as a rare and valuable example of the manner of that Master in his Middle or Transition Period, previous to that remarkable condensation, not so say coagulation, of his style which has rendered it impenetrable to all but the piercing intellect of the author in his best moments.

Nemo repente fuit Turpissimus.[3]

Airys Equations[4] are of the form for Turps[5]

$$\rho \frac{d^2\xi}{dt^2} = X = A\frac{d^2\xi}{dz^2} - B\frac{d^3\eta}{dz^3}$$

$$\rho \frac{d^2\eta}{dt^2} = Y = A\frac{d^2\eta}{dz^2} + B\frac{d^3\xi}{dz^3}.\quad {}^{(6)}$$

These under the hypothesis $\zeta = 0$;[7] ξ & η functions of z and t only.

Hence in the potential energy of the system there must be terms of the form $-\xi\frac{d^3\eta}{dz^3}$ & $\eta\frac{d^3\xi}{dz^3}$[8] but in as much as we suppose pot energy to depend on relative, not on absolute displacement, these must be integrated by parts leaving internal parts $\frac{d\xi}{dz}\frac{d^2\eta}{dz^2}$ & $-\frac{d\eta}{dz}\frac{d^2\xi}{dz^2}$.

---

(1) ULC Add. MSS 7655, I, b/58.

(2) P. G. Tait, 'On orthogonal isothermal surfaces. Part I', *Trans. Roy. Soc. Edinb.*, **27** (1873): 105–23.

(3) 'No one ever suddenly became depraved'; Juvenal, *Satires*, ii, 83.

(4) Airy's mathematical treatment of the Faraday magneto-optic effect (on which see Number 434); see G. B. Airy, 'On the equations applying to light under the action of magnetism', *Phil. Mag.*, ser. 3, **28** (1846): 469–77, esp. 472. Airy cites James MacCullagh, who had previously obtained equations containing terms of the form d^3/dz^3 in his paper 'On the laws of the double refraction of quartz', *Transactions of the Royal Irish Academy*, **17** (1837): 461–9. Compare Maxwell's discussion of Airy's and MacCullagh's equations of motion in his treatment of the Faraday magneto-optic effect in the *Treatise*, **2**: 413–14 (§830).

(5) Turpentine: see Number 441 esp. note (8).

(6) ξ and η are displacements at time t parallel to the x and y axes.

(7) ζ is the displacement parallel to the z axis. (8) Compare Number 441.

The question then arises. Since in Turps there are no fixed axes, these terms must form part of an invariant which is reduced to this form when $\zeta = 0$ & ξ & η independent of x & y. Now $S\nabla\sigma$ is an invariant but will not do but σ, $V\nabla\sigma$ $\nabla^2\sigma$ $V\nabla^3\sigma$ &c are vectors[9] the scalar part of the product of any two of which is independent of the directions of the axes of $x\,y\,z$.

Now $\nabla^2\sigma \cdot V\nabla\sigma$ ($= S\nabla^2\sigma\nabla\sigma$)[10] is of the right dimensions in ∇ (or d) and is when expanded of the form (never mind signs)

$$\left(\frac{d^2\xi}{dx^2}+\frac{d^2\xi}{dy^2}+\frac{d^2\xi}{dz^2}\right)\left(\frac{d\zeta}{dy}-\frac{d\eta}{\delta z}\right)$$
$$+\left(\frac{d^2\eta}{dx^2}+\frac{d^2\eta}{dy^2}+\frac{d^2\eta}{dz^2}\right)\left(\frac{d\xi}{dz}-\frac{d\zeta}{dx}\right)$$
$$+\left(\frac{d^2\zeta}{dx^2}+\frac{d^2\zeta}{dy^2}+\frac{d^2\zeta}{dz^2}\right)\left(\frac{d\eta}{dx}-\frac{d\xi}{dy}\right)^{(11)}$$

which is an invariant and when $\zeta = 0$ & ξ & η independent of x & y is reduced to

$$\frac{d\xi}{dz}\frac{d^2\eta}{dz^2}-\frac{d\eta}{dz}\frac{d^2\xi}{dz^2}$$

the form required.

The fact that the rotation is *roughly* as inverse square of wave length[12] with corrections for dispersion[13] shows that this is the form of the principal part of the term in **B**.[14]

But what if the body is turned about axis of x through a few degrees. Then values of $\frac{d\eta}{dz}$ arise without any strain of the body.

Moral: – These things are molecular & not to be explained by the diff: co: and ∇ of a continuous medium.

For your diamagnetic experiment[15] the best thing you can do is to throw your polarized light into a mass of Jargon.

The absorption lines are much more distinct in scientific Jargon[16] than in

---

(9) See Numbers 347 and 396 note (8).
(10) Compare Number 441.
(11) ξ, η, ζ are the components of the vector σ; and see Number 441 note (9).
(12) Émile Verdet, 'Recherches sur les propriétés optiques développées dans les corps transparents par l'action du magnétisme. De la dispersion des plans de polarisations des rayons de diverses couleurs', *Ann. Chim. Phys.*, ser. 3, **69** (1863): 415–91, esp. 438. See the *Treatise*, 2: 413 (§830).
(13) Verdet, 'Recherches sur les propriétés optiques...': 439–41.
(14) Magnetic induction.   (15) See Number 440 esp. note (2).
(16) See notes (17) and (18).

ordinary materials. One very sharp one appears in light polarized one way and not in the other kind of polarized light.

See Sorby on Absorption.[17]

I believe that what is called scientifically Jargon and vulgarly Zircon[18] is derived from some of the settlements containing Christians of S Thomas and indeed contains Didymium.[19]

I think all recriminations between men of science on opposite sides of the Atlantic should be refused admittance into *Nature* or any other paper till they have been passed through the cable.[20] If one cabling is not sufficient to defæcate them, give them two more, and then if necessary send them round by Peru & Pernambuco till they are either cleansed themselves or have corroded the cables, in wh: case let the authors spend their time in discovering and mending the faults. You will see presently in Phil: Mag: a meritorious research of a modern Trojan[21] into the magnetizability of Iron Steel & Nickel.[22] He has hit on a good way of shooting at the maximum of magnetization by means of a curve, which as the result of plotting is good, but as the result of an equation is ludicrous.

$$L'\text{Equation du Beau}$$
$$\text{exprimée par la formule Arithmétique}$$
$$B = 2^{\pm m}(1 \times 3^{\pm n} \times 5^{\pm p}).$$

---

(17) H. C. Sorby claimed to discover an element 'jargonium' from investigation of the absorption spectra of zirconium ore; see his paper 'On jargonium, a new elementary substance associated with zirconium', *Proc. Roy. Soc.*, **17** (1869): 511–15.

(18) Sorby admitted that the 'jargon' spectral lines were due to uranium; see his paper 'On some remarkable spectra of compounds of zirconium and the oxides of uranium', *Proc. Roy. Soc.*, **18** (1870): 197–207.

(19) A rare metal found in association with lanthanum and cerium, difficult to separate from lanthanum, and hence named 'didymium' ($\delta\iota\delta\upsilon\mu o\varsigma$, twin); see Henry Watts, *A Dictionary of Chemistry*, 5 vols. (London, 1863–9), **2**: 321.

(20) Maxwell is alluding to the virulent exchanges, currently filling the letters column of *Nature*, between Alexander Agassiz (of Harvard) and George Forbes (of St Andrews) over the relations – both scientific and personal – between their fathers Louis Agassiz and James David Forbes in the formulation of theories of glacial motion in the early 1840s. See Alexander Agassiz, 'Originators of glacial theories', *Nature*, **8** (1873): 24–5; George Forbes, 'Agassiz and Forbes', *ibid.*: 44; Forbes, 'Forbes and Agassiz', *ibid.*: 64–5; Agassiz, 'Agassiz and Forbes', *ibid.*: 222–3. This correspondence had been sparked off by the publication of *The Life and Letters of James David Forbes* (London, 1873), written jointly by J. C. Shairp, P. G. Tait and A. Adams-Reilly. See also Number 477.

(21) 'Rowland of Troy, that doughty knight' (*Life of Maxwell*: 645).

(22) See Numbers 466 and 467.

'Le bon goût semble être l'apanage de la France dans les expositions universelles.   Edouard Lagout.'
Voyez Les Mondes 17 July[23]

I return the epistle of the Knight.

$$\frac{\partial p}{\partial t}$$

---

[23] See a report in *Les Mondes*, **31** (17 July 1873): 480–96, esp. 486–7, on a theory of rules of beauty.

469

POSTCARD TO PETER GUTHRIE TAIT

24 JULY 1873

From the original in the University Library, Cambridge[1]

[Glenlair]

O T Can you supply me with the no. of grammes of Hydrogen in a litre at a named temperature and pressure.[2] I require the value of $\frac{p}{\rho}$ in absolute measure and I have not the data here.

Also do you know if L. Boltzmann has done any thing new in electricity?[3] Wiedemann[4] in a letter seems to imply it. I only know Boltzmann as a student of the ultimate distribution of vis viva in a swarm of molecules.[5]

Viscosity in centimetre-gramme-second measure, deduced from Loschmidt on Diffusion of gases by the elastic-sphere theory compared with $\frac{dp}{dt}$ direct.[6]

	Loschmidt	$\frac{dp}{dt}$ direct
Hyd	0.0001112	0.0000967
Ox	0.0002581	
CO	0.0002076	
CO_2	0.0002049	0.0001612

Note on Ångström[7] received today. No explanation of $\alpha\ \alpha'\ \alpha_2$ &c.[8]

---

(1) ULC Add. MSS 7655, I, b/59. Previously published in *Molecules and Gases*: 493–4.

(2) See Number 470, esp. notes (1) and (2).

(3) See especially Ludwig Boltzmann, 'Experimentaluntersuchung über die elektrostatische Fernwirkung dielektrischer Körper', *Wiener Berichte*, **63**, Abtheilung II (1873): 81–155.

(4) Gustav Wiedemann; the letter is not extant.

(5) Ludwig Boltzmann, 'Studien über das Gleichgewicht der lebendigen Kraft zwischen bewegeten materiellen Punkten', *Wiener Berichte*, **58**, Abtheilung II (1868): 517–60.

(6) Compare the values cited in Number 470.

(7) P. G. Tait, 'Note on Ångström's method for the conductivity of bars', *Proc. Roy. Soc. Edinb.*, **8** (1873): 55–61, read 17 February 1873.

(8) See A. J. Ångström, 'Neue Methode das Wärmeleitungsvermögen der Körper zu bestimmen', *Ann. Phys.*, **114** (1861): 513–30; (trans.) 'New method of determining the thermal conductibility of bodies', *Phil. Mag.*, ser. 4, **25** (1863): 130–42, esp. 132–3. α, α' are terms in Ångström's equations for the conducting power of bodies.

$$\text{Write } q_n = \sqrt{\frac{\pi n}{kT}}(1-e).^{(9)}$$

How long were the bars?[10]

If you go 17 miles per minute and take a totally new course 1700,000,000 times in a second where will you be in an hour?

---

(9) See Tait, 'Note on Ångström's method': 56. T is the period of heating and cooling of a metal bar, k the conducting power, and q_n a term in the equation for the periodic heating of a bar.

(10) On Tait's continuing interest see his paper 'Thermal and electrical conductivity', *Trans. Roy. Soc. Edinb.*, **28** (1878): 717–40.

DRAFT OF 'ON LOSCHMIDTS EXPERIMENTS ON DIFFUSION'[1]

LATE JULY 1873[2]

From the original in the University Library, Cambridge[3]

ON THE APPLICATION OF LOSCHMIDTS EXPERIMENTS ON THE DIFFUSION OF GASES[4] TO THE DETERMINATION OF MOLECULAR QUANTITIES

There are three phenomena from which data may be obtained for the investigation of the nature of gases on the kinetic theory of their molecular constitution.

According to this theory the molecules of a gas are in a state of very rapid motion. Each individual molecule would in consequence of this motion pass from one side to another of the containing vessel with a speed of several hundreds of metres per second if it were not interrupted in its course by collisions with other molecules.

These interruptions however occur so often that the molecule in spite of its rapid motion travels very slowly through the crowd of other molecules against which it is always jostling. But though the molecules are thus made to spend a long time on their journey they still travel about, and a process of diffusion is always going on so that any particular set of molecules which were in a certain part of the vessel at first will become gradually scattered throughout the whole vessel.

If these molecules are of a different chemical nature from the rest the fact of their diffusion may be verified by chemical analysis of the contents of different parts of the vessel.

This has been done by Graham who obtained the first rough estimate of the

---

(1) Published in *Nature*, **8** (1873): 298–300 (= *Scientific Papers*, **2**: 343–50).

(2) The paper was published in the issue of *Nature* dated 14 August 1873; and see Maxwell's postcards to Tait of 24 and 30 July 1873 (Numbers 469 and 471). The available documentary evidence – see notes (19) and (25) — suggests that this draft was written during the last week of July 1873.

(3) ULC Add. MSS 7655, IV, 2 *verso*. Published in part in *Molecules and Gases*: 477–82.

(4) Joseph Loschmidt, 'Experimental-Untersuchungen über die Diffusion von Gasen ohne poröse Scheidewände', *Wiener Berichte*, **61**, Abtheilung II (1870): 367–80; *ibid.*, **62**, Abtheilung II (1870): 468–78.

rate of diffusion.(5) The coefficients of diffusion of several pairs of gases have since been determined with great accuracy by Prof. Loschmidt of Vienna, and in making a revision of the kinetic theory of gases and comparing these results of Prof. Loschmidt with that theory I obtained evidence of the consistency of these results with each other and with the other experimental data of the theory which I consider encouraging both to experimenters and speculators.

Besides the diffusion of matter with which we are now dealing there are two other kinds of diffusion on which experiments have been made – that of momentum or the lateral communication of sensible motion from one portion of a gas to another, and that of kinetic energy.

The diffusion of momentum gives rise to internal friction or viscosity, that of energy to the conduction of heat. Investigations on viscosity have been made by Graham(6) O. E. Meyer(7) and myself.(8) They involve the consideration of the mutual action between the moving gas and the surfaces of the solids over which it moves. Hence in all these investigations it is only by carefully arranged methods of comparison that trustworthy results can be obtained. The conduction of heat in air has recently been investigated experimentally by Prof. Stephan of Vienna who finds his results in striking agreement with the kinetic theory(9) but the practical difficulties of the investigation are even greater than in the case of viscosity.

In Prof Loschmidts experiments on diffusion on the other hand everything appears favourable to the accuracy of the results. He appears to have got rid of all disturbing currents, and his methods of measurement, founded on those of Bunsen(10) are most precise. The interdiffusing gases are left to themselves

---

(5) Thomas Graham, 'A short account of experimental researches on the diffusion of gases through each other, and their separation by mechanical means', *Quarterly Journal of Science*, **20** (1829): 74–83; and Graham, 'On the molecular mobility of gases', *Phil. Trans.*, **153** (1863): 385–405.

(6) Thomas Graham, 'On the motion of gases', *Phil. Trans.*, **136** (1846): 573–632; Graham, 'On the motion of gases. Part II', *Phil. Trans.*, **139** (1849): 349–401.

(7) O. E. Meyer, 'Ueber die Reibung der Flüssigkeiten', *Ann. Phys.*, **113** (1861): 55–86, 193–228, 383–425; Meyer, 'Ueber die innere Reibung der Gase', *Ann. Phys.*, **125** (1865): 177–209, 401–20, 564–99; Meyer, 'Ueber die Reibung der Gase', *Ann. Phys.*, **127** (1866): 253–81, 353–82.

(8) J. Clerk Maxwell, 'On the viscosity or internal friction of air and other gases', *Phil. Trans.*, **156** (1866): 249–88 (= *Scientific Papers*, **2**: 1–25). See Number 252.

(9) Read: Josef Stefan, 'Untersuchungen über die Wärmeleitung in Gasen', *Wiener Berichte*, **65**, Abtheilung II (1872): 45–69. See Number 425, esp. note (5).

(10) Robert Bunsen, *Gasometrische Methoden* (Braunschweig, 1857); (trans. H. E. Roscoe), *Gasometry. Comprising the Leading Physical and Chemical Properties of Gases* (London, 1857).

and are not disturbed by the presence of any solid body. The results of different experiments with the same pair of gases are very consistent with each other. They prove conclusively that the coefficient of diffusion varies inversely as the pressure a result in accordance with the kinetic theory whatever hypothesis we assume for the mode of action between the molecules.

They also show that the coefficient of diffusion increases as the temperature rises, but the range of temperature in the experiments was too small to enable us to decide whether it varies as T^2 which it does according to the theory of a force varying inversely as the fifth power of the distance[11] or as $T^{\frac{3}{2}}$ as it does according to the theory of elastic spherical molecules.[12] In comparing the coefficients of diffusion of different pairs of gases Prof. Loschmidt has adopted a formula which is simple enough but which does not appear to me to agree with the kinetic theory and from which he deduces values of a quantity k' which according to him should be constant for all gases[13] but these values do not agree together in the manner which we should expect from the accuracy of the experiments.

According to the kinetic theory as deduced from the collisions of elastic spheres the coefficient of diffusion between two gases at standard pressure and temperature

$$D_{12} = \frac{p_1 p_2}{\rho_1 \rho_2} \frac{M_1 + M_2}{\pi s^2 V}$$

$$D_{12} = \sqrt{\frac{1}{W_1} + \frac{1}{W_2}} \frac{\mathfrak{M} V}{N} \frac{1}{2\sqrt{6\pi}} \frac{1}{s_{12}^2}$$

where W_1 & W_2 are the molecular weights of the gases that of hydrogen being unity $\mathfrak{M}$ is the mass of a molecule of hydrogen V the velocity of mean square for hydrogen $= \sqrt{\dfrac{3p}{\rho}}$ at standard pressure and temperature N the number of molecules in unit of volume (the same for all gases),[14] and s_{12} the distance between the centres at collision.

---

(11) J. Clerk Maxwell, 'On the dynamical theory of gases', *Phil. Trans.*, **157** (1867): 49–88, esp. 75 (= *Scientific Papers*, **2**: 60). See Number 263.

(12) The theory proposed by Maxwell in his 'Illustrations of the dynamical theory of gases', *Phil. Mag.*, ser. 4, **19** (1860): 19–32; ibid., **20** (1860): 21–37 (= *Scientific Papers*, **1**: 377–409).

(13) Defining $k' = k_0/\sqrt{m_1 m_2}$, where k_0 is the diffusion coefficient at standard temperature and pressure, and m_1 and m_2 are the masses of the molecules of two gases; see Loschmidt, 'Experimental-Untersuchungen über die Diffusion von Gasen', *Wiener Berichte*, **62**, Abtheilung II (1870): 476.

(14) 'Loschmidt's number'; see Number 259 note (13).

Hence if we write $A^2 = \dfrac{\mathfrak{M} V}{N 2\sqrt{6\pi}}$

and $\sum_{12}^2 = \dfrac{1}{D_{12}} \sqrt{\dfrac{1}{W_1} + \dfrac{1}{W_2}}$

We find $s_{12} = A \sum_{12}$.

The quantity A which is constant for all gases contains two hitherto unknown quantities, the mass of a molecule of hydrogen and the number of molecules in unit of volume. The product of these quantities is the density of hydrogen, a known quantity but their ratio which appears in A is not fully ascertained though Prof Loschmidt himself was the first to estimate it roughly[15] which has been since repeated independently by Mr Stoney[16] and Sir W Thomson.[17]

The quantity $\sum_{12}$ is proportional to the distance between the centres of the molecules at the instant of collision or to $r_1 + r_2$ if r_1 and r_2 are the radii of the molecules. Now from Prof Loschmidts data we can deduce the values of $\sum$ for the six pairs of gases which may be made up from the four gases H, O, CO and CO_2. These according to our theory are not independent, being the six sums of pairs of the four independent quantities $r_1\ r_2\ r_3\ r_4$.

Accordingly assuming

$2r(H) = 1.739 \qquad 2r(O) = 2.283$
$2r(CO) = 2.461 \qquad 2r(CO_2) = 2.775$

we find

	By calculation $\sum_{12} = r_1 + r_2$	By Loschmidt $\sum_{12} = \sqrt{\sqrt{\dfrac{1}{W_1}+\dfrac{1}{W_2}}\dfrac{1}{D_{12}}}$
$\sum(H, O)$	2011[18]	1992
$\sum(H, CO)$	2100	2116
$\sum(H, CO_2)$	2257	2260
$\sum(O, CO)$	2372	2375
$\sum(O, CO_2)$	2529	2545
$\sum(CO, CO_2)$	2618	2599

(15) Joseph Loschmidt, 'Zur Grösse der Luftmolecüle', *Wiener Berichte*, **52**, Abtheilung II (1865): 395–413.

(16) G. J. Stoney, 'The internal motions of gases compared with the motions of waves of light', *Phil. Mag.*, ser. 4, **36** (1868): 132–41.

(17) William Thomson, 'The size of atoms', *Nature*, **1** (1870): 551–3 (= *Math. & Phys. Papers*, **5**: 289–96). (18) Read: 2.011 in centimetre-second measure.

The agreement of these numbers furnishes I think strong evidence in favour of the kinetic theory of gases. But we may derive evidence of a higher order by a comparison between experiments of two entirely different kinds, those on diffusion, already spoken of and those on viscosity.

If μ is the viscosity of a gas and ρ its density at standard temperature and pressure the theory gives

$$\frac{\mu}{\rho} = A\sqrt{\frac{2}{W}}\frac{1}{(2r)^2}$$

so that we have the following relation between the viscosities of two gases and their coefficient of diffusion

$$2D_{12} = \frac{\mu_1}{\rho_1} + \frac{\mu_2}{\rho_2}.$$

Calculating on this system the viscosities of the gases experimented on by Loschmidt in centimetre gramme second measure and comparing them with those deduced by O E Meyer from his own experiments and those of Graham and with my own we find[19]

	μ	Meyer[20]	Maxwell
H	0.000116	0.000134	0.0000971
O	270	306	
CO	217	266	
CO_2	214	231	0.000161

The numbers do not appear to agree very well with each other. The numbers given by Meyer are greater than those deduced from diffusion. Mine, on the other hand, are smaller. I have no doubt however that the best method of determining all these quantities is by the comparison of the diffusion coefficients of a great many pairs of gases.

I have shown that by this method we may obtain a set of numbers which are proportional to the diameters of the molecules of different gases. From these we can determine their relative volumes and since we already know their relative masses we can determine the relative densities of the molecules.

---

(19) The values here cited correspond with those in the published paper 'On Loschmidt's experiments on diffusion': 300 (= *Scientific Papers*, 2: 347), but differ from those in the postcard to Tait of 24 July 1873 (Number 469), suggesting late July 1873 for the date of composition of this draft.

(20) O. E. Meyer, 'Ueber die Reibung der Gase', *Ann. Phys.*, **127** (1866): 253–81, 353–82, on 378–9.

These densities have been compared by Loschmidt and Lorenz Meyer[21] with the densities of the same substances in the liquid condition and with the 'molecular volumes' of the substance in its compounds as estimated by Kopp.[22] It appears from these comparisons that the relative molecular volumes of the gases whose viscosity has been determined are on the whole roughly proportional to those of the same substances in the liquid state or in their liquid compounds.

It is manifest, however that the density of the molecules must be greater than that of the liquified substance, for even if we could determine the density of the substance at $-273\,°C$ and at an infinite pressure there would still be interstices between the spherical molecules. Indeed the method of estimating molecular volume by observations on liquids at the boiling point under a pressure of 76 cm of mercury seems a very arbitrary one, for there is no reason why the average pressure of our atmosphere at the level of the sea should be placed on any very high rank as a physical constant.

It is probable that at all observed temperatures the molecules of bodies are kept further apart by their motion of agitation than they would be if in actual contact. It is therefore more likely that we should obtain consistent results if we measured the molecular volume of substances when that volume is the smallest attainable.

The volume relations of potassium its oxide and its hydrated oxide as described by Faraday[23] seem to indicate that the whole theory of molecular volume is not quite understood.

If, however we assume as the molecular volume of oxygen that deduced by Kopp from that of oxide of tin namely 2.7 when $O = 16$ which is the smallest of those quoted by L. Meyer[24] we find for the number of molecules of any gas in a cubic centimetre at 760 mm and 0 °C

$$N = 19 \times 10^{18}$$

Hence the side of a cube which would on an average contain one molecule is

$$N^{-\frac{1}{3}} = 37.47 \text{ tenth metres.}^{(25)}$$

---

(21) Read: Lothar Meyer, 'Ueber die Molecularvolumina chemische Verbindungen', *Annalen der Chemie und Pharmacie*, **5** Supplementband (1867): 129–47.

(22) Hermann Kopp, 'Ueber Atomvolum, Isomorphismus und specifisches Gewicht', *Annalen der Chemie und Pharmacie*, **36** (1840): 1–32.

(23) Michael Faraday, 'A speculation touching electric conduction and the nature of matter', *Phil. Mag.*, ser. 3, **24** (1844): 136–44, esp. 139–40 (= *Electricity*, **2**: 288–9).

(24) L. Meyer, 'Ueber die Molecularvolumina chemischer Verbindungen': 145.

(25) Tenth metre is 10^{-10} metre, as noted by Maxwell on the *verso* of a letter from George Griffith of 27 July 1873 (ULC Add. MSS 7655, II/72). This measure had been introduced by Stoney, 'The internal motions of gases compared with the motions of waves of light':

The mass of molecule of hydrogen is
$$= 4.607 \times 10^{-24} \text{ grammes}$$
and its diameter is 5.8 tenth metres.

        O   7.6
        CO   8.3
        CO_2 9.3

These estimates are much smaller than those of Prof Loschmidt Mr Stoney and Sir W Thomson. This arises from the molecular volume of oxygen being assumed much smaller than is usually done.

There is another quantity, however which plays a considerable part in the kinetic theory as developed by Clausius namely the mean length of the uninterrupted path of a molecule.[26] The determination of this quantity does not involve any estimate of such doubtful matters as the density of a molecule. We find the length of the mean path

    for Hydrogen $l = 965$ tenth metres
          Oxygen   560
          Carbonic Oxide 482
          Carbonic acid   430.

The length of a wave of green light is about ten times the mean length of path of a molecule of oxygen at 760 mm & 0 °C.[27]

138–9n. Maxwell calculated this value on the *verso* of Griffith's letter; again suggesting late July 1873 for the composition of the draft.

(26) Rudolf Clausius, 'Ueber die mittlere Länge der Wege...', *Ann. Phys.*, **105** (1858): 239–58.

(27) Compare Stoney, 'The internal motions of gases compared with the motions of waves of light'.

471

POSTCARD TO PETER GUTHRIE TAIT

30 JULY 1873
From the original in the University Library, Cambridge[1]

[Glenlair]

O T. $\Theta\alpha\gamma\xi$ for the density of H.[2] What do you expect me to do with Ewing & McGregor on Salts?[3] Figures & curves not sent to me but I see that the ordinates are densities. Now the best ordinates are Volumes of so much of the stuff as contains 1 of the original water. As for Å, if he neglects H, he does so at his peril. How can I save him? Let him sink![4] Have you seen Clausius ueber einen neuen mechanischen Satz in Bezug auf stationäre Bewegungen.[5] For the absolute values of molecular constants to be used for Viscosity diffusion & conduction I think diffusion exp^{ts} as done by Loschmidt for the best and least interfered with by sides of vessel &c. Thus for diameters of molecules of H, O, CO, CO_2.[6]

		Calculated	By diffusion	diff[7]
H	1739	$\frac{1}{2}(H+O) = 2011$	1992	-19
O	2283	$\frac{1}{2}(H+CO) = 2100$	2116	$+16$
CO	2461	$\frac{1}{2}(H+CO_2) = 2257$	2260	$+3$
CO_2	2775	$\frac{1}{2}(O+CO) = 2372$	2375	$+3$
CH	2605	$\frac{1}{2}(O+CO_2) = 2529$	2545	$+16$
NO	3063	$\frac{1}{2}(CO+CO_2) = 2618$	2599	-19
SO_2	3109			

Mass of Hydrogen molecule not less than 10^{-27} gramme.

---

(1) ULC Add. MSS 7655, I, b/60. Previously published in *Molecules and Gases*: 495–6.

(2) See Number 469.

(3) Maxwell had been asked to referee a paper by J. A. Ewing and J. G. MacGregor, 'On the electrical conductivity of certain saline solutions, with a note on the density', *Trans. Roy. Soc. Edinb.*, **27** (1873): 51–70. See Number 474.

(4) See Number 469.

(5) Rudolf Clausius, 'Ueber einen neuen mechanischen Satz in Bezug auf stationäre Bewegungen', *Sitzungsberichte der Niederrheinischen Gesellschaft für Natur- und Heilkunde zu Bonn*, **30** (1873): 136–54 (of which there is a reprint in Maxwell's library (Cavendish Laboratory)).

(6) See Number 470 note (18).

(7) See Tait's comment in his reply of 31 July 1873 (Number 474 note (3)).

DRAFTS OF 'ON THE FINAL STATE OF A SYSTEM OF MOLECULES IN MOTION SUBJECT TO FORCES OF ANY KIND'[1]

circa AUGUST 1873[2]

From the originals in the University Library, Cambridge[3][4]

[1] [5][a]ON THE MOTIONS AND ENCOUNTERS OF MOLECULES. APPLICATION OF HAMILTONS METHOD OF THE HODOGRAPH TO REPRESENT VELOCITIES OF MOLECULES.

1 Method of representing velocities of molecules

The velocity of a body is a Vector that is a quantity which is determinate in direction and magnitude. It may therefore be conveniently represented by the finite straight line which would be traced by the body in unit of time if the velocity of the body remained the same in magnitude and direction during that time.

The position of the first point of this straight line is a matter of indifference so long as the line is considered only with respect to its magnitude and direction; so that although it might appear most natural to draw the line from the actual position of the body at the given time it is more convenient to draw all lines representing velocities from one point, called the Origin.

(a) {Maxwell} Rough notes which you may make any use of, but return before May.[6]

(1) Published in *Nature*, **8** (23 October 1873): 537–8 and in the *Report of the Forty-third Meeting of the British Association for the Advancement of Science*; held at Bradford in September 1873 (London, 1874), part 2: 30–2 (= *Scientific Papers*, **2**: 351–4).

(2) For the circumstances of composition see Numbers 457 and 481; and see note (4).

(3) ULC Add. MSS 7655, V, f/7, 11.

(4) In notes on the 'Dynamical Theory of Gases', which form part of his notes on 'Maxwell's lectures/Oct term 1873' (ULC DAR. 210. 22), George Howard Darwin recorded Maxwell's presentation of the kinetic theory of gases. Maxwell began with an account of the application of the hodograph to represent the velocities of gas molecules. Darwin's notes on Maxwell's lectures on gas theory – part of a course on 'Heat and elasticity' (see *Cambridge University Reporter* (14 October, 1873): 23) – record Maxwell's presentation of the theory in terms similar to the argument of the manuscript drafts printed here. At the conclusion of these notes Darwin appended: 'See Nature for some week in Nov or Oct 1873 for this subject – *Maxwell*'. See also Number 482 note (5).

(5) ULC Add. MSS 7655, V, f/11.

This method has long been known in the construction of what is called the 'parallelogram of velocities' but its value was first clearly shown by Sir W. R. Hamilton who by drawing from one point a series of lines representing the successive velocities of a body, determined a series of points in a curve which he called the Hodograph.[7]

The Hodograph is a curve each point of which corresponds to a point in the path of the body, and by studying the correspondence of these curves the force acting on the body and the whole circumstances of the motion may be ascertained.

In our present investigation we use the same method to compare the simultaneous velocities of different bodies as well as the successive velocities of each.

We may regard this method as an example of one of the most powerful instruments of mathematical research – the simultaneous contemplation of two systems so related to each other that every element in the one has its corresponding element in the other. In pure geometry this study of corresponding elements in two figures has led to the establishment of a Geometry of Position by which results are obtained by pure reasoning without calculation the verification of which by the Cartesian analysis would fill many pages with symbols.

In Statics the same method has enabled us to construct diagrams of stress, by which without calculation the stresses of the pieces of a frame are all represented and in Geometrical Optics the study of the correspondence between the object and the image has been of almost equal service to the theory of optical instruments and to pure geometry.[8]

In all these instances we have to construct a figure the relative position of whose elements indicates not the relative *position* of the corresponding elements of the original system but their relative velocity, the force acting between them or some other physical quantity not apparent to the eye in the original system.

In molecular science this method is especially valuable when we want to form a mental representation of the motion of an immense number of molecules at a given instant. Instead of confusing the image we have already formed of the positions ⌊configuration⌋ of the system [of] molecules by trying to attach to each molecule an arrow or some other symbol to indicate its velocity, we form our image of the velocities on an entirely new field in which

---

(6) Maxwell's pencilled note was probably addressed to H. W. Watson: see note (12).

(7) W. R. Hamilton, 'A new mode of geometrically conceiving, and of expressing in symbolical language, the Newtonian law of attraction', *Proceedings of the Royal Irish Academy*, **3** (1847): 344–53. See Number 276 note (2).

(8) See Numbers 273 note (2) and 480.

their positions are not represented at all. In this figure, to every molecule corresponds a point, and the velocity of the molecule is represented in magnitude and direction by a line drawn from the origin to this point.

Since in all the motions of real bodies the phenomena depend not on their absolute but on their relative velocities, and as these are indicated in the diagram of velocities by the distances between the points of the figure, the position of the origin itself may be transferred from one part of the figure to another without altering the relative position of the points just as the ⌐motion [of a]⌐ system of molecules as a whole may be varied while the relative motion of the molecules may be unaltered.

If there are a great number of molecules having velocities different from each other, the diagram of velocities will contain as many points distributed over the diagram. If we take a small element of volume of the diagram and consider those points which lie within it, these points correspond to molecules whose velocities differ little from each other, either in magnitude or direction.

In studying the motion of the system it is found convenient to divide the molecules into groups according to their velocities, those molecules whose velocities lie within certain limits with respect to magnitude and direction being placed in the same group.

In the diagram of velocities these magnitudes are indicated at once by the points which correspond to them being included within a certain small region of the diagram, the boundaries of this region corresponding to the given limit of velocity.

We shall also find it convenient to use the term velocity-density to indicate the result of dividing the number of molecules whose velocities lie between the given limits by the volume of the corresponding region in the diagram of velocities.

[2][9]   ENCOUNTER OF TWO MOLECULES

If two molecules act on each other only when at a very small distance apart, and if the kinetic energy of the system is not altered by the encounter then if *OA* represents the velocity of the first and *OB* that of the second, *BA* will represent the velocity of *A* with respect to *B*. If *G* is the centre of gravity of the two molecules when placed at *A* and at *B* respectively *OG* will represent the velocity of the centre of ⟨gravity⟩

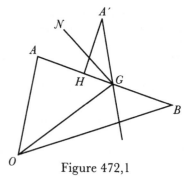

Figure 472,1

---

(9) ULC Add. MSS 7655, V, f/7. Previously published in *Molecules and Gases*: 398–9 (but there printed as a draft fragment preliminary to 'On the dynamical theory of gases' (1867)).

⟨inertia⟩ mass of the two molecules which is not altered by their mutual action.

During the whole motion, therefore, in whatever manner the velocities of the two molecules represented by the lines OA and OB may alter the centre of ⟨inertia⟩ mass, G, will remain fixed.

We shall also assume that the action between the molecules is such that after the encounter the kinetic energy of the system is the same as before. The kinetic energy of the system of two molecules may be divided into two parts the first being the kinetic energy of a mass equal to that of the system and having the velocity of its centre of ⟨gravity⟩ ⟨inertia⟩ mass, and the second being the kinetic energy arising from the motion of the parts of the system relatively to the centre of ⟨inertia⟩ mass.

The first part is necessarily unaffected by any mutual action of the parts of the system. Hence if the whole kinetic energy is the same before and after the encounter the second part must be so.

Now the kinetic energy of the motion relative to the centre of inertia is $\frac{1}{2}(A.\overline{GA}^2 + B.\overline{GB}^2)$ before the encounter or since $A.GA = B.\overline{BG}$ the energy is $\frac{1}{2}\frac{A.B}{A+B}\overline{AB}^2$ and if OA', OB' represent the velocities after the encounter the kinetic energy is $\frac{1}{2}(A.\overline{GA'}^2 + B.\overline{GB'}^2) = \frac{1}{2}\frac{A.B}{A+B}\overline{A'B'}^2$.

Now the ratio of GA to GB is the same before and after the encounter so that if this part of the kinetic energy remains the same after the encounter we must have
$$AB = A'B', \quad GA = GA' \ \& \ GB = GB'.$$

The velocity of the molecules relative to the centre of inertia is therefore unaltered and the result of the encounter is therefore completely defined if the *direction* of this relative velocity be given.

This direction is determined by the angle $AGA' = 2\theta$, and the angle, ϕ, which the plane of AGA' makes with a plane through AG parallel to the axis of x. This plane which may be called the plane of the encounter may be determined by drawing through the line AB a line parallel to the line joining the molecules at any instant. The plane through these two lines is the plane of the encounter. It is manifest that all values of the angle ϕ which determines the angular position of this plane round the line AB are equally probable.

The angle AGA' or 2θ, between the directions of the line GA before and after the encounter depends on the mode in which the force is exerted between the bodies and on their angular momentum about G.

[3]⁽¹⁰⁾ [THE MOTIONS AND ENCOUNTERS OF MOLECULES]

The elements therefore by which the circumstances of an encounter are completely defined are as follows.

The motion of the centre of mass of the two molecules. This motion is not affected by the encounter and the other elements of the encounter are not affected by it. We need not therefore take it into consideration till we have to do with the relation of the encountering molecules to other bodies.

In what follows we shall consider the centre of mass of the two molecules as the origin of the diagram of configurations and of that of velocities. The lines of motion of the two molecules will then be parallel and in opposite directions.

The velocity of the molecule A with respect to B before the encounter is called the velocity of approach and the direction of this velocity is called the direction of approach. The velocity of A with respect to B after the encounter is called the velocity of separation and its direction the direction of separation.

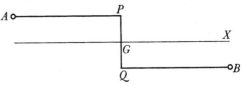

Figure 472,2

The distance, PQ between the lines of motion of the molecules before the encounter is called the arm of approach. The corresponding distance after the encounter is called the arm of separation.

The plane containing the direction of approach and the arm of approach is called the plane of the encounter. During the whole encounter the line joining the molecules remains parallel to this plane.

The angle between the direction of approach and the direction of separation is called the deviation.

The direction and velocity of approach is determined when we know the velocities of the two molecules.

To determine the arm of approach we require also to know the relative position of the two molecules at any instant before the encounter.

The plane of the encounter is thus determined. It is manifest that of all the planes passing through the direction of approach any one is equally likely to

---

(10) ULC Add. MSS 7655, V, f/11. The introductory portion of the manuscript has been published in *Molecules and Gases*: 402–4 (but there printed as a draft fragment preliminary to 'On the dynamical theory of gases' (1867)).

be the plane of the encounter. The angle of deviation depends on the velocity of approach and on the arm of approach. If the force with which the molecules act on each other does not pass through their centres of mass the angular positions of the molecules at the instant of encounter may affect the deviation, but we do not attempt to take account of this kind of irregularity otherwise than by classing those encounters as of the same kinds in which this irregularity as well as the other elements has the same value.

Neglecting this irregularity the velocity of separation is equal to that of approach but its direction is turned through the angle of deviation in the plane of the encounter.

Whatever be the circumstances of an encounter it is always possible to arrange the positions of the molecules for a second encounter such that the velocities of approach and separation in the second encounter shall be those of separation and approach in the first. For if we suppose the whole figure of the encounter turned round through two right angles in the plane of the encounter, and the directions of motion reversed, the velocity of approach in the original figure will be equal and parallel to the velocity of separation in the inverted figure and *vice versâ*.

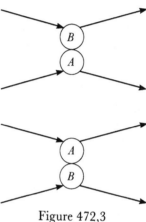

Figure 472,3

The arm of approach in the one figure is equal and parallel to that in the other figure, but it is drawn in the opposite direction.

We are now prepared to investigate the fundamental problem in the theory of molecules – the determination of the ultimate state of a multitude of moving molecules confined in a vessel in such a way that neither the molecules themselves, nor their energy, can escape.

For greater generality we shall suppose the molecules to be of several different kinds and we shall distinguish the quantities belonging to the different sets of molecules by different suffixes. We shall also suppose that the molecules are acted on by attractions or repulsions towards fixed points. The effect of gravity on the motion of a set of molecules will thus be included in our solution but for the sake of generality we shall only assume that the force acting on any set of the molecules is such that it may be derived from a potential and we may even suppose the form of this potential to be different for different sets of molecules.

Let x, y, z be the coordinates of a molecule of mass M and let ξ, η, ζ be the components of its velocity and let N be the number of such molecules in unit of volume and let ψ be the potential of the force which acts on this set of molecules.

The number of molecules of this kind which on an average have their coordinates between the limits x and $x+dx$, y and $y+dy$, z and $z+dz$ and also the components of their velocity between ξ and $\xi+d\xi$, η and $\eta+d\eta$, ζ and $\zeta+d\zeta$ must be a function of $x, y, z; \xi, \eta, \zeta; dx, dy, dz$ and $d\xi, d\eta, d\zeta$ of the form

$$\mathfrak{N} = f(x\ y\ z\ \xi\ \eta\ \zeta)\,dx\,dy\,dz\,d\xi\,d\eta\,d\zeta. \tag{1}$$

We have to investigate the form of this function.

We shall begin by determining the manner in which this function depends on the components of velocity (ξ, η, ζ) before we proceed to investigate in what manner it depends on the coordinates (x, y, z).

For this purpose we shall consider the effect of an encounter between two molecules which we shall assume to be of the first and the second kind respectively, distinguished by the suffixes 1 and 2. The whole number of molecules of the first kind in unit of volume of the given place which have their component velocities within the given limits may be written

$$f_1(\xi_1\ \eta_1\ \zeta_1)\,d\xi_1\,d\eta_1\,d\zeta_1 = n_1. \tag{2}$$

The number of molecules of the second kind selected in a similar manner according to the velocities may be written

$$f_2(\xi_2\ \eta_2\ \zeta_2)\,d\xi_2\,d\eta_2\,d\zeta_2 = n_2. \tag{3}$$

The number of pairs which can be formed by taking one molecule out of each of these groups is $n_1 n_2$.

The result of an encounter between the two molecules forming one of these pairs will depend on the elements of position of the molecules, that is to say on the arm of approach and on the plane of the encounter if the action between the molecules passes through their centres of mass. If the mode of action depends on the angular position of each molecule about its centre of mass then this also must be taken into account.

Let us class all encounters as of the same kind when these elements of position differ from certain specified values by less than certain given small quantities.

Now it is shewn in treatises on dynamics*[11] that if in any motion a certain

* Thomson & Taits Natural Philosophy Vol 1 p 250[11]

---

(11) Thomson and Tait, *Natural Philosophy*: 250. Thomson and Tait there (§328) discuss Hamilton's 'characteristic function', and establish that for a system of rigid bodies or connected particles, if ξ, η are momenta corresponding to coordinates ψ, χ, then '$\dfrac{d\xi}{d\chi} = \dfrac{d\eta}{d\psi}$ if both coordinates belong to one configuration, or $\dfrac{d\xi}{d\chi} = -\dfrac{d\eta}{d\psi}$, if one belongs to the initial configuration, and the other to the final'. Compare Maxwell's similar argument in his paper 'On Boltzmann's

variation δq_a in one of the elements of position of the initial motion causes a variation $\delta p'_b$ in one of the elements of momentum in the final motion then if the direction of motion be reversed a variation δq_b equal in magnitude to δq_a in the initial element of position will cause a variation $-\delta p'_a$ equal in magnitude to δp_b in the final element of momentum

$$\frac{dp'_a}{dq_b} = -\frac{dp_b}{dq'_a}.$$

We have already shown that if the system be turned round 180° in the plane of the encounter and the direction of motion reversed we have an encounter in which the initial velocities agree in direction and magnitude with the final velocities in the original encounter and in which the final velocities agree with the original velocities in the first encounter.

We now see that equal variations in the initial elements of position lead to equal variations in the final elements of velocity in the two encounters.

Let us now consider a set of encounters all the elements of which except the velocity of the centre of mass agree within very close limits but let the velocity of the centre of mass of the two molecules be anywhere between the limits $\bar{\xi}$ and $\bar{\xi}+d\xi$, $\bar{\eta}$ and $\bar{\eta}+d\eta$ and $\bar{\zeta}$ and $\bar{\zeta}+d\zeta$.

Since the velocities relative to the centre of mass are the same for all the encounters the limits of the velocity of the molecule A before the encounter will be ξ_1 & $\xi_1+d\xi$, η_1 and $\eta_1+d\eta$, ζ_1 and $\zeta_1+d\zeta$ and those of B will be ξ_2 and $\xi_2+d\xi$, η_2 and $\eta_2+d\eta$, ζ_2 and $\zeta_2+d\zeta$. We shall call these the original limits.

If the symbols of the velocities after the encounter are distinguished by accents their limits will be

ξ'_1 and $\xi'_1+d\xi$ η'_1 and $\eta'_1+d\eta$ ζ'_1 and $\zeta'_1+d\zeta$ for A

and ξ'_2 and $\xi'_2+d\xi$ η'_2 and $\eta'_2+d\eta$ ζ'_2 and $\zeta'_2+d\zeta$ for B.

We shall call these the final limits.

The number of pairs of molecules which have their original velocities lying within the given limits is

$$f_1(\xi_1\ \eta_1\ \zeta_1)f_2(\xi_2\ \eta_2\ \zeta_2)\ (d\xi\, d\eta\, d\zeta)^2. \tag{4}$$

The proportion of these whose elements of position lie within the assigned limits may be represented by the factor ρ.

Hence the number of pairs which change their velocities from the given original to the given final velocities is

$$\rho f_1(\xi_1\ \eta_1\ \zeta_1)f_2(\xi_2\ \eta_2\ \zeta_2)\ (d\xi\, d\eta\, d\zeta)^2. \tag{5}$$

---

theorem on the average distribution of energy in a system of material points', *Trans. Camb. Phil. Soc.*, **12** (1879): 547–70, esp. 551 (= *Scientific Papers*, **2**: 718).

But we have seen that it is possible for two molecules to have an encounter in which the original and final velocities are the final and original velocities of the first encounter and that the factor which expresses the condition that the elements of the encounter shall be within given limits is the same in both cases. Hence the number of encounters of the second kind is

$$\rho f_1(\xi'_1\ \eta'_1\ \zeta'_1) f_2(\xi'_2\ \eta'_2\ \zeta'_2)\ (d\xi\ d\eta\ d\zeta)^2. \tag{6}$$

In these encounters the velocities change from the final to the original limits. Thus there is an exchange of molecules between the two groups whose velocities lie within the original and the final limits respectively. In the ultimate state of the system as many pairs of molecules must pass from the final to the original as from the original to the final velocities. Hence in the ultimate state we may equate (5) and (6) or omitting the common factors

$$f_1(\xi_1\ \eta_1\ \zeta_1) f_2(\xi_2\ \eta_2\ \zeta_2) = f_1(\xi'_1\ \eta'_1\ \zeta'_1) f_2(\xi'_2\ \eta'_2\ \zeta'_2) \tag{7}$$

One and only one necessary relation exists between the variables before and after the encounter namely that which expresses the conservation of the kinetic energy of the system

$$M_1 V_1^2 + M_2 V_2^2 = M_1 V_1'^2 + M_2 V_2'^2 \tag{8}$$

where the symbol V denotes the velocity and

$$V^2 = \xi^2 + \eta^2 + \zeta^2. \tag{9}$$

Since $f(\xi, \eta, \zeta)$ cannot depend on the directions assumed for the axes of $\xi\ \eta\ \zeta$ we may write it

$$f(\xi, \eta, \zeta) = e^{F(V)} \tag{10}$$

Hence taking the logarithm of equation (7) it becomes

$$F_1(V_1) + F_2(V_2) = F_1(V'_1) + F_2(V'_2) \tag{11}$$

whatever be the values of $V_1\ V_2\ V'_1\ V'_2$

provided
$$M_1 V_1^2 + M_2 V_2^2 = M_1 V_1'^2 + M_2 V_2'^2. \tag{12}$$

From this we obtain

$$F_1(V_1) = B_1 - AM_1 V_1^2, \quad F_2(V_2) = B_2 - AM_2 V_2^2 \tag{13}$$

where A is a constant common to both functions and B_1, B_2 are independent.

We may now write the expression (1) in the more definite form

$$\mathfrak{N} = e^{B - AMV^2} d\xi\ d\eta\ d\zeta\ dx\ dy\ dz \tag{14}$$

where B is a function of x, y, z which may be different for different kinds of molecules while A, though it may, for ought we know be a function of $x\ y\ z$ is the same for the different kinds of molecules.

The relation between the velocities immediately before and immediately after a sudden encounter is not affected by the continuous action of finite forces on the molecules. Hence the above expression for the distribution of velocities at any given point is true whether external forces act or not. The effect of external forces is to alter the velocity of the molecules while they are describing their free paths.

Let us now confine our attention to molecules of the first kind and let us suppose that they are acted on by a force whose potential is ψ_1.[12]

Consider the $\mathfrak{N}$ molecules whose coordinates of position are $x\,y\,z$ and whose components of velocity are $\xi\,\eta\,\zeta$.

Let us follow any one of these molecules in its motion. The rates of variation of the coordinates are

$$\frac{dx}{dt} = \xi \quad \frac{dy}{dt} = \eta \quad \frac{dz}{dt} = \zeta. \tag{15}$$

The rates of variation of the component velocities are

$$\frac{d\xi}{dt} = -\frac{d\psi}{dx} \quad \frac{d\eta}{dt} = -\frac{d\psi}{dy} \quad \frac{d\zeta}{dt} = -\frac{d\psi}{dz}. \tag{16}$$

Hence if we consider $\mathfrak{N}$ as a function of $x\,y\,z\,\xi\,\eta\,\zeta$

$$\frac{d.\log \mathfrak{N}}{dt} = \frac{dB}{dx}\xi + \frac{dB}{dy}\eta + \frac{dB}{dz}\zeta$$
$$+ 2AM\left(\xi\frac{d\psi}{dx} + \eta\frac{d\psi}{dy} + \zeta\frac{d\psi}{dz}\right)$$
$$- MV^2\left(\frac{dA}{dx}\xi + \frac{dA}{dy}\eta + \frac{dA}{dz}\zeta\right). \tag{17}$$

---

(12) On Maxwell's acknowledgment to Boltzmann for this method see Number 481. See Ludwig Boltzmann, 'Studien über das Geichgewicht der lebendigen Kraft zwischen bewegten materiellen Punkten', *Wiener Berichte*, **58**, Abtheilung II (1868): 517–60, esp. 555–60. In his *A Treatise on the Kinetic Theory of Gases* (Oxford, 1876): 12–13, H. W. Watson discussed the problem of deriving Maxwell's distribution law for a system of molecules in the presence of an external field of force, noting that his theorem was 'due originally to Dr. Ludwig Boltzmann and subsequently modified by Professor Maxwell.' He was here alluding to Maxwell's published paper 'On the final state of a system of molecules in motion subject to forces of any kind' (see note (1)). Watson considers any number of molecules, divided into two sets in a unit of volume, the molecules being acted on by impressed forces tending to fixed centres, and expressed as space variations of a potential function. His method of presentation, making reference to Thomson and Tait's dynamical argument (see note (11)), is however closer to Maxwell's argument in the present draft than to the procedure in the published paper (compare the later draft, Number 473, which is closer in style to the published paper). Watson acknowledged his 'access to some of his [Maxwell's] manuscript notes on this subject, from which I have taken many valuable suggestions' (*Kinetic Theory of Gases*: iv). It seems likely that Maxwell had made available MS notes now collected in ULC Add. MSS 7655, V, f/11; see also Number 478 §§5 and 6 and esp. note (31).

Now though the molecules have by their motion passed into this new condition their number must remain the same as before, so that the right hand member of the above equation (17) must be identically zero, whatever be the values of ξ, η, ζ.

Hence
$$\frac{dA}{dx}=0 \quad \frac{dA}{dy}=0 \quad \frac{dA}{dz}=0 \qquad (18)$$

or A is independent of x, y, z and is constant throughout the system.

Also
$$\frac{dB}{dx}=-2AM\frac{d\psi}{dx} \quad \frac{dB}{dy}=-2AM\frac{d\psi}{dy} \quad \frac{dB}{dz}=-2AM\frac{d\psi}{dz} \qquad (19)$$

whence
$$B = C - 2AM\psi \qquad (20)$$

where C is independent of x, y, z.

Hence we obtain
$$\mathfrak{N}_1 = e^{C_1 - AM_1(2\psi_1 + \xi^2 + \eta^2 + \zeta^2)} dx\, dy\, dz\, d\xi\, d\eta\, d\zeta^{(13)} \qquad (21)$$

as the number of molecules of the first kind which at a given instant lie within the element of volume $dx\, dy\, dz$ and have their velocities represented by points within the element $d\xi\, d\eta\, d\zeta$ of the diagram of velocities.

In this expression C_1 is a constant for each kind of molecule but may be different for different kinds of molecules, A is a constant which is the same for all kinds of molecules in the alternate state of the system, ψ_1 is the potential of the force which acts on molecules of the first kind. The other kinds of molecules may be acted on by forces having potentials different from ψ_1.

To find the whole number of molecules within the element $dx\, dy\, dz$ we must integrate (21) between the limits $\pm \infty$ with respect to ξ η and ζ so as to include all values of the velocity.

Dividing the result by $dx\, dy\, dz$ we obtain $\mathcal{N}_1$ the number of molecules of the first kind in unit of volume

$$\mathcal{N}_1 = \left(\frac{\pi}{AM_1}\right)^{\frac{3}{2}} e^{C_1 - AM_1 2\psi_1}. \qquad (22)$$

From this it appears that the density of the first medium which is the product of the number of molecules in unit of volume into the mass of a molecule, varies from one part of the vessel to another according to a law which is independent of the existence of molecules of other kinds in the vessel.

For instance if a certain quantity of oxygen is placed in a closed vessel it will be distributed according to the well known law of a gas under the action of gravity, being denser below and rarer above. If now a quantity of nitrogen be

---

(13) Compare the result stated in Number 474, which corresponds more closely to that obtained in the published paper (*Scientific Papers*, **2**: 354).

added to the oxygen in the vessel and time be allowed for a thorough diffusion to take place the distribution of the oxygen will be exactly as before. That of the nitrogen will follow its own law diminishing in density in the upper part of the vessel but at a slower rate than in the case of oxygen because the mass of its molecule is less.

This is Dalton's law of mixed gases according to which if several portions of gas whether of the same kind or of different kinds occupy the same region each portion behaves as a vacuum to the rest.[14]

The kinetic energy of the medium in unit of volume is found by multiplying $\mathfrak{N}$ by $\frac{1}{2}M_1V_1^2$ and integrating as before. By dividing this by N_1 we get the mean kinetic energy of a molecule

$$\frac{1}{2}M_1\overline{V_1^2} = \frac{3}{2}\frac{1}{A}. \qquad (23)$$

As the quantity A is in the ultimate state of the system the same for every kind of molecule and for every part of the vessel, it follows that the mean kinetic energy is the same for all molecules whatever be their masses.

Now when two bodies are placed in communication their temperatures tend to become equal and the temperature of each depends in some manner on the agitation of its parts. The relation between the kinetic energy of agitation and temperature is not known for all bodies but in the case of two gases mixed together we now see that what tends to become equal is the mean kinetic energy of a single molecule in each gas. Hence we may assert that in gases the temperature is a function of the kinetic energy of agitation of a single molecule.

It follows from this that in the ultimate state of the system of molecules acted on by gravity the temperature is the same in all parts of the vessel.[15] The effect of gravity is to increase the density in the lower parts of the vessel but not to make any difference in the mean velocity of the molecules. This may appear in contradiction to the fact that in the free motion of any one molecule its velocity increases as it descends and diminishes as it ascends. To show that the contradiction is only apparent requires a little consideration which will form a good exercise for the student.

Another and still more important result is that equal volumes of different gases at equal temperatures and pressures contain equal numbers of molecules. This is Gay-Lussacs law of the molecular volumes of gases.[16]

---

(14) John Dalton, 'Experimental essays on the constitution of mixed gases,...', *Memoirs of the Manchester Literary and Philosophical Society*, **5** (1802): 535–602.   (15) See note (2).

(16) On Gay-Lussac and 'Avogadro's hypothesis' see Number 259 §4 and notes (13) and (14) and Number 263.

For the pressure on unit of area is

$$p = \tfrac{1}{3}MN\overline{V^2} = \tfrac{1}{2}\frac{N}{A}$$

where A is a function of the temperature. Hence when the temperature and the pressure are given, $N = 2Ap$ is given or the number of molecules in unit of volume is independent of the nature of the gas.

Again when heat is communicated to a gas that part of it which is spent in increasing the motion of agitation of the centres of the molecules is for each molecule the increment of $\tfrac{1}{2}M_1\overline{V^2}$ or of $\tfrac{3}{2}\tfrac{1}{A}$ which is the same for all gases for the same increment of temperature. Hence the specific heat per molecule is the same for all gases except in so far as their thermal energy may depend on the internal motions of each molecule. This is the law of molecular specific heats discovered by Dulong & Petit.[17]

---

(17) A. T. Petit and P. L. Dulong, 'Sur quelques points importants de la théorie de la chaleur', *Ann. Chim. Phys.*, ser. 2, **10** (1819): 395–413, esp. 405. See Number 377 note (18).

473

DRAFT OF 'ON THE FINAL STATE OF A SYSTEM OF MOLECULES IN MOTION SUBJECT TO FORCES OF ANY KIND'[1]

AUGUST 1873[2]

From the original in the University Library, Cambridge[3]

[ON THE FINAL STATE OF A SYSTEM OF MOLECULES IN MOTION][4]

Let molecules of several kinds be in motion within a vessel with elastic sides and let each kind of molecules be acted on by forces which have a potential the form of the potential being in general different for different kinds of molecules. Let the coordinates of a molecule be $x\,y\,z$ and the components of its velocity ξ, η, ζ and let it be required to determine the number of molecules of the first kind which, on average, have their coordinates between x & $x+dx$ y and $y+dy$ and z and $z+dz$ and also their component velocities between ξ and $\xi+d\xi$ η and $\eta+d\eta$ and ζ and $\zeta+d\zeta$. This number must depend on the coordinates $x\,y\,z$ on the component velocities $\xi\,\eta\,\zeta$ and on the limits and we may therefore write it

$$f_1(x_1\,y_1\,z_1\,\xi_1\,\eta_1\,\zeta_1)\,dx\,dy\,dz\,d\xi\,d\eta\,d\zeta.$$

We shall begin by investigating the law according to which this number depends on the velocity (ξ, η, ζ) before we proceed to determine in what manner it depends on the position (x, y, z).

For this purpose we consider the mode in which the velocity of a molecule of the first kind will be changed in consequence of a collision with a molecule, say, of the second kind. The whole number of molecules of the first kind in unit of volume at the given place which have velocities within given limits may be written

$$f_1(\xi_1\,\eta_1\,\zeta_1)\,d\xi_1\,d\eta_1\,d\zeta_1 = n_1.$$

The number of those of the second kind within their limits of velocity are

$$f_2(\xi_2\,\eta_2\,\zeta_2)\,d\xi_2\,d\eta_2\,d\zeta_2 = n_2.$$

The number of pairs which can be formed by taking one molecule of each kind is $n_1\,n_2$.

---

(1) For publication details see Number 472 note (1). The present draft is closer to the published paper than the drafts reproduced as Number 472.
(2) See Number 472 note (13). (3) ULC Add. MSS 7655, V, f/12.
(4) For the circumstances of composition see Number 472 note (2).

We have already shown[5] that when two molecules encounter each other the velocity of their centre of gravity remains unchanged in magnitude and direction but that the line AB representing on the diagram of velocities the relative velocity of the molecule B with respect to A is turned about G as a fixed point without change of magnitude into a new direction which we may suppose to be defined by the angular coordinates θ & ϕ.

The values of θ and ϕ depend upon the direction and magnitude of the angular momentum of B with respect of A and on the direction of the axis about which this angular momentum exists, and the number of pairs [of] molecules for which θ lies between θ and $\theta+d\theta$ and ϕ between ϕ and $\phi+d\phi$ will be

$$n_1 n_2 F(\theta, \phi) \, d\theta \, d\phi.$$

Now let us suppose the components of relative velocity $(\xi_2-\xi_1)$, $(\eta_2-\eta_1)$, $(\zeta_2-\zeta_1)$ to remain constant while the components of absolute velocity of both molecules are made to vary then $d\xi_2 = d\xi_1 \quad d\eta_2 = d\eta_1 \quad d\zeta_2 = d\zeta_1$.

Let us also suppose that θ and ϕ remain constant during the variation then if the values of the component velocities after collision be distinguished by accents

$$d\xi'_1 = d\xi'_2 = d\xi_2 = d\xi_1 = d\xi$$

and the same for the other differentials.

Hence the number of molecules of the first kind whose velocities as represented in the diagram lie within the element A which encounter molecules of the second kind whose velocities lie within the element B equal to A and which have encounters such that θ and ϕ lie between given limits

$$f_1(\xi_1\,\eta_1\,\zeta_1) f_2(\xi_2\,\eta_2\,\zeta_2) F(\theta,\phi) (d\xi\,d\eta\,d\zeta)^2 d\theta\,d\phi$$

and after collision the velocities are represented by points lying within the elements A' and B', each equal to A.

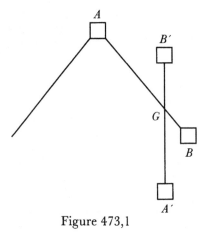

Figure 473,1

Let us now consider the number of encounters between pairs of molecules the original velocities of which lie within $d\xi\,d\eta\,d\zeta$ of $-\xi'_1\,-\eta'_1\,-\zeta'_1$ and $+\xi'_2+\eta'_2+\zeta'_2$ respectively and for which θ' and ϕ' lie between the same limits as before except that $\phi' = \phi+\pi \quad \theta' = \pi-\theta$. Their number is evidently

$$f'_1(-\xi'_1\,-\eta'_1\,-\zeta'_1) f_2(+\xi'_2+\eta'_2+\zeta'_2) F(\theta,\phi)(d\xi\,d\eta\,d\zeta)^2 d\theta\,d\phi.$$

---

(5) See Number 472 §2.

These pairs of molecules will change their velocities from $OA'\ OB'$ to $OA\ OB$.

If the system is in a permanent state as many pairs will change from $AO\ OB$ to $OA'\ OB'$ as change from $OA'\ OB'$ to $AO\ OB$ or dividing out the common factors

$$f_1(\xi_1\ \eta_1\ \zeta_1)f_2(\xi_2\ \eta_2\ \zeta_2) = f_1(\xi_1'\ \eta_1'\ \zeta_1')\ f_2(\xi_2'\ \eta_2'\ \zeta_2').$$

One and only one necessary relation exists between the variables before and after collision namely

$$M_1(\xi_1^2+\eta_1^2+\zeta_1^2) + M_2(\xi_2^2+\eta_2^2+\zeta_2^2)$$
$$= M_1(\xi_1'^2+\eta_1'^2+\zeta_1'^2) + M_2(\xi_2'^2+\eta_2'^2+\zeta_2'^2). \quad [(1)]$$

Writing $\qquad \xi = Vl \quad \eta = Vm \quad \zeta = Vn$

this becomes $\qquad M_1 V_1^2 + M_2 V_2^2 = \text{const.}$

We may also write $\qquad f(\xi, \eta, \zeta) = F(V^2, l, m, n)$

whence taking the logarithm of $([(1)])$

$$F_1(M_1\ V_1^2\ l_1\ m_1\ n_1) + F_2(M_2\ V_2^2\ l_2\ m_2\ n_2)$$

is constant provided $M_1 V_1^2 + M_2 V_2^2$ is constant.

Since $l_1\ m_1\ n_1$ are independent of $l_2\ m_2\ n_2$ we must have

$$F_1(M_1 V_1^2) = AM_1 V_1^2\ \&\ F_2(M_2 V_2^2) = AM_2 V_2^2$$

or
$$f_1(\xi_1\ \eta_1\ \zeta_1) = C_1 e^{AM_1 V_1^2}$$
$$f_2(\xi_2\ \eta_2\ \zeta_2) = C e^{AM_2 V_2^2}.$$

Since the relation between the velocities immediately before and immediately after collision is not affected by the continuous action of finite forces on the molecules the distribution of velocities at any given point of the vessel must be such that the number of molecules in the element $dx\,dy\,dz$ having velocities between $\xi\ \&\ \xi+d\xi$ &c is

$$dN = C_1 e^{AM(\xi_1^2+\eta_1^2+\zeta_1^2)}\,d\xi\,d\eta\,d\zeta\,dx\,dy\,dz^{(6)}$$

where C is a function of $x\,y\,z$ which may be different for different kinds of molecules while A though it may be a function of the position of the element is the same for the different kinds of molecules.

Let us now suppose that a force whose potential is ψ_1 acts on the molecules of the first kind which we are now alone considering and let us consider the variation of dN during the time δt the quantities $x\,y\,z\,\xi\,\eta\,\zeta$ varying in the

---

(6) See the similar result in the published paper in *Nature*, **8** (1873): 537 (= *Scientific Papers*, 2: 353).

same way as the coordinates and the component velocities of a molecule do, that is, let

$$\delta x = \xi \delta t \qquad \delta y = \eta \delta t \qquad \delta z = \zeta \delta t$$

$$\delta \xi = -\frac{d\psi}{dx}\delta t \quad \delta \eta = -\frac{d\psi}{dy}\delta t \quad \delta \zeta = -\frac{d\psi}{dz}\delta t.$$

We thus find

$$\frac{\delta \log \delta N}{\delta t} = \frac{dC_1}{dx}\xi + \frac{dC_1}{dy}\eta + \frac{dC_1}{dz}\zeta$$

$$- 2AM\left(\xi\frac{d\psi}{dx} + \eta\frac{d\psi}{dy} + \zeta\frac{d\psi}{dz}\right)$$

$$+ M(\xi^2 + \eta^2 + \zeta^2)\left(\frac{dA}{dx}\xi + \frac{dA}{dy}\eta + \frac{dA}{dz}\zeta\right).$$

Now since the same set of molecules have by their motion passed into this new condition the variation of N must be zero and this must be true whatever the particular values of $\xi\ \eta\ \zeta$. Hence

$$\frac{dA}{dx} = 0 \quad \frac{dA}{dy} = 0 \quad \frac{dA}{dz} = 0$$

or A is a constant throughout the vessel.

Also $\qquad \dfrac{dC}{dx} = 2AM\dfrac{d\psi}{dx} \qquad \dfrac{dC}{dy} = 2AM\dfrac{d\psi}{dy} \qquad \dfrac{dC}{dz} = 2AM\dfrac{d\psi}{dz}$

or $\qquad C = 2AM(\psi + B).$

474

LETTER TO PETER GUTHRIE TAIT

circa AUGUST 1873[1]

From the original in the University Library, Cambridge[2]

Glenlair
Dalbeattie

Dear Tait[3]

(1) I have sent a report on Ewing & MacGregor[4] to Prof Balfour.[5]

(3) The person most injured in the Contemporary Review,[6] (next to JT)[7] is Principal Shairp,[8] who has been subjected to textual criticism and also to comparison with the author of the article.

(7) Does T drag at each remove a lengthened chain, and leave a continuity of copper between himself and the old world, or is his conversation confined to the new?[9]

(5) By the study of Boltzmann[10] I have become unable to understand him. He could not understand me on account of my shortness and his length was and is an equal stumbling block to me. Hence I am very much inclined to join the glorious company of supplanters and to put the whole business in about 6 lines.

---

(1) See note (3) and Number 471; and the date given by Knott, *Life of Tait*: 114.

(2) ULC Add. MSS 7655, I, b/60A.

(3) The following numbered paragraphs indicate that this letter was written in reply to Tait's postcard post marked 31 July 1873 (and to another missing letter or card): 'O dp/dt; This is what is required of thee – / 1. Report to Balfour whether Ewing and MacGregor's paper is worthy to go into Trans. R.S.E. / 2. Report to ♀. (at St Andrews) whether his formulas for periodic temperature in bars are *correct*, and whether he has employed proper courtesy to Å. / 3. Look at the *Contemp-Review* and advise whether it is worth while to answer, or whether it would be better to hand the author over at once to the son of the injured man for what he calls chastisement. / 4. Communicate any doubts or difficulties or discoveries of your own about ∇ for the benefit of my final chapter, now about to pass through the Clarendon Press. ♀. / The diffusion numbers certainly show a splendid agreement. Why are the differences symmetrical? Is it a new Semal-bis-ter law?????'. (ULC Add. MSS 7655, I, a/36). On (1) see note (4). On (2) see Number 469 esp. note (7). On (3) see note (6). On (4) see P. G. Tait, *An Elementary Treatise on Quaternions* (Cambridge, $_2$1873): 260–88, on the quaternion operator ∇; the first edition of 1867 was published by the Clarendon Press, Oxford, the second edition by Cambridge University Press. On Tait's final comment see Maxwell's table of molecular diameters in his post card of 30 July 1873 (Number 471).

(4) See Number 471 esp. note (3).
(5) See Number 349 note (1).
(6) See Number 477 esp. note (1).
(7) John Tyndall: see Number 477.
(8) See Number 468 note (20).
(9) See Number 460 esp. note (18).
(10) See Numbers 472 note (12) and 481.

Boltzmanns aim is to settle the equilibrium of kinetic energy among a finite number of bodies.

But if the question is restricted to the average number of bodies M, within the element $dx\,dy\,dz$ which have velocity components $\xi\,\eta\,\zeta$ between limits $d\xi$, $d\eta$, $d\zeta$, there being N_1 bodies of mass M_1 acted on by a force whose potential is ψ_1, N_2 bodies of mass M_2 acted on by a force whose potential is ψ_2 &c the answer is

$$\epsilon^{-AM_1(\xi_1^2+\eta_1^2+\zeta_1^2+2\psi_1+B_1)}\,dx\,dy\,dz\,d\xi\,d\eta\,d\zeta.$$

The values of the constants $A_1\,B_1$ must be found after the integration over the vessel containing the bodies. B is different for each set of bodies A is the same for all.[11]

Hence (1) the mean kinetic energy of the body is the same for all sizes of bodies and for all points in the vessel.

(2) The distribution of each kind of body in the vessel is the same as if all the other kinds had been removed, each taking its share of kinetic energy out of the common stock.

In thermal language.

Temperature uniform, in spite of crowding to one side by forces.

Molecular volume of all gases equal.

Equilibrium of mixed gases follows Daltons law of each gas acting as vacuum to the rest. (In fact it acts as vacuum to itself also.)

In my former treatise[12] I got these results only by way of conclusions. Now they come out before any assumption is made as to the law of action between molecules.

$$\frac{dp}{dt}$$

Is Joule very ill? He must count on not being able to be President of the Asses in Sept. which is not just yet.[13] It is a great pity for the Asses who have had and lost the opportunity of being led by a Lion.

---

(11) See J. Clerk Maxwell, 'On the final state of a system of molecules subject to forces of any kind', *Nature*, **8** (1873): 537–8 (= *Scientific Papers*, **2**: 351–4, esp. 354); and Numbers 472 and 473.

(12) J. Clerk Maxwell, 'On the dynamical theory of gases', *Phil. Trans.*, **157** (1867): 49–88 (= *Scientific Papers*, **2**: 26–78).

(13) In a letter to Maxwell of 27 July 1873 George Griffith, Assistant General Secretary of the British Association for the Advancement of Science, informed Maxwell that: 'We have only lately heard from Joule that owing to his health he will be unable to act. Our Council have proposed Prof. Williamson of Univ. Coll. London in his place.' (ULC Add. MSS 7655, II/72). See also Number 478 note (2).

475

ON ATOMS AND ETHER: REPLY TO ALBERT JULIUS MOTT[1]

13 AUGUST 1873

From *Nature* (4 September 1873)[2]

ATOMS AND ETHER[3]

I am not enough of a metaphysician to say whether a substance which can be compressed and expanded *necessarily* contains void spaces.

If so, the idea of air, furnished to a beginner by instruction in 'Boyle's Law', is self-contradictory; and any molecular theory afterwards developed in order to account for 'Boyle's Law', may claim not only ingenuity but necessity in order to abate a crying grievance to all right-minded persons.

I do not myself believe in Prof. Challis's æther,[4] but at the same time I do not believe in the power of the human mind to pronounce that a continuous medium capable of being compressed is an impossibility.

But, on the other hand, I am sure that a medium consisting of molecules is essentially viscous; that is, any motions on a large scale which exist in it are

---

(1) A. J. Mott, 'Atoms and ether', *Nature*, **8** (1873): 322, written in response to Maxwell's anonymous review of 'Challis's "Mathematical Principles of Physics"', *Nature*, **8** (1873): 279–80 (= *Scientific Papers*, **2**: 338–42): 'Attempts to dispense, in physics, with the ideas of direct attraction and repulsion, however interesting, lead generally to a *petitio principii*, and I fear Prof. Challis's view, to which attention is called in *Nature*, of August 7, cannot be received as an exception. / For an ether of which the density can be varied is a substance that can be compressed and expanded, and what idea is in our minds when we speak of compression and expansion in a really continuous substance? Continuity implies space, and space that is full. Can space be more than full? When we say that a fluid is compressible and elastic, do we mean anything else than that it is made of parts which can be pushed closer together, and which, being so pushed, will push each other back? But this is repulsion and action at a distance. We do not alter the fact by calling the substance ether, and relieving it from the influence of gravitation. / Is a continuous substance, which is capable of compression, conceivable? I think not; or if it is, the conception is at once more difficult and more opposed to sensible experience than that of attraction and repulsion. / The substance of a bar of iron is not continuous. If I draw one end of it towards me, why does the other end follow? What can be the relation between the movement of my end of the bar and the ethereal vibrations which must propel the other end and all intermediate parts in the same direction?'

(2) *Nature*, **8** (1873): 361.

(3) As published in *Nature* under this title: see note (1).

(4) See Maxwell's review (see note (1)) of James Challis, *An Essay on the Mathematical Principles of Physics* (Cambridge, 1873).

always being converted into molecular agitation, otherwise called heat, so that every molecular medium is the seat of the dissipation of energy, and is getting hotter at the expense of the motions which it transmits. Hence no perfect fluid can be molecular. So far as I can see, Prof. Challis intends his æther to be a perfect fluid, and therefore continuous (see p. 16 of his Essay),[5] though he does not himself pronounce upon its intimate constitution.

Hansemann*[6] makes his æther molecular, and in fact a gas with the molecules immensely diminished in size.

With regard to Mr. Mott's iron bar, when he pulls one end he diminishes, in some unknown way, the pressure between the particles of the iron, and allows the pressure of the æther on the other end to produce its effect.

N.B. This is only the language of a theory, and that theory not mine; nevertheless, I think it is consistent with itself.

J.C.M.

Glenlair, Aug. 13

* Die Atome und ihre Bewegungen, von Gustav Hansemann. E. H. Mayer: Coln, 1871.[6]

(5) See note (4).   (6) See Number 377 note (36).

476

LETTER TO JOHN WILLIAM STRUTT, LORD RAYLEIGH[1]

28 AUGUST 1873

From the original in private possession[2]

Glenlair
Dalbeattie
28 August 1873

Dear Lord Rayleigh

I have left your papers on the light of the sky &c[3] at Cambridge and it would take me even if I had them some time to get them assimilated sufficiently to answer the following question which I think will involve less expence to the energy of the race if you stick the data into your formula and send me the result (not worked out arithmetically I can do that).

Suppose that there are N spheres of density ρ and diameter s in unit of volume of the medium find the index of refraction of the compound medium and the coefficient of extinction of light passing through it.[4]

The object of the enquiry is of course to obtain data about the size of the molecules of air.[5] Perhaps it may lead also to data involving the density of the ether.

The following quantities are known being combinations of the unknowns.

M = mass of molecule of hydrogen
N = number of molecules of any gas in a cubic centimetre at 0 °C & 760 B[6] } Three unknowns
s = diameter of molecule of any gas

---

(1) John William Strutt succeeded his father as the third Baron Rayleigh in June 1873 (*DNB*).

(2) Rayleigh Papers, Terling Place, Terling, Essex. Published in part in Lord Rayleigh, 'On the transmission of light through an atmosphere containing small particles in suspension, and on the origin of the blue of the sky', *Phil. Mag.*, ser. 5, **47** (1899): 375–84, esp. 376n.

(3) J. W. Strutt, 'On the light from the sky, its polarization and colour', *Phil. Mag.*, ser. 4, **41** (1871): 107–20, 274–9.

(4) Strutt, 'On the light from the sky': 113; 'If the primary light be unpolarized, the intensity in a direction making an angle β with its course becomes $A^2 \frac{(D'-D)^2}{D^2}(1+\cos^2\beta)\frac{mT^2}{\lambda^4 r^2}$', where D and D' are the original and altered densities of the medium, m the number of particles, T the volume of the disturbing particle, λ the wave-length, and r the distance from the disturbing particle.

(5) See Numbers 470 and 471.

(6) See Number 470 note (14). Barometric pressure in mm. of mercury.

Known combinations
MN = density
Ns^2 from diffusion or viscosity

Conjectural combination

$\dfrac{6M}{\pi s^3}$ = density of molecule $\propto$ density of liquid?
density in compounds?

If you can give us 1° the quantity of light scattered in a given direction by a stratum of a certain density & thickness and 2° the quantity cut out of the direct ray and 3° the effect of the molecules on the index of refraction which I think ought to come out easily we might get a little more information about these little bodies.[7]

You will see by Nature Aug 14 1873 that I make the diameter of molecules about $\frac{1}{1000}$ of a wavelength.[8]

The inquiry into scattering must begin by accounting for the great observed transparency of air. I suppose we have no numerical data about its absorption.

But the index of refraction can be numerically determined, though the observation is of a delicate kind, and a comparison of the result with the dynamical theory may lead to some new information.

Yours very truly
J. CLERK MAXWELL

P.S. What vowel did the echo at Bedgebury Park return an octave higher?[9] There are some echoes here from trees which act best when the leaves are on. They are very different and more ringing than from walls but I must try them again by your new light.

---

(7) Rayleigh subsequently published his own solution in his 'On the transmission of light through an atmosphere containing small particles in suspension': 377–84. See also Maxwell's letter to Rayleigh of 22 November 1873 (Number 482).

(8) See Maxwell, 'On Loschmidt's experiments on diffusion in relation to the kinetic theory of gases', *Nature*, **8** (1873): 298–300 (= *Scientific Papers*, 2: 343–50); and Number 470.

(9) [Lord] Rayleigh, 'Harmonic echoes', *Nature*, **8** (21 August 1873): 319–20. Rayleigh reported 'an echo at Bedgebury Park.... The sound of a woman's voice was returned from a plantation of firs, situated across a valley, with the pitch *raised an octave*... it soon occurred to me that the explanation was similar to that which I had given of the blue of the sky'.

477

NOTE TO PETER GUTHRIE TAIT[1]

LATE AUGUST – EARLY SEPTEMBER 1873[2]

From the original in the National Library of Scotland, Edinburgh[3]

Can a man do *good* service in popularising certain parts of science and *thereby* lose his claim to scientific authority?[4] If a man has a claim to scientific authority the only way he can lose it is by writing bosch. If he writes it in a dry manner it is bad enough, but the harm is confined to students. But if he seasons it for the public, and the public swallow it (like the Saturday Reviewer)[5] then it is a sad misuse of words to say that this is a useful work.

Unless indeed it was a good work when the D–l invented popular tunes, because the pious were thereby enabled to set hymns thereto. If so, are you prepared to write an orthodox Libretto of the Tyndallic lectures[6] containing the spirit which gives liveliness, and avoiding the letter which would pluck any man.

---

(1) An annotation to the proofs of Tait's 'Tyndall and Forbes' dated 20 August 1873 and published in *Nature*, **8** (11 September 1873): 381–2. Tait was responding to John Tyndall's 'Principal Forbes and his biographers', *Contemporary Review*, **22** (August 1873): 484–508, when Tyndall defended his relations with J. D. Forbes on the theory of glaciers (see Number 319 notes (11) and (12)). Tyndall was responding to Tait's account of Forbes' glacier theory in J. C. Shairp, P. G. Tait and A. Adams-Reilly, *The Life and Letters of James David Forbes* (London, 1873): 492–520; and see also Number 468 note (20).

(2) See note (1).

(3) National Library of Scotland, MS.1709 f. 78.

(4) In his 'Tyndall and Forbes': 382 Tait had resorted to personal attack on Tyndall, holding up to ridicule Tyndall's discussion in his *Six Lectures on Light. Delivered in America in 1872–1873* (London, 1873): 25, of whether a 'rainbow which spans a tranquil sheet of water is ever seen reflected in it'. Tait commented: 'Dr. Tyndall has, in fact, martyred his scientific authority by deservedly winning distinction in the popular field'. In his bitter response (*Nature*, **8** (1873): 399) Tyndall replied that 'Mr Tait's criticism of my "popular" writings...is the product of mere ignoble spite'.

(5) The reviewer of 'Tyndall on Light' in *The Saturday Review*, **36** (26 July 1873): 115–16, had singled out Tyndall's discussion of the 'reason why a rainbow is never seen reflected in the sheet of water, however tranquil, which it spans', in praising the *Lectures on Light* as being marked with Tyndall's 'freshness of thought, clearness of exposition, and firm grasp of physical truth'.

(6) See note (4).

= 478 =

DRAFTS OF LECTURE ON 'MOLECULES'[1]

circa AUGUST – SEPTEMBER 1873[2]

From the originals in the University Library, Cambridge[3]

[1][4] [MOLECULAR PHENOMENA]

[In a liquid the diffusion of the molecules takes place with][5] extreme slowness, whereas internal friction, or the lateral diffusion of momentum from one stratum to another, is rather favoured by the molecules being close together and the conduction of heat which takes place in liquids not so much by the transference of molecules as by the communication of energy from one molecule to another with which it is as it were in gear takes place still more freely.

Another kind of diffusion which can be studied best in liquids is that which takes place under electric action. Here is a solution of iodide of potassium through which an electric current passes. Iodine appears at one electrode and potassium at the other but as potassium cannot exist in contact with water we have instead potass and hydrogen.

Clausius has thrown great light on this phenomenon which is called electrolysis[6] by his theory that the molecules of iodide of potassium are always dancing about in the solution and that with such vigour that every

---

(1) A lecture delivered to the meeting of the British Association for the Advancement of Science in Bradford on 22 September 1873; see J. Clerk Maxwell, 'A discourse on molecules', *Phil. Mag.*, ser. 4, **46** (1873): 453–69, esp. 453n (= *Scientific Papers*, **2**: 361–78). The MS of the text of the published lecture (first published as 'Molecules', *Nature*, **8** (25 September 1873): 437–41) is in ULC Add. MSS 7655, V, f/14.

(2) It is likely that Maxwell prepared the lecture in late August or early September 1873. According to a letter to Maxwell from George Griffith (Assistant General Secretary of the British Association) of 27 July 1873 Maxwell had tried to escape from his commitment to present the lecture on 'Molecules': 'I am very sorry to hear that it will be extremely inconvenient for you to deliver a Discourse at the Bradford meeting. I will have a conference with my colleagues on Tuesday & we will endeavour to find a substitute but I fear that it will be very difficult to do so.' (ULC Add. MSS 7655, II/72). In *Nature*, **8** (7 August 1873): 292 it was stated that 'It is also hoped that Prof. Clerk-Maxwell will deliver a discourse on "Molecules"'. See also note (12).

(3) ULC Add. MSS 7655, V, f/11, 13. Published in part in *Molecules and Gases*: 133–6, 257–9, 260–1 and 400–1.   (4) ULC Add. MSS 7655, V, f/13.

(5) Maxwell, 'Molecules': 439 (= *Scientific Papers*, **2**: 370).

(6) Rudolf Clausius, 'Ueber die Elektricitätsleitung in Elektrolyten', *Ann. Phys.*, **101** (1857): 338–60; (trans.) 'On the conduction of electricity in electrolytes', *Phil. Mag.*, ser. 4, **15** (1858): 94–109.

now and then they bounce up against some other molecule with such force that the iodine and potassium part company and dance about through the crowd seeking partners among the other dissociated molecules who have suffered like things. It is under these circumstances according to Clausius that the electromotive force produces the effects you have seen. As long as the molecules are in pairs the electromotive force which pulls the two molecules in opposite directions can do nothing, and by itself it is not sufficient to tear them asunder; but when by some violent shock the molecules are once parted the electromotive force exerts its guiding influence and bends the course of each of the unattached molecules each towards its proper electrode till the moment when meeting an unappropriated molecule of the opposite kind it enters into a new and closer alliance in which it is indifferent to mere electric suasion.

Another class of molecular phenomena from the study of which we may derive much light is the evaporation of liquids and the condensation of vapours. According to the theory of Clausius both these phenomena are always going on at the surface of every liquid.[7] Molecules are continually darting out of the liquid and other molecules from the gaseous mass above are darting into the liquid. When more molecules leave the liquid than enter it we call the process evaporation, when more enter it than leave it we call it condensation.

The conditions under which evaporation and condensation take place have been long studied. Certain correct statements about them are to be found in every elementary book, so that we are in danger of thinking we know all that is to be known but we need only to consider the vast accession to our knowledge of the relations between gases and liquids which we owe to Dr Andrews[8] to see that however well rounded our scientific doctrines may appear their true interpretation may involve some principle so profound that we are not even conscious that it yet remains to be discovered.

[2]   [THE DATA OF MOLECULAR SCIENCE]

[The average distance travelled by a molecule between one collision and another][9] is very small. Roughly speaking it is about one tenth of a wavelength of light.[10]

---

(7) R. Clausius, 'Ueber die Art der Bewegung, welche wir Wärme nennen', *Ann. Phys.*, **100** (1857): 353–80, esp. 361–3; (trans.) 'On the kind of motion which we call heat', *Phil. Mag.*, ser. 4, **14** (1857): 108–27, esp. 113–16.

(8) Thomas Andrews, 'On the continuity of the gaseous and liquid states of matter', *Phil. Trans.*, **159** (1869): 575–90.

(9) Maxwell, 'Molecules': 439 (= *Scientific Papers*, **2**: 369).   (10) See Number 470.

From the mean path and the mean velocity it is easy to calculate the number of collisions which each molecule must undergo in a second in a gas of standard temperature and pressure. These numbers are also given in the table.[11] They are reckoned by thousands of millions in a second. The numbers of vibrations of light is only about a hundred thousand times greater.

Having advanced thus far in the study of molecules let us spend a moment in taking account of the knowledge we have obtained. We have determined the relative masses of the molecules of different gases, their absolute velocities in metres per second and the amount of energy which takes the form of ⟨internal⟩ or rotatory or vibratory motion of the parts of the molecule about its centre of gravity.

These data of molecular science are obtained from those experiments on the pressure density and specific heat of gases which have long been recognised as the regular business of a laboratory.

In the second rank we must place the determination of the relative size of the molecules of different gases, and the absolute values of their mean paths and of the number of collisions in a second. For these quantities we must have recourse to experiments of a more difficult order, on the diffusion of gases, their viscosity and their conductivity for heat. Some progress has already been made in obtaining accuracy in researches of this kind, but we must remember that the numerical results of such experiments cannot as yet be regarded as so precise as those of the first rank.

But the results already obtained agree with each other sufficiently to show that the molecular theory of gases is worth the attention of scientific men.

There is another set of quantities which we must place in the third rank, as our knowledge of their numerical magnitude is neither precise, as in the first rank nor approximate as in the second, but is only as yet of the nature of a probable conjecture. These are the absolute mass and dimension of the molecules and the number of them in a cubic centimetre.

The most direct way of calculating these quantities is by a comparison of the volume of the substance as a gas at the standard temperature and pressure with its volume when the molecules are packed as closely together as possible.[12] We cannot be certain that in any case the molecules are in actual

---

(11) See Maxwell, 'Molecules': 441 (= *Scientific Papers*, **2**: 378).

(12) In a letter to Maxwell of 4 September 1873 (addressed from Lindau, Bavaria), Alexander Crum Brown (Professor of Chemistry at Glasgow University) gave Maxwell some information on molecular volume, responding to a letter of Maxwell's of 18 August 1873: '1st as to molecular (and atomic) volume of *solids*. The *atomic* volume of similar *elements* is often nearly the same, i.e. the sp. gr. varies as the *atomic* weight.... By adding 5.2 for each atom of oxygen, to the atomic volume of a metal, the molecular vol. of the oxide is obtained in a *good many*

contact. Indeed we are certain that in liquids they are not in contact, for the phenomena of diffusion show that they not only have room to move about among each other, but that they are always moving about even when the liquid is apparently at rest. But we have already shown that we can ascertain the relative dimensions of the molecules from experiments on diffusion viscosity and conduction. We can also compare the volumes to which a cubic centimetre of different gases is reduced when in the liquid form. In the case of those gases which have not been observed ⟨directly⟩ in the liquid form Kopp has calculated their molecular volume from the volumes of their liquid compounds.[13]

Now Loschmidt[14] and Lorenz Meyer[15] have shown that there is a remarkable though by no means perfect correspondence between the ratios of the volumes of the molecules deduced from experiments on viscosity and the molecular volumes of the substances in the liquid form. It would appear therefore that in most liquids the molecules are nearly in the same state of relative condensation so that the same proportional condensation would reduce them to the ideal state of maximum density in which no room at all is left between the molecules.

What the amount of this further condensation may be it is hard to say but we cannot suppose that any liquid is capable of any very great degree of condensation.

Now Loschmidt has shown in a very simple way that if the mean path of a molecule were shortened in the same proportion as the volume of the gas

---

cases....But this breaks down in many cases besides that which you mention of the alkaline metals. In these as you mention, the mol. vol. is diminished by the addition of oxygen. 2nd. mol. vol. of liquids. Owing to the large coeff. of expansion of liquids, no comparison can be made that is of any use unless at corresponding temperatures. Kopp compares them at temperatures at which they have the same vapour tension that is at the boiling points under the same pressure, and has made out a number of regularities or indications of regularities, but nothing like a law. You ask if the mol. volumists have a dodge to explain the anomalies. They have, and I have indicated it above. It is that we do not know the molecular weight of solids or liquids, but only of gases.' (ULC Add. MSS 7655, II/73). On work on molecular volumes by Kopp and Lothar Meyer see notes (13) and (15). The letter is published in *Molecules and Gases*: 506–8.

(13) Hermann Kopp, 'Beiträge zur Stoichiometrie der physikalischen Eigenschaften chemischer Verbindungen', *Annalen der Chemie und Pharmacie*, **96** (1855): 1–36, 153–85, 303–35; *ibid.*, **100** (1856): 19–38.

(14) Joseph Loschmidt, 'Experimental-Untersuchungen über die Diffusion von Gasen ohne poröse Scheidewände', *Wiener Berichte*, **61**, Abtheilung II (1870): 367–80; *ibid.*, **62**, Abtheilung II (1870): 468–78.

(15) Read: Lothar Meyer, 'Ueber die Molecularvolumina chemische Verbindungen', *Annalen der Chemie und Pharmacie*, **5** Supplementband (1867): 129–47.

would be diminished if it were reduced to its ideal condensation this shortened mean path would be about one eighth of the diameter of a molecule.[16]

It was in this way that Loschmidt in 1865[17] first announced that the diameter of a molecule of either of the gases contained in air is about a millionth of a millimetre or ten tenth-metres.[18] Independently of him and of each other Mr Stoney in 1868[19] and Sir W. Thomson in 1870[20] published results of a similar kind, those of Sir W. Thomson being deduced not only by the consideration of the volume of a liquefied gas but from the phenomena of soap bubbles and the electric properties of metals.

According to an estimate which I have made on Loschmidts plan[21] the size of the molecules of hydrogen is such that about two million of them placed in a row would be about a millimetre long and a million million million million of them would weigh about four grammes. In a cubic centimetre of gas at standard pressure and temperature there are nineteen million million million molecules and if they were placed in regular cubical order the distance between consecutive molecules would be 37 tenth-metres. We must remember that all these numbers which I have placed in the third rank are conjectural. In order to warrant us in putting any confidence in numbers of this kind we should have to show that independent calculations founded on data obtained from experiments on many different gases, lead to consistent results.

But what we have already obtained is enough to show that we have some foundation for our conjectures about the weight and dimensions of molecules, and that our knowledge of the subject has made much progress since the time when Graham began to experiment on Diffusion[22] and Transpiration.[23] The adventurers who now undertake the quest of the ultimate atom are at

---

(16) Joseph Loschmidt, 'Zur Grösse der Luftmolecüle', *Wiener Berichte*, **52**, Abheilung II (1865): 395–413, esp. 398.

(17) Loschmidt, 'Zur Grösse der Luftmolecüle'.

(18) Tenth-metre is 10^{-10} metre; see Number 470 note (25).

(19) G. J. Stoney, 'The internal motions of gases compared with the motions of waves of light', *Phil. Mag.*, ser. 4, **36** (1868): 132–41.

(20) William Thomson, 'The size of atoms', *Nature*, **1** (1870): 551–3 (= *Math. & Phys. Papers*, **5**: 289–96).

(21) J. Clerk Maxwell, 'On Loschmidt's experiments on diffusion in relation to the kinetic theory of gases', *Nature*, **8** (1873): 298–300 (= *Scientific Papers*, **2**: 343–50). See Number 470.

(22) Thomas Graham, 'On the law of the diffusion of gases', *Trans. Roy. Soc. Edinb.*, **12** (1832): 222–58.

(23) Thomas Graham, 'On the motions of gases', *Phil. Trans.*, **136** (1846): 573–632; Graham, 'On the motions of gases. Part II', *ibid.*, **139** (1849): 349–401.

least aware of some of the phenomena which they have to study and they may be sure that in following up the paths already known they will light on others hitherto unthought of.

Some years ago the homoeopathists in their endeavour to administer small enough doses of medicine prescribed them in the dilution. (Here describe the process.)[24]

If the estimate we have formed of the size and weight of the molecules of simple substances be a just one the chance of the patient receiving even one molecule of the drug would be but small.

There are other men who have made a study of the transmission of the characteristic features and peculiarities of individuals from one generation to another and of the remarkable manner in which these peculiarities sometimes reappear after having been apparently lost for one or more generations.[25] Some of the results of these enquiries have been expressed in terms of the hypothesis that a large number of [....]

[3]   [THE METHOD OF MOLECULAR SCIENCE]

Thus far we have been describing scientific work from the point of view of the worker himself. The aim we have kept in view is the study of the constitution of bodies and we have estimated the value of experiments methods and theories according to the help they have afforded us in this study.

But though the professed aim of scientific work is to unravel the secrets of nature it has another result hardly less important in its reaction on the mind of the worker. It leaves him in possession of methods which he could never have developed without the incitement of the pursuit of natural knowledge and it places him in a position from which many regions of nature besides that which he has been studying appear under a different aspect. The study of molecules has developed a method of its own and it has also opened up new views of nature.

To describe mathematical methods is at all times tedious and I have no intention of making use of a black board. But I think that the method which we are forced to adopt in the study of molecular phenomena affords one of the

(24) In his letter of 4 September 1873 (see note (12)) Crum Brown commented: 'I understand the homœopathists to mean by a drug in the nth dilution, a substance containing $1/(100)^n$ of the active stuff. You take 1 part of your drug and 99 of sugar of milk if the drug be solid, 99 of water or spirit if it be liquid, mix *well* the result is the first delusion or dilution take 1 part of that & do it again &c &c. I think they sometimes go to the 10th dilution!'

(25) Francis Galton, *Hereditary Genius: an Inquiry into its Laws and Consequences* (London, 1869). See Maxwell's reference to Galton in Number 439.

best illustrations of the nature and limitations of a large part of human knowledge.

The molecular theory of gases resolves itself into that of the motions and encounters of the molecules. As long as we have to deal only with one pair of molecules and to determine from their known motion before the encounter what will be their motion after the encounter we require no methods but those of elementary dynamics.

When air is compressed the sides of the vessel are moving to meet the molecules like a cricket bat swung forward to meet the ball, and the molecules like the cricket ball rebound with a greater velocity than before. When air is allowed to expand the sides of the vessel are retreating from the molecules like the cricketers hands when he is stopping the ball and the molecules rebound with diminished velocity. Hence air becomes warmer when compressed and cooler when allowed to expand. The observed amount of this heating and cooling however is less than it would be if the only motion of the molecules were that of their centres of inertia. Hence as Clausius has shown[26] the molecules must have other motions such as rotation and vibration as well as motion of simple translation and a definite portion of the energy of the gas arises from these rotatory or vibratory motions of the molecules which have no effect on the pressure of the gas.

Thus far any person acquainted with the most elementary dynamics may pursue the kinetic theory of gases. It is easy to understand the effects of the collisions of the molecules against the sides of the vessel. But when we attempt to trace the motion of each molecule among innumerable others and to determine the effects of all the collisions which must occur in the flying crowd we find that special methods are requisite for the treatment of so intricate a problem.

Lucretius has given us a hint how to form a mental representation of the dance of atoms by looking at the motes which we see chasing each other through a sunbeam in a darkened room.[27] Their number their minuteness

---

(26) Clausius, 'Ueber die Art der Bewegung, welche wir Wärme nennen'.

(27) *Titi Lucreti Cari De Rerum Natura Libri Sex*, ed. and trans. H. A. J. Munro, 2 vols. (Cambridge, $_2$1866), **1**: 87–8 (Book II, 114–22): 'contemplator enim, cum solis lumina cumque / inserti fundunt radii per opaca domorum: / multa minuta modis multis per inane videbis / corpora misceri radiorum lumine in ipso / et velut aeterno certamine proelia pugnas / edere turmatim certantia nec dare pausam, / conciliis et discidis exercita crebris; / concicere ut possis ex hoc, primordia rerum / quale sit in magno iactari semper inani'; ('observe whenever the rays are let in and pour the sunlight through the dark chambers of houses: you will see many minute bodies in many ways through the apparent void mingle in the midst of the light of the rays, and as in never-ending conflict skirmish and give battle combating in troops and never halting, driven about in frequent meetings and partings; so that you may guess from this what it is for the first-beginnings of things to be ever tossing about in the great void'; *ibid.*, **2**: 31).

and the variety and perpetual alteration of the motion of each atom might well confuse the [....]

[4]   [THE STATISTICAL METHOD]

[When the working members of Section F[(28)] get hold of a report of the Census, or any other document containing the numerical][(29)] data of Economic or Social Science they obtain their results by distributing the whole population of a country into groups according to age, income tax, reading and writing, number of convictions and so forth. They do so because the number of individuals is far too great to allow of their tracing the history of each separately, so that in order to reduce their labour within human compass they concentrate their attention on artificial groups so that the varying numbers in each group and not the varying state of each individual is the primary datum from which they work. ⟨This may not be the way in which Shakespeare obtained his knowledge of human nature.⟩ This is of course not the only method of studying human nature.

We may observe the conduct of individual men and compare it with that conduct which their previous character, as judged according to the best attainable rules and maxims would lead us to expect. In this way we may correct and improve these rules and maxims just as an astronomer corrects the elements of a planet by comparing its actual position with that deduced from the received elements.

This method which we may call the astronomical or dynamical method is evidently of a higher order than the statistical method, but we can employ it only in the case of the limited number of individuals of whose history we have sufficient knowledge.

Now in our physical researches every portion of matter which we can subject to experiment consists of millions of millions of molecules not one of which ever becomes individually sensible to us. Hence the statistical method is the only available one.

What is the nature of our data. We can take a drop of water and weigh it. We thus obtain a measure of the sum of the masses of all the molecules it contains, though we may be ignorant of the mass of any one of them. Again by multiplying this mass by the apparent velocity of the drop we obtain its momentum and this is the resultant of the momenta of all the individual

---

(28) The section concerned with 'Economic Science and Statistics'; see the *Report of the Forty-third Meeting of the British Association for the Advancement of Science; held at Bradford in September 1873* (London, 1874), part 2: 174.

(29) Following the published text of 'Molecules': 440 (= *Scientific Papers*, **2**: 373).

molecules though in point of fact these molecules may be moving in every direction within the drop.

[5] [THE STATISTICAL METHOD]

In passing from the consideration of the motions of individual molecules to that of the medium which consists of multitudes of moving molecules we are forced, on account of our limited powers of observation and even of imagination, to abandon the strict dynamical method of tracing the course of every molecule and to adopt the statistical method of dividing the molecules into groups according to some system, and then confining our attention to the number of molecules in each group. This is a step the philosophical importance of which cannot be overestimated. It is equivalent to the change from absolute certainty to high probability. The kinetic theorems by which the motion of a single molecule is expressed are, no doubt, founded on axioms absolutely certain but as soon as we loose sight of the individual molecule and assert anything of groups of molecules which are continually exchanging molecules one with another our assertions can lay claim to nothing more than a high probability.

In the first place let us form a group of molecules by confining our attention to those which at a given instant are within a given region bounded by a closed surface of any form but large enough to contain a very great number of molecules.

The mass of this group of molecules is the sum of the masses of the individual molecules which at the given instant are within the given region. The only way in which the mass of the group can change is by molecules entering or leaving the given region.

The numerical value of the density of the medium within this region is obtained by dividing the number representing the mass by the amount representing the volume of the region. The density of the matter at any mathematical point within the region is [...]. There is no point within the region at which the actual density of matter has this value for if the point is within a molecule the density is much greater and if it is not within a molecule the density is zero. The density we have obtained is therefore an average density and is our first example of a statistical quantity. If there are several kinds of molecules within the region forming a mixture of several media the mass and the density of each medium may be estimated separately.

---

(30) ULC Add. MSS 7655, V, f/11.

[6]⁽³¹⁾   [THE STATISTICAL METHOD]

It is easy to see that if encounters take place among a great number of molecules their velocities even if originally equal will become unequal for except under conditions which can be only rarely satisfied two molecules having equal velocities before their encounters will have unequal velocities after the encounter.

Every molecule changes both its velocity and its direction of motion at every encounter so that unless we are supposed to be able to calculate the elements of the motion of every other molecule which it encounters these changes of motion must appear to us very irregular if we follow the course of a single molecule.

As long as we have to deal with only two molecules and have all the data of the encounter given us, we can calculate the result of their mutual action, but when we have to deal with millions of molecules each of which has millions of encounters in a second, the complexity of the problem seems to shut out all hope of a legitimate solution.

We are therefore obliged to abandon the strictly kinetic method and to adopt the statistical method.

According to the strict kinetic or historical method as applied to the case before us we follow the whole course of every individual molecule. We arrange our symbols so as to be able to identify every molecule throughout its whole motion and the complete solution of the problem would enable us to determine at any given instant the position and motion of every given molecule from a knowledge of the positions and motions of all the molecules in their initial state.

According to the statistical method the state of the system at any instant is ascertained by distributing the molecules into groups, the definition of each group being founded on some variable property of the molecules. Each individual molecule is sometimes in one of these groups and sometimes in another but we make no attempt to follow it. We simply take account of the number of molecules which at a given instant belong to each group.

Thus we may consider as a group those molecules which at a given instant lie within a given region in space. Molecules may pass into or out of this

---

(31) ULC Add. MSS 7655, V, f/11. The first part of the MS draft here printed as §6 – up to and including the sentence on Laplace, and with the second paragraph omitted – was published in H. W. Watson's 'Introduction' to his *A Treatise on the Kinetic Theory of Gases* (Oxford, 1876): v–vii. Making only trivial modifications to Maxwell's text, Watson acknowledged the source as 'MS. notes by Professor Clerk Maxwell' (*Kinetic Theory of Gases*: vii footnote). See also Number 472 note (12).

region but we confine our attention to the increase or diminution of the number of molecules within it. In the same way the population of a watering-place considered as a mere number varies in the same way whether its visitors return to it season after season or whether the annual flock consists each year of fresh individuals.

We might also form our groups out of those molecules which at a given instant have velocities lying within given limits. When a molecule has an encounter and changes its velocity it passes out of one of these groups and enters another, but as other molecules are also changing their velocities the number of molecules in each group varies very little from a certain average value.

We thus meet with a new kind of regularity – the regularity of averages – a regularity which when we are dealing with millions of millions of individuals is so unvarying that we are almost in danger of confounding it with absolute uniformity.

Laplace in his theory of Probability[32] has given many examples of this kind of statistical regularity and has shown how this regularity is consistent with the utmost irregularity among the individual instances which are enumerated in making up the results. In the hands of Mr Buckle facts of the same kind were brought forward as instances of the unalterable character of natural laws.[33] But the stability of the averages of large numbers of variable events must be carefully distinguished from that absolute uniformity of sequence according to which we suppose that every individual event is determined by its antecedents.

For instance if a quantity of air is enclosed in a vessel and left to itself we may be ⟨perfectly⟩ ⌊morally⌋ certain that whenever we choose to examine it we shall find the pressure uniform in horizontal strata and greater below than above, that the temperature will be uniform throughout, and that there will be no sensible currents of air in the vessel.

But there is nothing inconsistent with the laws of motion in supposing that in a particular case a very different event might occur. For instance if at a given instant a certain number of the molecules should each of them encounter one of the remaining molecules and if in each case one of the molecules after the encounter should be moving vertically upwards and if in addition the molecules above then happened not to get into the way of these upward moving molecules, – the result would be a sort of explosion by which a mass of air would be projected upwards with the velocity of a cannon ball

---

(32) P. S. de Laplace, *Théorie Analytique des Probabilités* (Paris, 1812).
(33) Thomas Henry Buckle, *History of Civilization in England*, 2 vols. (London, 1857–61), **1**: 19–22.

while a larger mass would be blown downwards with an equivalent momentum. We are morally certain that such an event will not take place within the air of the vessel however long we leave it. What are the grounds of this certainty.

The explosion will certainly happen if certain conditions are satisfied. Each of these conditions by itself is not only possible but is in the common course of events as often satisfied as not. But as the number of conditions which must be satisfied at once is to be counted by millions of millions the improbability of the occurrence of all these conditions amounts to what we are unable to distinguish from an impossibility.

Nevertheless it is no more improbable that at a given instant the molecules should be arranged in one definite manner than in any other definite manner. We are as certain that the exact arrangement which the molecules have at the present instant will never again be repeated as that the arrangement which would bring about the explosion will never occur.

479

POSTCARD TO PETER GUTHRIE TAIT
2 SEPTEMBER 1873
From the original in the University Library, Cambridge[1]

[Glenlair]

O T! 0 can be finer than T″'s bow. It is decidedly a long one. But no man in his senses would undertake to sanction a *whole affair* between 2 other men, in any other respect than where grammar &c occur.[2]

Beware of the Redding Strake.[3]

Observe in Les Mondes Aug 28 M. Belpaire on $\Theta.\Delta$ as reported on by that eminent savant M. Folie.[4] Also the hardness of solids calculated to 6 places of decimals and the effects of a moral discourse on a dogue.[5] If the observed values of $a+b$, $a+c$, $a+d$, $b+c$, $b+d$, $c+d$ are p, q, r, s, t, u, and if $f = p+u$ $g = q+t$ $h = r+s$ then the most probable value of $6a$ is

$2p+2q+2r-s-t-u$ and the (observed–probable) value
of p is $\frac{1}{6}(2f-g-h)$ = that of u
of q $\frac{1}{6}(2g-h-f)$ = that of t
r $\frac{1}{6}(2h-f-g)$ = that of s.

Whence follows the curious arrangement of errors in my diffusion calculations.[6]

---

(1) ULC Add. MSS 7655, I, b/61.
(2) See Number 477 note (1).
(3) See Sir Walter Scott, *Guy Mannering*, chap. 27 (note): 'a blow received by a peacemaker who interferes betwixt two combatants, to red or separate them, is proverbially said to be the most dangerous blow a man can receive'.
(4) See a report in *Les Mondes*, **31** (28 August 1873): 721–2, on Th. Belpaire, 'Note sur le second principe de la thermodynamique', *Bulletins de l'Académie Royale des Sciences... de Belgique*, **34** (1872): 509–26, and on comments on Belpaire's paper by François Folie, *ibid.*: 448–51.
(5) See the reports in *Les Mondes*, **31** (28 August 1873): 720, 729–33.
(6) See Number 471, and Tait's comment in his card of 31 July 1873 (Number 474 note (3)).

BRITISH ASSOCIATION PAPER ON GEOMETRICAL OPTICS

[SEPTEMBER 1873]

From the *Report of the British Association for 1873*[1]

ON THE RELATION OF GEOMETRICAL OPTICS TO OTHER BRANCHES OF MATHEMATICS AND PHYSICS

The author said that the elementary part of optics was often set before the student in a form which was at once repulsive to the mathematician, unmeaning to the physical inquirer, and useless to the practical optician. The mathematician looked for precision, and found approximation; the physicist expected unity in the science, and found a great gulf between geometrical and physical optics; the optician found that if he had to design a microscope, he was expected to combine the analytical power of a Gauss with the computative skill of a Glaisher[2] before he could make head or tail of the formulæ. The author maintained that elementary optics might be made attractive to the mathematician by showing that the correlation between the object and the image is not only an example, but the fundamental type of that principle of duality which was the leading idea of modern geometry. The object and image were homographic figures, such that every straight line or ray in the one was represented by a straight line or ray in the other. The relations between pairs of figures of that kind formed an important part of the geometry of position, an excellent treatise on which had been brought out by M. Theodor Reye.[3] To the physicist he would exhibit the unity of the science, by adopting Hamilton's characteristic function as explained in his papers on systems of rays,[4] and using it in the most elementary form from the very beginning of the subject, leading at once to the undulatory theory of light.[5] At the same time the practical optician would learn what were the

---

(1) *Report of the Forty-third Meeting of the British Association for the Advancement of Science; held at Bradford in September 1873* (London, 1874), part 2: 38–9.

(2) James Whitbread Lee Glaisher, Trinity 1867, second wrangler 1871, Fellow 1871 (Venn), who had written the 'Report of the Committee...on mathematical tables', in the *Report of the Forty-third Meeting of the British Association*: 1–175.

(3) Theodor Reye, *Die Geometrie der Lage*, 2 vols. (Leipzig, 1866–8). There is a copy in Maxwell's Library (Cavendish Laboratory). Maxwell is alluding to projective geometry.

(4) W. R. Hamilton, 'Theory of systems of rays', *Transactions of the Royal Irish Academy*, **15** (1827): 69–74; *ibid.*, **16** part 1 (1830): 2–62; *ibid.*, **16** part 2 (1831): 93–125; *ibid.*, **17** (1832): 1–44. (5) See Number 482 notes (8) and (9).

cardinal points of an optical instrument, and would be able to determine them without taking the instrument to pieces. Helmholtz[6] and Listing[7] had pointed out the advantages of the method to the oculist; and Beck[8] had recently placed some of the elementary points in a clear light. Casorati[9] had also exemplified some of the advantages of the method of homographic figures in elementary optics; but though Gauss, the modern founder of that method,[10] and several others, had made honourable mention of the name of Roger Cotes,[11] and of that theorem[12] with respect to which Newton said that 'if Mr. Cotes had lived, we should have known something',[13] no one seemed to have suspected that it would form the meeting-point of all the three methods of treating the science of optics.

(6) Hermann Helmholtz, *Handbuch der physiologischen Optik* (Leipzig, 1867): 35–64.

(7) Johann Benedict Listing, 'Ueber einige merkwürdige Punkte in Linsen und Linsensystemen', *Ann. Phys.*, **129** (1866): 466–72.

(8) A. Beck, 'Die Fundamentaleigenschaften der Linsensysteme in geometrischer Darstellung', *Zeitschrift für Mathematik und Physik*, **18** (1873): 588–600.

(9) Felice Casorati, 'Ricerche e considerazioni sugli strumenti ottici', *Rendiconti dell' Instituto Lombardo di Scienze e Lettere*, ser. 2, **5** (1872): 179–92.

(10) Carl Friedrich Gauss, 'Dioptrische Untersuchungen', *Abhandlungen der Mathematischen Classe der Königlichen Gesellschaft der Wissenschaften zu Göttingen*, **1** (1843): 1–34.

(11) Gauss makes no mention of Cotes; but see Volume I: 334, esp. note (3).

(12) See Number 482 note (10).

(13) Maxwell here misremembers the context of Newton's (rather improbable) judgment on Cotes as reported by Robert Smith, Cotes' cousin. The circumstances are described by Joseph Edleston in his *Correspondence of Sir Isaac Newton and Professor Cotes* (London, 1851): lxxvii.

ON THE EFFECT OF GRAVITY ON THE TEMPERATURE OF A COLUMN OF GAS: REPLY TO FRANCIS GUTHRIE[1]

OCTOBER 1873[2]

From *Nature* (23 October 1873)[3]

ON THE EQUILIBRIUM OF TEMPERATURE OF A GASEOUS COLUMN SUBJECTED TO GRAVITY[4]

Since reading Principal Guthrie's first letter on this subject (vol. viii, p. 67),[5] I have thought of several ways of investigating the equilibrium of

---

(1) A letter from Francis Guthrie (see Number 457 note (1)), headed 'On the equilibrium of temperature of a gaseous column subject to gravity', was published in *Nature*, **8** (9 October 1873): 486. Guthrie stated his argument in the following form: 'From Mr. Clerk-Maxwell's reply to my note on this subject which appeared in your columns a short time since, it would appear that he does not profess so much fully to explain the difficulty suggested by me as to show that it is capable of explanation, referring your readers to his other works for further information. I would not, therefore, have troubled you further on the subject had it not occurred to me on reading Mr. Maxwell's letter that I could state the case in such a way as to render clearly apparent the grounds for taking different views on this point. / Let a vertical column of gas, subject to gravity and in a state of equilibrium as to pressure and temperature, be divided by a horizontal plane P into two parts, A above and B below. / In the time Δt let a mass M_1 of particles pass in their free course from A to B, and a mass M_2 from B to A. / Let the portion of A from which the particles composing M_1 proceed be called the upper stratum, and the corresponding part of B the lower stratum, then the following consequences may be deduced:– / 1. From the equilibrium of density $M_1 = M_2$. / 2. From the equilibrium of temperature the amounts of work in M_1 and M_2 while passing through P are equal. / 3. From the effect of gravity the work in M_1 while in A reckoning from the commencement of the free course of each particle composing M_1, is less than at P, while that in M_2 is greater. / 4. Whence it follows that of the two equal masses M_1 and M_2 in the upper and lower strata respectively M_1 contains less work than M_2. / 5. The work in M_1 while in the upper stratum reckoned as before, is the same as that of any other equal average mass in that stratum, and the same is the case also of M_2. / 6. The average amounts of work in equal masses in the two strata, and the consequent temperatures of the strata are unequal, the lower stratum having the higher temperature. / I suppose Mr. Maxwell would deny the truth of statement (5). I presume he would argue as follows:– / "Of all the particles in the lower stratum which in the time Δt have at the commencement of their free course a velocity and direction such as would take them through P, gravity in selecting those which compose M_2 excludes those whose velocities are insufficient to overcome the effects of their weights, while in forming M_1 particles of low velocities are selected (included?), which, but for the effects of gravity, would not have cut P in their free courses, consequently the particles in M_1 have an average velocity less than that of the upper stratum from which they come, while the particles of M_2 have a greater average velocity than that of the lower stratum, and consequently the inequality of the average velocity of the particles in the two strata cannot be inferred from the

temperature in a gas acted on by gravity. One of these is to investigate the condition of the column as to density when the temperature is constant, and to show that when this is fulfilled the column also fulfils the condition that there shall be no upward or downward transmission of energy; or, in fact, of any other function of the masses and velocities of the molecules. But a far more direct and general method was suggested to me by the investigation of Dr. Ludwig Boltzmann* on the final distribution of energy in a finite system of elastic bodies.[6] A sketch of this method as applied to the simpler case of a number of molecules so great that it may be treated as infinite, will be found on p. 535.[7] Principal Guthrie's second letter (vol. viii, p. 486)[8] is especially valuable as stating his case in the form of distinct propositions, every one of which, except the fifth, is incontrovertible. He has himself pointed out that it is here that we differ, and that this difference may ultimately be traced to a difference in our doctrine as to the distribution of velocity among the molecules in any given portion of the gas. He assumes, as Clausius, at least in

* Studien über das gleichgewicht der lebendigen Kraft zwischen bewegten materiellen Punkten. Von Dr. Ludwig Boltzmann. Sitzb. d. Akad. d. Wissensch, October 8, 1868 (Vienna).[6]

inequality of the average velocities of the particles composing M_1 and M_2 while in those strata." / This argument, therefore assumes the theory that in a given mass of uniform temperature there are particles moving with every velocity from nothing upwards to a certain limit, and mixed in certain proportions. That this is actually Mr. Maxwell's view I own I might have remembered, but I suppose I overlooked it from an impression in my own mind that the molecular motion was to be regarded as being of a planetary (or in the case of gases a cometary) nature. That in masses of the same temperature velocities were to be regarded as practically uniform, except in so far as affected by the distance of the particles apart, and that the so-called impacts of particles were more properly to be regarded as perihelion passages of bodies moving among each other in hyperbolic orbits. / If this view is the more accurate one, then obviously the argument which I have assumed that Mr. Maxwell would use, falls to the gound. / Is there no possibility of testing the nature of the thermal equilibrium of a column of still air? The result would at any rate throw an unexpected light on the nature of molecular motion.'

(2) See notes (1) and (3).

(3) *Nature*, **8** (23 October 1873): 527–8; printed in the *Report of the Forty-third Meeting of the British Association for the Advancement of Science; held at Bradford in September 1873* (London, 1874), part 2: 29–30, where it is printed as a preliminary to the paper cited in note (7).

(4) The title under which Maxwell's letter to *Nature* was published.

(5) Number 457 note (1).

(6) See Number 472 note (12).

(7) Read: 537. The paper is titled 'On the final state of a system of molecules subject to forces of any kind', *Nature*, **8** (1873): 537–8, and was printed in the *Report of the Forty-third Meeting of the British Association*, part 2: 30–2 (= *Scientific Papers*, **2**: 351–4). See Numbers 472 and 473.

(8) See note (1).

his earlier investigations, did, that the velocities of all the molecules are equal,[9] whereas I hold, as I first stated in the *Phil. Mag.* for Jan. 1860, that they are distributed according to the same law as errors of observation are distributed according to the received theory of such errors.[10]

It is easy to show that if the velocities are all equal at any instant they will become unequal as soon as encounters of any kind, whether collisions or 'perihelion passages'[11] take place. The demonstration of the actual law of distribution was given by me in an improved form in my paper on the Dynamical Theory of Gases, 'Phil. Trans.' 1866, and *Phil. Mag.* 1867,[12] and the far more elaborate investigation of Boltzmann has led him to the same result. I am greatly indebted to Boltzmann for the method used in the latter part of the sketch of the general investigation (see p. 535)[13] which was communicated in a condensed form to the British Association on Sept. 20, 1873.[14]

J. CLERK MAXWELL[15]

---

(9) R. Clausius, 'Ueber die Art der Bewegung, welche wir Wärme nennen', *Ann. Phys.*, **100** (1857): 353–80; Clausius, 'Ueber die mittlere Länge der Wege...', *ibid.*, **105** (1858): 239–58.

(10) J. C. Maxwell, 'Illustrations of the dynamical theory of gases. Part I. On the motions and collisions of perfectly elastic spheres', *Phil. Mag.*, ser. 4, **19** (1860): 19–32 (= *Scientific Papers*, **1**: 377–91).

(11) Guthrie's phrase: see note (1).

(12) *Phil. Trans.*, **157** (1867): 49–88 (= *Scientific Papers*, **2**: 26–78); and *Phil. Mag.*, ser. 4, **35** (1868): 129–45, 185–217.

(13) See note (7).   (14) See note (7).

(15) Guthrie responded in a letter dated 7 February 1874, published in *Nature*, **10** (18 June 1874): 123, with Maxwell's rejoinder (to be published in Volume III).

482

LETTER TO JOHN WILLIAM STRUTT, LORD RAYLEIGH

22 NOVEMBER 1873

From the original in private possession[1]

11 Scroope Terrace
Cambridge
22 Nov 1873

Dear Lord Rayleigh

Your letter of Nov 17 quite accounts for the observed transparency of any gas.[2] With respect to the composition of vibrations from sources irregularly distributed if each vibration is absolutely independent of the others as to phase, then at a distance so great that the ratio of the distances of different sources may be neglected, the energy of radiation is the sum of the energies due to each source separately.

But the case is different with respect to the undulations excited by a system of plane waves when we consider the propagation of the secondary waves in the same direction as the primary wave. For then the time at which a secondary wave reaches a given point will differ only by a certain fraction of a wave-period from the time at which the primary waves reaches the same point because both waves travel at the same rate except close to the source of the secondary wave.

Hence the theory of the direct ray requires special consideration.

But in any case its intensity is diminished only by the energy of the scattered radiation together with that employed in heating the medium.

Your theorems on vibrations are first rate. Will you send me a separate copy if you can spare one (I have that in the Math Societys Trans).[3]

I made use of your dissipation function[4] in lecture today in proving the existence of a system of conjugate harmonic solutions in every problem on the

---

(1) Rayleigh Papers, Terling Place, Terling, Essex.

(2) See Maxwell's letter to Rayleigh of 28 August 1873 (Number 476). In his paper 'On the transmission of light through an atmosphere containing small particles in suspension, and on the origin of the blue of the sky', *Phil. Mag.*, ser. 5, **47** (1899): 375–84, esp. 376n, Rayleigh observed: 'So far as I remember, my argument was of a general character only.'

(3) J. W. Strutt (Lord Rayleigh), 'Some general theorems relating to vibrations', *Proceedings of the London Mathematical Society*, **4** (1873): 357–68; see Maxwell's referee's report (Number 460). See also Lord Rayleigh, 'On the vibrations of approximately simple systems', *Phil. Mag.*, ser. 4, **46** (1873): 357–61; and 'On the fundamental modes of a vibrating system', *ibid.*: 434–9.

(4) Strutt, 'Some general theorems relating to vibrations': 364; and see Numbers 460, esp. notes (11) and (12), and 461.

conduction of heat (or of electricity when electromagnetic induction may be neglected) and that any given initial state of the system may be expressed as a sum of a set of harmonic solutions.⁽⁵⁾

---

(5) George Howard Darwin recorded Maxwell's argument in notes on his lecture of 22 November 1873; these form part of Darwin's notes on 'Maxwell's lectures/Oct term 1873' (ULC DAR. 210. 22). Darwin jotted pencilled notes at the lecture, subsequently elaborating them in a written-out expansion on the facing pages of his notebook. This latter version is reproduced here. '*Nov 22* / There is an analogy between electricity & heat which may be utilised for working out & understanding the problems in both sciences. / Electricity at high pot^l is worth more for the perform^{ce} of mechan. work & heat at high temp. has the same properties. / The pot^l of a body has a simple expression, but the temp. is not so simple & ∴ in this respect heat is more complic^d than el^y. / Fourier's method consists in the cutting of the body into several parts, such that the heating and cooling of these parts may be considered sep^y fr. one an$\overline{or}$. The capac. of a body for heat is the qu^y of heat requ^d to raise its temp 1°. That for elec^y is the qu^y of elec^y required to raise its pot^l by unity. This latter depends on the pot^l of all the surrounding bodies, hence in this respect the electrical problem is more complicated. / If the pot^l of all the bodies of a system be given – the electrostat. energy of the system is a homog^s quadr. f^n of the pot^{ls} of the sev^l parts. Since in heat each body is indep^t of all the others, in heat this expression consists only of squares. When products appear in expressions of this nature it shows that the sev^l parts react on one an$\overline{or}$. The arrangement of the solution so that there shall be no products is equiv^t to finding the geom^l solution of the diff^l eq^{ns}, since the gen^l solution (in linear eq^{ns}?) is the sum of the part$\overline{ar}$ solutions each ×plied by a const – i e we have to find a no. of indep^t solutions wh. do not react on one an$\overline{or}$. / The energy of a system may be repres^{ted} as / $V = \frac{1}{2}\sum_r \sum_s a_{sr} p_s p_r$ – there are n terms if there are 1, 2, 3…r…s…n bodies p is the electrical pot^l & a_{sr} is a const. In elect^y $a_{sr} = a_{rs}$. Since in heat there are no products $s = r$ & there are only n terms $\frac{1}{2}\sum_r a_r p_r^2$ – but the expression no longer means the energy of the system. / If there be a conductor (of no capacity in the case of heat i e $\frac{\text{width}}{\text{length}}$ v. small) joining the two bodies at pot^{ls} (or temp^s) p_r & p_s. Then $p_r - p_s$ is the electromot. force (or diff. of temp^s) & $K_{rs}(p_r - p_s)$ is the flow of the elec^y (or heat). / The work done by the electr^y is the flow × diff. of pot^{ls}. / But in heat flow × diff. of temp^s does not repres^t the work done. The work done is some func. of this expression. / There is a complete analogy betw. this & the flow of fluid betw. 2 vessels, where flow × diff. of press^s is the work done by the fluid in passing from one vessel to the $\overline{or}$. Thus the work done by the elec. in flowing from the body r to $s = K_{rs}(p_r - p_s)^2$. / We may suppose that conductors are arranged betw. every body two & two – some of these cond^{rs} might however be suppressed without disturbing the condition (why). / Then $F = \sum_r \sum_s K_{rs}(p_r - p_s)^2$. / In the case of heat we may sum for all values of r & s since all terms for diff^t values of r & s go out – (how? is it from the ppties of Laplace's coeff^{ts}). / The presence of electrokinetic energy (i e induced currents) is supposed excluded; hence we must have our conductors well apart – bad short & narrow conductors. / In the case of stat. el^y the presence of induced currents is imperceptible. We must suppose the connections betw. the sev^l bodies to be made with cotton thread & not with wires (why?) – tho' a needle won't be deflected by the flow in a thread. / It is possible to find a new set of variables to replace the p's such that all the terms with products disappear (i.e. refer to ppal axes in case of surfs of 2nd order). $q = \sum(ap)$ where a is const. Then we sh^d get / $V = \frac{1}{2}\sum(B_u q_u^2)$ or the energy of the system /

Do you know any pure mathematical proof that any two homogeneous quadratic functions which cannot become negative can be expressed in the form of the sums of squares by one, and only one linear transformation of the variables?

When is your book on Acoustics coming out? I am afraid that every effort you make towards finishing it will only turn up fresh materials which it would be wrong not to insert.

I am getting more light on Geometrical Optics. The geometry of the subject is the geometry of position, the theory of perspective and of homographic figures apart from all considerations of magnitude.[6]

The calculation of the subject is all founded on Hamiltons characteristic function[7] which, for an instrument symmetrical about an axis, has the form[8]

$$V = V_0 + \mu_1 z_1 + \mu_2 z_2 + \frac{1}{2} \frac{\mu_1(z_2-\alpha_2)(x_1^2+\eta_1^2) + \mu_2(z_1-\alpha_1)(x_2^2+\eta_2^2) - 2\phi\mu_1\mu_2(x_1 x_2+\eta_1\eta_2)}{(z_1-\alpha_1)(z_2-\alpha_2) - \phi^2\mu_1\mu_2}$$

where
$z_1 = \alpha_1$ gives the first principal focus
$z_2 = \alpha_2$ .... second ......
$f_1 = \mu_1\phi$ first principal focal length
$f_2 = \mu_2\phi$ second ....[9]

$F = \frac{1}{2}\sum(C_u q_u^2)$ or the rate of dissipation. / Then clearly $F = -\frac{dV}{dt}$ / $\therefore \frac{dF}{dq_u} = \frac{d^2V}{dq_u dt}$ / $\therefore C_u q_u = -B_u \frac{dq_u}{dt}$ $\therefore q_u = Q_u e^{(C_u/B_u)t}$. / ($B_u$ will not be a f^n of time if we suppose the theory stated right tho' I missed the argum^t on this part.) / $\left(\frac{C_u}{B_u}\right.$ is called the modulus. In the case of vibr$\overline{\text{ons}}$ we sh^d have $C_q = -\frac{dq^2}{dt^2}$. If the vibr$\overline{\text{ons}}$ are of the decaying type it w^d be $\left.\frac{dq^2}{dt^2} + A\frac{dq}{dt} + Bq = 0.\right)$ / Thus the actual state can be analysed into a number of independent states each of wh. decays indeptly according to the above law. This may be done in only one way – & might be called a harmonic distribution. The various terms may fitly be called conjugate. / $F = \sum_r \sum_s K_{rs}(p_r-p_s)^2 = K_{rs}(p_r-p_s)(p_r-p_s)$ / $= \sum\sum$ flow × electromot force. / ∠ I don't understand but it is an analogy with Lapl. fns.'

(6) See Number 480. (7) See Number 480 note (4).

(8) See also Maxwell's paper 'On the relation of geometrical optics to other parts of mathematics and physics', *Proc. Camb. Phil. Soc.*, **2** (1874): 338–40 (= *Scientific Papers*, 2: 391–2).

(9) For further discussion see Maxwell's paper 'On Hamilton's characteristic function for a narrow beam of light', *Proceedings of the London Mathematical Society*, **6** (1875): 182–90, esp. 189–90 (= *Scientific Papers*, 2: 389–90).

The denominator divided by f_1 or f_2 is Cotes' or rather Smith's 'apparent distance'[10] or $\frac{\text{real}}{\text{angular}}$ diameter. When it is zero, z_1 & z_2 are 'conjugate' foci.

For a telescope the fraction is

$$\frac{\mu_1^2 x_1^2 + m^2 \mu_2^2 x_2^2 + 2m\mu_1 \mu_2 x_1 x_2}{(z_1 - \alpha_1)\mu_1 + (z_2 - \alpha_2) m^2 \mu_2}$$

where m is the angular magnifying power.[11]

In all cases z_1 & z_2 are measured *from* the instrument.

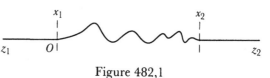

Figure 482,1

I have got the most general form of the fraction with ten arbitrary constants with a geometrical method of finding the focal lines of the emergent pencil when those of the incident pencil are given but except in the case of pencils passing through a spectroscope they are too complicated.[12]

The Cavendish Laboratory will be evacuated by the contractors before Christmas. The lecture room is in action already.

Yours very truly
J. CLERK MAXWELL

---

(10) On Cotes' theorem, and 'apparent distance', see Robert Smith, *A Compleat System of Optics*, 2 vols. (Cambridge, 1738), **2**: ('Remarks') 76–8; and see Volume I: 391n. For Maxwell's further discussion see his papers 'On the relation of geometrical optics to other parts of mathematics and physics': 339–40, and 'On Hamilton's characteristic function': 190 (= *Scientific Papers*, **2**: 392, 390).

(11) See also Maxwell, 'On Hamilton's characteristic function': 190 (= *Scientific Papers*, **2**: 390).

(12) As discussed in his paper 'On Hamilton's characteristic function'.

LETTER TO PETER GUTHRIE TAIT

1 DECEMBER 1873

From the original in the University Library, Cambridge[1]

Natural Sciences Tripos[2] 1 Dec 1873

O. T. For the flow of a liquid in a tube,[3] axis z

$$\mu\left(\frac{d^2w}{dx^2}+\frac{d^2w}{dy^2}\right)=\frac{dp}{dz}.\text{[4]} \qquad (1)$$

Surface condition $\quad \mu\dfrac{dw}{d\nu}=\lambda w$ [5] $\qquad (2)$

where ν is the normal drawn towards the liquid.[6]

When the curvature is small, (2) is equivalent to supposing the walls removed back by $\dfrac{\mu}{\lambda}$ and then λ made ∞ or $w=0$. For glass & water by Helmholtz & Pietrowski $\dfrac{\mu}{\lambda}=0$.[7]

If so, and if the value of w is $C\left(1-\dfrac{x^2}{a^2}-\dfrac{y^2}{b^2}\right)$, $2\mu C\left(\dfrac{1}{a^2}+\dfrac{1}{b^2}\right)+\dfrac{dp}{dz}=0$ which gives C. If not, you may write

$$w = A + Br^2 + C_2 r^2 \cos 2\phi + C_4 r^4 \cos 4\phi + \&\text{c}\text{[8]}$$

where $x = ar\cos\theta$ and $y = br\sin\theta$ and then $2\mu B\left(\dfrac{1}{a^2}+\dfrac{1}{b^2}\right)+\dfrac{dp}{dz}=0$ and you satisfy (2) the best way you can when $r=1$.

---

(1) ULC Add. MSS 7655, I, b/62. Previously published (in part) in Knott, *Life of Tait*: 114–16. (2) See Number 488.

(3) See P. G. Tait, 'On the flow of water through fine tubes', *Proc. Roy. Soc. Edinb.*, **8** (1873): 208–9, read 1 December 1873.

(4) Following Hermann Helmholtz and G. von Piotrowski, 'Über Reibung tropfbarer Flüssigkeiten', *Wiener Berichte*, **40**, Abtheilung II (1860): 607–58, on 652. Here μ is the coefficient of viscosity, w the component of velocity along the axis of the tube z, and p the pressure.

(5) Following Helmholtz and Piotrowski, 'Über Reibung tropfbarer Flüssigkeiten': 653, where λ is the 'Gleitungscoefficient', the coefficient of slipping of the liquid at the surface of the tube.

(6) Compare a similar discussion by Horace Lamb, *A Treatise on the Mathematical Theory of the Motion of Fluids* (Cambridge, 1879): 223–4.

(7) Helmholtz and Piotrowski, 'Über Reibung tropfbarer Flüssigkeiten': 651.

(8) A, B and C are constants; and using polar coordinates $r^2 = x^2+y^2$; see Helmholtz and Piotrowski, 'Über Reibung tropfbarer Flüssigkeiten': 652.

As to Ampère[9] – of course you may lay on d_1 (anything) when d_1 is with respect to the element of a circuit. Have you studied H² on the potential of two elements?[10] or Bertrand who, with original bosh of his own,[11] rushes against the thicker bosches of H²'s buckler?[12] and says that H² believes in a force which does not diminish with the distance[13] so that the reason why Ampère or H² or Bertrand observe peculiar effects is because some philosopher in α Centauri happens to be completing a circuit $XQqD$ [14] as I am surrounded by Naturals and cannot give references.

In introducing 4^{ions},[15] do so by blast of trumpet & tuck of drum. Why should $V.\alpha\beta\gamma$[16] come in sneaking without having his style & titles proclaimed by a fugleman. Why, even . should be treated with due respect and we should be informed whether he is attractive or repulsive.

What do you think of 'Space-variation' as the name of Nabla?[17]

It is only lately, under the conduct of Professor Willard Gibbs[18] that I have been led to recant an error which I had imbibed from your $\Theta\Delta^{\text{cs}}$[19]

---

(9) See Tait's 'Note on the various possible expressions for the force exerted by an element of one linear conductor on an element of another', *Proc. Roy. Soc. Edinb.*, **8** (1873): 220–8, read 1 December 1873. On Ampère's formula for the force law between two infinitesimal line elements carrying currents see Number 430 note (5).

(10) Hermann Helmholtz, 'Ueber die Bewegungsgleichungen der Elektricität für ruhende leitende Körper', *Journal für die reine und angewandte Mathematik*, **72** (1870): 57–128, on 76.

(11) Joseph Bertrand, 'Examen de la loi proposée par M. Helmholtz pour représenter l'action de deux éléments de courant', *Comptes Rendus*, **77** (1873): 1049–54.

(12) Hermann Helmholtz, 'Vergleich des Ampère'schen und Neumann'schen Gesetzes für die elektrodynamischen Kräfte', *Monatsberichte der Königlich Preuss. Akademie der Wissenschaften zu Berlin* (1873): 91–104.

(13) Bertrand, 'Examen de la loi proposée par M. Helmholtz': 1054.

(14) Read: excuse details.

(15) P. Kelland and P. G. Tait, *Introduction to Quaternions, with numerous examples* (London, 1873); see Number 485.

(16) The vector of the product of three vectors; see Kelland and Tait, *Introduction to Quaternions*: 156. (17) See Number 348 esp. note (3).

(18) Josiah Willard Gibbs, 'Graphical methods in the thermodynamics of fluids', *Transactions of the Connecticut Academy of Arts and Sciences*, **2** (1873): 309–42, esp. 310n; 'The term *entropy*, it will be observed, is here used in accordance with the original suggestion of Clausius, and not in the sense in which it has been employed by Professor Tait and others after his suggestion. The same quantity has been called by Professor Rankine the *Thermo-dynamic function*.'

(19) See P. G. Tait, *Sketch of Thermodynamics* (Edinburgh, 1868): 100, 29; 'It is very desirable to have a word to express the *Availability* for work of the heat in a given magazine; a term for that possession, the waste of which is called the *Dissipation*. Unfortunately the excellent word *Entropy*, which Clausius has introduced in this connexion, is applied by him to the negative of the idea we most naturally wish to express.... [Thus] we shall...use the excellent term Entropy in the

namely that the entropy of Clausius is *unavailable energy* while that of T' is available energy.[20] The entropy of Clausius is neither the one nor the other it is only Rankines Thermodynamic function[21] and if we compare the vocabulary

Thermodynamic Function	Entropy (Clausius)[22]
Entropy (Tait)	Available Energy

I think we shall prefer the 2nd column. Available Energy there is none in a system of uniform temperature and pressure.

I have also great respect for the elder of those celebrated acrobats, Virial and Ergal,[23] the Bounding Brothers of Bonn.[24] Virial came out in my paper on Frames R.S.E. 1870[25] under the form $\sum Rr = 0$[26] where there is no motion. Where there is motion the time-average of $\frac{1}{2}\sum Rr$ = time-average of $\frac{1}{2}\sum Mv^2$ where R is positive for attraction.[27]

---

opposite sense to that in which Clausius has employed it, – viz., so that the *Entropy of the Universe tends to Zero*, which is Thomson's theory of dissipation [of available energy]'. See also William Thomson, 'On a universal tendency in nature to the dissipation of mechanical energy', *Proc. Roy. Soc. Edinb.*, **3** (1852): 139–42 (= *Math. & Phys. Papers*, **1**: 511–14).

(20) J. Clerk Maxwell, *Theory of Heat* (London, 1871): 186; 'Clausius has called the remainder of the energy, which cannot be converted into work, the Entropy of the System. We shall find it more convenient to adopt the suggestion of Professor Tait, and give the name of Entropy to the part which can be converted into mechanical work.'

(21) W. J. M. Rankine, 'On the geometrical representation of the expansive action of heat, and the theory of thermo-dynamic engines', *Phil. Trans.*, **144** (1854): 115–75. In his *Sketch of Thermodynamics*: 29, Tait had himself noted that the 'Aequivalenzwerth of Clausius is nearly identical with the Thermodynamic Function of Rankine'. In his paper 'Ueber eine veränderte Form des zweiten Hauptsatzes der mechanischen Wärmetheorie', *Ann. Phys.*, **93** (1854): 481–506, on 494, Clausius had introduced the concept of 'Aequivalenzwerth' for the quantity he subsequently termed 'Entropie'.

(22) R. Clausius, 'Ueber verschiedene für die Anwendung bequeme Formen der Hauptgleichungen der mechanischen Wärmetheorie', *Ann. Phys.*, **125** (1865): 353–400, esp. 390, 400. He used this term 'nach dem griechischen Worte ἡτροπή, die Verwandlung, die *Entropie* des Körpers zu nennen'; hence '1) Die Energie der Welt ist constant. 2) Die Entropie der Welt strebt einem Maximum zu'.

(23) Clausius' concepts of 'virial' and 'ergal'; see his paper 'Ueber einen auf die Wärme anwendbaren mechanischen Satz', *Ann. Phys.*, **141** (1870): 124–30. See Number 356, esp. note (3).

(24) Clausius had been appointed director of the Bonn physics institute in 1869; see C. Jungnickel and R. McCormmach, *Intellectual Mastery of Nature. Theoretical Physics from Ohm to Einstein*, 2 vols. (Chicago/London, 1986), **2**: 79–82.

(25) J. Clerk Maxwell, 'On reciprocal figures, frames and diagrams of forces', *Trans. Roy. Soc. Edinb.*, **26** (1870): 1–40, esp. 13 (= *Scientific Papers*, **2**: 175–6). See Number 356 note (4).

(26) R is the force between two mass points at a distance r.

(27) See Number 356 note (3).

But it is rare sport to see those learned Germans contending for the priority of the discovery that the 2nd law of $\Theta\Delta^{cs}$ is the Hamiltonsche Princip,$^{(28)}$ when all the while they *assume* that the temperature of a body is but another name for the vis viva of one of its molecules, a thing which was suggested by the labours of Gay Lussac Dulong &c but first deduced from dynamical statistical considerations by $\frac{dp}{dt}$.$^{(29)}$ The Hamiltonsche Princip,$^{(30)}$ the while, soars along in a region unvexed by statistical considerations while the German Icari flap their waxen wings in nephelococcygia,$^{(31)}$ amid those cloudy forms which the ignorance and finitude of human science have invested with the incommunicable attributes of the invisible Queen of heaven.

Dictum of K & T′ concerning 3 points, p 160.$^{(32)}$

If these perps intersect in G, the three points A, B, G will be in one plane.

---

(28) This comment was probably prompted by publication in the *Philosophical Magazine* of a paper by C. Szily, 'On Hamilton's dynamic principle in thermodynamics', *Phil. Mag.*, ser. 4, **46** (1873): 426–34, esp. 434; 'What in thermodynamics we call the second proposition, is in dynamics no other than Hamilton's principle, the identical principle which has already found manifold application in several branches of mathematical physics.' This paper was translated from Szily's 'Das dynamische Princip von Hamilton in der Thermodynamik', *Ann. Phys.*, **146** (1872): 74–86. This was Szily's second intervention in the controversy between Boltzmann and Clausius over the reduction of the second law of thermodynamics to mechanical principles: see Szily, 'Das Hamilton'sche Princip und der zweite Hauptsatz der mechanischen Wärmetheorie', *Ann. Phys.*, **145** (1872): 295–302. Though perhaps prompted by Szily's paper, Maxwell's comment bears generally on the priority controversy between Boltzmann and Clausius over the reduction of the second law of thermodynamics to a mechanical theorem. See Ludwig Boltzmann, 'Über die mechanische Bedeutung des zweiten Hauptsatzes der Wärmetheorie', *Wiener Berichte*, **53**, Abtheilung II (1866): 195–220; Rudolf Clausius, 'Ueber die Zurückführung des zweiten Hauptsatzes der mechanischen Wärmetheorie auf allgemeine mechanische Principien', *Ann. Phys.*, **142** (1871): 433–61; Boltzmann, 'Zur Priorität der Auffindung der Beziehung zwischen dem zweiten Hauptsatze der mechanischen Wärmetheorie und dem Principe der kleinsten Wirkung', *Ann. Phys.*, **143** (1871): 211–30; Clausius, 'Bemerkungen zu der Prioritätsreclamation des Hrn. Boltzmann', *Ann. Phys.*, **144** (1871): 265–74; and Clausius, 'Ueber den Zusammenhang des zweiten Hauptsatzes der mechanischen Wärmetheorie mit dem Hamilton'schen Princip', *Ann. Phys.*, **146** (1872): 585–91 (a response to Szily's first paper).

(29) See Number 377 para. 11 and notes (16), (17) and (18) for further discussion.

(30) There is a treatment of Hamilton's principle of 'varying action' in Thomson and Tait, *Natural Philosophy*: 231–41, to which Szily made reference in his paper 'On Hamilton's dynamic principle in thermodynamics': 428.

(31) Aristophanes, *The Birds*, line 817; 'Νεφελοκοκκυγιαν', rendered as 'Cuckoocloudland' in *The Birds of Aristophanes*, (trans.) H. F. Cary (London, 1824): 76.

(32) See Kelland and Tait, *Introduction to Quaternions*: 160; 'To find the condition that the perpendiculars from the angles of a tetrahedron on the opposite faces shall intersect one another... the condition that all three perpendiculars shall meet in a point is that the sum of all the squares of each pair of opposite edges shall be the same.'

Inference $\left(\text{by a new logical formula invented by } \frac{dp}{dt}\right)$. 'All planes pass through O'.

General Exercise. Interpret every 4^{ion} expression in literary geometrical language, e.g. express in neat set terms the result of $\frac{\beta}{\alpha}.\gamma$.[33]

$$\frac{dp}{dt}$$

---

(33) β/α is a 'quotient or fraction', where α and β are unit vectors.

484

FROM A LETTER TO WILLIAM GRYLLS ADAMS[1]

3 DECEMBER 1873

From Campbell and Garnett, *Life of Maxwell*[2]

Natural Science Tripos
[Cambridge]
3 December 1873

I got Professor Guthrie's[3] circular some time ago.[4] I do not approve of the plan of a physical society considered as an instrument for the improvement of natural knowledge. If it is to publish papers on physical subjects which would not find their place in the transactions of existing societies, or in scientific journals, I think the progress towards dissolution will be very rapid. But if there is sufficient liveliness and leisure among persons interested in experiments to maintain a series of stated meetings to show experiments, and talk about them as some of the Ray Club[5] do here, then I wish them all joy; only the manners and customs of London, and the distances at which people live from any convenient centre, are very much against the vitality of such sociability.

To make the meeting a dinner supplies that solid ground to which the formers of societies must trust if they would build for aye. A dinner has the advantage over mere scientific communications, that it can always be had when certain conditions are satisfied, and that no one can doubt its existence. On the other hand, it completely excludes any scientific matter which cannot be expressed in the form of conversation with your two chance neighbours, or else by a formal speech on your legs; and during its whole continuance it reduces the Society to the form of a closed curve, the elements of which are incapable of changing their relative position.

For the evolution of science by societies the main requisite is the perfect freedom of communication between each member and any one of the others who may act as a reagent.

The gaseous condition is exemplified in the soiree, where the members rush about confusedly, and the only communication is during a collision, which in some instances may be prolonged by button-holing.

---

(1) See Number 256 note (4). (2) *Life of Maxwell*: 384–5.

(3) Frederick Guthrie: see Number 442 note (1).

(4) See J. H. Gladstone's presidential report to the Physical Society of London, read 13 February 1875, recording that a 'circular which Prof. Guthrie addressed in 1873 to the leading physicists elicited a gratifying number of replies'; see *Proceedings of the Physical Society of London*, **1** (1874–5).   (5) See Volume I: 314n.

The opposite condition, the crystalline, is shown in the lecture, where the members sit in rows, while science flows in an uninterrupted stream from a source which we take as the origin. This is radiation of science.

Conduction takes place along the series of members seated round a dinner table, and fixed there for several hours, with flowers in the middle to prevent any cross currents.

The condition most favourable to life is an intermediate plastic or colloïdal condition, where the order of business is (1) Greetings and confused talk; (2) A short communication from one who has something to say and to show; (3) Remarks on the communication addressed to the Chair, introducing matters irrelevant to the communication but interesting to the members; (4) This lets each member see who is interested in his special hobby, and who is likely to help him; and leads to (5) Confused conversation and examination of objects on the table.

I have not indicated how this programme is to be combined with eating. It is more easily carried out in a small town than in London, and more easily in Faraday's young days (see his life by B. Jones)[6] than now. It might answer in some London district where there happen to be several clubbable senior men who could attract the juniors from a distance.

---

(6) Henry Bence Jones, *The Life and Letters of Faraday*, 2 vols. (London, 1870).

ON QUATERNIONS

DECEMBER 1873[1]

From *Nature* (25 December 1873)[2]

QUATERNIONS

A mathematician is one who endeavours to secure the greatest possible consistency in his thoughts and statements, by guiding the process of his reasoning into those well-worn tracks by which we pass from one relation among quantities to an equivalent relation. He who has kept his mind always in those paths which have never led him or anyone else to an inconsistent result, and has traversed them so often that the act of passage has become rather automatic than voluntary, is, and knows himself to be, an accomplished mathematician. The very important part played by calculation in modern mathematics and physics has led to the development of the popular idea of a mathematician as a calculator, far more expert, indeed, than any banker's clerk, but of course immeasurably inferior, both in resources and in accuracy, to what the 'analytical engine' will be, if the late Mr. Babbage's design should ever be carried into execution.

But although much of the routine work of a mathematician is calculation, his proper work – that which constitutes him a mathematician – is the invention of methods. He is always inventing methods, some of them of no great value except for some purpose of his own; others, which shorten the labour of calculation, are eagerly adopted by all calculators. But the methods on which the mathematician is content to hang his reputation are generally those which he fancies will save him and all who come after him the labour of thinking about what has cost himself so much thought.

Now Quaternions, or the doctrine of Vectors, is a mathematical method, but it is a method of thinking, and not, at least for the present generation, a method of saving thought. It does not, like some more popular mathematical methods, encourage the hope that mathematicians may give their minds a holiday, by transferring all their work to their pens. It calls upon us at every step to form a mental image of the geometrical features represented by the symbols, so that in studying geometry by this method we have our minds

---

(1) See the references to Kelland and Tait's *Introduction to Quaternions* (London, 1873) in his letter to Tait of 1 December 1873 (Number 483).

(2) Published (unsigned) in *Nature*, **9** (1873): 137–8. The review can however be confidently attributed to Maxwell's authorship: the *Nature* archives confirm this attribution.

engaged with geometrical ideas, and are not permitted to fancy ourselves geometers when we are only arithmeticians.

This demand for thought – for the continued construction of mental representations – is enough to account for the slow progress of the method among adult mathematicians. Two courses, however, are open to the cultivators of Quaternions: they may show how easily the principles of the method are acquired by those whose minds are still fresh, and in so doing they may prepare the way for the triumph of Quaternions in the next generation; or they may apply the method to those problems which the science of the day presents to us, and show how easily it arrives at those solutions which have been already expressed in ordinary mathematical language, and how it brings within our reach other problems, which the ordinary methods have hitherto abstained from attacking.

Sir W. R. Hamilton, when treating of the elements of the subject, was apt to become so fascinated by the metaphysical aspects of the method,[3] that the mind of his disciple became impressed with the profundity, rather than the simplicity of his doctrines. Professors Kelland and Tait in the opening chapter (II.)[4] of their recently published work* have, we think, successfully avoided this element of discouragement. They tell us at once what a vector is, and how to add vectors, and they do this in a way which is quite as intelligible to those who are just beginning to learn geometry as to the most expert mathematician.

The subject, like all other subjects, becomes more intricate as the student advances in it; but at the same time his ideas are becoming clearer and more firmly established as he works out the numerous examples and exercises which are placed before him.

The technical terms of the method – Scalar, Vector, Tensor, Versor[5] – are introduced in their proper places, and their meaning is sufficiently illustrated to the beginner by the examples which he is expected to work out.

---

* 'Introduction to Quaternions, with numerous Examples.' By P. Kelland, F.R.S., formerly Fellow of Queen's College, Cambridge; and P. G. Tait, formerly Fellow of St. Peter's College, Cambridge; Professors in the Department of Mathematics in the University of Edinburgh. (Macmillan, 1873).

---

(3) In the 'Preface' to his *Lectures on Quaternions* (Dublin, 1853): 1–64, esp. 1–3, Hamilton describes 'Algebra as the SCIENCE OF PURE TIME', referring to his paper 'Theory of conjugate functions, or algebraic couples; with a preliminary and elementary essay on algebra as the science of pure time', *Transactions of the Royal Irish Academy*, 17 (1837): 293–422, esp. 293–7. In his *Lectures on Quaternions*: 2–3n he makes explicit reference to 'passages in Kant's Criticism of the Pure Reason, which appeared to justify the expectation that it should be *possible* to construct, *à priori*, a Science of Time, as well as a Science of Space'.

(4) Chapter II, 'Vector addition and subtraction', in Kelland and Tait, *Introduction to Quaternions*: 6–31. (5) See Number 353 note (9).

The pride of the accomplished mathematician, however (for whom this book is not written), might have been somewhat mollified if somewhere in the book a few pages had been devoted to explaining to him the differences between the Quaternion methods and those which he has spent his life in mastering, and of which he has now become the slave. He is apt to be startled by finding that when one vector is multiplied into another at right angles to it, the product is still a vector, but at right angles to both. His only idea of a vector had been that of a line, and he had expected that when one vector was multiplied into another the result would be something of a different kind from a line, such, for instance, as a surface. Now if it had been pointed out to him in the chapter on vector multiplication that a surface is a vector, he would be saved from a painful mental shock, for a mathematician is as sensitive about 'dimensions' as an English schoolboy is about 'quantities'.

The fact is, that even in the purely geometrical applications of the Quaternion method we meet with three different kinds of directed quantities: the vector proper, which represents transference from A to B; the area or 'aperture', which is always understood to have a positive and a negative aspect, according to the direction in which it is swept out by the generating vector; and the versor, which represents turning round an axis.

The Quaternion ideas of these three quantities differ from the old ideas of the line, the surface, and the angle only by giving more prominence to the fact that each of them has a determinate *direction* as well as a determinate magnitude. When Euclid tells us to draw a line AB, he supposes it to be done by the motion of a point from A to B or from B to A. But when the line is once generated he makes no distinction between the results of these two operations, which, on Hamilton's system, are each the opposite of the other.

Surfaces also, according to Euclid, are generated by the motion of lines, so that the idea of motion is an old one, and we have only to take special note of the direction of the motion in order to raise Euclid's idea to the level of Hamilton's.

With respect to angles, Euclid appears to treat them as if they arose from the fortuitous concourse of right lines; but the unsatisfactory nature of this mode of treatment is shown by the fact that in all modern books on trigonometry an angle is represented as generated by motion round an axis in a definite direction.

There are thus three geometrical quantities having direction, and the more than magical power of the method of Quaternions resides in the spell by which these three orders of quantities are brought under the sway of the same system of operators.

The secret of this spell is twofold, and is symbolised by the vine-tendril and the mason's rule and square. The tendril of the vine teaches us the relation which must be maintained between the positive direction of translation along a line and the positive direction of rotation about that line. When we have not a vine-tendril to guide us, a corkscrew will do as well, or we may use a hop-tendril, provided we look at it not directly, but by reflexion in a mirror.[6]

The mason's rule teaches us that the symbol, as written on paper, is not a real line, but a mere injunction, commanding us to measure out in a certain direction a vector of a length so many times that of the rule. Without the rule the symbol would have no definite meaning. Thus the rule is the unit of the Quaternion system, while the square *reminds* us that the right angle is the unit versor.

The doctrine of the unit is a necessary part of every exact science, but in Quaternions the application of the same operators to versors, vectors, and areas is utterly unintelligible without a clear understanding of the function of the unit in the science of measurement.

Whether, however, it is better to insinuate the true doctrine into the mind of the student by a graduated series of exercises, or to inculcate it upon him at once by dogmatic statements, is a question which can only be determined by the experience of a new generation, who shall have been born with the extraspatial unit ever present to their consciousness, and whose thoughts, guided by the vine-tendril along the Quaternion path, shall turn always to the right hand, and never to the left.

Prof. Kelland tells us in the preface to the work to which we have alluded that, whereas Sir W. R. Hamilton and Prof. Tait have written treatises on Quaternions for mathematicians, the time has come when it behoves some one to write for those who desire to become mathematicians. Whatever, therefore, advanced mathematicians may think of this book, they ought to reserve their judgment as to its difficulty till they have ascertained how it is assimilated by those for whom it is written – those in whom the desire to become mathematicians has not yet become alloyed with the consciousness that they are mathematicians. For while Prof. Kelland – as he has elsewhere told us – finds but little difficulty in teaching the elements of the doctrine of Vectors to his junior classes, Hamilton himself, the great master of the spell, when addressing mathematicians of established reputation, found, for his Quaternions, but few to praise and fewer still to love.

Prof. Kelland, by the clearness and orderliness of his statements, and by boldly getting rid of everything which is unnecessarily abstruse, has done more than any other man towards rendering the subject easy to the student,

---

(6) See Numbers 370 and 371.

and reconciling even the case-hardened mathematician to the new method, as applied to geometrical questions of old-established truth.

The other aspect of Quaternions, as a method which every mathematician *must* learn in order to deal with the questions which the progress of physics brings every day into greater prominence, is hinted at by Prof. Tait in the last chapter of the book.[7] He there introduces us to the linear and vector function of the first degree under its kinematical aspect of a homogeneous strain. The importance of functions of this kind may be gathered from the fact that a knowledge of their properties supplies the key to the theory of the stresses as well as the strains in solid bodies, and to that of the conduction of heat and electricity in bodies whose properties are different in different directions, to the phenomena exhibited by crystals in the magnetic field,[8] to the thermo-electric properties of crystals, and to other sets of natural phenomena, one or more of which the scientific progress of every year brings before us.

But as we believe that Prof. Tait is about to bring out a new edition of his treatise on Quaternions, in which this higher aspect of the subject will be brought more prominently forward, we reserve our remarks on Quaternions as an instrument of physical research till we have the subject presented to us by Prof. Tait in a form which adequately represents its latest developments.[9]

---

(7) Chapter X, 'Vector equations of the first degree', in Kelland and Tait, *Introduction to Quaternions*: 180–208.

(8) See Numbers 441 and 468.

(9) P. G. Tait, *An Elementary Treatise on Quaternions* (Cambridge, $_2$1873): 228–88 (Chap. XI, 'Physical Applications').

486

LETTER TO HERBERT SPENCER[1]

5 DECEMBER 1873

From the original in the University of London Library[2]

11 Scroope Terrace
Cambridge
5 Dec 1873

Dear Sir[3]

I do not remember the particulars of what I said to Prof. Clifford[4] about nebular condensation. The occasion of it was I think a passage in an old edition of your First Principles,[5] and having since then made a little more acquaintance with your works I regarded it merely as a temporary phase of

---

(1) Herbert Spencer, philosopher and sociologist (*DNB*).

(2) Herbert Spencer MS 791/92, University of London Library.

(3) In reply to a letter from Spencer of 4 December 1873: 'Sometime this year, Prof. Clifford named to me a criticism you passed upon a certain hypothesis of mine respecting the process of nebular concentration, as tending to produce a hollow liquid spheroid during its closing stages. The moment he named to me this criticism, I saw that I had made a mistake. The process of condensation from the vapourous to the liquid form, I had at first considered in the case of Saturn's rings, where a precipitation into a denser form, recurring at the equatorial portion of the concentrating spheroid, might produce a ring that would maintain its place; supposing the concentration to occur when the centripetal and centrifugal forces were balanced. And I had inadvertently carried this conception to the case of other planets, where there could be no such balance of forces. / There has since occurred to me another hypothesis respecting the mode of condensation and the resulting structure. I have discussed this with my friends Tyndall, Hirst and Clifford; and, while not committing themselves to it, they do not raise any objections against it. Prof. Clifford, however, expressing great faith in your intuitive insight into physical processes, recommended me to obtain, if possible, your opinion respecting the tenability of this hypothesis. / I write to ask whether, after the close of the Cambridge term, you are likely to be in London; and whether, in that case, you could afford me half-an-hour's conversation; and further to ask whether, if you are not coming to London, you could grant me the same favour were I to come to Cambridge before the term ends. / I enclose the outline, in proof, of a speculation on another physical question, respecting which, also, I [...]' (ULC Add. MSS 7655, II/74). On Thomas Archer Hirst see Number 369 note (6). On Spencer's interpretation of Laplace's nebular hypothesis, and his correspondence with Maxwell, see David Duncan, *The Life and Letters of Herbert Spencer* (London, 1908): 428–31.

(4) William Kingdon Clifford: see Number 280 note (7).

(5) On Spencer's interpretation of the nebular hypothesis see his *First Principles* (London, 1862): 362–7. Maxwell may have noted Spencer's discussion of Saturn's rings in illustration of his theory 'that a state of homogeneity is one of unstable equilibrium'; see *First Principles*: 366–7, and also Spencer's letter of 4 December 1873 (note (3)). For Maxwell's comments on the nebular hypothesis in relation to Saturn's rings see Volume I: 443.

the process of evolution which you have been carrying on within your own mind.

Mathematicians, by guiding their thoughts always along the same tracks, have converted the field of thought into a kind of railway system and are apt to neglect cross-country speculations.

It is very seldom that any man who tries to form a system can prevent his system from forming round him and closing him in before he is 40. Hence the wisdom of putting in some ingredient to check crystallization and keep the system in a colloidal condition. Candle-makers I believe use arsenic for this purpose. In psychological matters 'mental suspense' is often recommended but this is generally interpreted as 'acidia' or want of interest.

But you seem to be able to retard the crystallization of parts of your system without stopping the process of evolution of the whole, and I therefore attach much more importance to the general scheme than to particular statements.

With respect to electricity[6] and its relation to molecular motions of various kinds you should look at Professor Challis' speculations as he inclines to a theory of that kind.[7]

You quote me as denying that Electricity is a form of energy,[8] but you give, as an example, an electrified system, the energy of which is the main subject of calculation in my book.

I say that the electrification of a system is a form of energy, just as the-being-wound-up of a watch spring is, but electricity, that is the quantity which we deal with when we compare the charges of electrified bodies, is not of the nature of energy, but of the nature of body, just as the watch spring is.

It is one of the factors of energy, the other being electric potential. It cannot therefore of itself be energy.

But heat, of itself, that is the quantity of heat which will melt so much ice, is energy.

---

(6) Presumably the subject of Spencer's supplementary query mentioned in his letter of 4 December (note (3)). The proof of a paper 'What is electricity?', revised and published in Spencer's *Essays: Scientific, Political, and Speculative*, 3 vols (London, 1858–74), **3**: 191–215, is among the Maxwell MSS in ULC Add. MSS 7655, V, c/51. According to Spencer, 'electricity results from the mutual disturbance of unlike molecular motions' (*Essays*, **3**: 195).

(7) James Challis, *An Essay on the Mathematical Principles of Physics* (Cambridge, 1873). See Maxwell's review, 'Challis's "Mathematical Principles of Physics"', *Nature*, **8** (1873): 279–80 (= *Scientific Papers*, **2**: 338–42), critical of Challis' speculations. See also Number 475, and Volume I: 693n.

(8) The proof of Spencer's 'What is electricity?' (see note (6)) includes galleys of a postscript to the text of the essay (as first published in 1864). There is a statement – which was deleted from the text as published in *Essays*, **3**: 203–11 – of 'the paradox enunciated by Prof. Clerk Maxwell; namely, that electricity cannot be classed as a form of energy'.

My peculiar doctrine about electricity, that is the 'matter of electricity', is that it fills all space, so that every cubic foot of space is at all times equally full of it. Every displacement of this medium is therefore in a circuit, as in the case of an incompressible fluid. If this displacement occurs in a non-conductor or 'dielectric' it requires electromotive force to produce it, and it reacts with an equal electromotive force, just as a watch spring requires a force to wind it up and then exerts force on the wheels when the watch is not going.

In a conductor, the electromotive force decays rapidly, so that a continuous current is produced, as if a man should keep winding his watch when it is going, or when the balance wheel is removed, and the watch is running down at great speed.

The reasons for such a doctrine are given in different parts of my book and are referred to in the index under 'Displacement'.

In column Three of the slips you sent me and in the 2nd paragraph (on residual discharge) there is a very graphic description of phenomena which resemble real phenomena in all but one, and that a most significant, respect.$^{(9)}$ First read Faradays experimental researches from (1169) to (1178).$^{(10)}$ (This is a most remarkable passage, one that has hardly ever been appreciated, and which Faraday himself understood only in his highest scientific moods.) Then on residual discharge (1234) &c.$^{(11)}$

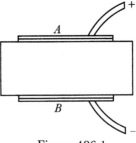

Figure 486,1

The facts are as follows. Take a plate of spermaceti gutta percha &c. Let A B be metallic electrodes to be connected at pleasure with a machine. Electrify $A+$ (or $B-$, there is no difference) for some time: Then discharge both A and B completely and simultaneously, and insulate them again. In a little A will be found $+$ and $B-$ but feebler than at first. This may be repeated several times, the residual charges becoming always feebler.

---

(9) In the postscript to his 'What is electricity?' (see notes (6) and (8)) Spencer discusses electric charge in terms of his notion that 'electricity results from the mutual disturbance of unlike molecule motions'. He explains 'residual discharge' in terms of 'perturbations in the layers of molecules'. He adds: 'We have, too, a complete explanation of the truth, insisted on by Faraday, that there can be no charge of one kind of electricity obtained, without a corresponding charge of the opposite kind. For...no wave of molecular perturbations of the nature described, can be produced, without there being simultaneously produced an exactly-equal counter-wave.' He slightly amended the final sentence, here quoted from the proof, in the published text (*Essays*, **3**: 210). In response to comments by Maxwell and others, Spencer appended a supplementary postscript (*Essays*, **3**: 211–15).

(10) Faraday, *Electricity*, **1**: 364–7 ('On the absolute charge of matter').

(11) Faraday, *Electricity*, **1**: 387.

Now take a case apparently similar. Hold a thick plate of metal before the fire till one side is hotter than the other. Then take it away and pour cold water over the heated side till it is cooled to the same temperature as the other.

Then leave the plate to itself for a while. The side which was formerly next the fire will again become hotter than the other, just as the plate of gutta percha became again electrified in the first case.

The thermal phenomenon is explained by the return of the heat which had been conducted a certain distance into the plate. The electrical phenomenon has often been explained in the same way, but not correctly.

If you heat a body and then cool its surface to the atmospheric temperature and then leave it alone, the heat will work its way outwards and warm the surface again.

But if you charge a body ever so highly with electricity over its whole outer surface and keep it charged ever so long, and if you then instantaneously discharge the outer surface and again insulate it, no new electrification will appear. You cannot cause electricity to become absorbed in the substance of the body so as to produce no effect outside at the instant of discharge, and afterwards to creep out of the molecules in which it was latent as heat does.[12]

Observe that I do not say that these phenomena are inconsistent with your theory. I only say that they are very important and significant, and that though you expressly refer to Faraday's dogma in the next paragraph[13] I think it probable that fresh thought on the subject would lead you to modify some expressions in the paragraph on residual charge, so as to exclude from the mind of the reader the idea that electricity is absorbed after the manner of heat.

With respect to the vibrations of molecules I know that you do not believe that a molecule can of itself dance up and down with nothing to dance on, but as I observe that you are always improving your phraseology I shall lay before you my notions on the nomenclature of molecular motions.

(1) I would confine the word *vibration* to those internal motions of a molecule which alter the distances between the parts of which it is composed. The simpler the molecule the smaller the number and the greater the definiteness of the modes of harmonic vibration. Every system has a set of harmonic modes of vibration but whether it actually vibrates and how the

---

(12) See Maxwell, *Treatise*, **1**: 50–2 (§§ 52–4).   (13) See note (9).

motion is divided among these modes depends on the circumstances which set it in motion.

(2) The molecule may also *rotate* about any axis, constant or variable, without altering the distances between its parts. There is nothing which defines the period of such rotation. It varies at every encounter with another molecule.

(3) Next comes the motion of the centre of gravity which is in itself of course perfectly definite, but as regards human knowledge it consists of two parts, visible and invisible.

The *visible* velocity is that of the centre of gravity of the group of molecules, consisting of millions which we deal with as an observable portion of the substance.

(4) The other component, that by which the actual velocity of an individual molecule differs from the mean velocity of the group, is called the invisible motion, or more expressively, the motion of *agitation* of the molecule.

Our knowledge of (2) and (4) is *statistical* only – there is nothing definite in any other sense than the death-rate of a city is definite.

In (1) the periods are definite but the amplitudes are not. (1) (2) & (4) are connected together and the total energy of each rises and falls with the temperature. (3) alone is independent of the others.

It is only in gases that the vibrations of the molecules have definite periods because it is only in gases that a molecule is ever so far from its neighbours as to form a vibrating system by itself like a tuning fork. In solids liquids and even in gases when highly compressed there is so much interaction between the molecules that the vibrating system has a far greater variety of periods and besides this the relative motion of the molecules introduces continual changes in the connexions of the system and therefore in its periods so that the final result is what appears to us complete irregularity of vibration. Hence there are no bright lines in the spectra of hot solids and liquids, and even in gases the spectrum becomes continuous when the gas is dense.

Of course all this has nothing to do with the vibrations (which may or may not be of regular periods) which arise when waves such as sound waves are propagated through a medium consisting of molecules. These vibrations are far slower and on a far larger scale than the vibrations of the constituents of a molecule. The motions belong to class (3) and may be treated as if the medium were continuous (not molecular) without any risk of error.

All these distinctions of motion into regular and irregular &c arise from the limitation of our bodily and mental faculties. If the molecular theory is true and if we could see or trace the motion of each molecule we could not longer distinguish motion into visible and invisible, regular and irregular, motion of masses and heat. We do not say that a cannon ball is hot because it is moving rapidly for we follow it in thought with our thermometer and find it cold. We say that a battle is hot when there are many such balls flying about and when we think of the battle, not of one ball at a time.

I had not intended to send you this letter (which was written at odd times during the examination of papers) but I find I have not time to reduce it to a reasonable form for a day or two so I must leave it as it is.

Yours faithfully
J. CLERK MAXWELL

487

LETTER TO HERBERT SPENCER
17 DECEMBER 1873
From the original in the University of London Library[1]

11 Scroope Terrace
Cambridge
17 December 1873

Dear Sir

The reason for which I use the word agitation to distinguish the local motion of a molecule in relation to its neighbours is that I think with you that the word agitation conveys in a small degree, if at all, the notion of rhythm.[2]

If motion is said to be rhythmic when the path is, on the whole, as much in one direction as in the opposite, then all motion is rhythmic when it is confined within a small region of space.

But if as I understand the word rhythmic, it implies not only alternation, but regularity and periodicity, then the word agitation excludes the notion of rhythm, which was what I meant it to do.

In the writings and words of many persons who are trying to conceive of heat in a body as a motion of its parts, I can trace a tendency to attribute some kind of regularity to the motion. They have picked up their ideas of motion confined to narrow limits chiefly from their study of the vibrations of elastic bodies (like tuning forks) and the motion of the particles of a medium during the propagation of a wave. The popularization of true notions on these matters has been the great work of the early part of this century.

But these motions, at least in those cases which are explained in books, are periodic and regular, that is one vibration is exactly like another.

They have also the property that they can be conveyed away from the vibrating body and passed on, in their entirety, to other bodies, as in the propagation of a sound wave which leaves the air behind it at rest.

But the motion called heat is not propagated but only diffused, that is, it cannot be passed from hand to hand so as to make the receiver hot while leaving the giver cold. It can only be communicated from those who have much to those who have less.

---

(1) Herbert Spencer MSS 791/93, University of London Library.

(2) In his reply to this letter, dated 30 December 1873 (ULC Add. MSS 7655, II/76; printed in *Molecules and Gases*: 160–2), Spencer wrote: 'I had no intention when I made my passing comment on the word *agitation*, of drawing from you a second letter.', apparently referring to his (missing) reply to Maxwell's letter of 5 December (Number 486). On Spencer's concept of 'the rhythm of motion', his doctrine that 'rhythm results wherever there is a conflict of force not in equilibrium', see his *First Principles* (London, 1862): 317–34, esp. 317.

The explanation of this *diffusion* lies in the *irregularity* of that motion of agitation which we call heat. Heat (physically speaking) is something which a body cannot possess without being hot. Now you will find mention made in books of something called Radiant Heat which is further explained as a regular system of undulations in an æther.

But I say that Radiant Heat is not heat at all, for the medium which transmits it is not hot while it is in it, and though it is in motion, this motion is entirely passed on to the next portion of the medium.

The case is like that of a fire which drives a steam-engine which drives a band which drives a turning lathe which has a piece of wood chucked on it which gets hot by friction.

The ultimate source of this heat is the fire, and one of the media of transmission is the band, but the band does not become hot in virtue of its transmitting energy.

Similarly the transparent media transmit radiation without becoming hot.

A great scientific desideratum is a set of words of *little* meaning – words which mean no more than that a thing belongs to a very large class. Such words are much wanted in the undulatory theory of light in order to express fully what is proved by experiment without connoting anything which is a mere hypothesis. Hamiltons word Vector, signifying a directed quantity without specifying whether it is a displacement, a rotation, a velocity, a magnetization &c is exceedingly useful in such a statement. See arts 816 & 821 of my book on Electricity.[3]

Yours truly
J. CLERK MAXWELL

---

(3) Maxwell, *Treatise*, 2: 404, 407–8.

EXAMINER'S REPORT ON THE NATURAL SCIENCES TRIPOS (PHYSICS) 1873

DECEMBER 1873[1]

From the original in the University Library, Cambridge[2]

NATURAL SCIENCES TRIPOS 1873

PHYSICS

Of the twenty three candidates, seventeen obtained marks for their answers to questions in Physics. The knowledge of the subject as shown by these answers was in a good many cases of a very unsatisfactory kind, arising partly from an unintelligent use of popular text books and partly from a familiarity with the appearance of instruments without any knowledge of the principles on which their action depends.

Several of the candidates however, and in particular Mr Davies of St. Johns[3] sent up answers which showed that Experimental Physics, treated without the higher mathematics, may be learned in a sound & scientific manner.

A certain amount of knowledge of the first principles of physics ought I think to be required of candidates during the first three days, as necessary in every branch of Natural Science.

During the last three days,[4] the object of the Examiner should be to give credit to those who can show a practical as well as a theoretical knowledge of the methods and results of physical research. The questions in the last three days should therefore be so arranged as to give full occupation to the real student of physics during the hours of examination while they afford no chance of making marks to the man of hearsay information.

JAMES CLERK MAXWELL

---

(1) See Numbers 483 and 486 for reference to the examination.

(2) ULC, Natural Sciences Tripos Mark Book, Cambridge University Archives, Min. VIII.56, 41^v. There is a draft in ULC Add. MSS 7655, V, k/10.

(3) John Paget Davies, St John's 1870 (Venn).

(4) According to the regulations for the examination for the Natural Sciences Tripos, in 'the last six papers the questions shall take a wider range... and some of the questions shall have special reference to the Philosophy and History of those subjects'; see *The Cambridge University Calendar for the Year 1873* (Cambridge, 1873): 34–5.

THE EQUATION OF CONTINUITY AND PHYSICAL ANALOGY

1873[1]

From the original in the University Library, Cambridge[2]

NOTES ON Mr APPLETON'S DISSERTATION[3]

On p. 4 it would be more general in the equation of continuity instead of $K\left(\dfrac{dV}{dz}+\dfrac{d^2V}{dz^2}\delta z\right)$ to write $K\dfrac{dV}{dz}+\dfrac{d}{dz}\left(K\dfrac{dV}{dz}\right)\delta z$.

The first equation then becomes

$$CD\frac{dV}{dt} = \frac{d}{dx}\left(K\frac{dV}{dx}\right)+\frac{d}{dy}\left(K\frac{dV}{dy}\right)+\frac{d}{dz}\left(K\frac{dV}{dz}\right)$$

which is the general equation of the flow of heat in an isotropic but not necessarily homogeneous solid within which there are no sources or sinks.[4] C, D, and K are functions of whatever the state of the body at the point $x\,y\,z$ depends on such as

> the chemical nature of the substance
>
> its physical state as determined by its state of aggregation as solid liquid or gaseous, powdered, spongy or dense &c and also on its temperature.

In so far as pressure affects the state of aggregation, $C\,D$ & K are functions of pressure, but we have no reason to believe that pressure affects C, D, K in any other way. Magnetization may also affect these quantities. On the other hand, C, D, K are not functions of anything which does not affect the physical state of the body directly as for instance

1. Flow of heat through the element does not affect it.
2. Flow of electricity through a conducting element does not directly affect it, only by raising the temperature.
3. Electric and Magnetic potentials, being mere artificial concepts, cannot affect the physical state of a body.

---

(1) This date is conjectural. See note (3). (2) ULC Add. MSS 7655, V, i/6.
(3) Probably for a Trinity College Fellowship: Richard Appleton, Trinity 1867, Fellow 1873 (Venn).
(4) See Number 339 esp. note (3). K is the conductivity of the body for heat, C the heat capacity per unit mass, and D the density of the body.

General note on the analogies of Heat Electrostatics Elektrokinetics and Magnetic Induction.

(1) V in the equation represents –

Temperature   Electric Potential and Magnetic Potential. Of these Temperature is a physical state of a body and therefore its properties may be functions of Temperature.

Electric and Magnetic Potentials are not physical states. They are reckoned from a purely arbitrary zero, and a change of potential does not affect any property of the body.

(2) $\frac{dV}{dx}$ represents –

(α)   The component flow of heat across a surface normal to x.[5]

We have no reason to believe that the physical state of any body is affected by the flow of heat across it. In fact we have every reason to believe that the flow of heat is going on in all directions in a body of uniform temperature, and that what we call a flow of heat is only a preponderant flow in one direction.

(β)   The electromotive force at a point in a dielectric.[6]

If, as I suppose, this produces a state of strain in the dielectric, the physical properties of the dielectric may vary with its value from the state of complete freedom from polarization to that at which disruptive discharge occurs. No such variation of properties has as yet been experimentally demonstrated, but there is no reason against it.

(γ)   The electromotive force at a point in a conductor.[7]

Here the state of strain, if it exists in a conductor is continually decaying and breaking down. We have abundance of experimental evidence that Ohms law is true to a great degree of accuracy, and therefore the conductivity of a body is not affected by the intensity of the electromotive force acting on it, or by the strength of the current produced. (If the current raises the temperature, of course the rise of temperature, and not the current itself, increases the resistance.)

(δ)   The magnetizing force at a point in a ferro- or diamagnetic body.[8]

Magnetization is a change in the physical state of a body. It has been shown by Thomson to alter the physical properties of the body as regards

---

(5) [William Thomson,] 'On the uniform motion of heat in homogeneous solid bodies, and its connection with the mathematical theory of electricity', *Camb. Math. J.*, **3** (1842): 71–84 (= *Electrostatics and Magnetism*: 1–14).

(6) See the *Treatise*, **1**: 384 (§332).   (7) See the *Treatise*, **1**: 345 (§297).

(8) See the *Treatise*, **2**: 21 (§395).

conduction of electricity &c,[9] and we know that the magnetic permeability varies with the magnetization.[10]

(3) K represents

α thermal conductivity
β specific inductive capacity
γ electric conductivity
δ magnetic permeability.[11]

All these are independent of

Electric and magnetic potential
Flow of heat and of electricity but depend upon Temperature, electric displacement & magnetization.

(4) $CD = 0$ in the case of electricity.[12]

p. 14 It should be distinctly stated that Thomson was the first to point out the analogy between the mathematical theories of heat & electricity[13] and this ought to be done early in the Dissertation.

p. 35 The description of electrolysis here given is much older than Clausius. Clausius introduced the doctrine that in an electrolyte in its ordinary state the ions are often dissociated by the effect of the collisions of the molecules and that it is when they are in this state that the electromotive force guides their motion.[14]

p. 36 strain instead of stress

stress = distribution of force, strain = distribution of displacement.[15]

p. 37 and to be itself rendered impervious to electricity.

p. 38 Sp. ind. cap. certainly does not vary with potential it may vary with temperature and with electromotive force.

p. 41 doubtful analogy between 1st law of motion and conduction of heat without expenditure of energy

better analogy the diffusion of gases or of black & white balls in a bag.

p. 47 changing the temperature of a standard body.

---

(9) See Thomson's discussion of 'Magnetic permeability, and analogues in electro-static induction, conduction of heat, and fluid motion', in his *Electrostatics and Magnetism*: 482–6.
(10) See the *Treatise*, **2**: 51 (§428).   (11) See the *Treatise*, **2**: 237 (§618).
(12) Yielding Laplace's equation for points in space where there is no electrification: see the *Treatise*, **1**: 86, 99, 115, 384 (§§83, 96, 102, 332).
(13) See note (5).   (14) See Number 478 esp. note (6).
(15) See Number 206 esp. note (7).

REPORT ON A PAPER BY OSMOND FISHER ON THE ELEVATION OF MOUNTAINS

circa DECEMBER 1873[1]

From the original in the University Library, Cambridge[2]

REPORT ON Mr FISHERS PAPER ON THE ELEVATION OF MOUNTAINS BY LATERAL PRESSURE[3]

The aim of this paper is to investigate the numerical data of the lateral contraction of the earths crust since it became solid in order to compare it with the amount of crumpling exhibited by the strata which have been elevated into mountain ranges.

The investigations given in the paper are of several different kinds. The first relates to the volumes of mountains above and of valleys below a certain datum level, defined as the present surface of the earth, supposing that during its shrinking the crust had yielded freely to lateral compression without either crumpling up or in any way increasing its vertical thickness.

The equation derived from these considerations appears consistent with this definition of the datum level. But it does not seem to me to be of any use in relation to the aim of the paper. It only tells us that the volume of the crust has remained the same since it has become cold in spite of upheavals and subsidences. But what we want is a measure of the amount of disturbance and this is not to be got by an expression in which hollows are negative and heights positive but by one in which both are positive. For instance the expression might be that of the potential energy of the present distribution of matter which might be derived from it by levelling up and down to a

---

(1) This dating is tentative. A minute of a meeting of the Council of the Cambridge Philosophical Society, dated 1 December 1873, records: 'Mr O. Fisher's (second) paper "On the elevation of mountains by lateral pressure" to be read this evening, was ordered to be referred.' ('Council Minute Book, 1871–85', Scientific Periodicals Library, Cambridge). Fisher had previously published a paper 'On the elevation of mountains by lateral pressure, its cause, and the amount of it, with a speculation on the origin of volcanic action', *Trans. Camb. Phil. Soc.*, **11** (1871): 489–506.

(2) ULC Add. MSS 7655, V, i/5.

(3) See Osmond Fisher, 'On the inequalities of the earth's surface viewed in connection with the secular cooling', *Trans. Camb. Phil. Soc.*, **12** (1875): 414–33. A minute of a meeting of the Council of the Cambridge Philosophical Society, dated 8 February 1875, records: 'It was agreed that Mr O. Fisher's paper "On the elevation of mountain chains by compression" be printed in the Society's Transactions.' ('Minute Book').

spheroidal surface of the same volume as the actual earth. (This is not Mr Fishers datum level.)

Thus $\sum$ (Mass of elevated portion × height of centre of gravity of do:)
+$\sum$ Mass of earth displaced from hollows × depth of c.g. of hollows would give a quantity *essentially* +^{ve} representing the energy of the present distribution of mountains and valleys.

But what is really wanted is a numerical estimate of the actual amount of crumpling of the crust, that is to say an estimate of the original area of what is now a square mile of crust derived from observation of the contortions of the strata and the distortions of fossils therein.

Such an estimate is referred to in the paper; it is derived from Prof Ramsays restored sections[4] and gives linear compression between $\frac{1}{13}$ and $\frac{1}{21}$.[5]

The valuable part of the paper is the comparison of this estimate with the linear shrinking of the surface due to the cooling of the earth.

I have not had time to go through the calculations but on a rough estimate the results do not seem to be affected by any important error and they show that to assume a linear shrinking of $\frac{1}{13}$ or even $\frac{1}{21}$ due to cooling of hot rocks since the surface became solid would be very extravagant.

The author suggests other causes of shrinkage besides loss of heat namely the escape of water.[6] It is probable or rather certain that water-substance if it exists at great depths under great pressure and at high temperture is neither a gas nor a liquid being above its critical point.[7]

In this state substances are easily dissolved in it, not however so much on account of greater tendency to combine with water as on account of a greater tendency of their own to dissipation. At still higher temperatures the water-substance becomes itself dissociated into oxygen and hydrogen but it does not follow that the dissolved substances will be precipitated. The 'magma' may be all the more complete the higher the temperature, because though the bonds of affinity have fallen away, the prison walls prevent the elements from escaping.

But of all the unknown regions of the universe the most unsafe to reason about is that which is under our feet.

On the whole, I consider the value of the paper to lie in the comparison

---

(4) A. C. Ramsay, 'On the denudation of South Wales and the adjacent counties of England', *Memoires of the Geological Survey of Great Britain*, 1 (1846): 297–335.

(5) As stated by Fisher, 'On the inequalities of the earth's surface': 428.

(6) The passages in Maxwell's report, from 'It is probable...' to '... that which is under our feet', were quoted by Fisher in 'On the inequalities of the earth's surface': 431n, with the appended comment: 'The following remarks... were received from a quarter which disposes me to place a great reliance on them.' (7) See Number 381 note (3).

between the observed crumpling of the strata and the theoretical shrinking of the crust by cooling and in the conclusion that if the shrinkage was similar to that of melted rocks and slags it would not be sufficient to account for the observed crumpling. There is also a suggestion as to the shrinkage by escape of water the objections to which so far as they are stated in the paper I do not think of great moment considering the slowness of diffusion through a thickness equal to that of the earths crust.

I have not been able to see the value of the first part of the paper, namely that which involves the 'datum line' equation. Unless I become convinced by further explanation, I should say that this part of the paper, if printed, would greatly detract from the value of the whole.[8]

J. CLERK MAXWELL

(8) But see Fisher, 'On the inequalities of the earth's surface': 415–19, where discussion of the datum line is included.

APPENDIX

§1 The following letters, which are not extant as autograph manuscripts, have been abbreviated from the versions printed in the *Life of Maxwell*.

(1) Letter to Charles Hope Cay
    5 January 1865 (Number 240).
(2) Letter to Charles Benjamin Tayler
    2 February 1866 (Number 256).

§2 The following letters printed in extract in the *Life of Maxwell*, have not been reproduced.

(1) Letter to Lewis Campbell
    22 November 1864 (*Life of Maxwell*: 340).
(2) Letters to Charles Hope Cay
    18 November 1863, 14 October 1865 (*Life of Maxwell*: 337–8, 343–4).
(3) Letters to Katherine Mary Clerk Maxwell
    22 June 1864, 23 June 1864, 26 June 1864, 28 June 1864, December 1873 (*Life of Maxwell*: 338–40, 387).

§3 Letters written to Maxwell

Locations of the letters and details (where appropriate) of their citation and reproduction in this volume are given. Many of these letters – notably those from G. G. Stokes, P. G. Tait and William Thomson – have been reproduced *in extenso*. Letters which have been reproduced in abbreviated form are marked * below, those merely cited are marked †.

(1) Letters from George Biddell Airy
    (1) 12 November 1868, Royal Greenwich Observatory Archive, ULC, Airy Papers 6/5, 411R–V; *Number 314 note (4).
    (2) 14 October 1872, ULC, Airy Papers 6/259, 203R–V; Number 424 note (2).
    (3) 26 October 1872, ULC, Airy Papers 6/259, 205R; Number 426 note (2).
    (4) 29 October 1872, ULC, Airy Papers 6/259, 210R–V; *Number 426 note (7).
(2) Letter from John Aitken
    6 March 1873, ULC Add. MSS 7655, II/70.
(3) Letter from Jane Barnard
    20 June 1871, ULC Add. MSS 7655, II/47.

(4) Letters from William Benson
 (1) May 1870, ULC Add. MSS 7655, II/37; † Number 341 note (6).
 (2) 13 March 1871, ULC Add. MSS 7655, II/43; † Number 358 note (3).
(5) Letter from Edward William Blore
 13 February 1871, ULC Add. MSS 7655, II/38A; Number 357 note (3).
(6) Letter from George Phillips Bond
 9 July 1863, Bond MSS, Harvard University Archives UAV. 630.6; *Number 217 notes (3), (4), (6) and (14).
(7) Letter from Robert E. Branston
 21 October 1867, ULC Add. MSS 7655, II/27.
(8) Letter from Lewis Campbell
 4 July 1872, ULC Add. MSS 7655, II/58.
(9) Letter from Arthur Cayley
 20 April 1868, ULC Add. MSS 7655, II/29; Number 320 note (3).
(10) Letter from Robert Bellamy Clifton
 22 November 1871, ULC Add. MSS 7655, II/53.
(11) Letter from Alexander Crum Brown
 4 September 1873, ULC Add. MSS 7655, II/73; *Number 478 notes (12) and (24).
(12) Letter from V. Dwelshauvers-Dery
 12 May 1872, ULC Add. MSS 7655, II/57.
(13) Letters from Joseph David Everett
 (1) 19 July 1872, ULC Add. MSS 7655, II/60; † Number 341 note (19).
 (2) 26 July 1872, ULC Add. MSS 7655, II/61; *Number 341 note (19).
(14) Letter from James David Forbes
 4 June 1864, ULC Add. MSS 7655, II/22.
(15) Letter from William Francis
 11 July 1873, Henry Augustus Rowland Papers MS. 6, Milton S. Eisenhower Library, The Johns Hopkins University, Baltimore; Number 467 note (2).
(16) Letter from George Griffith
 27 July 1873, ULC Add. MSS 7655, II/72; † Number 470 note (25) and *Numbers 474 note (13) and 478 note (2).
(17) Letter from G. A. Hirn
 25 November 1872, ULC Add. MSS 7655, II/68; † Number 426 note (7).

(18) Letters from Charles Hockin
   (1) 15 May 1868, ULC Add. MSS 7655, II/30; *Number 289 note (8).
   (2) 27 July 1868, ULC Add. MSS 7655, II/31; *Number 297 notes (6) and (9).
   (3) 11 March 1870, ULC Add. MSS 7655, II/34; †Number 297 note (6) and *Number 378 note (9).
(19) Letters from Fleeming Jenkin
   (1) 10 January 1868, ULC Add. MSS 7655, II/28; Number 287 note (8).
   (2) 28 October 1871, ULC Add. MSS 7655, II/51; †Number 385 note (10).
(20) Letter from James Prescott Joule
   n.d. [June 1871], ULC Add. MSS 7655, II/49; *Number 339 note (15).
(21) Letter from William Longman
   20 June 1871, ULC Add. MSS 7655, II/48; Number 381 note (2).
(22) Letter from Arthur Luke
   6 October 1868, ULC Add. MSS 7655, II/24.
(23) Letters from Cecil James Monro
   (1) 2 June 1870, Greater London Record Office, Acc. 1063/2105; *Number 341 notes (2) and (20).
   (2) 3 March 1871, GLRO, Acc. 1063/2106, 2109b, 2109c; *Number 359 notes (2) and (7).
   (3) 9 March 1871, GLRO, Acc. 1063/2107; *Number 359 notes (2), (14) and (15).
   (4) 21 March 1871, GLRO, Acc. 1063/2108; *Numbers 359 note (15) and 363 notes (2), (3) and (4).
   (5) 10 September 1871, GLRO, Acc. 1063/2109a; *Number 359 note (8).
(24) Letter from E. J. Nanson
   5 December 1873, ULC Add. MSS 7655, II/75.
(25) Letter from George E. Preece
   7 March 1873, ULC Add. MSS 7655, V, i/12.
(26) Letter from Bartholomew Price
   4 January 1871, ULC Add. MSS 7656, P 659; *Introduction note (90) and *Number 367 note (3).
(27) Letters from Herbert Spencer
   (1) 4 December 1873, ULC Add. MSS 7655, II/74; Number 486 note (3).

974 *Appendix*

- (2) 30 December 1873, ULC Add. MSS 7655, II/76; *Number 487 note (2).
- (28) Letters from George Gabriel Stokes
  - (1) 16 February 1871, ULC Add. MSS 7655, II/40; Number 357 note (3).
  - (2) 18 February 1871, ULC Add. MSS 7655, II/41; Number 357 note (4).
  - (3) 23 February 1871, ULC Add. MSS 7655, II/42; Number 357 note (5).
  - (4) 14 March 1871, ULC Add. MSS 7655, II/44; Number 358 note (11).
- (29) Letter from John William Strutt, Lord Rayleigh
  14 February 1871, typed copy in private possession; *Numbers 355 notes (9), (10) and (12) and 357 note (3), and † Number 358 note (6).
- (30) Letter from William Swan
  11 May 1872, ULC Add. MSS 7655, II/56.
- (31) Letters and postcards from Peter Guthrie Tait
  - (1) n.d. [June 1865], ULC Add. MSS 7655, I, a/1; Number 249 note (2).
  - (2) 6 April 1866, ULC Add. MSS 7655, I, a/2; Number 262 note (15).
  - (3) 27 November 1867, ULC Add. MSS 7655, I, a/3; Number 276 note (2).
  - (4) 6 December 1867, ULC Add. MSS 7655, I, a/4; Number 277 note (2).
  - (5) 13 December 1867, ULC Add. MSS 7655, I, a/5; Number 277 note (22).
  - (6) 1 February 1871, ULC Add. MSS 7655, I, a/7; Number 353 note (11).
  - (7) 17 February 1871, ULC Add. MSS 7655, I, a/8; Number 356 note (7).
  - (8) 31 March 1871, ULC Add. MSS 7655, I, a/9; Number 365 note (5).
  - (9) 5 April 1871, ULC Add. MSS 7655, I, a/10; Number 366 note (5).
  - (10) 9 May 1871, ULC Add. MSS 7655, I, a/11; Number 368 note (6).
  - (11) 13 May 1871, ULC Add. MSS 7655, I, a/12; Number 369 note (8).
  - (12) 14 May 1871, ULC Add. MSS 7655, I, a/13; Number 371 note (8).

(13) 1 June 1871, ULC Add. MSS 7655, I, a/14; Number 373 note (5).

(14) 5 June 1871, ULC Add. MSS 7655, I, a/15; Number 375 note (2).

(15) 7 June 1871, ULC Add. MSS 7655, I, a/16; Number 375 note (2).

(16) 13 June 1871, ULC Add. MSS 7655, I, a/17; Number 376 note (2).

(17) 14 June 1871, ULC Add. MSS 7655, I, a/18; Number 378 note (11).

(18) 20 June 1871, ULC Add. MSS 7655, I, a/20; Number 378 note (11).

(19) 9 July 1871, ULC Add. MSS 7655, I, a/21; Number 380 note (2).

(20) 10 November 1871, ULC Add. MSS 7655, I, a/22; Number 389 note (14).

(21) 2 January 1872, ULC Add. MSS 7655, I, a/23; Number 398 note (10).

(22) 6 January 1872, ULC Add. MSS 7655, I, a/25; Number 399 note (8).

(23) n.d. [January 1872], ULC Add. MSS 7655, I, a/55; Number 403 note (8).

(24) 25 January 1872, ULC Add. MSS 7655, I, a/26; Number 401 note (7).

(25) 11 June 1872, ULC Add. MSS 7655, I, a/27; Number 413 note (3).

(26) 28 June 1872, ULC Add. MSS 7655, I, a/28; Number 414 note (2).

(27) 13 July 1872, ULC Add. MSS 7655, I, a/29; Number 417 note (2).

(28) 15 July 1872, ULC Add. MSS 7655, I, a/30; Number 417 note (4).

(29) 16 July 1872, ULC Add. MSS 7655, I, a/31; Number 417 note (3).

(30) 17 July 1872, ULC Add. MSS 7655, I, a/32; Number 417 note (3).

(31) 19 July 1872, ULC Add. MSS 7655, I, a/33; Number 417 note (3).

(32) 30 June 1873, ULC Add. MSS 7655, I, a/34; Number 465 note (2).

(33) 7 July 1873, ULC Add. MSS 7655, I, a/35; Number 465 note (2).

(34) 31 July 1873, ULC Add. MSS 7655, I, a/36; Number 474 note (3).
(32) Letters from James Thomson
(1) 21 July 1871, James Thomson Papers MS 13/22b, The Queen's University of Belfast Library; Number 382 note (2).
(2) 11 January 1873, James Thomson Papers MS 13/22e, Queen's University Library; *Number 421 notes (3) and (12).
(33) Letters and postcards from Sir William Thomson
(1) 14 December 1868, ULC Add. MSS 7655, II/32; Number 316 note (4).
(2) 11 January 1871, ULC Add. MSS 7655, I, a/6; Number 350 note (14).
(3) 17 June 1871, ULC Add. MSS 7655, I, a/19; Number 377 note (1).
(4) 4 January 1872, ULC Add. MSS 7655, I, a/24; Number 393 note (7).
(5) 24 August 1872, ULC Add. MSS 7655, II/62; Number 420 note (8).
(34) Letter from Coutts Trotter
20 April [1871], ULC Add. MSS 7655, II/46; *Number 361 note (2).
(35) Letter from Robert Tucker
8 April 1870, ULC Add. MSS 7655, II/35; Number 311 note (11).
(36) Letter from John Tyndall
'Monday', *Life of Maxwell*: 381.

INDEX

Part I and Part II

Bold figures refer to text numbers. Italic figures indicate pages on which biographical details are given.

Aberdeen, University of, 249, 392
Accademia del Cimento, 648
acoustics, 412–15, 417, 538, 598–604, 605–6, 608, 856–7, 860–3, 920
Adams, John Couch, 249n, 370
Adams, William Grylls, 4, 249
   letter from Maxwell: (3 December 1873) **484**, 949–50
Adams-Reilly, A., 774n, 886n, 921n
Agassiz, Alexander, 886n
Agassiz, Louis, 886n
agitation, molecular, 959–63
Airey, J. A. L., 510n
Airy, George Biddell, 23, 33, 463, 540n, 639
   letters from Maxwell: (14 May 1863) **209**, 87; (12 March 1868) **283**, 351–2; (9 November 1868) **314**, 462; (16 October 1868) **424**, 758–9; (28 October 1868) **426**, 761–2
   letters to Maxwell: (12 November 1868), 462n; (14 October 1872), 758n; (26 October 1872), 761n; (29 October 1872), 761–2n
   letter to H. A. Faye: (26 September 1872), 758n
   letter to W. H. Miller: ([1848]), 414n
   letters to G. G. Stokes: (22 February 1863), 63–4n, 95–6n; (27 February 1863), 95n; (3 July 1872), 725n
   letters from Stokes: (12 May 1848), 414n; (26 February 1863), 64n; (18 March 1863), 95n; (10 December 1872), 718n; (13 December 1872), 718n
   report on paper by Stokes: (16 July 1868), 415n
   Royal Society papers: 'On the directive power of large steel magnets' (Maxwell's report on) **410**, 718–26; 'Magnetical observations...' (Maxwell's report on) **453**, 847; 'On the strains in the interior of beams' (Maxwell's report on) **205**, 62–9; **206**, 70–1; **212**, 95–6
   Greenwich Observatory, 351–2

magnetisation, 718–26
magneto-optic effect, 884
Mathematical Tracts, 46–7n, 309n
on Maxwell's *Saturn's Rings*, 115n, 758n, 761–2n
stress function, 63–9, 520–1
Aitken, John, letter to Maxwell: (6 March 1873), 971
Akin, C. K., 245n
Alhazen, 629n
Ampère, André Marie, 485n, 507, 514, 654n, 678, 723–5, 767, 773, 843n, 945
Amsler, J., 874
Andrews, Thomas, 16, 277, 668, 671, 681n, 923
Ångström, A. J., 41n, 307, 311, 877n, 888–9, 897
anomalous dispersion, 11–12, 419–21, 862–3, 864–5
Appleton, R., 965
Arago, D. F., 108, 148n, 154n, 223n, 309, 713
Arago's disc, 27, 548, 704, 706, 710, 711, 712–13
Arbuthnot, John, 636n
Archimedes, 367
Argyll, Bishop of, 749n
Aristophanes, 693, 947
Aristotle, 551
Armstrong, Sir W. G., 369n
Armstrong and Whitworth Committee, 373
Athenæum Club, 6, 636, 660
Avogadro's hypothesis, 15, 135, 258, 282, 305, 657n, 892, 909

Babbage, Charles, 648, 951
Bacon, Francis, 655
Baily, Francis, 234, 657
Bain, Alexander, 395, 578
Bakerian Lecture, *see* Royal Society of London
Balfour, Evelyn, 664n
Balfour, John Hutton, *580n*, 915
   letter from Maxwell: (28 November 1870) **349**, 580–1
   letter from W. Thomson: ([1870]), 580n
Ball, W. W. Rouse, 35

band (endless), 501, 872
Barclay, T., 627n
Barnard, Jane, letter to Maxwell: (20 June 1871), 971
Barrett, W. F., 551n
Bashforth, Francis, 24, *369n*, 386
   Royal Society paper: 'On the resistance of the air to the motion of...projectiles' (Maxwell's report on) **288**, 369–73
battery (standard), 734–7, 742, 866–7, 873
Baynes, T. S., 463n
beauty (rules of), 886–7
Beck, A., 936
Becker, Carl Ludwig, 98, 122, 151, 213n, 310, 377, 870
Beer, Gillian, 840n
Bell, Oswald, 463
Bell, William, 691
Belpaire, Th., 934
Benet, Stephen Vincent, 373n
Benson, William, 551, 614, 617
   letters to Maxwell: (May 1870), 551; (13 March 1871), 614n
Bentley, Richard, 368, 798
Benvenuto, E., 24n
Berkeley, George, 361, 363, 365, 395, 816
Bernoulli, Daniel, 72, 135, 250, 279, 655
Bernoulli, Jakob (James) I, 367
Bernoulli, Johann (John) I, 370n
Bernoulli equation, 242
Bernstein, H. T., 654n
Bertrand, Joseph, 391, 399, 407, 716, 745n, 945
Bessel, F. W., 752, 857
Betti, Enrico, 320n, 333, 386n, 423, 426, 439
Bible, 731
Bierhalter, G., 18n
Biot, Jean Baptiste, 559, 563, 720–1
Birkbeck, George, 5n
Birkbeck, Mrs, 5n
Bismarck, Otto, Prince von, 707
Blackburn, Hugh, 449
Blackburn's pendulum, 872
Blore, Edward William, 34, *611n*
   letter from Maxwell: (15 February 1871) **357**, 611–13
   letter to Maxwell: (13 February 1871), 611n
Boltzmann, Ludwig, 15, 18, 284n, 740n, 760n, 888, 907n, 915–16, 938, 947n
Bond, George Phillips,
   letter from Maxwell: (25 August 1863) **217**, 104–9
   letter to Maxwell: (9 July 1863), 104–7n

Bond, W. C., 105n
Bonney, T. G., 5n, 147n
Boole, George, 304
Boscovich, R. J., 396, 799–800, 812n
Bose, M. von, 211n, 349n, 407n
Bottomley, W., letter to G. G. Stokes: (26 March 1873), 867n
Bourgoin, E., 504
Boussinesq, Joseph, 19n
Bowman, William, 203
Boyle, Robert, 655, 816
Boyle's law, 673, 731
brachistochrone, 224n, 667n
   see also quickest ascent, line of
Bramah, Joseph, 869
Branston, Robert E., letter to Maxwell: (21 October 1867), 972
Brewster, Sir David, 47, 50n, 312n, 461, 462, 559
Bright, Sir Charles, 6, 735n
Bristed, Charles Astor, 228n
British Association for the Advancement of Science, 9, 466n, 489, 532n, 548, 550n, 578n, 627, 654n, 659n, 667, 671n, 677n, 749, 833, 916
   Committee on electrical standards, 6–9, 88–92, 93–4, 96, 97, 98–101, 103, 107–8, 113–14n, 122, 157, 164, 170n, 188n, 202, 207n, 211n, 214, 217, 375n, 377n, 378n, 409, 417n, 489, 548, 627, 734–7, 748, 773, 810n, 850, 871
   electrodynamometer, 627, 734–5, 738, 742, 867, 871
   Maxwell's papers, 312, 313–17, 564–5, 566–7, 898n, 911–14, 922–33, 935–6, 937–9
Brodie, Sir Benjamin Collins, Bt, 337n, 830
   chemical calculus, 304–5, 660
Bromberg, Joan, 26n
Bruhns, C., 752n
Brush, Stephen G., 12n, 15n, 17n, 81n, 128n, 138n, 250n, 280n, 900n, 902n
Buchwald, Jed Z., 11n, 26n, 37n, 485n, 559n
Buckle, Thomas Henry, 818, 932
Buff, Heinrich, 408n, 828
Bunsen, Robert, 626, 869, 874, 891
Burdon-Sanderson, J. S., *836n*
   report on paper by J. Jago: (12 May 1873), 836–7n
Burlington, Earl of, *see* Devonshire, 7th Duke of
Burns, Robert, 391n
Butler, Joseph, 834n
Butler, Samuel, 321n

Byron, George Gordon, 6th Baron, 408, 646

cables (telegraph), 410n, 489, 496, 504, 517, 555
Cagniard-Latour, Charles, 670–1n
calculus of variations, 589n, 625, 787–9
calorescence, 245–8
Cambridge Philosophical Society, 37, 744n, 787n, 815n, 840, 968n
  Maxwell's report on paper by O. Fisher: **490**, 968–70
Cambridge, University of,
  Adams Prize, 8, 33, 589, 624–6
  Board of Mathematical Studies, 33, 35, 612n, 729, 839
  Cambridge Calendar, 154–5n, 239n, 241n, 251n, 277n, 293n, 411n, 418n, 420–1, 444–5n, 456n, 464n, 466n, 477n, 517n, 542n, 634n, 729n, 752n, 787n, 839, 862n, 964n
  Cavendish Laboratory, 1, 33–4, 36, 611–13, 619, 626–7, 630–1, 632–3, 634–5, 666, 681, 690, 701, 760, 840, 868–75, 876, 943
  Mathematical Tripos, 11, 33, 35, 154–5n, 227, 236n, 239–40, 241n, 248n, 251–2, 277, 293, 321, 391, 411n, 418, 419–21, 444–5n, 456, 464, 466n, 517, 542, 684, 729, 752–3, 787–9, 839, 862–3, 865
  Maxwell's lectures, 35–6, 689, 690, 760, 898n, 940–1, 942n
  Natural Sciences Tripos, 35–6, 612n, 766, 944, 961, 964
  Professorship of Experimental Physics, 33–6, 611–13, 615–16, 623
  Smith's Prize, 28, 477n, 589n, 634n
Campbell, Lewis, 1, 110n, 361n, 444n, 457, 463n, 840
  letters from Maxwell, 971: (21 April 1862), 72n, 817n; (21 November 1865) **251**, 228–9; (3 November 1868) **312**, 460; (19 October 1872) **425**, 760; (3 April 1873) **449**, 840–1
  letter to Maxwell: (4 July 1872), 972
Candolle, A. P. de, 641–2
capillary action, 386n
carbon bisulphide prisms, 607, 874
Cardwell, D. S. L., 791n
Carnot, Lazare, 646
Carnot, Sadi, 791
Carnot cycle, 36
Carnot function, 544n
Caro, Elme Marie, 358
Carpenter, W. B., 2
Carroll, Lewis (Charles Dodgson), 832

Casella's barometer, 869
Casorati, F., 936
catenary, 330
cathetometer, 631, 870
Catton, Alfred, 640n
'cat-turning', 528
Cauchy, A. L., 51n
causality, 820–3
Cavendish, Henry, 179, 655, 784n, 785–6, 800, 839, 843, 858
Cavendish Laboratory, Cambridge, 619, 666, 681
  apparatus for, 626–7, 630–1, 632–3, 634–5, 868–75, 876
  building of, 33–4, 36, 690, 701, 760, 840, 943
  plans for, 630–1, 632–3, 868–75, 876
Cay, Charles Hope, *202n*
  letters from Maxwell, 971: (5 January 1865) **240**, 202–3
Cay, Jane, 240
Cay, John, 240
Cay, Robert Dundas, *103*, 119n
  letters from Maxwell: (21 August 1863) **216**, 103; (12 July 1864) **229**, 157; (28 April 1865) **247**, 221; (8 December 1865) **253**, 240; (23 November 1871) **391**, 690; (27 May 1872) **412**, 729; (22 May 1873) **456**, 852
Cay, William Dyce, *119n*, 157, 221
Cayley, Arthur, 296n, 466n, *320n*, 566n, 589n, 687, 702, 745n
  letter from Maxwell: (12 April 1869) **320**, 476–8
  letter to Maxwell: (20 April 1868), 476n
  report on paper by N. M. Ferrers: (14 July 1869), 492n
census, 929
Challis, James, 245n, 529n, 589n, 624n, 917, 957
Chambers, Charles, 23
  Royal Society paper: 'On the nature of the sun's magnetic action' (Maxwell's report on) **220**, 117–18
charge (electric), *see* displacement (electric); electrification
Charlemagne, 408
Charles I, King of England, 408
Charles, J. A. C., 408, 646
Charles' law, 408n, 646n, 650–1n, 673, 731
Charlton, T. M., 21n, 24n
Chasles, Michel, 294, 295n, 313n, 476, 647
Chemical Society, 304–5,
chemistry, 304–5, 782

Christiansen, C., 862n
chronographs, 371–2, 631, 635
Chrysostom, John, 834
Chrystal, George, 35
Church of Scotland (General Assembly), 852
circular motion, 1n, 702
Clairaut, A. C., 752
Clapeyron's theorem, 120n
Clarendon Press, 31, 636, 856, 915n
Clark, Edwin, 119
Clark, Josiah Latimer, 6, 23, 630, 734–7, 738, 742–3, 748, 872n, 873
   letter from Maxwell: (16 July 1872) **418**, 742–3
   letter to G. G. Stokes: (23 January 1873), 735n
   Royal Society papers: 'On a standard voltaic battery' (Maxwell's report on) **462**, 866–7; 'On a voltaic standard of electromotive force' (Maxwell's report on) **415**, 734–7
Clarke, Samuel, 817
Clausius, Rudolf Julius Emmanuel,
   electrolysis, 657, 922–3, 967
   entropy, 16–18, 359, 564, 672n, 710, 946–7
   kinetic theory of gases, 12–13, 72–4, 75n, 77, 83, 84n, 133, 250, 280, 305, 408, 656–8, 896, 923, 938
   light of the sky, 619
   on Maxwell, 73–5, 83n, 133, 280, 353, 658, 709, 710, 732n
   off-prints of papers, 757, 897n
   and Tait, 328n, 335n, 408, 732n, 740n
   thermodynamics, 16–18, 328n, 335n, 408, 609, 709–10, 732n, 757n, 946–7
Clifford, William Kingdon, *343*, *666*, 677n, 956
Clifton, Robert Bellamy, 34, 623n, *632*, 636, 701
   letter to Maxwell: (22 November 1871), 972
   letter to G. G. Stokes: (20 January 1871), 603n
   report on paper by J. W. Strutt: (20 January 1871), 603n
colloids, 285–7
colour,
   blindness, 621–2
   boxes, 58n, 94, 146, 155–6, 551–2, 607–8, 614
   mixing, 1n, 94, 146, 155–6, 551–2, 774–5
   names, 617, 629
   vision, 1n, 58–9, 551–2, 614–15, 617–18, 704, 774–5, 781
comet II (1868), 451
comets (tails of), 105–7, 451–2
Comte, Auguste, 362

conduction of electricity, 417, 422–3, 504, 524–7
conjugate functions, 426n, 428, 487–8, 531, 546
Conservatoire des Arts et Métiers, 477
continuity, equation of, 123, 198, 262, 439, 965–7
Cookson, Henry Wilkinson, 35n, *876n*
   letter from Maxwell: (5 July 1873) **464**, 876
   letter from W. M. Fawcett: (16 December 1873), 35n
corkscrew rule, 641, 644, 679, 953–4
Cornu, Alfred, 479, 851
Corsock, 103, 202
Cotes, Roger, 510n, 799, 817, 936, 943
Coulomb, Charles Augustin, 482, 720, 800, 843
Crofton, M. W., 297n
Croonian Lecture, *see* Royal Society of London
Cross, J. J., 28n, 634n,
Crowe, M. J., 29n
Crum, Alexander, 446
Crum Brown, Alexander, 328n, 640n
   letter to Maxwell: (4 September 1873), 924–5n, 927n
crystals (optical properties of), 380–2, 559–63
Cunningham, John William,
   letters from Maxwell: (5 December 1862) **204**, 61; (24 March 1863) **208**, 86; (27 June 1863) **213**, 97; (10 August 1863) **215**, 102
curl (vector operator), 569, 574, 591, 593–4, 784, 825, 878
   see also quaternions
current (induction of), 158–9, 695–6
cyclides, 319–20, 322, 476n

Dallas, D. M., 304n
D'Almeida, J. Chr., 504
Dalton, John, 621, 909, 916
   letter from J. Herschel: (20 May 1833), 621
Daniell, John Frederic, 178n, 504
Daniell cell, 178, 196, 633n, 736
Darwin, Charles, 334n, 815n
Darwin, George Howard, 35–6, 898n, 941–2n
Daston, Lorraine J., 21n
Davies, J. P., 964
Deas, Francis, *559n*
   paper on chromatic effects of polarized light (Maxwell's comments on): **343**, 559–63
Deleuil, J. A., 869
Democritus, 654
'demon' paradox, 17–18, 331–2, 582–3, 585
Desaguliers, J. T., 368
Descartes, René, 294–7, 361, 570, 587, 656, 797, 816, 831

Deschanel, A. Privat, 552n, 856–7
Des Cloiseaux, Alfred, 23, *380n*
   Royal Society paper: 'On the dispersion of the optic axes...' (Maxwell's report on) **290**, 380–2
determinism, 19, 814–23
Deville, H. Sainte-Claire, 285n, 287
Devonshire, William Cavendish, 7th Duke of, 33–4, 649, 651n, 839, 858
   letter from Maxwell: (late January–early February 1873) **435**, 785–6
   letters to John Power: (10 October 1870), 33–4; (1 June 1871), 649n
Dewar, Daniel, 552
diamagnetism, 336–7, 405–6, 781
dielectric constant, 485
   and index of refraction, 196, 543, 627–8
dielectrics,
   conduction, 497
   polarization, 484–6
differential (exact), 645
dimensions, 8, 218, 232, 270, 541
dip circle, 543, 870
Dirichlet's principle, 605n, 660, 763n
disgregation, 16, 709, 710
dispersion of optic axes, 380–2
displacement (electric), 26, 160, 190, 198, 485–6, 572, 958
Disraeli, Benjamin, 461n
Ditscheiner, L., 307,
Domb, C., 3n, 61n, 461n
Donati's comet, 105n
Donders, F. C., 203
Donkin, W. F., 856, 862n
doubly refracting crystals, 1n, 559–63
Dove, H. W., 156, 381
Droop, Henry Richmond, letters from Maxwell: (28 January 1862), 230n; (19 July 1865) **250**, 226–7
duality (principle of), 20–2, 320, 863, 899, 935, 942
Du Bois Reymond, Emil, 555, 556–7n
Dulong, P. L., 657, 910, 947
Dupin, Charles, 319n, 715, 787
Dwelshauvers-Dery, V., letter to Maxwell: (12 May 1872), 972
'dynamical method', 586, 818, 929–31
dynamics,
   collision, 383–5, 654–5
   definition of, 291, 654n, 778–9
   Hamilton on, 31, 732–3, 740n, 744–7
   instability, 19, 819–23
   Lagrange on, 31, 337, 716, 740, 744–7, 769–70
   Maxwell on, 16–19, 31, 291, 363–6, 395–6, 423, 598–9, 716, 732–3, 740, 744–7, 769–71, 777–9, 811–12
   projectiles, 369–74
   reduction to, 18, 31, 609, 769, 779–82, 947
   reversibility, 18, 359–61, 366–7, 583,
   rotating bodies, 492–5
dynamo, 298–9, 356n, 635

Earnshaw, Samuel, 540n
Edleston, Joseph, 510n, 936n
Edlund, E., 692
elasticity,
   Airy's stress function, 23–4, 63–9, 520–1
   experiments on, 269–70, 272–5, 300–3, 348–50
   mathematical theory, 64–9, 70–1, 95–6, 261–2, 270, 272–3, 282–3, 292–3
   strain/stress, 62n, 70–1, 95–6, 518
electric circuits, 158–9, 204–6, 516–17, 522–4, 678–9, 768
electric images,
   applied to magnetism, 32, 704, 706, 710, 711, 712–13
   Maxwell on, 26, 389, 423, 453–6, 479–81, 503
   W. Thomson on, 25–6, 389, 423, 453n, 479, 713
electrical atmospheres, 800
electrical resistance (standard), 6–9, 88–92, 93–4, 96, 97, 98, 100–1, 103, 107–8, 122, 157, 164, 170n, 177n, 202, 214, 217, 378n, 409, 649, 735–6, 850
electrical resistance (and temperature), 211n, 349, 407–8, 661–2
electrical standards, 6–9
   see also battery (standard); British Association, Committee on electrical standards; electrical resistance (standard)
electrical units (ratio of), 6–9, 110–11, 162–3, 172–5, 176–9, 180, 187–8, 194–5, 198, 204–6, 211, 219–20, 375–8, 403, 409, 489n, 810, 849–51
electrification,
   bowl, 25, 453–6, 489, 497, 499
   dielectrics, 484–6
   discs, 26–7, 428–32, 443, 481–2, 546–8
   generation of charge, 271, 424–6, 503, 873
   grating, 27, 487–8, 490, 496–7
   spheres, 26, 480–1
electrodynamics (continental), 26, 353–5, 426, 499–500, 686–8

electrodynamometer (British Association), 627, 734–5, 738, 742, 867, 871
electrolysis, 417, 504, 657, 781, 922–3, 967
electromagnetic theory of light, 9–12, 155, 182–5, 186–8, 194–6, 199–200, 202–3, 378–9, 543n, 627, 772–3, 781, 784, 810, 849, 851
electromagnetism (theory of), 189–96, 507, 767–73, 781, 800–11
electrometers,
 attracted disc (guard ring), 209, 377, 429–30, 443, 481–2, 850, 858, 859n, 873
 portable, 828, 873
 quadrant, 482, 555, 873
 W. Thomson's 'Report' (1867), 377n, 423, 482, 555n, 736, 828n, 850n, 858n, 859n
 in the *Treatise*, 689
electrophorus. 424n, 503, 873
electrophysiology, 554–8
electro-tonic state, 99, 161, 192, 199n, 507
electrotonus, 557–8
Eliot, George, 840–1
Elliott Bros, 98n, 312
elliptic integrals, 276, 458n, 508–9, 550n
Ellis, R. L., 550n
Encyclopaedia Britannica, 36–7, 311n, 776–82
energy,
 conservation of, 182–4, 191–2, 335, 354–5, 359, 364–6, 417, 522, 578n, 817
 dissipation of, 359–61, 366–7, 542, 564–5, 780, 917–18, 946
 electric circuits, 516–17, 769–71, 957
 electromagnetic, 193–4, 769–71, 784
 electrostatic, 162, 485
 energetics, 291, 335, 778
 in evaporation, 672–4
 gravity, 194, 451–2
 kinetic, 75n, 364–6, 598, 657, 744–7, 769–71, 784, 864, 900–1, 916, 941n
 potential, 365–6, 784, 822, 864
 vis viva, 75, 182n, 364, 609n, 657, 888, 947
entropy, 16, 359, 564, 672n, 710, 946–7
Epicurus, 798
Eranus club, 814
ergal, 16, 609, 709, 710, 946
ergon, *see* work (mechanical)
errors (distribution of), 626, 938
Esson, William, *346*
ether,
 drag, 9–10, 148–53, 154–5, 306–11
 electromagnetic, 105–6, 180–1, 182–5, 186–8, 194–6, 199–200

energy, 105–6, 190, 354–5, 364
gravity, 105–7, 194, 366, 451–2, 798–9
luminiferous, 9–11, 23, 46–9, 50–3, 148–53, 154–5, 182–5, 189–90, 194–6, 306–11
models of, 30–1, 180, 337
molecular, 917–18, 919–20, 957, 959–60, 962–3
Newton's theory, 798–9
and refraction of light, 9–10, 147–53, 154–5, 306–11
velocity of light in, 9, 147–53, 154–5, 306–11
Euclid, 655, 953
Euler, Leonhard, 469n, 470n, 688n
Eulerian integrals, 426
evaporation, 668–9, 670–4
Everett, Joseph David, 23, 269, 749n, 751n, 857n
 letters to Maxwell: (19 July 1872), 552n; (26 July 1872), 552n
 Royal Society papers: 'On the flexural and torsional rigidity of a glass rod' (Maxwell's report on) **261**, 272–5; 'On torsion and flexure for the determination of rigidities' (Maxwell's reports on) **269**, 300–3; **282**, 348–50
Everitt, C. W. F., 1n, 8n, 9n, 12n, 13n, 81n, 128n, 132n, 138n, 250n, 280n, 632n, 682n, 900n, 902n
Ewing, J. A., 897n, 915

Fabius Maximus, Quintus (Cunctator), 878n
factorials, 682, 684, 687, 688n, 689
farad, 736, 742–3, 748–50, 843–4
Faraday, Michael, 367, 950
 letters from Maxwell: (9 November 1857), 20n, 107n, 194n, 802n; (19 October 1861), 110n, 188n, 484n, 627n
 letter to Maxwell: (13 November 1857), 802n
 diamagnetism, 336–7, 405–6, 806
 dielectrics, 193, 958–9
 electrolysis, 417
 electromagnetic induction, 193, 507, 768
 electromagnetic rotation, 507
 electrostatic induction, 193, 829
 gold film, 181
 lines of force, 405, 507, 678–9, 802–6
 magneto-optic effect, 189–90, 336, 405–6, 781, 784n
 matter, 812n, 895
 paramagnetism, 336, 405–6
 polarity, 405
Faraday effect, *see* magneto-optic rotation

Fawcett, William Milner, 35n, *701n*
   letter from Maxwell: (1 January 1872) **397**, 701
   letter to H. W. Cookson: (16 December 1873), 35n
Faye, H. A., 155, 758, 761
   letter from G. B. Airy: (26 September 1872), 758n
Felici, Riccardo, 193, 386, 710, 711, 713
Ferrers, Norman Macleod, 23, *492n*, 729n
   Royal Society paper: 'Motion of a free rigid body' (Maxwell's report on) **325**, 492–5
field equations, 160–1, 193, 514–15
figure of the earth, 98, 277, 683, 780
Fischer, W. L. F, 463n
Fisher, Osmond,
   Cambridge Philosophical Society paper: 'On the elevation of mountains by lateral pressure' (Maxwell's report on) **490**, 968–70
fish-eye lens, 752
Fizeau, Hippolyte, 9, 148–51, 154–5, 195, 311, 851, 874
Flint, Robert, 463n
fluids,
   analogy to electromagnetism, 124, 399, 401, 403, 426, 439, 485–6, 512, 524–5, 598–604, 605–7
   displacement in, 447, 456, 457–8, 551
   Helmholtz on, 124, 241–2n, 243, 391, 399–404, 426, 432, 446–7, 448n, 530, 545n, 778
   lines of motion in, 123–7, 529–34
   Maxwell on, 123–7, 236–40, 241–4, 391, 399–404, 446–8, 456, 510–12, 529–34; 730
   Rankine on, 123–7, 389, 445, 448n, 511, 529–34
   stability of, 239–40, 241–4
   Stokes on, 124, 533–4n, 778
   stream function, 123–4, 426, 428–9, 448, 457–8, 529–31, 545–6, 603
   W. Thomson on, 390, 391, 398, 778
   vena contracta, 510–12
   vortex motion, 239–40, 241–4, 391, 398–404
   vortex turbine, 236–9
fluorescence, 245n
Folie, F., 934
Fontaine's turbine, 239
Forbes, George, *228*, 886n
Forbes, James David, 1n, 2, 228n, 284, 296n, 460, 461, 462, 474, 646n, 774–5, 886n, 921n
   letter to Maxwell: (4 June 1864), 972

Forde, Henry Charles, *375*, 410n
Forrest, James, 691n
Foucault, Léon, 195, 345, 351, 378, 631, 810, 851, 871
Fourier, Charles, 542n
Fourier, Joseph, 36, 358, 541–2, 564, 941n
Fourier's theorem, 487
Fourneyron's turbine, 239
frameworks (theory of), 119–21, 313–17, 519–21, 691
Francis, William, 881
   letter to Maxwell: (11 July 1873), 881n
Fraunhofer, Joseph, 155
free will, 19, 814–23
Fresnel, Augustin Jean, 9, 46n, 47, 148, 149n, 154n, 182–4n, 187n, 309, 311
   wave surface, 319, 322, 342, 477
Fresnel rhomb, 46n
Froude, William, 532
Fuller, A. T., 98n, 112n, 128n, 139n, 236n, 239n, 344n, 410n, 624n, 783n

Galilei, Galileo, 361, 367
Galton, Francis, 815, 928n
   letter from Maxwell: (26 February 1879), 19n, 819n
galvanometers, 166–70, 204–6, 219, 375, 557–8
   mirror, 165–6, 664–5, 704n, 871–2
   sine, 735, 867
   tangent, 666, 667, 871
   in the *Treatise*, 517, 666, 667
Garber, Elizabeth, 12n, 81n, 128n, 138n, 250n, 280n, 900n, 902n
gases,
   absorption of, 24, 285–7
   Clausius on, 12–13, 72–4, 75n, 77, 83, 84n, 133, 280, 656–8
   conductivity (thermal), 13, 72–85, 133, 263–4, 268, 270, 277, 283–4, 658, 661–3, 760
   diffusion, 15, 133, 223, 271, 277, 281–2, 286–7, 564, 657, 661–2, 760, 780, 888, 890–6, 897, 926, 934
   electrical discharge in, 827–30
   equilibrium of temperature, 14–15, 16–17, 264–6, 267–9, 283, 292, 853–5, 898–910, 911–14, 916, 937–9
   force law, 13, 227, 254–6, 276–7n, 659
   kinetic theory (history of), 12–16, 19, 250–2, 279–80, 654–9
   and liquids (continuity of states), 668–9, 670–4, 923, 969
   mean free path, 12–13, 77–83, 657, 923–6

relaxation time, 13, 257n, 282–3
separation of, 285–7, 344, 588
specific heats, 76–7, 259–60, 284
statistical theory, 12–15, 16–19, 133, 281, 292, 656–9, 903–10, 911–14, 915–16, 927–33, 946–7, 960
transpiration, 222–3, 224, 232–3, 283, 890–1, 926
velocity distribution function, 12–15, 17, 74–5, 133, 281, 657, 903–10, 911–14, 915–16, 938
viscosity, 13–14, 78, 96, 202, 215, 216–17, 218–19, 221, 222–3, 224–5, 230–5, 261–2, 270, 277, 282–4, 658, 780, 888, 891–4, 897
Gassiot, John Peter, 211, 375, 403, 607n
Gauss, Carl Friedrich, 654n, 809, 935
   'consistent representation', 26
   factorials, 689
   optics, 936
   potential, 399n, 843n
   spherical harmonics, 330n
   terrestrial magnetism, 505–6
   topology, 326n, 647
Gauss' theorem, 645, 648–9n
Gay-Lussac, J. L., 135, 258, 650–1n, 657, 909, 947
generator (electrostatic), 424–7
geometry, 1n, 20–2, 702, 715, 716, 717
   non-Euclidean, 618–19
   projective, 21, 313–14, 647, 899, 935–6, 942
   topographical, 29, 466n, 566–7
   see also topology
'geometry of position', *see* geometry, projective; topology
Gibbs, J. Willard, 945
Gibson, J. C., 627n
Girard, P. S., 223n
glaciers, viscosity of, 473–5
Gladstone, J. H., 56n, 949n
Gladstone, W. E., 461n
Glaisher, J. W. L., 935
Glasgow, University of, 392, 443, 446, 449
Goethe, J. W., 578
Gonville and Caius College, Cambridge, 683
Goodeve, Thomas Minchin, 3, 668n
Gordon, Edward Strathearn, 463n
Goupillière, J. Haton de la, 717
governors, 8, 101, 107–8, 113–16, 343–5, 351–2, 410–11, 631, 635, 871
Graham, Thomas, 24, 222–3, 224, 231–3, 262n, 270, 281–3, 564n, 588, 657, 658n, 891, 926

letter from Maxwell: (1 May 1865) **248**, 222–3
Royal Society paper: 'On the absorption and dialytic separation of gases' (Maxwell's report on) **264**, 205–7
Gramme, Z. T., 872
gravity, 20, 106–9, 194, 366, 451–2, 780, 797–9, 817
   and thermal equilibrium, 14, 264–6, 269, 283, 292, 853–5, 909, 916, 937–9
Gray, Charles, 251
green (colour), 629
Green, G., 377n, 665n, 871n, 873n
Green, George, 399n, 453n, 456n, 459, 683, 721–2, 843n, 859n, 880
Green's function, 320, 502
Green's reciprocity theorem, 320
Green's theorem, 24, 346, 399n, 422, 502, 532
Greenwich Observatory
   chronogrraph, 351, 372
   governors, 351–2
Gregory, David, 368
Gregory, D. F., 426n
Griffith, George, 753n, 895–6n
   letter to Maxwell: (27 July 1873), 895n, 916n, 922n
Grove, William Robert, 6, 356n, 463
   letters from Maxwell: (27 March 1868) **285**, 356–7; (7 November 1868) **313**, 461
Grove battery, 378, 403, 626, 632, 635
Grubb, Thomas, 607
Gudermann, Christoph, 550n
Gulliver's Travels, 355
Guthrie, Francis, *853*, 937
Guthrie, Frederick, 23, 513, *827n*, 949
   Royal Society paper, 'On a new relation between heat and electricity' (Maxwell's report on) **442**, 827–30
Guyou, É., 528n

Haidinger's brushes, 837n
Hall, Marie Boas, 22n
Hamilton, Sir William, Bt, 335n, 361, 597
Hamilton, Sir William Rowan,
   algebra, 952n
   characteristic function, 224n, 667n, 935, 942, 943n
   dynamics, 28, 31, 744–7
   hodograph, 21, 898–900
   metaphysics, 361, 952
   optics, 667, 935, 942–3

quaternions, 29–30, 214, 568n, 575n, 577, 580, 609, 626, 707n, 755, 951–5, 963
    spatial direction, 637, 639, 641, 643, 644
    time, 952n
    varying action, 354, 626, 757n, 947
Hamilton's operator, 30, 332–3, 568–9, 573–6, 577, 590–2, 593–7, 600–1, 609, 755, 760, 915n, 945
'Hamlet, Prince of Denmark', 610n
Hance, H. F., 642n
Hankins, Thomas L., 21n, 29n
Hanlon, George Oldham, 510–12
Hansemann, Gustav, 659, 918
Harcourt, A. Vernon, 346
Hardy, Gathorne, 463n
Harman, P. M., 12n, 20n, 28n, 618n, 686n, 746n
harmotome, 380–2
Harris, Thomas, 785, 858
Harris, Sir William Snow, 785, 858, 859n
Haughton, Samuel, 23, 46–7, 50–3
    Royal Society paper: 'On the reflexion of polarised light' (Maxwell's report on) **199**, 46–9; **200**, 50–3
    letter to G. G. Stokes: (6 November 1862), 52n
    'Remarks on Mr Stokes' Report', 52n
heat,
    conduction of, 353, 358–9, 389, 392, 416, 513–14, 541–3, 564–5, 780, 940–1, 941–2n, 962
    dynamical theory of, 266n, 269, 359, 655, 780, 957–9, 962–3
    and electricity, 353, 827–30, 940–1, 941–2n, 958–9
    radiant, 245–8, 253, 781, 962–3
    see also energy; thermodynamics; thermoelectricity
Heaviside, Oliver, 824n
Heilbron, J. L., 800n
Heimann, P. M., 26n
    see also Harman, P. M.
Helmholtz, Hermann von, 2, 22, 26, 34, 632, 681
    letter from Maxwell: (12 April 1864) **225**, 146
    acoustics, 603n, 856, 874n
    chronograph, 631
    colour vision, 775
    conservation of energy, 191–2, 335n, 354–5n, 686
    Croonian Lecture, 146n, 341, 837n
    electrodynamics, 26, 354–5n, 583, 596, 686–7, 773, 945

geometry, 618n
induction of currents, 191–2, 507
optics, 146n, 341, 775, 837n, 936
potential theory, 241–2n, 391n, 399–404, 407, 426, 432, 434n, 530, 545n, 593
siren, 874
topology, 434n, 439
viscosity, 944
vision, 341, 837n
vortex motion, 22, 124, 241n, 242–3, 321, 391n, 399–404, 407, 434n, 445, 446–7, 530n, 533, 593, 778
Herapath, John, 280, 656
Herschel, Sir John F. W., Bt, 107, 246, 296n, 621, 856, 860
    letter to John Dalton: (20 May 1833), 621
Herschel, Sir William, 104–5n, 246n
Hicks, W. M., 35
Hirn, G. A., 761, 762n
    letter to Maxwell: (25 November 1872), 762n
Hirst, Thomas Archer, 2, 5, 6, 639, 642, 956n
    letter to G. G. Stokes: (5 October 1868), 385n
    report on paper by R. Moon: (5 October 1868), 385n
Hockin, Charles, 9, 122n, *164*, 181, 200n, 219, 376, 403, 409–10, 423, 662
    letter from Maxwell: (7 September 1864) **232**, 164
    letters to Maxwell: (15 May 1868), 376n; (27 July 1868), 410n; (11 March 1870), 410n, 662n
hodograph, 323n, 328n, 898–900
Holden, E. S., 104n
Holtz, W., 271n, 873
Home, David Milne, 580n
Home, R. W., 800n
homoeopathy, 927n
Hooke's law, 537
Hopley, I. B., 89n, 113n, 165n, 204n, 213n, 376n, 386n
Hort, F. J. A., 814n
Hudson, W. H. H., 729n
Huggins, Sir William, 6, 10, 149n, 150n, *306n*, 451–2n, 714
    letters from Maxwell: (10 June 1867) **271**, 306–11; (13 October 1868) **309**, 451–2; (2 May 1872) **406**, 714
Hunt, B. J., 11n, 824n
Hunter, John, 681
Huxley, Thomas Henry, 6, 836n

impulse (force), 423, 733, 747

index of refraction, 196, 543, 627–8
inertia, 363–4, 800, 812
    inertial effect of current, 548, 770
instruments (electrical)
    electrodynamometer, 627, 734–5, 738, 742, 867, 871
    electrometers, 209, 377, 423, 429–30, 443, 481–2, 555, 736, 828, 850, 858, 873
    galvanometers, 165–70, 204–6, 219, 375, 557–8, 664–5, 666, 667, 704n, 735, 867, 871–2
integral theorems, 28–9, 325–6, 441, 589, 634
integration (order of), 638, 639n
irreversibility, 16–19, 359–61, 366–7, 541–3, 564–5, 582, 967

Jacobi, Carl Gustav Jacob, 214
Jago, James, 23
    letter to T. H. Huxley: (11 March 1873), 836n
    Royal Society paper: 'On visible direction' (Maxwell's report on) **447**, 836–8
Jamin, Jules,
    magnetism, 883
    polarized light, 50, 51–2n, 53
    wave theory of light, 50, 155, 182–5n, 186–7
jargonium, 748n, 886
Jenkin, Henry Charles Fleeming, 6, *7n*, 8
    letters from Maxwell: (27 August 1863) **218**, 110–11; (*c.* September 1871) **385**, 678–9
    letters to Maxwell: (10 January 1868), 363n; (28 October 1871), 680n
    letters to G. G. Stokes: (16 July 1868), 375n; (27 May 1873), 830n; (30 May 1873), 850n
    letters to W. Thomson: (8 August 1860), 113n; (20 February 1868), 363n
    report on paper by Frederick Guthrie: (27 May 1873), 830n
    report on paper by D. M'Kichan: (30 May 1873), 850n
    report on paper by Maxwell: (16 July 1868), 375n
    cable, 410n, 489
    electrical measurements, 6, 88n, 92, 94, 97, 107, 110–11, 122n, 210, 214, 217, 375, 408n, 409, 417, 548n
    Electricity and Magnetism, 356n, 630n, 678n, 679n, 680, 743, 748, 842–4
    frameworks, 517, 520
    governors, 8, 101, 107–8, 113–16, 343n, 631, 871
    on Lucretius, 363n

Jochmann, E., 704n, 710, 711, 713
Jones, Henry Bence, 950
    letter from Maxwell: (4 February 1873) **438**, 813
Jordan, D. W., 879n
Joule, James Prescott, 36, 84n, 210, 390, 489
    letter to Maxwell: (n.d.), 543n
    letter to W. Thomson: (3 December 1851), 751n
    air pump, 869
    British Association (Presidency), 916
    dip circle, 543, 719n, 870
    dynamical theory of heat, 280, 333n, 656
    magnet, 810
    magnetic measurements, 499, 505, 543, 719n
    mechanical equivalent of heat, 36, 84–5, 179–80, 210n, 338–9, 346, 378, 390
Joule's equivalent, *see* mechanical equivalent of heat
Jullien, Michel, 702–3n
Jungnickel, C., 946n
Jurin, James, 510n
Juvenal, 884

Kant, I., 952n
Kelland, P., 775n, 947, 951–5
Kew Observatory, 93n, 96, 214
kinetics, 291, 654n, 778
King's College Hospital, 102
King's College London, 147
    Maxwell's appointment, 2, 61, 86, 249
    Maxwell's electrical experiments, 92n, 97, 157, 210
    Maxwell's lectures, 3–4, 60, 61, 87
    Maxwell's resignation, 4, 180, 249
Kirchhoff, Gustav,
    elasticity, 269, 272, 275, 300, 302n, 348
    electricity, 516, 704
    magnetism, 480
    spectra, 41n, 44
Klein, Martin J., 16n, 17n, 18n, 544n, 709n
Klinkerfues, Wilhelm, 152–3n
knots, 322, 325–7, 330
Knott, C. G., 17n, 328n, 335n, 568n, 577n, 593n, 667n, 677n, 699n, 731n, 755n, 756n, 763n, 825n, 831n, 915n
Knudsen, Ole, 11n, 406n
Kohlrausch, F. W. G., 230–1
Kohlrausch, R., 110–11n, 188, 195, 378, 773n, 851
Kopp, H., 895, 925
Krönig, A., 280, 656

Lagout, Edouard, 887
Lagrange, Joseph Louis, 27–8, 30–2, 337, 716, 741n, 744–6, 770
Lake, Henry, 766
Lamb, Horace, 35, 123n, 730n
Lambert, J. H., 774n
Lamé, Gabriel, 70, 120n, 333, 479–80, 568, 573, 717, 825
Laplace, Pierre Simon de, 131, 277, 386, 686, 689, 751n, 818, 932
Laplace's coefficients, *see* spherical harmonic analysis
Laplace's equation, 30, 430, 480, 502, 511, 967n
Laplacian operator, 24, 30, 161, 199, 333, 569, 575, 700
Larmor, Sir Joseph, 528n, 607n
least action (principle of), 626
Legendre, A. M., 276, 278n, 426n, 458n
Leibniz, G. W., 361, 577
Leibnizians, 364
Le Sage, G. L., 250, 279, 363n, 655, 702n
Leslie, John, 412
Lévy, M., 528n
Lewes, G. H., 362n
Leyden jar, 485n, 555–7
Libri, G., 648
Lichtenberg, G. C., 774n
light,
　anomalous dispersion, 11–12, 419–21, 862–3, 864–5
　atmospheric refraction, 751–4
　blue of the sky, 614–15, 619, 666n, 919, 940n
　double refraction, 1n, 559–63
　electromagnetic theory of, 9–11, 155, 182–5, 186–8, 194–6, 199–200, 202–3, 375–9, 543n, 627, 781, 809–10, 849, 851
　emission theory, 751
　polarization of, 46–7, 50–3, 559–63, 781, 810
　refraction of, 1n, 148–53, 154–5, 224, 667, 751–4
　velocity of, 9–11, 148–53, 154–5, 187–8, 194–5, 306–11, 781, 809–10, 851
　wave theory of, 46–7, 50–3, 182–5, 186–8, 199n, 306–11, 378, 751
Lightfoot, J. B., 814n
Lindsay, James, 707n
lines of force, 125n, 192, 405, 446, 516, 666, 667, 678–9, 719–20, 802–9
Linnaeus, Carl, 641n,
Liouville, Joseph, 453n, 480, 543–4n
liquid and gaseous states (continuity of), 16, 668–9, 670–4, 923, 969

Listing, Johann Benedict, 29, 326n, 433n, 470–1, 591n, 639, 641–2, 644, 936
Littré, Émile, 362
Liveing, G. D., 833
Lloyd, Humphrey, 753
Lloyd, J. T., 377n, 665n, 871n, 873n
Locke, John, 361, 368, 416n, 816
Lockyer, J. N., 820n
logarithmic curves, 328–30
London Mathematical Society, 5, 620
　Maxwell's papers at, 318n, 340, 342, 457n, 466n, 470–1, 510–12, 570n, 715n, 716, 717, 942–3
　Maxwell's questions to, 343, 508–9, 550–1, 637, 639, 641–3, 644
　Maxwell's report on paper by J. W. Strutt, **460**, 860–3
Longman, William, 661, 710
　letter to Maxwell: (20 June 1871), 668n
Longridge, James Atkinson, 24, 369n
　Royal Society paper: 'On the resistance of the air to rifled projectiles' (Maxwell's report on) **288**, 373–4
Lorenz, L. V., 355n, 379
Loschmidt, Joseph, 15, 292n, 632, 659, 760, 888, 890–6, 897, 925–6
Loschmidt's number, 258, 892
Lowe, Robert, Viscount Sherbrooke, 704–5n
Lucretius, 19, 250–1, 291, 363, 654–5, 820, 928–9
Luke, Arthur, letter to Maxwell: (6 October 1868), 973

McCormmach, R., 946n
MacCullagh, James, 182–4n, 186–7n, 380n, 884n
McCunn, Mrs, 446, 449
McDonald, W., 463n
MacGregor, J. G., 897, 915
Mackenzie, Colin, 727, 731n
M'Kichan, Dugald, 23
　Royal Society paper: 'Determination of the number of electrostatic units…' (Maxwell's report on) **455**, 849–51
MacLaurin, Colin, 798–9, 816
MacLeod, R. M., 6n
Macmillan (publishers), 650n, 758
magnetism,
　axis of, 675–6
　coercive force, 828
　diamagnetism, 336, 405–6, 781
　effluvia, 800
　lamellar distribution of, 514n, 597, 700

magnetisation, 514, 718–26, 781, 847, 879–80, 881–3, 886
  measurements, 499
  paramagnetism, 336, 405–6
  of ships, 505, 517, 781
  solar, 117–18
  solenoidal distribution of, 485, 514n, 591, 597, 700
  terrestrial, 499, 505, 549, 781
  W. Thomson on, 485n, 498n, 514n, 597n, 700, 724n
  vortices, 180, 189–90, 337, 768–9, 784
magnetometer, 870
magneto-optic rotation, 11, 180, 189–90, 336–7, 405–6, 733, 781, 784, 824, 825, 884–5
Magnus, Gustav, 504
Mance, Henry, 584n
Mansel, H. L., 335n
Marey, É. J., 528n
Marianini, S., 557
Marischal College, Aberdeen, 2
Martin Chuzzlewit, 834
materialism, 19–20, 360–1, 363–5, 654–5, 814–23
Mathison, W. C., *341*
matter (nature of), 15, 19–20, 250–1, 279–80, 291, 304–5, 360–1, 363–5, 395–6, 586–8, 654–9, 799–800, 811–12
Matthiessen, Augustus, 211, 217, 349, 376n, 407, 409, 514
Maupertuis, P. L. M., 626
Maxwell, Frances Clerk, 451
Maxwell, James Clerk,
  correspondence, 971–6; *see also* Adams, W. G.; Airy, G. B.; Aitken, J.; Balfour, J. H.; Barnard, J.; Blore, E. W.; Bond, G. P.; Branston, R. E; Campbell, L.; Cay, C. H.; Cay, R. D.; Cayley, A.; Clark, J. L.; Clifton, R. B.; Cookson, H. W.; Crum Brown, A.; Cunningham, J. W.; Devonshire, Duke of; Droop, H. W.; Dwelshauvers-Dery, V.; Everett, J. D.; Fawcett, W. M.; Forbes, J. D.; Francis, W.; Graham, T.; Griffith, G.; Grove, W. R.; Hockin, C.; Huggins, W.; Jenkin, H. C. F.; Jones, H. B.; Joule, J. P.; Longman, W.; Luke, A.; Maxwell, K. M. Clerk; Monro, C. J.; Munro, H. A. J.; Nanson, E. J.; Pattison, M.; Preece, G. E.; Price, B.; Rowland, H. A.; Sharpey, W.; Siemens, C. W.; Spencer, H.; Stokes, G. G.; Strutt, J. W.; Swan, W.; Sylvester, J. J.; Tait, P. G.; Tayler, C. B.; Thomson, J.; Thomson, W.; Tomlinson, C.; Trotter, C.; Tucker, R.; Tyndall, J.
  reports on papers: *see* Cambridge Philosophical Society; London Mathematical Society; Royal Society of London; *see also* Airy, G. B.; Bashforth, F.; Chambers, C.; Clark, J. L.; Des Cloiseaux, A.; Everett, J. D.; Ferrers, N. M.; Fisher, O.; Graham, T.; Guthrie, F.; Haughton, S.; Jago, J.; Longridge, J. A.; M'Kichan, D.; Merrifield, C. W.; Miller, W. A.; Moon, R.; Moseley, H.; Radcliffe, C. B.; Rankine, W. J. M.; Robinson, T. R.; Stokes, G. G.; Strutt, J. W.; Tarn, E. W.; Tyndall, J.
  manuscripts not reproduced as texts: 'Chief Musician upon Nabla', 577n; 'Concerning Demons', 17n, 332n; on ether drag, 154n; 'Fresnels Biaxial Wave Surface', 319n; on Heaviside, 824n; Helmholtz's conjugate functions, 432n; Helmholtz on electrodynamics, 596n; 'Instruments in the Cavendish Laboratory', 868n; 'Lines of Curvature of an Ellipsoid', 319n; 'Lines of Curvature of an Elliptic Paraboloid', 318n; line of quickest ascent, 625n; Listing's terms, 591n; 'Memorandum of Improvements', 377n; 'Oxford Physical Laboratory', 636n; notes on F. E. Neumann, 498n; 'Results of Experiments July 1850', 275, 349; 'Schröter on Steiner Surface', 477n; 'Torricelli Evangelista Lezioni Accademiche', 395n; viscosity of gases, 96n
  notebooks: 154n, 239–40, 256n, 321n, 377n, 395n, 410–11, 432n, 477n, 502–7, 625n, 630–1, 636n, 642–3, 646n, 648n, 651n, 730
  appointments: *see* Cambridge, University of; King's College London; St Andrews United College; Trinity College, Cambridge
  Bakerian Lecture, 230–5
  'Construction of stereograms of surfaces' (1868), 340n, 342n, 476n
  'On the cyclide' (1868), 312n, 319n, 476n
  'Displacement in a case of fluid motion' (1870), 448n, 456n, 457–8n, 545n
  'A dynamical theory of the electromagnetic field' (1865), 9–11, 27, 30, 99n, 112n, 158n, 160–3, 164n, 178n, 180n, 183n, 188n, 189–96, 197–201, 202–3, 337, 355n, 399, 401, 417, 773

'On the dynamical theory of gases' (1867), 13–14, 250n, 254–66, 267n, 270–1n, 276–7, 279–84, 291–2, 331n, 408, 658–9, 854, 892n, 938
'On a dynamical top' (1857), 492–3n
'On the equilibrium of elastic solids' (1850), 65n, 273n, 275n
'Equilibrium and stiffness of frames' (1864), 119–21n
'On Faraday's lines of force' (1856), 21, 28, 99n, 192n, 336–7n, 355n, 484n, 527n, 529n, 530n
'Final state of a system of molecules in motion' (1873), 14–15, 898–910, 911–14, 916n, 938–9
'On governors' (1868), 8, 113–15n, 343–5, 351, 862
'Illustrations of the dynamical theory of gases' (1860), 12–13, 72–85, 133, 216, 219n, 232, 250n, 258n, 280, 331n, 657–8, 892n, 938
Keith prize, 727–8, 731n
lectures: (at Cambridge University), 35–6, 685, 689, 690, 760, 898n, 940–1, 942n; (at King's College London), 3–4, 60, 61, 87
library, 362n, 646n, 897n
'On Loschmidt's experiments on diffusion' (1873), 890–6, 926
'Mathematical classification of physical quantities' (1870), 568n, 570n, 573n, 651n, 652n
'Method of making a direct comparison of electrostatic with electromagnetic force' (1868), 9, 176–8n, 213n, 326n, 354–5n, 375–9, 484–6n, 489n, 851
'Molecules' (1873), 15, 19, 820n, 922–33
'On physical lines of force' (1861–62), 9, 27, 31, 99n, 110n, 180, 188n, 198n, 337, 484n, 627n, 769, 808n
'On reciprocal figures and diagrams of forces' (1864), 21, 60n, 313, 330
'On reciprocal figures, frames and diagrams of forces' (1870), 21, 63n, 330, 346, 392, 517–18, 519–21, 609, 946
On the Stability of the Motion of Saturn's Rings (1859), 12, 105n, 115n, 130n, 131, 758, 761
'On the theory of compound colours' (1860), 58–9n, 552n, 775n
Theory of Heat (1871), 15–16, 27, 332n, 416n, 540n, 541–3, 564–5n, 584–8, 633n, 634, 636, 645n, 646n, 648n, 651n, 661, 668, 672–4, 709, 710, 732n, 780, 853n, 946n

thermodynamic signature, 16, 543–4n, 596n, 609n, 716, 733, 740
travels (continental), 97, 98, 476
Treatise on Electricity and Magnetism (1873), 11–12, 21; (composition of), 24–33, 323n, 328n, 346, 416–17, 423, 424–7, 428–32, 453–6, 479–82, 483–6, 487–8, 489–91, 496–7, 499–500, 502–7, 508–9, 514–15, 516–17, 522–7, 589, 634, 639, 641–3, 644, 732–3; (dynamics in), 27, 30–1, 716, 732–3, 740, 744–7, 769–71; (Part II 'Electrokinematics') 27, 158n, 320n, 417, 422–3, 483, 503–4, 584n, 626n, 633n, 661–3, 699–700, 707, 765n, 828–9n, 966–7n; (Part IV 'Electromagnetism'), 27, 174n, 177n, 188n, 199n, 210n, 323n, 324–5n, 336n, 355n, 426n, 500n, 507, 508–9, 514–15, 516–17, 522–7, 549n, 572n, 583n, 597n, 627n, 666n, 679n, 686n, 695n, 704n, 706n, 725n, 732–3, 738, 742, 748–9n, 756, 770–2, 784n, 801n, 805n, 809n, 826n, 871n, 884–5n, 963n, 967n; (Part I 'Electrostatics'), 26–7, 125n, 172n, 207n, 271n, 320n, 423, 424–6, 428–32, 453–6, 459, 479–82, 484–6, 488, 489–91, 496–7, 499, 502–3, 516, 531n, 547n, 605–6n, 680n, 682, 689, 764n, 858n, 871n, 959n, 967n; (Part III 'Magnetism'), 27, 117n, 325–6n, 433n, 498–9, 505–6, 514n, 543n, 583n, 590n, 597n, 675–6, 828n, 880n, 881–2n, 966–7n; ('Preliminary'), 433n, 569n, 570n, 591n, 634n, 641n, 644, 700n, 784n; (proofs), 32, 652, 660, 676, 681, 689, 700, 707, 733, 741, 755, 757, 784n; (publication), 31–3, 416, 636, 781, 839
'On the viscosity or internal friction of air and other gases' (1866), 13, 202n, 215n, 216–17n, 222n, 230–5, 262, 429, 432, 658, 891
Maxwell, John Clerk, 451
Maxwell, Katherine Mary Clerk, 446, 449, 552n
  letters from Maxwell, 971; (28 January 1864) **222**, 122; (3 January 1870) **336**, 528; (20 March 1871) **361**, 623; (22 March 1871) **363**, 629
Mayer, Julius Robert, 335n
Mayer, Tobias, 774n
Mayr, O., 8n
mechanical equivalent of heat, 84–5,
  and British Association unit, 210n, 378, 489
  experiments, 179–80, 338–9, 346, 390
mechanics (theory of), 291, 492–5, 777–9

'Memoirs of Martin Scriblerus', 636
Mensbrugghe, G. Van der, 386
Merrifield, Charles Watkins, 24, *369*
  Royal Society paper: 'Resistance of the air to rifled projectiles' (Maxwell's report on) **288**, 374
metaphysics, 19–20, 335–6, 360–1, 362–4, 367–8, 395–6, 798–800, 811–12, 814–23, 917, 952, 956–7
Meyer, Lothar, 895, 925
Meyer, O. E., 78n, 231, 234, 262n, 270, 280, 658, 891, 894
Michelson, A. A., 10
Mill, John Stuart, 335n, 362, 731
Miller, J. D., 879n
Miller, William Allen, 24, 42, 415n, 417, 504
  Royal Society paper: 'On the photographic transparency of various bodies' (Maxwell's report on) **199**, 47–9
  report on paper by T. Graham: (4 July 1866), 287n
Miller, William Hallowes, *382*, 415n, 510n, 641n
  letter from G. B. Airy: ([1848]), 414n
molecules,
  diameter of, 15, 659, 890–6, 897, 915n, 919–20, 925–6, 934
  encounters, 254–9, 898–910, 911–14,
  ether, 915–16
  gases, 15, 72–85, 230–5, 258–60, 261–4, 279–84, 291, 654–60, 888, 890–6, 922–9
  forces, 16, 668–9, 670–4
  properties, 291, 586–8, 888, 890–6, 922–7, 959–61, 962–3
Moncreiff, James, *392*
Monro, Cecil James, 58n, 614, 629
  letters from Maxwell: (6 July 1870) **341**, 550–3; (15 March 1871) **359**, 617–20
  letters to Maxwell: (2 June 1870), 550n; (3 March 1871), 617–18n; (9 March 1871), 619n; (21 March 1871), 620n, 629n; (10 September 1871), 618–19n
  letters to J. W. Strutt: (5 February 1871), 614n; (27 February 1871), 614n
Moon, Robert, 23, *383*
  Royal Society paper: 'On the impact of compressible bodies' (Maxwell's report on) **291**, 383–5
Morgan, Augustus de, 648n
Moseley, Henry, 23, 113n, *472*
  Royal Society paper: 'On the mechanical possibility of the descent of glaciers' (Maxwell's report on) **319**, 472–5

Mossotti, O. F., 193
Mott, A. J., 917
mountains (elevation of), 968–70
Muirhead, J. P., 791n
Mulcahy, John, 313n
Müller, F. Max, 617n, 840–1n
Müller, J., 246, 552
Munro, Hugh Andrew Johnstone, *250*
  letter from Maxwell: (7 February 1866) **257**, 250–2
  translation of Lucretius, 251n, 363n, 655n, 928n
Murphy, Robert, 683, 689

Nabla, 30, 568, 577, 593, 755, 760, 945
  see also Hamilton's operator
Nanson, E. J., letter to Maxwell: (5 December 1873), 973
Napier, R. D., 510n
Nature,
  letters to, 14–15, 551, 619, 853–5, 886, 917–18, 921, 937–9
  papers in, 618n, 671n, 712–13, 890–6, 898n, 913n, 922n
  poem in, 704n
  reviews in, 37, 395n, 842–4, 951–5
Navez pendulum, 373
Navier, C. L. M. H., 273n
nebular hypothesis, 956–7
nerves (electrical properties of), 554–8
Neugebauer, Otto, 98n
Neumann, Carl, 26, 320, 426, 480, 499–500, 531, 654n, 764–5
Neumann, Franz Ernst, 182–4n, 186–7n, 479–80, 498, 721n, 773, 843n, 881n, 945n
Newton, Sir Isaac, 20, 70, 297, 361, 368, 395–6, 510n, 610n, 655, 816, 936
  gravity, 20, 798, 801
  laws of motion, 31, 746, 817
Newtonians, 368, 798–800, 816–17
Newton's rings, 796, 813
Niagara, 346
Nicol's prism, 562–3, 615
Niven, William Davidson, 75n, 729n
Nobert, F. A., 874

O'Brien, Matthew, 683
Odling, William, 5n
Oersted, H. C., 193, 507, 767, 801
Ohm, Georg Simon, 516, 750
Ohm's law, 7, 417, 503, 517, 966
opacity, 180–1, 196, 200

ophthalmoscope, 203
optical instruments, 21-2, 224
  see also stereoscope
optics (geometrical), 21-2, 224, 667, 751-3, 781, 899, 935-6, 942-3
orthogonal curves, 123-4, 545, 715, 825, 884
ovals, 20-1, 294-7
Oxford Physical Laboratory, 623n, 632n, 636

Paley, F. A., 840
pangenesis, 815n
paramagnetism, 336-7, 405-6
Parker, Henry Tooke, 104n
Parliament (election to), 390, 392, 399
Pattison, Mark, 18-19, *358*
  letters from Maxwell: (7 April 1868) **286**, 358-61; (13 April 1868) **287**, 362-8
Peel, Sir Robert, Bt, *212n*
Peelers, 212
Peltier, J. A. C., 483n, 765n
Peltier effect, 483-4, 692, 699-700, 765, 833
periphractic region, 591, 593-4
peripolar molecules, 555-6
perversion (topological), 637, 642, 644, 645
Petit, A. T., 657, 910
Philosophical Magazine, 446, 732, 824, 879, 881, 886
  Maxwell's letter to the editors: (12 October 1870), 566n
  Maxwell's letter to W. R. Grove: (27 March 1868) **285**, 356-7
phlogiston, 364
physical sciences, 776-82
Physical Society of London, 6, 949
Piotrowski, G. von, 944
Pirie, George, 729n
Plana, Giovanni (Jean), 479
planimeter, 874
Plato, 361n
Plücker, Julius, 41n, 214, 750
Poggendorff, J. C., 866
Poinsot, Louis, 492n, 495
Poiseuille, J. L. M., 223
Poisson, Siméon Denis,
  elasticity, 261n, 272n, 283
  electrostatics, 479, 800, 802, 843
  fluids, 241n, 540n
  integral theorems, 634
  magnetism, 117, 498, 802
  specific heats, 260n
  vibrations, 414n
Poisson's equation, 430n

Poisson's ratio, 272-5, 302, 349
polarizing prisms, 559
Pole, William, 552
Pollock, Sir Frederick, 2nd Bt, 5-6n
Pollock, Sir Frederick, 3rd Bt, *252*, 666n
polygon of forces, 519
Poncelet, J. V., 313n
Pope, Alexander, 636n
Porter, T. M., 19n
positivism, 358, 362
potential (concept of), 24, 25-7, 36, 123-4, 160-2, 392, 394, 396, 400, 424-7, 428-32, 453-6, 457-9, 479-82, 487-8, 490-1, 496, 502-4, 506-7, 508-9, 512, 516, 522-6, 529-33, 591-2, 593-7, 601-2, 606-7, 666, 667, 680, 730, 843, 941-2n, 965-6
  see also spherical harmonic analysis; stream function; velocity potential
potential (propagation of), 26, 353-5, 499-500
  see also electrodynamics (continental)
potentiometer, 630, 734
Pouillet, C. S. M., 196
Power, John, 34n
  letters from the Duke of Devonshire: (10 October 1870), 33-4; (1 June 1871), 649n
Pratt, J. H., 256n, 650n, 683
Preece, George, E., letter to Maxwell: (7 March 1873), 973
Prevost, Pierre, 250n, 279, 655, 781
Price, Bartholomew, *31*, 404n, 687, 688n, 856
  letter to Maxwell: (4 January 1871), 30n, 31n, 636n
Prior, Matthew, 619
projectiles (motion of), 24, 369-74
Ptolemy, Claudius, 797

quaternions, 25, 29-30, 32, 35, 214, 332-3, 334n, 568-9, 570-6, 577-8, 580, 590-2, 593-7, 600-1, 609, 634n, 636n, 648-9, 652, 660, 685, 700, 707, 755, 756-7, 784, 825-6, 831, 833, 877n, 878, 884-5, 915n, 947-8, 951-5, 963
Quetelet, Adolphe, 296n
quickest ascent (line of), 224n, 625, 667n, 787-9
Quincke, G., 631n

Rabelais, François, 271n
Radcliffe, Charles Bland, 23, *554*
  Royal Society paper: 'Researches on animal electricity' (Maxwell's report on) **342**, 554-8
Ramsay, A. C., 969

Rankine, William John Macquorn, 658n, 783
  letters to G. G. Stokes: (21 April 1868), 374n; (26 April 1868), 373n; (26 June 1868), 374n
  report on paper by G. B. Airy: (26 January 1863), 63n, 69n, 71n
  report on paper by F. Bashforth: (26 April 1868), 373n
  report on paper by J. A. Longridge: (21 April 1868), 374n
  report on paper by C. W. Merrifield: (26 June 1868), 374n
  report on paper by H. Moseley: (24 February 1869), 473n, 475n
  Royal Society papers: 'On the mathematical theory of stream-lines' (Maxwell's report on) **337**, 529–34; 'On plane water-lines' (Maxwell's report on) **223**, 123–7; 'On the thermodynamical theory of waves' (Maxwell's report on) **338**, 535–40
  Applied Mechanics, 60n, 63n, 65n, 70–1n, 236n, 242n, 289, 317, 369n, 520, 807
  fluids, 23, 123–7, 236n, 239n, 242n, 389, 511, 529–33
  diagrams of forces, 60n, 313, 392, 519–20
  energy, 190n, 365n, 417, 778
  specific heats of gases, 76n, 77, 260
  stream-lines, 123–7, 448n, 529–33
  stress, 71n, 807
  thermodynamics, 23, 75n, 84n, 260, 328n, 331n, 334n, 535–40, 672, 946
  waves, 23, 445, 533, 535–40
Ray Club, 949
Rayleigh, 3rd Baron, *see* Strutt, John William
reciprocal figures, 21–2, 60, 313–17, 320, 330, 346, 392, 517–18, 519–21, 609, 946
reciprocal polars, 21–2, 313, 520
Regnault, H. V., 223n, 260, 731, 791, 869
resonance, 598–604, 605–7, 856–7
Reye, Theodor, 935
Richards, Joan L., 21n
Riemann, G. F. B., 26, 605n
  Cauchy–Riemann equations, 428n
  electrodynamics, 26, 353–5, 379
  geometry, 618n
  potential theory, 320, 502
  topology, 433n, 439, 466n
Rive, A. de la, 557
Robertson, Alexander, 335
Robins, Benjamin, 369
Robinson, Thomas Romney, 24, *43*, 58, 211
  Royal Society paper: 'On the spectra of electric light' (Maxwell's reports on) **198**, 43–5; **201**, 54–7
Robison, John, 113n, 396n
Rothlauf, Kaspar, 721
Rowland, Henry Augustus, 37, 325n
  letters from Maxwell: (9 July 1873) **466**, 879–80; (12 July 1873) **467**, 881–3
Royal Institution, 3, 5, 271, 513, 614, 617n, 621–2, 628, 668, 790n, 813
Royal School of Mines, 409
Royal Society of Edinburgh, 6, 226, 328n, 330, 339, 346, 392, 517, 519–21, 580–1, 660, 675n, 700, 702, 710n, 727, 884, 897n, 915n, 946
Royal Society of London, 6, 269, 648n, 671n, 714n, 738, 785, 879
  Maxwell's papers at, 158n, 160–3; **238**, 189–96; 197–201; **252**, 230–5; 254–66, 267–9; **263**, 279–83; 291–2; 298–9; 343–5; **289**, 375–9; 706, 710, 711, 712–13
  Maxwell's reports on papers, 22–4; *see* reports on papers by G. B. Airy, **205**, 62–9; **206**, 70–1; **212**, 95–6; **410**, 718–26; **453**, 847; by F. Bashforth, **288**, 369–73; C. Chambers, **220**, 117–18; J. L. Clark, **415**, 734–7; **462**, 866–7; A. Des Cloiseaux, **290**, 380–2; J. D. Everett, **261**, 272–5; **269**, 300–3; **282**, 348–50; N. M. Ferrers, **325**, 492–5; T. Graham, **264**, 285–7; F. Guthrie, **442**, 827–30; S. Haughton, **199**, 46–7; **200**, 50–3; J. Jago, **447**, 836–8; J. A. Longridge, **288**, 373–4; D. M'Kichan, **455**, 849–51; C. W. Merrifield, **288**, 374; W. A. Miller, **199**, 47–9; R. Moon, **291**, 383–5; H. Moseley, **319**, 472–5; C. B. Radcliffe, **342**, 554–8; W. J. M. Rankine, **223**, 123–7, **337**, 529–34; **338**, 535–40; T. R. Robinson, **198**, 43–5; **201**, 54–7; G. G. Stokes, **197**, 41–2; **298**, 412–15; J. W. Strutt, **354**, 598–604; E. W. Tarn, **265**, 288–90; J. Tyndall, **255**, 245–8; **258**, 253
  Bakerian Lectures, 5, 230–5, 661, 671n
  Committee of Papers, 22, 533–4n
  Croonian Lecture, 146n, 341
  Philosophical Club, 5, 147
  Register of Papers Received, 62n, 117n, 123n, 348n, 380n, 554n, 734n, 827n, 836n, 849n
Ruhmkorff coil, 356n
Rühlmann, R., 829

Sabine, Edward, 463, 870n
Sabra, A. I., 629n

Salet, Georges, 417
Salmon, George, 295n, 481n
Sang, Edward, 578, 702n
Saturday Review, 358, 362n, 812n, 921n
Saturn's rings
    Airy, 115n, 758n, 761–2n
    Bond, 105, 107n
    Maxwell, 12, 104–5, 128–45, 758–9, 761–2, 956n
    Spencer, 956n
    Struve, 130n
scalars, 29, 568–9, 570–6, 590–2, 593–7, 952
Scholz, E., 21n
Schröter, H., 477n
Schröter, J. H., 105n
Scott, M., 321
Scott, Sir Walter, Bt, 321n, 934n
Seebeck, Thomas, 765n
Seebeck effect, 765
self-induction of currents, 99–100, 112, 158–9, 200–1
Sellmeier, W., 863n
Shairp, J. C., 463, 774n, 886n, 915, 921n
Shakespeare, William, 610n, 822, 929
Sharpey, William, 22, *41*
    letter from Maxwell: (8 July 1862) **197**, 41–2
    report on paper by C. B. Radcliffe: ([1870]), 554n, 556n, 558n
ships,
    design of, 123–7, 529–34
    magnetism of, 505, 517, 543
Siegel, D. M., 9n, 11n, 26n, 161n, 198n
Siemens, Sir Charles William, 16, 114, 298, 351, 376n, 661–3
    letter from Maxwell: (23 June 1871) **378**, 661–3
Siemens, Werner, 661n
Simpson, Thomas K., 11n
Simpson's rule, 720
Simson, Robert, 816n
Smalley, George Robarts, 4, *61*, 86, 87, 249n
Smith, Archibald, *392*
Smith, C. W., 6n, 19n
Smith, Robert, 936n, 943
Smith, William Robertson, 516n, *577*
Smith, Willoughby, *375*
Somerville, Mary, 812n
Sophocles, 840
Sorby, H. C., 748n, 886
sound waves (propagation of), 412–15, 417–18, 538, 598–604, 780, 856–7, 960, 962
space (dimensions of), 618–19

space (directions in), 29, 637, 639, 641–3, 644, 953–4
spectra, 24, 41–2, 43–5, 47–9, 54–7, 58–9, 245–8, 339, 559–63, 614–15, 644n, 748n, 781, 960
Spencer, Herbert,
    letters from Maxwell: (5 December 1873) **486**, 956–61; (17 December 1873) **487**, 962–3
    letters to Maxwell: (4 December 1873), 956n; (30 December 1873), 962n
spherical harmonic analysis, 25, 26, 32, 277, 330, 347, 390, 392–4, 397, 406, 412–13, 503, 677, 682, 683–5, 688n, 689, 692, 723–5, 940–1, 942n
Spinoza, B., 618, 797
Spottiswoode, William, *5–6n*, 563n, 717
Sprengel, Hermann, 869
stability (dynamical), 625, 819–22
St Andrews (United College), 4–5, 457, 460, 461, 462, 463
'statistical method', 15, 16–18, 582–3, 818–19, 929–33
steel (manufacture of), 287
Steele, W. J., 703n, 872n
Stefan, Josef, 760, 891
Steiner, Jacob, 619
Steiner's surface, 477
Steinheil, C. A. von, 870
Stephen, Leslie, 666n
stereograms, 22, 318–20, 322, 330, 342, 476n
stereoscope (real image), 22, 312, 340–1, 342
stereoscopic vision, 340–1, 447
Stevenson, R. L., 7n
Stewart, Balfour, *6–7*, 214, 217n, 271, 277
    electrical measurements, 6–7, 88n, 92, 93–4, 103n, 122, 489n
    stability (dynamical), 819n, 820
Stewart, Dugald, 816n
Stewart, John, 816n
Stewart, Matthew, 816n
St John's College, Cambridge, 689
Stokes, Sir George Gabriel, Bt, 7, 9–10, 14, 22–4, 28, 48, 50, 463, 528n, 645, 671n, 710
    letters from Maxwell: (8 May 1857), 148n; (7 September 1858), 78n; (30 May 1859), 74n, 78n, 258n; (14 July 1862) **198**, 43–5; (16 July 1862) **199**, 46–9; (21 July 1862) **200**, 50–3; (10 September 1862) **202**, 58–9; (29 December 1862) **206**, 70–1; (9 June 1863) **212**, 95–6; (6 May 1864) **228**, 154–6; (15 October 1864) **237**, 186–8; (18 December 1866) **266**, 291–3; (27 February

1867) **268**, 298–9; (26 June 1869) **323**, 487–8; (8 July 1869) **324**, 489–91; (11 January 1871) **351**, 589; (8 January 1872) **400**, 706; (12 February 1872) **404**, 711; (8 July 1872) **416**, 738; (13 May 1873) **453**, 847

letters to Maxwell: (16 February 1871), 611n; (18 February 1871), 612n; (23 February 1871), 612n; (14 March 1871), 615n

letters to G. B. Airy: (12 May 1848), 414n; (26 February 1863), 64n; (18 March 1863), 95n; (10 December 1872), 718n; (13 December 1872), 718n

letters from Airy: (22 February 1863), 63 4n, 69n, 95n, 96n; (27 February 1863), 95n; (3 July 1872), 725n

letter from W. Bottomley: (26 March 1873), 867n

letter from J. L. Clark: (23 January 1873), 735n

letter from T. A. Hirst: (5 October 1868), 385n

letters from F. Jenkin: (16 July 1868), 375n; (27 May 1873), 830n; (30 May 1873), 850n

letters from W. J. M. Rankine: (21 April 1868), 374n; (26 April 1868), 373n; (26 June 1868), 374n

letter to Lord Rayleigh: (5 June 1877), 538n

letters to W. Thomson: (22 February 1862), 230n; (25 February 1862), 230n

letters from Thomson: (2 July 1850), 589n; (10 March 1862), 230n; (19 April 1862), 98n; (8 July 1862), 98n; (29 October 1863), 117n; (17 February 1864), 125–6n; (15 March 1865), 189n; (11 April 1866), 230n; (13 October 1866), 291–3n; (19 October 1868), 375n; (7 March 1870), 537–8n; (9 May 1870), 538n; (3 March 1871), 613n; (25 May 1872), 734n; (1 January 1873), 735n; (21 January 1873), 735n; (21 April 1873), 847n

report on paper by S. Haughton: (30 June 1862), 50–2n

reports on paper by W. J. M. Rankine: ([1870]), 530n; (19 January 1871), 531n, 533–4n

report on paper by J. Tyndall: (18 January 1866), 245–8n

Royal Society papers: 'On the communication of vibrations' (Maxwell's report on) **298**, 412–15; 'On the long spectrum of electric light' (Maxwell's report on) **197**, 41–2

conduction (equations of), 527
crystal optics, 380–1n
elasticity, 262, 273n, 283n, 391n
ether, 199n
ether drag, 154, 309
fluids, 124, 241n, 242n, 529n, 530n, 533–4n, 539n, 778
fluorescence, 245n
infinite series, 487–8
periodic series, 414–15
polarized light, 155
potential, 590, 593
sound waves, 412–15, 417–18, 538
vibration, 412–15, 417–18, 419n
viscosity, 78, 218, 224, 231, 234, 262, 270, 473, 657

Stokes' theorem, 28, 441n, 589, 634
Stoney, G. J., 446n, 659, 893, 926
Strange, Alexander, 552
stream function, 123–4, 426, 428–9, 448, 457–8, 529–32, 545–7, 601, 603, 606–7
stream lines, 123–7, 456, 517, 529–34, 551
Strutt, John William, 3rd Baron Rayleigh, 18, 23–4, 623, 740

letters from Maxwell: (18 May 1870) **340**, 545–9; (6 December 1870) **350**, 582–4; (4 February 1871) **355**, 605–8; (15 March 1871) **358**, 614–16; (8 and 10 July 1871) **379**, 664–6; (26 May 1873) **458**, 856–7; (28 August 1873) **476**, 919–20; (22 November 1873) **482**, 940–3

letter to Maxwell: (14 February 1871), 607n, 608n, 611–12n, 614–15n

letters from C. J. Monro: (5 February 1871), 614n; (27 February 1871), 614n

letter from G. G. Stokes: (5 June 1877), 538n

London Mathematical Society paper: 'Theorems relating to vibrations' (Maxwell's report on) **460**, 860–3

Royal Society paper: 'On the theory of resonance' (Maxwell's report on) **354**, 598–604

anomalous dispersion, 863n
Bessel functions, 857
blue of the sky, 614, 619, 666n, 919, 940
colour mixing, 607n, 614n
dissipation function, 862, 940
echoes, 920
electromagnetism, 583–4, 599–602, 605–7

marriage, 664
Theory of Sound, 856, 860n, 942
vibrations, 598–604, 605–7, 860–3, 864n, 940
Strutt, R. J., 4th Baron Rayleigh, 582n, 664n
Struve, Otto, 130n
Stuart, James, *623*, 718n, 723–5
Sturrock, George, 103
surface tension, 15, 325, 334n, 386–8, 389, 780
Sviedrys, R., 34n
Swan, William, 457, 463n
  letter to Maxwell: (11 May 1872), 974
Swift, Jonathan, 355n
Sydney Observatory, 87
Sylvester, James Joseph, 1n, 294n, 476, 492–4, 651n, 652–3, 687
  letter from Maxwell: (21 December 1866) **267**, 294–7
Szily, C., 947n

Tait, Archibald Campbell, 634–5n
Tait, Peter Guthrie, 1n, 6, 774–5n, 872n, 886n
  letters from Maxwell: (7 March 1865) **244**, 214–15; (3 April 1865) **245**, 216–17; (17 June 1865) **249**, 224–5; (4 April 1866) **262**, 276–8; (13 November 1867) **275**, 321–2; (4 December 1867) **276**, 323–7; (11 December 1867) **277**, 328–34; (23 December 1867) **278**, 335–9; (12 March 1868) **284**, 353–5; (14 July 1868) **293**, 389–90; (18 July 1868) **294**, 391–7; (c. 20 July 1868) **296**, 407–8; (3 August 1868) **299**, 416–18; (10 December 1869) **333**, 516–18; (7 November 1870) **346**, 568–9; (14 November 1870) **348**, 577–9; (23 January 1871) **352**, 590–2; (23 January 1871) **353**, 593–7; (14 February 1871) **356**, 609–10; (4 April 1871) **366**, 634–5; (3 May 1871) **367**, 636; (8 May 1871) **368**, 637; (11 May 1871) **369**, 639; (12 May 1871) **371**, 644; (25 May 1871) **372**, 645; (27 May 1871) **373**, 646–7; (27 May 1871) **374**, 648–9; (3 June 1871) **375**, 650–1; (14 June 1871) **376**, 652–3; (13 July 1871) **380**, 667; (late August 1871) **383**, 675–6; (5 September 1871) **384**, 677; (19 October 1871) **386**, 681; (23 October 1871) **387**, 682; (2 November 1871) **388**, 683–5; (7 November 1871) **389**, 686–7; (7 December 1871) **393**, 692–3; (12 December 1871) **394**, 694; (21 December 1871) **396**, 699–700; (1 January 1872) **398**, 702; (c. 4 January 1872) **399**, 704; (19 January 1872) **401**, 707; (12 February 1872) **403**, 710; (c. early May 1872) **407**, 715; (9 May 1872) **408**, 716; (14 May 1872) **409**, 717; (24 May 1872) **411**, 727–8; (c. late June 1872) **413**, 731; (29 June 1872) **414**, 732–3; (15 July 1872) **417**, 739–40; (7 August 1872) **417**, 741; (4 October 1872) **422**, 755; (9 October 1872) **423**, 756–7; (12 November 1872) **427**, 763; (late 1872–early 1873) **428**, 764–5; (c. December 1872) **429**, 766; (12 February 1873) **440**, 824; (c. early 1873) **441**, 825–6; (3 March 1873) **443**, 831; (5 March 1873) **444**, 832; (10 March 1873) **445**, 833–4; (12 March 1873) **446**, 835; (2 May 1873) **451**, 845; (7 May 1873) **452**, 846; (15 May 1873) **454**, 848; (8 July 1873) **465**, 877–8; (22 July 1873) **468**, 884–7; (24 July 1873) **469**, 888–9; (30 July 1873) **471**, 897; (c. August 1873) **474**, 915–16; (late August–early September 1873) **477**, 921; (2 September 1873) **479**, 934; (1 December 1873) **483**, 944–8; (11 November 1874), 618n
  letters to Maxwell: (n.d.), 224n; (6 April 1866), 278n; (27 November 1867), 323n; (6 December 1867), 328n; (13 December 1867), 333–4n; (1 February 1871), 596n; (17 February 1871), 610n; (31 March 1871), 633n; (5 April 1871), 634n; (9 May 1871), 637–8n; (13 May 1871), 639–40n; (14 May 1871), 644n; (1 June 1871), 646n; (5 June 1871), 650n; (7 June 1871), 650–1n; (13 June 1871), 652n; (14 June 1871), 662n; (20 June 1871), 663n; (9 July 1871), 667n; (10 November 1871), 687–8n; (2 January 1872), 702–3n; (6 January 1872), 704n; (n.d.), 710n; (25 January 1872), 707n; (11 June 1872), 731n; (28 June 1872), 732n; (13 July 1872), 739n; (15 July 1872), 740–1n; (16 July 1872), 740n; (17 July 1872), 740n; (19 July 1872), 740n; (30 June 1873), 877n; (7 July 1873), 877n; (31 July 1873), 915n
  letter to G. G. Stokes: (4 March 1865), 214n
  letters to W. Thomson: (6 January 1870), 856n; (25 April 1875), 856n
  letters from Thomson: (5 July 1868), 25, 398n; (21 August 1871), 25, 675n
  brachistochrone, 224n, 667
  and Clausius, 328n, 335n, 408, 732n, 740n
  conductivity, 389, 392, 888n
  fluids, 944n

'On Green's and other allied theorems', 29–30, 574n, 581, 590n, 660n
Keith prize, 580–1
laboratory, 634n, 636
magnetism, 824n
Maxwell's relations with, 25, 335n, 580–1, 624
pendulum motion, 702, 704
proofs of the *Treatise*, 32, 652, 660, 676, 681, 689, 700, 733
quaternions, 29–30, 214, 332, 334n, 568–9n, 573–5n, 577n, 580–1, 590n, 594–6n, 624, 634n, 650–1n, 652n, 660, 704n, 707n, 825n, 831, 833, 877n, 915n, 947–8, 951–5
Rede Lecture, 765n, 831, 833, 835, 845, 846, 848, 852
Sketch of Thermodynamics, 16–17, 328n, 335–7, 405, 408, 416, 465n, 543–4, 581, 646n, 650n, 945–6
smoke rings, 321n
spatial directions, 637, 638n, 639, 640n, 641, 644
spherical harmonics, 25, 32, 682, 684–5, 688n, 689
and B. Stewart, 214, 217n, 271n, 277, 819n
thermo-electricity, 393, 654n, 662–3, 694, 699–700, 707, 731, 732, 739, 740–1n, 831n
translation of Helmholtz on vortex motion, 243n, 321n, 391n, 398–9n, 434n, 446–7n, 530n
vision, 703n, 704
Talbot, W. Fox, 333n, 702
Tarn, Edward Wyndham, 24, *288*, 291
 Royal Society paper: 'On the stability of domes' (Maxwell's report on) **265**, 288–90
Tatlock, John, 513
Tayler, Charles Benjamin, letter from Maxwell: (2 February 1866) **256**, 249
Taylor, W. P., 392, 517, 520
Teixeira, F. Gomes, 297n
Tennyson, Alfred (Lord), 294
tension (electric), 556–7
Thalén, T. R., 498, 881
Thales' eclipse, 98
thermodynamic relations (Maxwell's), 673–4
thermodynamics (second law of), 934
 Clausius on, 17, 328n, 335n, 359, 408, 564, 609, 757n, 946
 'demon' paradox, 17–18, 331–2, 582–3, 584–5
 gas under gravity, 14–15, 265–6, 269, 292n, 853–5, 937–9
 irreversibility, 18, 359–60, 366–7, 583

 Maxwell on, 14, 17–18, 266, 269, 359, 564–5, 583, 585
 reduction of, 609, 757n, 946–7
 W. Thomson on, 17, 266n, 269, 359, 564
thermo-electricity, 32, 483–4, 527, 661–3, 692, 694, 699–700, 707, 731, 732, 739–40, 764–5, 833
 Tait on, 32, 393, 654n, 662, 694, 699–700, 707, 731, 732n, 739–41n, 831n, 833
 W. Thomson on, 483, 692n, 699, 764–5
thermometer (Accademia del Cimento), 645, 648
Thompson, S. P., 34n, 390n, 391n, 489n, 513n, 624n, 665n, 704n, 783n, 792n, 846n, 849n, 863n, 873n
Thompson, William Hepworth, *228*
Thomson, James, 1n, 16, 681
 letters from Maxwell: (13 July 1871), **381**, 668–9; (24 July 1871) **382**, 670–4; (2 September 1872) **421**, 751–4
 reference: (7 January 1873) **433**, 783
 letters to Maxwell: (21 July 1871), 670–1n; (11 January 1873), 751n, 753–4n
 atmospheric refraction, 751, 753
 continuity of gases and liquids, 668–9, 671, 672n
 vortex turbine, 236, 239
Thomson, William, Lord Kelvin, 25, 34, 390, 612, 681, 704, 751, 791–2, 839
 letters from Maxwell: (15 May 1855), 564n, 730n; (1 August 1857), 105n; (14 November 1857), 132n; (24 November 1857), 18; (30 January 1858), 105n; (10 December 1861), 110n, 188n, 484n, 548n, 784n; (17 December 1861), 659n; (29 May 1863) **210**, 88–92; (June 1863) **211**, 93–4; (31 July 1863) **214**, 98–101; (11 September 1863) **219**, 112–16; (27 September 1864) **234**, 172–5; (15 October 1864) **235**, 176–81; (25 February 1865) **242**, 207–12; (17 and 18 April 1865) **246**, 218–20; (27 February 1866) **260**, 267–71; (14 September 1867) **274**, 318–20; (20 February 1868) **281**, 346–7; (18 July 1868) **295**, 398–406; (19 August 1868) **301**, 422–3; (5 September 1868) **302**, 424–7; (12 September 1868) **303**, 428–32; (28 September 1868) **306**, 443–5; (6 October 1868) **307**, 446–8; (7 October 1868) **308**, 449; (16 October 1868) **310**, 453–6; (30 October 1868) **311**, 457–9; (9 November 1868) **315**, 463; (7 December 1868) **316**,

464–5; (12 May 1869) **321**, 479–82; (5 June 1869) **322**, 483–6; (17 August 1869) **326**, 496–7; (1 October 1869) **327**, 498–500; (5 October 1869) **328**, 501; (16 November 1869) **332**, 513–15; (14 April 1870) **339**, 541–4; (21 March 1871) **362**, 624–8; (30 March 1871) **365**, 632–3; (Summer 1871) **377**, 654–60; (late August 1871) **383**, 675–6; (7 November 1871) **390**, 689; (8 February 1872) **402**, 708–9; (10 August 1872) **420**, 748–50; (22 January 1873) **434**, 784; (25 March 1873) **448**, 839

letters to Maxwell: (14 December 1868), 464–5n; (11 January 1871), 584n; (17 June 1871), 654n; (4 January 1872), 692–3n; (24 August 1872), 749–50n

letter to J. H. Balfour: ([1870]), 580n

letters from F. Jenkin: (8 August 1860), 113n; (20 February 1868), 363n

letters to G. G. Stokes: (2 July 1850), 589n; (10 March 1862), 230n; (19 April 1862), 98n; (8 July 1862), 98n; (29 October 1863), 117n; (17 February 1864), 124–6n; (15 March 1865), 189n; (11 April 1866), 230n; (13 October 1866), 291–3n; (16 July 1868), 375n; (7 March 1870), 537–8n; (9 May 1870), 538n; (3 March 1871), 613n; (25 May 1872), 734n; (1 January 1873), 735n; (21 January 1873), 735n; (21 April 1873), 847n

letters from Stokes: (22 February 1862), 230n; (25 February 1862), 230n

letters to P. G. Tait: (5 July 1868), 25, 398n; (21 August 1871), 25, 675n

letters from Tait: (6 January 1870), 856n; (25 April 1875), 856n

reports on papers by G. B. Airy: (10 May 1872), 719n, 725n; (21 April 1873), 847n

report on paper by C. Chambers: (28 October 1863), 118n

reports on papers by Maxwell: (15 March 1865), 189n; (11 April 1866), 230n; (13 October 1866), 291–3n; (19 October 1868), 375n

reports on papers by W. J. M. Rankine: (17 February 1864), 124–6n; (7 March 1870), 537–8n; (9 May 1870), 538n

anomalous dispersion, 863n

axis of magnet, 675n

British Association Address, 654n

cable, 496, 863, 915

on Cavendish, 786

charge (generation of), 424n, 503, 873

condenser (standard), 166, 172

conduction of heat, 542–3n, 966

conservation of energy, 191–2, 337

'demon', 17n, 332n, 582n

diamagnetism, 336–7, 405

dissipation of energy, 359–60, 542n, 564–5

elasticity, 71n, 231, 272n

electric circuits, 158n, 205–6, 584n

electric images, 389, 423n, 453n, 479, 713

electrical discharge in gases, 829

electrical standards, 6–9, 88n

electrical units (ratio of), 6–9, 110, 205–6, 810

electrification of a bowl, 25, 453n, 497, 499

electrolysis, 417

electromagnetism, 191–2, 507, 516

electrometers, 207n, 377, 423, 430–3, 443, 482, 555, 736, 750, 828, 850, 858, 859n, 871, 873

electroplatymeter, 873

Electrostatics and Magnetism, 25, 32, 455n, 482, 675n, 708, 773, 786n, 850n, 858–9n, 877

ether, 105–6, 190, 364

evaporation, 668–9

extremal conditions, 605n, 763

fluids, 390, 391, 398, 778

gamma function, 426n

governor, 101, 107–8, 113–16, 343n, 344n, 351

guard-ring (electrometer), 211, 377, 430–3, 443, 850, 858, 859n, 873

induction of currents, 192, 507

Laplacian, 199n

on Le Sage, 702n

magnetisation, 498n, 881n

magnetism (lamellar), 514n, 597n, 700

magnetism (solenoidal), 485n, 514n, 597n, 700, 724n, 877n

magneto-optic rotation, 190, 768–9, 784n

matter, 291n

on Maxwell, 25, 125n

mirror galvanometer, 665, 704n, 871

molecular size, 659, 893, 926

orthogonal curves, 124

parrot, 846

quadrant electrometer, 482, 555

spatial directions, 637–8n, 642, 644

spherical harmonic analysis, 277, 677n

suspended coil, 871

thermodynamics, 17, 75n, 84n, 266, 269, 331n, 359, 542–3n, 564–5, 946n

thermo-electricity, 483–4, 527, 692, 694n, 699, 764–5, 833
tides, 98n, 624n
time-reversal, 332n, 582n
vortex atoms, 321n
vortex motion, 321, 390, 391, 398, 439
Thomson, William (Archbishop of York), 634–5n
Thomson and Tait, *Natural Philosophy*, 325
   dynamics, 31, 654n, 716, 732, 733n, 740n, 745n, 904n
   elasticity, 348
   extremal conditions, 605n, 763
   figure of the earth, 277n
   force, 423
   Gauss' theorem, 648n
   Hamilton's principle, 354n, 947n
   impact, 384
   inertia, 364n
   kinetic energy, 75n, 365n
   kinetics, 654n
   matter, 395–6
   particle motion, 323n
   publication of, 24, 277, 330, 856n
   spatial directions, 637, 639, 641, 644
   spherical harmonics, 277n, 330, 347, 390, 412n, 677, 682, 684, 689n, 723–4, 725n
   Stokes' theorem, 589n, 635n
   viscosity, 474n
Thomson effect, 765, 833
Thomson's theorem, *see* Dirichlet's principle
tides (theory of), 98, 624n
time-reversal, 18–19, 332n, 346, 360–1, 582–3
The Times, 748n
Todd, David Peck, letter from Maxwell: (19 March 1879), 10
Todhunter, Isaac, 589n, 625n, 689n
Tomlinson, Charles, 784, 786, *858*
   letter from Maxwell: (29 May 1873) **459**, 858–9
topography, 566–7
topology, 28–9, 647
   curves, surfaces and spaces, 433–8, 439–42, 443–4, 449–50, 466–9, 470–1, 591, 594, 626
   directions in space, 637, 639, 641–3, 644, 953–4
   knots, 321–2, 325–7, 330
   topographical geometry, 29, 566–7
Torricelli, E., 20, 365, 395, 812
torsion balance (electric), 213, 377, 482, 873
Tresca, Henri Edouard, 477, 691
Trinity College, Cambridge, 624n
   Maxwell at, 528
   Maxwell's fellowship, 228
Troost, L., 285n
Trotter, Coutts, 36n, *623*
   letter to Maxwell: (20 April 1871), 623n
Tucker, Robert, 343n, 566n, 641n
   letter to Maxwell: (8 April 1870), 458–9n
Tulloch, John, 462, 463
Turner, F. M., 840n
Tyndall, John, 5–6, 24, 56, 226, 473n, 474n, 513, 578, 617, 915, 921, 956n
   letters from Maxwell: (20 April 1864) **226**, 147; (23 July 1868) **297**, 409–10
   letter to Maxwell: ('Monday'), 976
   Royal Society papers: 'On calorescence' (Maxwell's report on) **255**, 245–8; 'On radiation and absorption' (Maxwell's report on) **258**, 253

Varley, C. F., 271, 424n, 503, 873
Vaughan, Daniel, 98, 132
vaulted structures, 24, 288–90, 691
vector potential, 590, 756
vectors, 29–30, 568–9, 570–6, 577, 590–2, 593–7, 825, 831, 898, 951–3, 954, 963
   electromagnetism, 572–3, 592, 594–5, 596–7, 825, 955, 963
   see also quaternions
velocity potential, 124, 242, 426, 428, 457, 511, 530, 545
vena contracta, 510–12
Verdet, Émile, 336, 380–1n, 405–6, 646n, 651n, 826n, 885n
vibrations (theory of), 412–15, 417–18, 419n, 598–604, 605–7, 780, 856–7, 860–3, 864–5
virial, 16, 609, 709, 710, 946
viscosity of gases (experiments on), 13, 96, 202, 215, 216–17, 218–19, 221, 222–3, 224, 230–5, 270, 582, 658, 869, 888, 891, 894
vision, 23, 703n, 704, 836–8
Vogt, Carl, 407n
Volta, Alessandro, 557, 750
Voltaire, F. M. A., 368
vortex atoms, 321n, 693
vortex motion,
   Helmholtz on, 243, 321, 391, 398n, 399–404, 434n, 439n, 446–7, 533
   Maxwell on, 11, 239–40, 243, 321–2, 399–404, 407
   W. Thomson on, 321, 390, 391, 398, 439n, 446
vortex turbine, 236–9

vortices (molecular), 11, 180, 337

Waltenhofen, A. von, 506
Waterston, J. J., 386
'The Waterwitch', 510n
Watson, H. W., 907n, 931n
Watt, James, 790–1
Watts, Henry, 100n, 380n, 693n, 886n
Way's mercury light, 56
Weber, Wilhelm Eduard, 736, 750
    diamagnetism, 336–7, 405, 505, 583
    electrical measurements, 7, 43–4, 211, 736, 773, 810–11
    electrical units (ratio of), 110, 171, 188, 195, 198, 378, 851
    force law, 337, 353–4, 654n, 686–7, 773, 843n
    magnetisation, 336, 498n, 583, 727
    paramagnetism, 336–7, 405, 505, 583
    terrestrial magnetism, 32, 505–6
Weierstrass, Karl, 477n
Wertheim, Guillaume, 273n, 274
Wheatstone, Sir Charles,
    reports on papers by J. L. Clark: (3 September 1872), 735n; (1 July 1873), 867n
    report on paper by W. A. Miller: (23 August 1862), 48n
    report on paper by T. R. Robinson: (22 October 1862), 45n, 57n
    report on paper by G. G. Stokes: (16 July 1862), 42n
    dynamo, 298
    polarization of light, 563
    spectra, 41n
    stereoscope, 312n
Wheatstone's bridge, 158, 193, 503, 584n, 824n, 871
Whipple, G. M., letters from Maxwell: (20 March 1874), 870n; (4 May 1874), 870n
White, James, 422, 445, 464, 498
White, Walter, 671n
Whittaker, E. T., 11n
Wiedemann, Gustav, 356n, 723, 735n, 773, 829, 866n, 871n, 888
Wilde, H., 872
Williamson, A. W., 337n, 916n
Willis, Thomas, 813
Wilson, D. B., 32n, 33n, 98n, 117n, 125–6n, 230n, 291–3n, 375n, 537–8n, 589n, 735n
Wilson, George, 621
Winstanley, D. A., 34n
Winter, Karl, 873
Wise, M. N., 6n, 19n
wöhlerite, 380
Wollaston, W. H., 751
work (mechanical), 365, 564, 609n, 710, 746
Wünsch, C. E., 775

yellow spot (of the eye), 552
Young, Thomas, 63, 367, 775
Young's modulus, 349

zoetrope ('wheel of life'), 22, 444–5, 446–7, 456, 464

CPSIA information can be obtained
at www.ICGtesting.com
Printed in the USA
LVOW06s1156180417
531173LV00002B/3/P